WHERE TO FISH

WHERE TO FISH

1982–1983

78th EDITION

EDITED BY

D. A. ORTON

THOMAS HARMSWORTH PUBLISHING
&
ADAM & CHARLES BLACK

78th edition published 1982 by
Thomas Harmsworth Publishing
13 Nicosia Road
London SW18 3RN

in association with
A. & C. Black (Publishers) Ltd.
35 Bedford Row, London WC1R 4JH

© 1982 Thomas Harmsworth Publishing

ISBN 0-7136-2180-X

Where to Fish.—1982–1983
  1. Fishing—Great Britain—Directories
799.1′025′41   SH605
ISBN 0-7136-2180-X

Printed and bound in Great Britain at
The Pitman Press, Bath

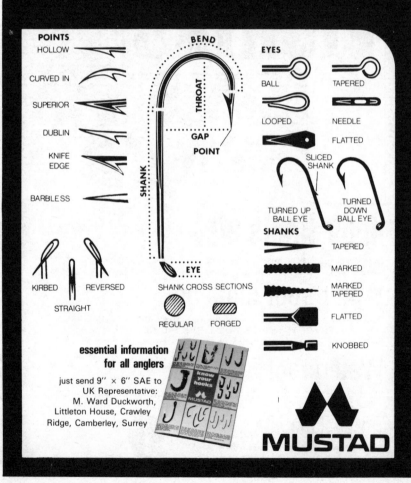

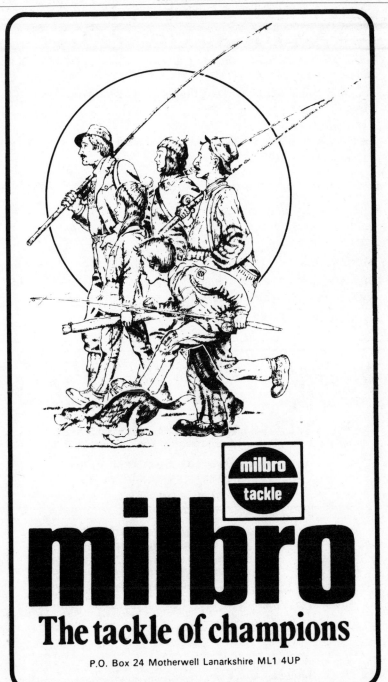

If you're looking for proven reliability - choose SYLCAST LINES

It's a fact that many UK records are held by anglers who rely on Sylcast line. 30 years of excellence speaks for itself so make sure when you tackle up you have the proven line for the job in hand – Sylcast.

MARCO
FISHING TACKLE

Sylcast sew on badge available 90p + 15p S.A.E.
Modern Arms Co. Ltd., Marco Works,
Pembroke Road, Bromley, Kent BR1 2RY

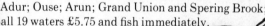

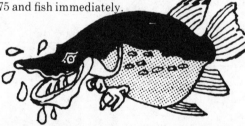

CONTENTS

FISHING IN THE BRITISH ISLES

FISHING ABROAD

For explanation of signs see pages 37–8

Moment of triumph. None the less sweet for the fish having ejected the fly on entering the landing-net. *Photograph: Eric Chalker.*

AS the previous edition of "Where to Fish" went to press in 1978 a panel appointed by the RSPCA to look for avoidable pain caused to animals in the course of shooting and angling was hearing evidence. The panel reported in the spring of 1980, disclosing an opinion, expressed with all due reservations, that such scientific evidence as had been available to it had indicated the probability that those who fished in the belief that fish, as such, were wholly incapable of experiencing pain were mistaken.

It went on to make recommendations on methods and tackle which were far from radical and reflected, in the main, sections of opinion within the sport which had been voiced loud and clear for many years. The evaluation of the panel's findings embarked upon by the angling establishment, working through the National Anglers' Council, was not available for study at the time these notes were compiled, so what additional light may thus be thrown on the contents of this storm-tossed tea-cup must remain a matter of conjecture.

Whatever that particular outcome, all may do well to reflect upon the fact that angling, in common with many other leisure activities (but not all) is often carried out squarely in the eye of public opinion and that the prudent man troubles himself more than a little to avoid the giving of unnecessary offence to his neighbours. That remains true however generally convincing or otherwise the evidence upon which a group of unprejudiced experts, including some of the highest scientific standing, gave their opinion. Impaling a small live fish on a pair of treble hooks to accomplish the capture of a larger fish might be thought an example of offence given. And, in view of the alternative methods open for the achievement of the same purpose, gratuitous offence.

While that panel still sat, a growing body of evidence was in course of assembly to show that casualties on a significant scale were being caused among swans and other waterfowl at places much visited by the general public by accidentally broken or idly discarded fishing tackle, principally monofil line, with or without hooks and lead, and by the ingestion of split lead shot, although there is reason to suspect that other factors may influence the degree to which a bird is harmed by that.

Inevitably, there have been journalists and others, impelled by a variety of not necessarily creditable motives, who have inflated both the magnitude of the likely sufferings of fish, as investigated by the RSPCA panel, and of the number of swans and other birds killed or injured as a side-effect of our sport.

Two duties are therefore laid upon us all. One is to keep ourselves properly informed, so as to be in a position to refute with authority all exaggerated allegations: the other, to be even more careful than the demands of economy and efficiency already make us to select tackle carefully, with avoidance of breakages a high priority, to leave no potentially dangerous litter (or any other sort!) and, where necessary, to clear up that left by less responsible practitioners of the sport.

So much for the clouds: now for the sunshine, gleaming through from a quarter which may surprise some. Not all the effects of inflation and the rating of fisheries have been malignant. Clubs in the remoter areas, better blessed with water than members to fish it are beginning to take a view of life less exclusive than that prevailing when last we published. The mood is now more one of encouragement to the visitor to come, fish, and help balance the budget. It is indeed an ill wind which blows no good to anybody!

Having made all allowances for the consequences of water-abstraction, the inflated cost of re-stocking game-fish waters, also of the cropping of salmon on their ocean feeding-grounds, it can be prophesied that the next few years are likely to offer the richest opportunities for holiday fishing that we have seen during the adult lifetimes of most of those who will benefit from the development. "Tight Lines" should again be something more than a slightly facetious expression of goodwill, uttered with a twinkle in the eye and a tongue in the cheek.

FISHERY AGENTS

ENGLAND

Richard Harris & Co, 125 Eign Street, Hereford. More than 20m of Wye under management. (0432 54455.) (*advt p 176*)

Woosnam and Tyler, Dolgareg, North Road, Builth Wells, Powys. Salmon fishings on Wye, Usk and tributaries. (098 223248.)

Herbert Hatton, St Owen Street, Hereford (2317). Up-to-the-minute information on Wye fishing; applications for advice etc should be accompanied by a stamped/addressed envelope.

Jackson-Stops and Staff, 14 Curzon Street, London W1Y 7FH. (01-499 6291.)

John Sale & Partners, 18–20 Glendale Rd, Wooler, Northumberland (*advt p 32*)

Knight Frank and Rutley, 20 Hanover Square, London W1R 0AH. (01-629 8171.) (*advt p 3*)

Leisure Sport, (Angling), RMC House, Feltham, Middx TW13 4HA.

Rod Box, The, 52 St George's Street, Winchester, Hants. Day or season lettings on some of finest dry fly, chalk stream fishing. Salmon, sea trout fishing in Scotland, Ireland, Norway and Iceland. (0962 61561.) (*advt p 13*)

Savills, 20 Grosvenor Hill, Berkeley Square, London, W1X 0HQ. (01-499 8644.) (*advt p 30*)

Strutt and Parker, 13 Hill Street, Berkeley Square, London, W1X 8DL. (01-629 7282.) (Telex: 8955508 STRUTT G) (*advt p 26*)

John D Wood and Co, 23 Berkeley Square, London W1X 6AL. (01-629 9050.) Scottish Office: 58 George Street, Edinburgh EH2 2LU. (031-225 7178/9.)

WALES

B J Crichton, FRICS, of Messrs W H Cooke & Arkwright, 148 High St, Bangor. (2414.)

South, Mid and West Wales: W V S Corbett, FRICS, of Messrs Cooke & Arkwright, 92 Park St, Bridgend, Mid-Glamorgan CF31 4BD. (55051).

Knight, Frank and Rutley, 14 Broad St, Hereford, HR4 9AL. (0432 3087.) (*advt p 3*)

SCOTLAND

Bell-Ingram, 7 Walker St, Edinburgh EH3 7JY (031-225 3271) and Durn, Isla Rd, Perth (21121). Tweed, Cassley, Tay, Dee, etc. (*advt p 343*)

John Dickson & Son (Inc Forrest & Son), 35 The Square, Kelso (2687). For Tweed and Teviot (Kelso AA trout fisheries). (*advt p 281*)

Fishing Shooting Services Ltd. For salmon fishing on Tweed and Teviot, 4 Weirgate Way, St Boswells, Roxburghshire (2332).

Gordonbush Estate, Brora, Sutherland (323).

Knight, Frank and Rutley, 2 North Charlotte St, Edinburgh EH2 4HR (031-225 7105). (*advt p 3*)

Lovat Estate, Beauly, Inverness (205).

Macsport, 68 Station Road, Banchory, Kinecardineshire (263). Advice on travel and sporting holidays also. (*advt p. 19*)

P D Malloch, 24 Scott Street, Perth (21631).

Mrs J Atkinson, 8 Sinclair Street, Thurso 3291. Halladale and Naver Rivers; trout fishing on lochs.

Major Neil Ramsay & Co, Farleyer, Aberfeldy, Perthshire (Aberfeldy 540). For salmon fishing on upper Tay, two beats.

Sport in Scotland Ltd, 6 Queensgate, Inverness.

Strutt and Parker, 26 Walker St, Edinburgh EH3 7HR (031-226 7431). (*advt p 26*)

Thurso Fisheries Ltd, Thurso East, Thurso, Caithness. (Thurso 3134). River Thurso.

CASTLE LOCH
Lochmaben, Dumfriesshire

The Loch offers first class coarse fishing throughout the year and is well stocked with vendace, roach, perch, eel and large specimens of bream. Subject to booking, clubs may also be accommodated.
   An attractive and secluded Caravan and Camping Park with modern facilities is situated near the Loch.
   Salmon and trout fishing is also available on the River Annan on the Estate Beat which runs a few hundred yards from the Park.
   Further details from: **McJerrow & Stevenson, 55 High Street, Locherbie, Dumfriesshire.**

IRELAND

Battersby & Co, Dublin (77042).
Lisney and Son, 24 St Stephen's Green, Dublin 2 (Telex 25804, 601222, 20 lines).

OVERSEAS

G. Aitken, 32 Offley Road, Kennington S.W.9 (*advt p 414*).
Dunston Brearley, 14 High St, Wombwell, Barnsley (*advt. p 431*).
AA, Fanum House, Basingstoke, Hants (*advt p 335*).
Dyton Angling, 25 High St, Dover, Kent (*advt p 436*)
Pemba Channel Fishing Club, P.O. Box 54, Ukunda, Kenya (*advt p 406*)
Fish America, The Rowans, Nether Tabley, Knutsford, Cheshire (*advt facing p 429*)
Tasmania, Tasmanian Government Tourist Bureau, 80 Elizabeth St, Hobart, Tasmania 7000, Australia (*advt p 414*)

BRITISH FISH FARMS

Annandale Trout Farm, Carse of Ae, Lochmaben (*advt p 34*)
Belleau Bridge Trout Farm, Alford, Lincs. Brown, brook and rainbow trout for stocking. (Swaby 225.)
Berkshire Trout Farm, Lower Denford, Hungerford, Berkshire. Brown, brook and rainbow trout. (Hungerford 04886-2520) (*advt p 34*)
Bibury Trout Farm, Bibury, near Cirencester, Gloucestershire. Rainbow trout bred on Coln. (Bilbury 215.) (*advts pp 14 and 35*)
Bristol Waterworks Company's Trout Hatchery, Woodford Lodge, Chew Stoke, Bristol BS18 8XH. Brown and rainbow trout ova. (Chew Magna 2172.) (*advt p 12*)
Burwarton Trout Farm, Cleobury North, Bridgnorth, Salop WV16 6RP. Browns and rainbows. (074633 601.)
Castle Fisheries (Argyll) Ltd, Low Balantyre, Inverary PA32 8XJ. Brown and rainbow trout. (0499 2233.)
Chirk Fishery Co Ltd, Chirk, Wrexham. Brown, brook and rainbow trout; ova, fry, yearlings and two-year-olds. (Chirk 069186 2420.) (*advt p 34*)
Costa Hatchery, High Costa Mill, Pickering, N. Yorks. Now owned by Yorkshire Water Authority, West Riding House, Albion St, Leeds. Trout supplied within YWA area. Inquiries to Fisheries Officer. Tel: 0751 73770 or 0751 73161
Dunsop Trout Farm, Dunsop Bridge, near Clitheroe, Lancashire, Brown, brook and rainbow trout and ova. (Dunsop Bridge 02008 234.)
Exe Valley Fishery Ltd, Exbridge, Dulverton, Somerset. Brown and rainbow trout available. (Dulverton 23328.)
Game Fisheries, Loch Fitty, Dunfermline. Brown and rainbow trout, all sizes. (Dunfermline 23162 or 031-449 3521.)

Hooke Springs Trout Farm, The Mill House, Hooke, Beaminster, Dorset. Brown and rainbow trout. (Beaminster 862553.) (*advt p 35*)

Howietoun and Northern Fisheries Co Ltd, Stirling FK7 9QH. Brown, rainbow and Loch Leven trout, and salmon and sea trout. (Bannockburn 2473.) (*advt p 35*)

Kenmure Fisheries Ltd, New Galloway, Kirkcudbrightshire. Brown and rainbow trout. (New Galloway 348.)

Kincardine Fisheries, Ardgay, Ross-shire. (Ardgay 251.)

Loch Leven Fishery, Kinross Estates Office, Kinross. Trout. (Kinross 2256.)

Midland Fishery, Nailsworth, Gloucestershire GL6 0PL. Brown and rainbow trout and ova. (Nailsworth 2053.)

North Cheshire Fisheries, 1972 Highland Road, Lymm, Cheshire. Coarse fish.

Rock Mill Trout Farm, Membury, nr Axminster, Devon. Rainbow trout. (Stockland 472.)

Solway Fisheries, New Abbey, Dumfries. Brown, brook and rainbow trout. (New Abbey 235.)

South Wales Fishery, nr Kington, Herefordshire. Trout.

Southburgh Trout Farm, Thetford, Norfolk. Brown and rainbow trout, all sizes, free delivery. (Hingham 295.)

Stambridge Trout Fisheries, Great Stambridge, near Rochford, Essex. King carp and tench; brown and rainbow trout and goldfish. (Canewdon 274.)

Thurso Fisheries Ltd, Thurso East, Thurso, Caithness, Salmon: eyed ova and fry. (Thurso 3134.)

Trent Fish Culture Co Ltd, Mercaston, Brailsford, near Derby DE6 3BL. Brown and rainbow trout and ova. Also American brook trout. Fry, yearlings and two-year-olds to 13 in; larger fish on application. (Brailsford 318.) (*advt p 34*)

Watermill Trout Farms Ltd, Westgate Mill, Louth, Lincs. Brown and rainbow trout. (Louth 2424.)

Welham Park Fish Hatcheries Ltd, Malton, Yorkshire. Brown, rainbow and Loch Leven trout. (Malton 3785.)

Westacre Fishery, King's Lynn, Norfolk. Brown and rainbow trout for immediate delivery. (Castleacre 240.)

Whitebrook Fisheries, Whitebrook, nr Llanvaches, Newport, Mon. Brown and rainbow trout, coarse fish. Fishery management services. (Penhow 400 276.)

Wye Valley Fisheries, Tyn-y-Cwm Mill, Beulah, Llanwrtyd Wells, Powys. Salmon, brown and rainbow trout, coarse fish when available. Technical advice on fishery management. (Talybont 229.)

N	Northumbrian Water Authority
NW	North West Water Authority
Y	Yorkshire Water Authority
S-T	Severn-Trent Water Authority
WWA	Welsh Water Authority
A	Anglian Water Authority
T	Thames Water Authority
S	Southern Water Authority
W	Wessex Water Authority
SW	South West Water Authority

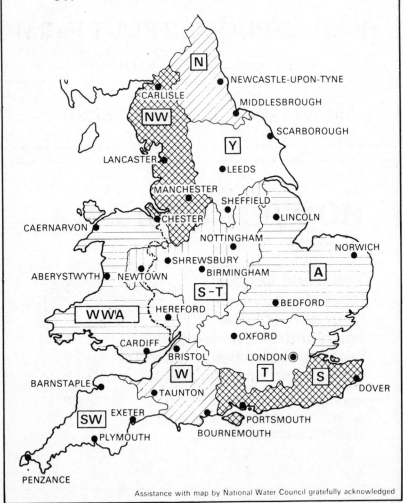

Assistance with map by National Water Council gratefully acknowledged

FISHING IN ENGLAND and WALES

Regional Water Authorities, Close Seasons, Licence Duties, etc.

THE 1973 Water Act, under which the Regional Water Authorities were set up, did not lay down a single pattern for organisation, sub-division and nomenclature. For the sake of simplicity and uniformity the letters RD (River Division) are used in the general text of this publication to denote sub-divisions of Authorities, whether or not these correspond precisely with individual river-basins. In addition to licences authorising the holder to fish a single river-system, there are now in being regional licences to cover some or all of the river-systems within an Authority area. Where developments of this sort have not yet occurred, they may well be in the offing.

Readers may be aware of the fact that there has been a change in the law respecting what used to be a firm statutory close season for coarse fish. The act gives Water Authorities a wide discretion on this matter, but in practice little has changed so far. Close seasons for coarse fish remain widely in force, often by desire of the anglers themselves, expressed to the Water Authorities through their organizations. The way, however, is now open for the abolition of the close season for coarse fish, should public opinion move in that direction. If it so happens, the process is likely to be piecemeal.

Statutory close seasons for other fish are as follows: salmon; 1 November to 31 January. Trout excluding rainbow trout; 1 October to the last day of February.

The 1973 Act, despite financial difficulties suffered ever since to a greater or lesser degree, has stimulated a greater activity in fisheries research and management than was common previously. There have been a number of amendments to bye-laws and the position has not yet stabilised.

It is therefore essential for anglers to make detailed local enquiries regarding the local statutory position respecting licences and seasons before visiting the waterside. The officers given in the various sections which follow under the headings of the RWAs are the authoritative source of information, but tackle shops may be relied upon to keep themselves briefed as changes occur. Where a licence is in force, it is an offence to fish without one. The burden is on the angler to make himself aware of the position wherever he may be fishing. Ignorance is not accepted as an excuse.

Anglers are reminded that the expression 'immature' in relation to salmon means that the fish is less than 12in long; taking immature salmon is prohibited throughout England and Wales. In relation to other fish the expression 'immature' means that the fish is of a length less than that prescribed by bye-law. Unless otherwise stated, it may be assumed that the length is measured from the tip of the snout to the fork of the tail.

The word 'salmon' means all fish of the salmon species. The word 'trout' means all fish of the salmon species commonly known as trout. The expression 'migratory trout' means trout that migrate to and from the sea. The expression 'freshwater (ie coarse) fish' means any fish living in fresh water except salmon, trout, all kinds of fish which migrate to and from tidal water, eels and their fry.

NOTE: *In the following lists, telephone numbers are given to enable anglers to contact officers outside office hours. This facility is included specifically to enable prompt advice to be given in cases of serious pollution. Anglers are asked to use these numbers with discretion and not to disturb officers in their off-duty hours unnecessarily.*

Abbreviations: The following abbreviations are used throughout the book; S, salmon; T, trout; MT, migratory trout; NT, non-migratory trout; C, char; FF or FW, freshwater (ie coarse fish); RD, River Division (or its equivalent); s, season; m, month (Water Authority list only); f, fortnight; w, week; d, day; t, ticket; ns, nearest railway station. In the

lists of fishing stations the abbreviation m means mile or miles, except
when it is used in conjunction with t, ie, mt, when it means monthly
ticket. Likewise, st means season ticket, wt weekly ticket, dt daily ticket,
and so on.

SOUTHERN WATER AUTHORITY, Guildbourne House, Worthing, Sussex BN11
1LD. (Supplanting former Kent, Sussex, Hampshire and IoW Authorities.)
Principal Fisheries Officer: J R Chandler, BSc, MIBiol, FZS, MIWPC.

Rivers controlled: Medway, Stour, Rother, RM Canal, Adur, Arun, Ouse, Cuckmere, all
rivers in Pevensey Levels, Test, Itchen, Hamble, Meon, Beaulieu, Lymington, Fletch,
Keyhaven, Eastern Yar, Medina, and the tributaries of all these rivers.

Area offices.

    Kent: 78, College Road, Maidstone.
Pollution reporting: Maidstone 55211 (emergency 999—Police link).

    Sussex: Anston House, 137/139, Preston Road, Brighton.
Pollution reporting: Brighton 606766.

    Hampshire: Eastleigh House, 2, Market Street, Eastleigh.
Pollution reporting: Twyford 713622 or Southampton 27017.

    I.O.Wight: St. Nicholas, 58, St. John's Road, Newport.
Pollution reporting: Newport 526611 or Sandown 2106.

Seasons: S—17 January to 2 October. MT—1 May to 31 October. NT—3 April to 31
October. FF—16 June to 14 March.

Licences: For the whole of the Southern Water Authority area. (No divisional licences
issued.) S s £17, ft £5.75, d £2.85. MT & T, s £5.60, ft £1.50, s (junior) £1.50. FF s £2.75, m
£1.50, s (junior) £0.75. OAP and regd. disabled—free.

Supplementary licences: s £0.50, period 0.20, junior 0.10.

SOUTH WEST WATER AUTHORITY, 3/5 Barnfield Road, Exeter EX1 1RE. (Supplant-
ing former Devon and Cornwall River Authorities.)
Pollution reporting: Telephone operator and ask for Freephone 920.

    DIVISION I: Victoria Square, Bodmin, Cornwall. (Tel: 3131.)
Fisheries and Recreation Officer: R. Furniss, BSc.
Rivers controlled: Camel, Fowey, East and West Looe, Western rivers and tributaries.

    DIVISION II: Southcott, Chapple, Launceston, Cornwall PL15 7AX. (Tel: 2151/5.)
Fisheries and Recreation Officer: E S Bray, BSc, AMIWPC.
Rivers controlled: Tamar, Tavy, Lynher, Taw, Torridge and tributaries.

    DIVISION III: 3/5 Barnfield Road, Exeter. (Tel: 50861.)
Fisheries and Recreation Officer: C V M Davies, BSc, MIBiol.
Rivers controlled: Axe, Exe, Lyn, Otter, Sid, Avon, Dart, Erme and Teign and
tributaries.

Licences: for whole SWWA area. S & MT, s £16, w £8, d £2. Concession: S & MT, s £8, d
£1. NT, s £4, w £2, d £0.75. Concession, s £2. FW, s £1, Concession £0.50. Concessions for
OAP, regd. disabled, juv. under 16 yrs (birth cert. req.) students under 18 yrs. (certified).
Seasons. Salmon: Avon—15 April to 30 November E. Remainder of district—15 March to
31 October. Axe—14 March to 31 October. Camel—1 April to 15 December. Dart—1
February to 16 September E. Exe—14 February to 30 September. Fowey—1 April to 15
December. Tamar & Plym (Plym—1 April to 15 December) (Yealm—1 April to 15
December E) remainder of district—1 March to 14 October. Taw & Torridge (Lyn—1
February to 31 October) remainder of district—1 March to 30 September. Teign—1
February to 31 August E. Migratory trout. Axe—15 April to 31 October. Avon—15 April
to 30 September E. Camel—1 April to 30 September. Fowey—1 April to 30 September.
Tamar & Plym—3 March to 30 September. Teign—15 March to 12 October. Other fishery
districts—15 March to 30 September. Brown trout. Rivers and streams, entire region—15
March to 30 September. Other waters, entire region—15 March to 12 October. Rainbow

trout. Entire region—no close season. Coarse fish. Axe, Avon, Dart, Exe, Teign, Taw and Torridge—16 June to 14 March. Camel, Fowey, Tamar and Plym—no close season. "E". As part of the Authority's strategy on salmon cropping, the season on some rivers has been changed experimentally. These are indicated with the letter "E" at the end of the note. Waters are not necessarily kept open for the full duration of the season. Check with the fishery owner before making plans.

WESSEX WATER AUTHORITY, Wessex House, Passage Street, Bristol BS2 0JQ.
(Supplanting Bristol Avon River Authority, Avon & Dorset River Authority, Somerset River Authority.)
Chief Fisheries and Recreations Officer: Major T Wills, MBE. (Tel: Bristol 290611.)
Principal Assistant: A J R Barber.
Pollution reporting: to the Regional Control Centre: Freephone 9917.

Avon and Dorset Division
Divisonal Fisheries and Recreations Officer: Dr D Wilkinson, Wessex Water Authority, Avon and Dorset Division, 2 Nuffield Road, Poole, Dorset. (Tel: 02013 (STD) 71144.)
Rivers controlled: Hampshire Avon and Stour, Frome, Piddle, Brit and Char. (All rivers entering the sea between Lyme Regis and Christchurch.)
Close seasons: S, Avon and Stour—30 September to 1 February. All other waters—30 September to 1 March. MT—31 October to 15 April. NT, River Avon and tributaries above Bickton Mill—15 October to 15 April. All other waters—15 October to 1 April. FF—14 March to 16 June.
Licences: Details below.

Bristol Avon Division
Divisional Fisheries and Recreations Officer: M J Amey, Wessex Water Authority, Bristol Avon Division, P.O. Box 95, Broad Quay, Bath BA1 2YP. (Tel: Bath 0225 (STD) 27541.)
Rivers controlled: Bristol Avon and tributaries.
Close seasons: S—30 September to 1 February. MT—31 October to 15 April. NT—15 October to 1 April. FF—14 March to 16 June.
Licences: Details below.

Somerset Division
Divisional Fisheries and Recreations Officer: C B Arden, Wessex Water Authority, Somerset Division, P.O. Box 9, King Square, Bridgwater, Somerset TA6 3EA. (Tel: Bridgwater 0278 (STD) 57333.)
Rivers controlled: Axe, Brue, Parrett and their tributaries, including Tone, Huntspill, King's Sedgemoor Drain and Bridgwater and Taunton Canal.
Close seasons: S—30 September to 1 February. MT—31 October to 15 April. NT—15 October to 1 April. FF—14 Match to 16 June.

Licences: S, MT, NT, FF; s £20. S; d £3.60. MT, NT, FF; s £7.10, w £1.80. FF; s £5.25, w £1.30. Half-price licences for juniors, (12–15 yrs incl.) OAP and regd. disabled. These licences are valid anywhere in the Region.

NORTH WEST WATER AUTHORITY, Dawson House, Gt Sankey, Warrington WA5 3LW. (Supplanting former Lancashire, Cumberland and Mersey & Weaver River Authorities.)
Regional Fisheries Officer: J D Kelsall. NWWA, Rivers Division, P.O. Box 12, New Town House, Buttermarket Street, Warrington WA1 2QG. Tel: 53999.
Pollution reporting: 8.45 am to 5.00 pm: Warrington 52999. Other times: 061 370 2645.

Northern Area
Fisheries Officer: Dr C Harpley, Rivers Div. NWWA, Chertsey Hill, London Road, Carlisle CA1 2QX.
Rivers controlled: Annas, Esk, Mite, Irt, Bleng, Calder, Ehen, Keekle, Marron, Derwent, Cocker, Greta, Ellen, Waver, Wampool, Eden, Caldew, Petteril, Eamont, Leith, Lyvennet, Lowther, Irthing, Esk (Border), Liddle, Lyne, Lune, Keer, Bela, Kent, Winster, Lever, Crake, Duddon and their tributaries, and the lakes Wastwater, Ennerdale Water, Loweswater, Crummock Water, Buttermere, Bassenthwaite, Derwentwater,

Thirlmere, Ullswater, Brotherswater, Haweswater, Windermere, Coniston, Grasmere, Rydal Water, Elterwater, etc.
Close seasons: Salmon, 1 November to 31 January, except (1) R. Eden system—15 October to 14 January, (2) Rivers Annas, Bleng, Esk, Mite, Irt, Calder and Ehen—1 November to 31 March, (3) Rivers Derwent, Ellen, Waver and Wampool—1 November to 14 February, (4) R. Lune—16 October to 31 March. **Migratory trout,** 16 October to 30 April, except rivers Annas, Bleng, Esk, Mite, Irt, Calder and Ehen—1 November to 30 April. **Trout,** 1 October to 14 March (Ullswater—15 October to 14 January). MT—1 November to 2 April (Ullswater—15 October to 31 March). T—15 September to 19 March (Ullswater—1 October to 19 March). Char (Crummock Water and Buttermere)—1 November to 30 June. Other lakes—15 September to 19 March.

Southern Area
Fisheries Officer: R D Parker, Rivers Div. NWWA, Bancroft House, Liverpool Road, Gt. Sankey, Warrington.
Rivers controlled: Ribble, Wyre, Mersey, Irwell, Bollin, Weaver, Dane, Gowy and their tributaries.
Close seasons: S—1 November to 31 January. MT—16 October to 30 April. NT—1 October to 14 March.
Coarse fish close season: (for whole NWWA area)—15 March to 15 June.

Licences: S s £18. 1 June to end of season (including MT and FW) £12. s (concession) £9. 1 June to end of season (including MT and FW) (concession) £6. w £3. MT. s £6. s (concession) £3. w £1.20. NT (brown, rainbow, char) and FW. s £3.60, s (concession) £1.80, w £0.60. Reduced duty licences—"concession"—are available to juniors 14–16 yrs. incl., men 65 yrs and more, women 60 yrs. and more; regd. disabled.

NORTHUMBRIAN WATER AUTHORITY, Northumbria House, Regent Centre, Gosforth, Newcastle-upon-Tyne NE3 3PX.
Chief Fisheries Officer: D J Iremonger, Directorate of Planning and Scientific Services at the above address. (Tel: 0632 (STD) 843151, ext 298.)
Pollution reporting: To the above.
Rivers controlled: Aln, Coquet, Wansbeck, Blyth, Tyne, Wear, Tees and tributaries, and all other rivers flowing into North Sea between Goswick Sands in the north and White Stones, Boulby Cliff, near Staithes, Yorks, other than the Tweed and its tributaries.
Close seasons: S—1 November to 31 January. MT—1 November to 2 April. NT—1 October to 21 March. FF—statutory for rivers and streams. Still-waters: no close season.
Licences: Decisions still pending as we go to press. Apply for details to NWA Chief Fisheries Officer.

YORKSHIRE WATER AUTHORITY, West Riding House, 67 Albion Street, Leeds LS1 5AA. (Tel: 0532 (STD) 448201.)
Assistant Amenity, Fisheries and Recreations Officer: Dr D J Shillcock, located at Head Office.
Pollution reporting: To Head Office, or outside office hours, in emergency, Barkston Ash 348.
Rivers controlled: Yorkshire Ouse, its tributaries (including Ure, Wharfe, Nidd, Derwent, Swale, Aire, Don and Calder and their tributaries); Yorkshire Esk and tributaries, Hull and tributaries, part of Humber and all tributaries of Humber from Blacktoft to Spurn Point, Hornsea Mere, all rivers entering sea between Spurn Point and White Stones to the west of Staithes near Whitby, and all lakes, canals and reservoirs within Authority's area.
Close seasons: S and MT—1 November to 5 April. NT—1 October to 24 March. FF—28 February to 31 May. Gaff permitted between 31 March and 1 October. Fishing on Esk between Ruswarp Weir and Ruswarp Road Bridge, Whitby, is prohibited. Fishing also forbidden on Whitby Esk at certain times.
Licences: S and MT, Esk and tributaries and waters in the area lying to the north of the Esk, s £24, w £9.60, d £4.80. Remainder of area: s £3, w £1.20. OAPs, regd. disabled and juniors aged less than 14 yrs. are not required to take out licences.

ANGLIAN WATER AUTHORITY, Diploma House, Grammar School Walk, Huntingdon PE18 6NZ. (Tel: 0480 (STD) 56181.)
Assistant Director, Admin (Estates and Recreation): F G Davy, DSO, DFC, FRICS.

Assistant Director, Scientific Services (Fisheries): A J Miller, MInst, WPC. Same address and phone number as Mr F G Davy.
Licences: (Uniform throughout Authority area.) Salmon, trout, fw fish and eels.
Regional. Standard: annual £2.75, 7-day 40p. Juveniles (12–15 incl.) annual £1.40. Retired persons (M 65+, F 60+), annual 70p.
Divisional (all annual): Standard £1. Juvenile 50p. Retired persons 25p.

Lincolnshire River Division: Anglian Water Authority (Lincolnshire River Division), 50 Wide Bargate, Boston, Lincs PE21 6SA. (Tel: 0205 (STD) 5661.)
Divisional Scientist: F Ackroyd, AMInst, WPC.
Fisheries Officer: P Kalinowski.
Pollution reporting: To Divisional Scientist.
Rivers controlled: Witham and tributaries, including Slea and Bain, Steeping River, Ancholme, South Forty Foot Drain, Hobhole Drain, East and West Fen Drains, etc.
Close seasons: T—statutory. FF—15 March to 14 June.
NB: Enclosed waters now exempted from any closed season.

Welland and Nene River Division: Anglian Water Authority (Welland and Nene River Division) North Street, Oundle, Peterborough PE8 4AS. (Tel: 08322 (STD) 3701.)
Divisional Scientist: R E Field, AMInst, WPC.
Assistant Fisheries Officer: D Moore, BSc.
Pollution reporting: To Divisional Scientist.
Rivers controlled: Welland and tributaries. Nene and tributaries.
Close seasons: NT—30 September to 25 March. FF—15 March to 15 June, except pike (15 March to 30 September).

Norfolk and Suffolk River Division: Anglian Water Authority (Norfolk and Suffolk Rivers Division), Yare House, 62/64 Thorpe Road, Norwich.
Divisional Scientist: F W Roberts, FRIC, MInst, WPC.
Fisheries Officer: C K Jones. (Tel: 0603 (STD) 615161.)
Pollution reporting: To Divisional Scientist.
Rivers controlled: Bure, Yare, Waveney, Blyth, Deben, Gipping, Galven, Stiffkey and their tributaries, all other rivers and their tributaries, and all lakes and other waters in the counties of Norfolk and Suffolk between but excluding the Heacham River in the north-west to and including the River Gipping and its estuary, the Orwell, in the south-east.
Close seasons: T—1 October to last day of March. FF—15 March to 15 June.

Gt Ouse River Division: Anglian Water Authority (Gt Ouse River Division), Gt Ouse House, Clarendon Road, Cambridge CB2 2BL. (Tel: 0223 (STD) 61561.)
Division Scientist: S B Livesey.
Fisheries Officer: C H A Fennell.
Pollution reporting: To Divisional Scientist.
Rivers controlled: Great Ouse (including Relief Channel from Denver Sluice to just beyond Saddle Bow Bridge), Cam and tributaries.
Close seasons: T—14 October to 31 March. FF (including eels with rod and line)—15 March to 15 June inclusive. Pike and zander—15 March to 30 August. Use of gorge bait in connection with fishing with rod and line for pike prohibited.

Essex River Division: Anglian water Authority (Essex River Division), Rivers House, Springfield Road, Chelmsford, Essex CM2 6JN. (Tel: 0245 (STD) 64721.)
Divisional Scientist: G M Eastman, BSc, ARIC, AMInst, WPC.
Fisheries Officer: E Pearson.
Pollution reporting: To Divisional Scientist.
Rivers controlled: Stour, Colne, Blackwater, Chelmer, Crouch and their tributaries, and all other streams in Essex except the Lee, the Stort and their tributaries.
Close seasons: T—1 October to last day of February. FF—15 March to 15 June, except pike, 15 March to 30 September.

SEVERN-TRENT WATER AUTHORITY, Abelson House, 2297 Coventry Road, Sheldon, Birmingham B26 3PR. (Supplanting former Severn and Trent River Authorities.)
Assistant Director of Scientific Services (Fisheries, Amenities and Recreation): M L Parry. (Tel: 021-743 4222.)

Severn Area
Fisheries Manager: A S Churchward, Severn-Trent Water Authority, Severn Area Laboratories, 64 Albert Road North, Malvern, Worcs. (Tel: 61511.)
Pollution reports: To this address.
Rivers controlled: Severn, Warwickshire Avon, Teme, Vyrnwy (excluding Lake Vrynwy and brooks running into it), Banwy, Tanat, Tern, Roden, Meese, Perry and all other tributary streams in the Severn watershed as well as canals and pools (including Clywedog Reservoir). The Authority also owns or rents water on the Avon and Severn (details on licence).
Close seasons: S—30 September to 2 February. T and C—16 October to 17 March in lakes and reservoirs. 1 October to 17 March in other waters (all dates inclusive).

Trent Area
Fisheries Manager: R G Templeton, Severn-Trent Water Authority, Trent Area Laboratories, Meadow Lane, Nottingham. (Tel: 0602 (STD) 865007.)
Pollution reports: To this address.
Rivers controlled: Trent, Soar, Tame, Derbyshire Derwent, Dove, Manifold, Churnet, Derbyshire Wye and their tributaries, all other waters in the area.
Close seasons: Brown trout—16 October to 17 March. Rainbow trout: in Rivers Derwent and Amber, and their tributaries, upstream of their confluence except between Blackwell Mill and Cressbrook Mill and above Ashford on Derbyshire Wye. On these fisheries, from 14 November to 15 May. No close season in any other waters in S-TWA area.
Licences: Whole area: T and FF, s £1.50, 28-day 50p, s (OAP) 20p.
Severn Catchment. S, s £10, s (restr) £7.50, d £1.50. T and FF, s £1. Trent Catchment. S, T and FF, s £1.

THAMES WATER AUTHORITY, New River Head Laboratories, 177 Rosebery Avenue, London EC1R 4TP. (Supplanting the former Thames Conservancy Board, Lea Conservancy Catchment Board, Essex, River Authority in respect of Roding, Ingrebourne and Beam, Kent River Authority in respect of Darent and Cray, and Port of London Authority in respect of fisheries).
Amenity and Fisheries Manager: D Parton, Thames Water Authority, Reading Bridge House, Reading. (Tel: 593333.)
Fisheries Officer: M J Bulleid, MSc, BSc, Thames Water Authority, Reading Bridge House, Reading. (Tel: 593333.)

Thames Conservancy Division: River Thames Catchment above Teddington Lock.
Fishery Inspector: Dr J W Banks, 5th Floor, Nugent House, Vastern Road, Reading, Berkshire. (Tel: 593333.)

Lea Division: Catchments of River Lea and River Roding.
Fishery Inspector: J A Reeves, The Grange, Crossbrook Street, Waltham Cross, Herts. (Tel: Waltham Cross 23611.)

Metropolitan Pollution Control: London area, Tidal Thames, Catchments of the Rivers Darent and Cray.
Fishery Inspector: Mr J Percival, Crossness Sewage Treatment Works, Abbey Wood, London SE2 9AQ. (Tel: 01-310 5500.)

River Pollution, Fish Mortality and Disease. Reports by Members of the Public: London Tidal Thames, Darent and Cray: 01-310 5500 (office hours), 01-837 3300 (all times).
Thames Catchment (Thames and all tributaries above Teddington Lock). Thames Conservancy Division. Office hours (0900–1700 hrs) Reading 55268. Outside office hours Reading 593333. If preferred, pollution may be reported during office hours to the three local pollution control offices of the Division. Oxford 721125. River Thames above Day's Lock (Dorchester). The River Kennet and all other upper tributaries apart from the River Thame. Amersham 5816. River Thames from Day's Lock to Sonning Bridge, the River Thame, The River Colne and streams in the Chilterns. Guildford 77655. River Thames from Sonning Bridge to Teddington and the Rivers Hogsmill, Mole, Wey, Loddon and minor streams in this area.

Lea and Roding Catchment. Office hours: Waltham Cross 23611. Other times Roydon 3241.

Seasons: brown trout; 1 April to 30 September, rainbow trout (rivers) 1 April to 30 September, rainbow trout (stillwater) no close season. FW 16 June to 14 March.

Licences: T and FW; s £4. ft £1. s (OAP and regd. disabled) £1. Annual licences run from 1 April to 31 March.

WELSH WATER AUTHORITY, Cambrian Way, Brecon, Powys. (Supplanting all former Welsh River Authorities and the Wye River Authority.)

Director Scientific Services: W Roscoe Howells.
Assistant Director (Recreation): J R Hampson, located at Head Office.

CLOSE SEASONS FOR ROD AND LINE FISHING

DIVISIONAL AREA	DEE & CLWYD	GWYNEDD	W WALES	GOWER	TAFF	USK	WYE
SALMON	R. Dee and tributaries 17th Oct–26th Jan. R. Clwyd and tributaries 17th Oct–20th March.			All waters 17th Oct–20th March.		All waters 17th Oct–26th Jan.	Above Llanwrthwl Bridge 26th Jan–25th Oct. Below: 26th Jan–17th Oct. All tributaries 26th Jan–25th Oct.
SEA TROUT				All waters 17th Oct–20th March.			
BROWN TROUT			Brown trout in rivers (General) 30th Sept–3rd March. Brown trout in rivers (lower reaches —see byelaws) 30th Sept–31st May. Brown trout in still waters (General) 17th Oct–20th March.				
RAINBOW TROUT	Llyn Tegid (Bala) 14th Aug–15th Jan.	Llyn Trawsfynydd 31st Aug–1st Feb.	Rainbow trout in rivers 30th Sept–3rd March. Rainbow trout in still waters No close season.				
FRESH-WATER FISH	All waters 14th March–16th Jan.	No close season.				All waters 14th March–16th June.	
EELS	No close period.			Close period 14th March–16th June.		No close period below George St, Newport.	No close period.

* N.B. Fishing is permitted on the above enumerated dates but not in the period between them.

LICENCES
1. Salmon and migratory trout

Every angler fishing for salmon or sea trout must possess a licence of the appropriate class and category for the water to be fished. Each water has been placed into one of four classes A, C, D or E depending upon the general quality of the fishing the better waters

CLASS	RIVER	CLASSIFIED AREA OF RIVER
A	WYE	main river below Llanwrthwl Bridge (see also class C waters)
	CONWY	main river between Conwy Falls and Dolgarrog (see also class D waters)
	DEE	main river below R Alwen junction (see also class D waters)
	DYFI	entire main river (see also class D waters)
C	TEIFI	main river below Lampeter Bridge
	TYWI	main river below Brianne Dam (see also class D waters)
	—(Cothi)	main river below Aberbranddu Falls
	USK	entire main river
	WYE	main river above Llanwrthwl Bridge (see also class A waters)
D	AERON	entire main river
	ALWEN	entire main river
	EAST CLEDDAU	entire main river
	WEST CLEDDAU	entire main river
	CLWYD	entire main river
	—(Elwy)	(see also class C waters)
	CONWY	entire main river
	—(Lledr)	main river below Swallow Falls
	—(Llugwy)	(see also class C waters)
	DEE	between Bala sluices and Alwen confluence
	—(Dee)	
	—(Alwen)	entire main river
	DWYFAWR	entire main river

CLASS	RIVER	CLASSIFIED AREA OF RIVER
	DWYRYD	main river below Rhydysarn (see also class C waters)
	DYFI	entire main river
	—(Twymyn)	entire main river
	—(Dulas North)	entire main river
	—(Dulas South)	entire main river
	—(Cleifion)	entire main river below Bont
	DYSYNNI	entire main river below Bont Abergynolwen
	EDEN	main river below Bont Dolgefeiliau
	ELWY	entire main river
	GLASLYN	entire main river (including Llynnoedd Dinas and Gwynant)
D	GWYRFAI	entire main river
	LLYFNI	entire main river
	LOUGHOR	entire main river
	MAWDDACH	entire main river
	—(Eden)	main river below Bont Dolgefeiliau
	NEATH	main river below confluence with R Melle
	NEVERN	entire main river
	OGMORE	main river below confluence of main Ogwr Fawr and Ogwr Fach
	OGWEN	entire main river
	RHEIDOL	main river below Cyfarllwyd Falls
	SEIONT	entire main river (including Llynnoedd Padarn and Peris)
	TAFF	entire main river
	TYWI	(see also class C waters)
	—(Gwili)	entire main river
	YSTWYTH	main river below Llanfan Bridge
E	OTHERS	*All rivers, tributaries and streams not specifically included by name as Class A, B, C or D waters above are classified as Class E.*

are in classes A and C, the poorest waters are in classes D and E. Some rivers contain waters in more than one class. (The old class B licence, covering the Usk has been abolished from 1980 and the waters incorporated into class C.)

A licence for a particular class of water entitles the angler to fish in all waters of the same or lower class but not waters of a higher class. For example, a class C licence covers all waters of classes C, D and E but not waters of class A.

Categories of licence are season, week and day. There are concessions for juveniles and OAP's for the season category only.

Weekly licences cover a period of 168 hours.

	A	C	D	E
Full Season	£37.25	£18.65	£12.40	£9.80
Concession Season	£18.65	£9.45	£6.20	£4.90
Week	£18.65	£9.45	£6.20	£4.90
Day	£6.20	£3.20	£2.05	£1.95

A licence for salmon/sea trout also covers non-migratory trout, freshwater fish and eels.

2. Non-Migratory Trout

These licences cover the entire WWA area, including rivers, lakes and ponds etc. There are three categories, season, week and day but juvenile and OAP concessions are allowed only on season categories.

Full Season	Concession Season	Week	Day
£5.20	£2.60	£3.10	£1.50

A licence for non-migratory trout also covers freshwater fish and eels.

3. Coarse Fish and Eels

These licences cover the entire WWA area. There are two categories of licence, season and day, but juvenile and OAP concessions apply only to the season category.

Full Season	Concession Season	Day
£3.10	£1.55	£1.05

In all cases a juvenile is defined as someone under 16 years of age and an OAP is a person in receipt of a state retirement pension at the time of issue of the licence.

DIVISIONS OF THE AUTHORITY

Dee and Clwyd Division: Shire Hall, Mold, Clwyd. (Tel: (0352) 58551.)
Divisional Manager: R J D Dixon.
Fisheries Officer: B Hodgson.
Rivers Controlled: Dee (Welsh) Clwyd, Elwy, Alwen, Alyn, Ceiriog, Ceirw, Lliw, Tryweryn, Twrch, Bala Lake and their feeders.

Gower Division: 86 The Kingsway, Swansea, Mid Glam. (Tel: (0792) 468000.)
Divisional Manager: D N W Earp.
Fisheries Officer: A Harvey.
Rivers Controlled: Neath, Afon, Kenfig, Ogmore and Ewenny.

Gwynedd Division: Penrhos Road, Penrhosgarnedd, Bangor, Gwynedd. (Tel: (0248) 51144.)
Divisional Manager: A Groves.
Fisheries Officer: P Parkinson.
Rivers Controlled: Waters in an area bounded by watersheds of rivers (including their tributaries and all lakes) running into the sea between the eastern boundary of the Division's area at Old Gwyrch, Denbighshire, and the southern extremity at Upper Borth, Cardiganshire. The principal rivers are: Dulas, Conway, Lledr, Llugwy (with Lakes Elsi, Crafnant, Cowlyd, Eigiau, Conway, Melynllyn, Dulyn), Aber, Ogwen (with Lakes Anafon, Ogwen, Idwal, Ffynnon, Loer), all waters in Anglesey, Seiont, Gwyrfai, Llyfni (with Lakes Padarn, Cwellyn, Gader, Nantlle), Erch, Soch, Rhydhir, Afon Wen, Dwyfawr, Dwyfach (with Lake Cwmystradllyn), Glaslyn, Dwyryd, Prysor (with Lakes Dinas, Gwynant, Llagi Adar, Trawsfynydd, Gamallt, Morwynion, Cwmorthin), Glyn, Eisingrug (with Lakes Tecwyn Isaf, Techwyn Uchaf), Artro, Mawddach, Eden, Wnion

(with Lakes Cwm Bychan, Bodlyn, Gwernan, Gregennen), Dysynny, Dovey, Dulas, Twymyn (with Lake Tal-y-Llyn).

Taff Division: Medallion House, Crwys Road, Cardiff. (Tel: (0222) 399961).
Divisional Manager: J E Roberts.
Fisheries Officer: J Davies.
Rivers Controlled: Ely, Taff and Rhymney.

Usk Division: Station Buildings, Station Road, Newport, Gwent. (Tel: (0633) 840404.)
Divisional Manager: P Beard.
Fisheries Officer: J Lambert.
Rivers Controlled: Usk and tributaries, including Cilienni, Honddu, Yscir, Bran, Cray, Senni, Tarrell, Cynrig, Crawnon, Rhiangoll, Gwryne-fawr, Grwyne-fechan, Olway, Afon Lwyd and Sirhowy.

West Wales Division: Meyler House, St Tomas Green, Haverfordwest, Dyfed. (Tel: (0437) 5551.)
Divisional Manager: H Prothero.
Fisheries Officer: R Millichamp.
Rivers Controlled: Towy, Teifi, Taf, Eastern and Western Cleddau, Gwaun, Nevern, Aeron, Clarach, Rheidol, Ystwyth, Tawe (Swansea), Wyre, Llwchwr, Amman, Gwendraeth Fach, Gwendraeth Fawr, and the tributaries of these rivers.

Wye Divison: 4 St John's Street, Hereford. (Tel: (0432) 6313.)
Divisional Manager: T Russell.
Fisheries Officer: E Staite.
Rivers Controlled: Wye and all rivers and brooks of the Wye watershed including Monnow, Trothy, Lugg, Arrow, Ithon and Irfon.

ENGLISH FISHING STATIONS

MAIN catchments are given in alphabetical order, fishing stations listed in mouth to source order, first main river, then tributaries. Where national borders are crossed—e.g. Wye and Border Esk—allocation has been arbitrary. Some small streams have been grouped in counties rather than catchments.

Water Authority rod licences are now required almost everywhere in England and Wales for all freshwater fishing. Details appear on pages 37–46. A list of fishing clubs appears at the end of each national section. "Free fishing" means only that a riparian owner is reputed to allow fishing without making a charge. It does not imply a right and such information should be checked locally before an attempt to fish is made. All charges shown are exclusive of VAT unless otherwise stated.

ADUR

(For close seasons, licences, etc, see Southern Water Authority, p 38)

Rises SW of Horsham and flows into the English Channel at Shoreham. A coarse-fish river of no great reputation, but occasionally provides good sport.

Shoreham (Sussex). Bass, codling, flats, eels, mullet from harbour and shore.

Steyning (Sussex). Carp, dace, roach, bream. Steyning and District AS has 3m from Beeding Bridge (tidal water; low water best) to Streatham Bridge; dt from Railway Hotel and Searles, High St; News Shop, Beeding Bridge, Upper Beeding. CALPAC has from footbridge at end of Northover Farm Road downstream to Streatham Bridge, sharing last 200 yards with Steyning AS. Members only

Henfield (Sussex). Roach, bream, perch, chub, dace (mullet good Sept). Henfield AS and Comrades AC have fishing rights on about 8m and canal. No dt. Apply hon sec Henfield AS for annual membership (£6). Lake at Bolney; brook fishing at Beeding.

Shermanbury Place Coarse fishing lakes in vicinity. St £12, dt £1.50. Phone Dorking 883621 for details.

ALDE

(For licences, etc, see Anglian Water Authority, p 40)

A small Suffolk stream, rising near Saxmundham and flowing into the North Sea at Orford Haven, 6½m NE of Felixstowe. Coarse fish.

Aldeburgh (Suffolk). Bass, codling, flatfish, eels, can be taken in estuary from jetty and boat; cod and whiting from beach; October and November best months. Hotels: Brudenell, White Lion, Wentworth, East Suffolk *(see also Suffolk, Sea Fishing Stations)*.

Snape (Suffolk). River tidal. Roach, dace, eels below sluice. Fishing free.

Saxmundham (Suffolk). Saxmundham Brook, 2m W; roach, etc; fishing free. Trout and coarse fishing in lakes at Lonely Farm Leisure Park. Dt. Good local beach fishing. Tackleist: Ernie Taylors, Suffolk House, High Street: licences; details of local lake fishing for carp, tench, rudd and pike. Hotels: White Hart, Bell.

ALN

(For close seasons, etc, see Northumbrian Water Authority, p 40)

Short Northumberland river, flowing into North Sea at Alnmouth. Trout and sea trout, occasional salmon; runs improving as pollution reduced.

Alnwick (Northumberland). Aln AA water (owned by the Duke of Northumberland) includes most reaches between Denwick Bridge and Alnmouth Bridge (4 to 5m). Portion running through

grounds at Lesbury House private. Visitors' (excl Sundays) st £5, mt £4, wt £3, dt £1 (concession-rates for jun) from Munray Sports, 2 Narrowgate, Alnwick, and R L Jobson, Tower Showrooms during business hours. Coquet and Till with-in easy reach. Hotels: White Swan and Hotspur, Alnwick; Schooner, Alnmouth.

ANCHOLME

(For close seasons, licences, etc, see Anglian Water Authority, p 40)

This river, in South Humberside, with its numerous tributaries, drains about 240 square miles of country. Falls into Humber at South Ferriby, where there is sluice and tidal lock. Lower part canalised for about 21 miles, and in this portion fishing is permitted by Lincolnshire River Division, which now controls river. River abundantly stocked with coarse fish (good bream). Fishing stations: **South Ferriby Sluice**, 4m from Barton-on-Humber; **Saxby Bridge**, 6m from Barton-on-Humber; **Broughton, Castlethorpe** and **Cadney Bridges**, near **Brigg**, through which town river passes; **Hibaldstow Bridge**, 3m from **Scawby Station; Brandywharf; Bishopsbridge**, 6m from **Market Rasen**. Licence issued by Lincolnshire RD necessary. Best station: **Brigg** (tackleist: Norman Leonard, 16–17 Bridge Street). **Scunthorpe** also convenient. At **Barton-on-Humber** are **Barton Broads** (16 acres; good coarse fishing). Wt £2.50, dt 50p and jun and OAP 25p from J & E Murray Ltd, Barton Broads. Carp lake: wt £7.50, dt £1.50.

ARUN

(For close seasons, licences, etc, see Southern Water Authority, p 38)

Rises on NW border of Sussex, flows past Horsham and enters English Channel at Littlehampton. Noted coarse-fish river, largely controlled by clubs. Some sea trout; May to October.

Littlehampton (Sussex). See under *Sea Fishing Stations*. HQ of Littlehampton and Dist AC is at Arun View Hotel, right by river. Lower reaches now leased by Sussex RD and Permits required—free from the Authority.

Arundel (Sussex). River tidal and mainly mud-bottomed. Roach and dace run large; bream, perch, pike, chub and occasional sea trout. Bass and mullet taken in fair numbers June, July, August between Ford and Arundel Bridge. Leger best method when tide running; swimming down successful in slack water. Association of Sussex Angling Societies has from Arundel Bridge to South Stoke Bridge, both banks, and Burpham backwater; dt from A. Shepherd (tackleist). 10 High Street. Hotels: Norfolk, Bridge, Black Rabbit.

Amberley (Sussex). Bream, roach, dace, perch, pike, occasional sea trout. London AA has water here; members only

(see Pulborough). The Central Association of London and Provincial Angling Clubs hold both banks downstream of Houghton Bridge to Stoke Bridge. This area to Stopham involved in Sussex RD improvement scheme.

Pulborough (Sussex). Pike, bream, roach, chub, dace, sea trout (May 1–Oct 29; sport improving). Central Association of London and Provincial ACs leases 3m to Stopham (mainly north bank) and stretch on south bank from railway bridge downstream; dt from bailiffs. London AA leases rights from above Greatham Manor down to Greatham Bridge and Amberley Castle meadows, and from Greatham Bridge to Bury Ferry on west bank (members only); tidal water. Pulborough and District AS has water; dt and wt from hon sec. Leisure Sport (Tel: 01-890 1313) have stretch at Hardham Church Farm. Hotels: Chequers, Pulborough, Arun and Oddfellows.

Tributaries of the Arun

WESTERN ROTHER:
Petworth (Sussex). Pike, perch, roach, dace, chub, few trout and sea trout. Mostly preserved by Leconfield Estate, which grants permits only to estate work-

ers. Petworth AC has 5½m in all; limited dt from Racehorse Inn, Coultershaw. Club also has 3½m of **Chichester Canal**; large carp, etc; dt. Petworth, Bognor and Chichester AA has stretch downstream of Shopham Bridge to Fittleworth Bridge (day and weekly tickets from Red Lion, Petworth and Post Office, Fittleworth). Tickets also available for assn stretch from Fittleworth Bridge to Pulborough. St available for Lodsbridge stretch *(see Selham)*. 3m stocked B and Rb trout av. 1¼ lb. St £80 from King & Chasemore (estate agents), Petworth. **Burton Mill Pond** holds good pike, perch, roach, rudd, carp, tench; permits, boats from W M S Ford, 390a High Hoes, Petworth, Sussex; Hotel: Petworth Park. Bank; £1.10; punt £3.75

Selham (Sussex), ns Pulborough. River stocked with brown and rainbow trout (av 1¼ lb). Fly only. St £80 incl VAT from King & Chasemore, Petworth

(estate agents). Inn: Three Moles (accommodation).

Midhurst (Sussex). Rother AC has river and lake; coarse fish incl carp, and grayling. £4 entrance. St £5. Dt 75p from Rice, North Street and Birchnall, West Street, Steyning, but not for all waters.

Chithurst (Sussex). Dace, trout, some roach. Petersfield & Dist AC has water; no tickets. Club shares 4m of **Chichester Canal** with six other clubs as follows: Isfield & Dist, Worthing, Bognor Regis, Stedham, Petworth, Portsmouth and Haslemere; dt from hon secs. Coarse fish, and carp and tench. Club affiliated to Hants and Sussex Alliance with waters on Arun, Rother, Meon and ponds, as well as the canal. Open fishing on pond at **Petersfield**.

AVON (Bristol)

(For close seasons, licences, etc, see Wessex Water Authority, p 39)

Sport improving as river conditions improve. Coarse fishing now excellent in places. Large trout in weir-pools and one or two stretches are worth fishing with fly. Some tributaries also hold good trout.

Bristol. On Avon and Frome. Much of Avon and tributaries controlled by Bristol and District Amalgamated Anglers (referred to later as Bristol Amalgamated), a merger of 11 clubs which makes all their waters available on one subscription, though each club retains its identity. Members have choice of more than 100m of fishing. Cards at £5 (concessions for ladies, juniors and pensioners) are available from tackleists in the main Avon centres or hon sec. No dt. Bristol Amal is among clubs affiliated to Bristol & West of England Federation, which itself has good water on Avon, **Kennet and Avon Canal, Frome** and **Ham Green Lake**. Good sport with trout on Blagdon Lake, Chew Valley and Barrow Reservoirs *(see Somerset streams, lakes and reservoirs)*. Among coarse fishing lakes in area are **Bowood** (2m W of Calne, dt at waterside); **Longleat** (apply P. Bundy, Bailiff, Rushpool Farmhouse, Longleat, Warminster (Tel. Chapmanslade 264); **Bitterwell Lake** (north of Bristol) dt 50p apply S Scully, The Chalet, Bitterwell Lake, Coalpit Heath, Bristol); **Henleaze Lake** (north of Bristol, dt June–Sep. from R W Steel, 63 Hill View, Henleaze, Bristol). Trout fishing on **Dodington Lake**, Chipping Sodbury. St £200, dt £10, evening only,

£7.50 from G M Dodington Estates Ltd, Chipping Sodbury. At Temple Cloud, nr Bristol, Cameley Trout Lakes. *(advt p 50)* Tackleists: Geo Gibbs Ltd, 3/4 Perry Road; S Veals, 61 Old Market Street, Scotts, 42 Soundwell Road, Staple Hill; S Shipp, Staple Hill; Sheppard's, 46 Bond Street; J B Sports, 31a Sandy Park Road, Brislington; Sportsfair, The Horsefair; Brachers, 68 Bedminster Parade; Ken Davis, 410 Wells Road; Sportsmans, 14 St Michael's Hill; Newmans, 331 Church Road; Bryants, 107 Coldharbour Rd, Redland.

Keynsham (Avon). Mainly roach and dace. Keynsham AA has water extending to Chewton, at Compton Dando and Woollard (trout) *(see tributary Chew)*; No dt. Bristol & West of England Federation has water here. Bristol Amal has six stretches of river here and one at **Wilsbridge**. *(see Bristol).* Free fishing from towpath below Hanham Weir.

Saltford (Avon). Bristol Amal has stretch at Avon Farm and one field at Swineford. Bathampton AA has 2½m; most coarse fish, including carp and tench, few large trout. Tickets from bailiffs, local tackleists and hon sec. Tackleist in Saltford: J D Roberts, 18 High St.

Bath (Avon). Coarse fish; barbel present from here to Limpley Stoke; few large trout. Some free fishing. Bristol Amal and Bath AA have water at Kensington Meadows and from Bathampton to city weirs. Good trout fishing in tributary streams, all preserved. **Kennet and Avon Canal** to Limpley Stoke aqueduct preserved by Bathampton AA. Cam, Midford, Wellow and By (Box) Brooks all within easy reach (trout) and Woodborough Lake, dt 30p. Knowle AA has **Emborough Pond**, Ston Easton; carp, tench, roach, perch, pike; dt from keeper. Tackleists: I M Crudgington, Broad Street; Wilson Lee & Co, Terrace Walk (information and tickets for Bath AA and Bathampton AA waters).

Batheaston (Avon). Bathampton AA has ½m; coarse fish, large trout; tickets from hon sec, bailiffs, tackleists. Bristol Amal has two fields here.

Bathampton (Avon). All-round fishing. Bristol Amal, Bath AA and Bathampton AA have water; dt from S Veals & Sons, 61 Old Market Street, Bristol, Bathampton AA also has water at **Kelston** (3½m), and other centres listed separately, and on **Kennet and Avon Canal, Hunstrete Lake** (good carp, tench), **Wellow** and **Box Brooks, River Banwell**, some ponds near Bridgwater and **River Isle**. Tickets for some waters; inquire hon sec.

Claverton (Avon). Bathampton AA has 2m; very good chub, few trout. Bath AA also has water.

Warleigh (Avon). Bathampton AA has 1m (as Claverton above). Bath AA has five meadows.

Limpley Stoke (Wilts). Good all-round fishing; large carp, with tench, chub, roach, bream and trout; fly-fishing on **River Frome**, Freshford to Farleigh Hungerford, and **Midford Brook** from Avon to Midford village; stocked with trout every year; preserved by Avon and Tributaries AA; visitors accompanied by member only. Bathampton AA holds **Kennet and Avon Canal** from Limpley Stoke to confluence with Avon at Bath (5½m); dt from hon sec, tackleists and bailiffs. Bath AA controls 3m from Limpley Stoke down to Kensington; coarse fish and trout; tickets from hon sec, two stretches. Bristol Amal has water *(see Bristol)*.

Midford (Avon). **Midford Brook**; trout only; preserved and stocked by the Avon and Tributaries AA. Dt to members' friends only.

Freshford (Avon). Bristol Amal has water on Avon here; dt issued for former Golden Carp AA water. **Frome:** trout, coarse fish, stocked and preserved by Avon and Tributaries AA (annual sub £45); from Avon up to Farleigh Hungerford (about 7m). Frome has mayfly hatch. Limited dt for members' friends. Association also has part of Avon, Freshford to Avoncliffe, and water on **Midford, Wellow** and **Cam Brooks**. All fly only.

Bradford-on-Avon (Wilts). Coarse fish, including pike, few trout. **Kennet and Avon Canal;** coarse fish. Some miles of Avon and canal preserved by Bradford-on-Avon and Dist AA. Dt 75p from hon sec or tackleists Wests, Roundstone Street; Roses, Fore Street, Smith and Ford, Fore St (all Trowbridge) and Smith and Ford, The Shambles, Bradford-on-Avon.

Melksham (Wilts). Coarse fish, few trout. Roughly 2m up and 1m downstream from river bridge rented by Bristol Amal, which has taken over Melksham

AA preserves following merger. Assn also has water at **Beanacre**. St from hon sec or tackleists. RD licences from hon sec and E Robinson (tackleist), 13 Bath Road. Lavington AC has water on **Semington Brook** at Lavington Mill and Baldham Mill.

Lacock (Wilts). Bristol Amal has 6m good coarse fishing with some trout. Licences from post office. Association also has **Silverlands Lake** (gravel pit) of 3–5 acres; carp and tench; limited tickets for members only from Scott's (below) and Coles, Market Place, Chippenham. Isis AC has water at **Pewsham;** apply hon sec for permit details. *(For details of Bristol Amal membership, see under Bristol).*

Chippenham (Wilts). Chub, barbel, bream, perch, roach. Chippenham AA has water; st £4, wt £2, dt £1, from tackleists. Bristol Amal has about 1½m between here and Lacock. Isis AC has water on Avon and **Marden;** members only. RD licences, tackle and bait from John Newman, 20 High Street, and Coles, Market Place.

Christian Malford (Wilts). Several fields controlled by Bristol Amal here, and at **Sutton Benger** assn has a meadow; further water near **Seagry Mill.** Somerfords FA has water upstream from Seagry to Kingsmead Mill (part of it, from Dauntsey road bridge, is trout water) and 2m above Kingsmead Mill on left bank and 1m on right bank. Good chub and perch. Assn also has water on **Frome.** Dt for trout and coarse fishing issued. Golden Valley FC has water at Seagry.

Malmesbury (Wilts). Bristol Amalgamated has acquired further extensive stretch to add to five fields already held; members only; trout and coarse fish. RD licences from Sports and Leisure, 36 High Street.

Tributaries of the Avon (Bristol)

FROME (Bristol). Rises near Chipping Sodbury and joins Avon estuary near Bristol. Coarse fishing mostly, but upper reaches restocked with trout.

Frampton Cotterell (Glos). Coarse fish. Most of lower Frome controlled by Bristol Amal *(see Avon).*

Yate (Glos). Frome Vale AC has water from Moorend Weir to viaduct. Dodington Park Lake, 6m; carp, perch; preserved. Badminton Park Lake, 8m; carp; preserved by the Duke of Beaufort; apply Estate Office, Badminton, Glos.

CHEW: Trout and coarse fish.

Keynsham (Avon). Bristol Amal has two fields. Keynsham AA has fishing *(see Avon).*

Malmesbury (Wilts). Five fields right bank downstream held by Bristol Amal. Bristol Amal also has long stretch of Woodbridge Brook.

Chewton Keynsham (Avon). Water held by Bristol Amal; no dt. Keynsham AA also has water; dt issued for fly and coarse fishing. Stretch in Keynsham Park free to licence holders.

Compton Dando (Avon). Mainly trout, grayling and dace. Keynsham AA has water here from above Woollard Weir some way downstream; no dt. Bristol Amal has water between here and Burnett; dt from hon sec, Golden Carp AA.

Pensford (Avon). Trout and coarse fish. Preserved by Knowle AA, tickets from Rising Sun Inn *(advt p 17 (see Stanton Drew).* Lakes: **Hunstrete Park Lake;** carp, tench, bream, roach, perch; Bathampton AA; members only.

Stanton Drew, Chew Magna, Chew Stoke (Avon). Trout dominant; some roach and dace; preserved, major portion by Knowle (Bristol) AA; wt (from hon sec only), and dt. Trout licences necessary. Average ¾ lb; brown and rainbow—occasional big fish. No spinning. Dt from local inns and Bristol tackleists from June 15 to Sept 30 (Mon–Fri only). Stretches of 2m at Compton Dando and ½m at Chew Magna held by Bristol Amal; trout; bait or fly. **Emborough Pond;** carp, tench, roach, perch; dt (limited) from bailiff. *(For Chew reservoirs see Somerset (lakes and streams)).*

BOYD BROOK: Trout, coarse fish, Bristol Amal has water at **Doynton** (Glos); dt issued (see Lacock). Golden Valley FC has stretch above and below **Bitton.**

CAM BROOK: Trout, Avon and tributaries AA has water (members' friends only) Bath AA has stretch at **Dunkerton** (Som). Bristol Amal has water at **Midford;** dt issued.

BY (BOX) BROOK: Trout, coarse fish. Bathampton AA has water at **Shockerwick** (Som) and Box (Wilts) Assn also has stretch of **Lamb Brook** at **Batheaston** (Som); trout, fly only; members: By Brook Fly FC and Two Mills Flyfishers have water for members. Manor House Hotel, **Castle Combe,** has ½m of good trout fishing in grounds.

WELLOW BROOK: Trout. Bath AA and Bathampton AA have stretches; fly only; members only.

SEMINGTON BROOK: Trout, coarse fish. Lavington AC has brook at Bulkington, Worton Brook, and Erlestoke Lake. St £5, limited dt 75p. Baldham Mill fishery now rented by St George's AC, Trowbridge.

FROME: Coarse fish, trout.

Frome (Som). Frome and Dist AA has several miles between Marston and Beckington. Regular matches. Informa-

tion from R Lee, tel Frome 61433. Dt trout fishing on private lake near Maiden Bradley from tackleist, The Sports Shop, 2 Bath Sreet, Frome. (Tel 62712).

Wolverton (Avon). Trout, coarse fish. Bristol Amal no longer holds the fishery here.

MARDEN: Coarse fish, trout.

Calne (Wilts). Trout, grayling, pike, perch, roach, dace, bream; 6m held by Calne AA; wt and dt issued. Isis AC has stretch at Newleaze Farm; members only. Above Calne is strictly preserved dry fly water. **Bowood Lake,** large pike (to 26 lb), perch, carp, tench, roach; Details from Bowood Estate, who issue st. North end of lake private. *Note: access to lake only through Pillars Lodge entrance on Calne-Melksham road.*

AVON (Hampshire)

(For close seasons, licences, etc, see Wessex Water Authority, p 39)

Pre-1955, probably the most famous mixed fishery in England. Roach, chub, dace, barbel and pike all bred prolifically and grew exceptionally large, especially in the lower reaches. There was a good sea trout run and while salmon did not enter the river in large numbers, the average size was exceptional. In its upper reaches, the Avon is a typical chalk stream, populated by free-rising trout and grayling. A decline in the coarse fishing which set in twenty years ago has been the subject of investigation and there is good hope that remedial measures in hand will before long restore the river to its former status.

Christchurch (Dorset). Avon and Stour. Excellent sea and coarse fishing in Christchurch Harbour. Bass, mullet, flounders and (higher up) dace, roach, bream and eels. Fishing permits for the Royalty Fishery on the Avon (excluding Parlour and Bridge Pool) can be obtained from Davis Tackle Shop, 75 Bargates, Christchurch (Tel: 5169). June 16 to Mar 14 inclusive. The price structure is complex, ranging between £15 per day for salmon fishing and £2 for coarse fishing. Davis will supply brochure on receipt of request and SAE. Pike fishing permitted Nov 1–Mar 14 at no extra charge (no spinning). This fishery was once the most famous in England for large coarse fish, noted specially for large barbel. Parlour and Bridge Pool permits from Fishery Manager: advance bookings only. S & MT. Parlour; dt £15. Bridge Pool; dt (for 2) £30. MT only. Parlour; dt £11. Bridge Pool; dt (for 2) £25. A coarse fishing dt for the Parlour, £4.25, available from bailiff. All prices include VAT. S & MT tickets for Parlour and Bridge Pool issued only until Sep 30;

the "MT only" tickets solely in the month of October. One fish per day salmon limit. Limited coarse fishing permits for Stour and Christchurch Harbour may be obtained by visitors from Davis Tackle Shop *(see also Stour (Dorset)).* For other salmon and sea trout fishing apply early in writing to the Royalty Fishery Manager, West Hants Water Co, Mill Road, Christchurch. *(Note: brochure on Royalty Fishing available from fishery manager or Davis.)* Good sea fishing at Mudeford; boats available *(see Sea fishing stations).* Tackleists: Davis, 75 Bargates (open from 7.45 am, Sundays incl); Hales Tackle, 258 Barrack Road. Hotels: Shortwood House, Magdalen Lane; King's Arms; Avonmouth; Broomway; Red Lion; White Hart; Hengistbury House. *Note: Several baits, including maggots, are now banned on the Royalty.*

Winkton (Dorset). Davis Fishing Tackle, 75 Bargates, Christchurch now sole agents for the Winkton fishery. Season is June 16 to Jan 31; good roach, chub, perch, pike; also dace, barbel, tench.

Sea trout fishing in the bridge pool on the River Avon by Christchurch Priory. *Photograph: John Tarlton.*

Salmon fishing is all preserved. Dt, £1.50. Hotel: Plaish House.

Ringwood (Hants). Salmon, trout and coarse fish. Mr N Ward, Avon Dairy Farm, The Bridges, Ringwood, issues dt on behalf of owners. Salmon fishing on Somerley let by the season; 5m of water; six beats; occasional vacancies; apply Bailiff's Cottage, Ibsley, Ringwood. Limited dt for trout and coarse fishing available on 2m stretch between Aug 1 and Sept 30 from fishing hut at Gorley downstream to junction of Harbridge Stream; apply Bailiff's Cottage, Ibsley. Gravel pits at **Blashford** and **Hightown** available on permit from Leisure Sport Ltd, dt from bailiff on bank. Ringwood & Dist AA has 20m of coarse fishing on rivers and 7 lakes. St £12 + £2 entrance. No dt. Tackleists: Ringwood Tackle, West Street, Ringwood. Hotels: Bridge House, Avon Crown, White Hart, Star Inn, Nag's Head.

Fordingbridge (Hants). Trout, grayling, perch, pike and roach. Salisbury AC has good water at **Burgate** and **Hale.** Dt for Burgate water from Burgate Manor Farm *(see Salisbury).* Albany Hotel has short river frontage (licences obtainable). Fordingbridge AC has water on Avon and **Stour;** members only. Few dt for Bickton Estate water from river bailiff, The Flat, **Bickton.** No RD licence needed as block licence purchased. Tackle shop on premises. Two excellent stillwater trout fisheries in the vicinity. **Damerham** and Allens Farm *(advt p 54).* Hotels: Royal Arms; George Inn; Victoria House, Sandleheath; Compasses Inn *(advt p 16).*

Breamore (Hants). Bat and Ball Hotel has 3m of salmon, trout and coarse fishing on dt basis. From £1.50. Phone Beamore 252. Accommodation.

Downton (Wilts). Trout, roach, grayling, dace. Bull Hotel has very good fishery here and provides punts; dt (coarse) £2; trout, £5; salmon, £9; boats for non-residents, £3 extra. All prices plus VAT. Water stocked with barbel up to 9½ lbs.

Tickets and RD licences obtainable at hotel. Weekly ticket terms for residents *(advt p 17)*.

Salisbury (Wilts). Avon, Wylye and Bourne; trout, grayling, coarse fish; preserved. Salisbury and Dist AC has water on Avon, **Bourne, Wylye, Nadder,** lakes and pits (ann sub £6); excellent trout, grayling, roach etc. Dt for some waters from I Rae, The Boathouse, Castle St, Salisbury and Burgate Manor Farm, Fordingbridge. Dt 75p for good coarse fishing (incl carp) on **Steeple Langford Lakes** from bailiff. London AA has Britford Fishery; 1½m SE; excellent coarse fishing, good sport with trout, some salmon (trout of 6½ lb and salmon of 31 lb taken recently). Members only; no dt. Fishing on short stretch of Avon at Fisherton Recreation Ground for small charge; apply Town Clerk, Salisbury City Council. Humberts, 8 Rollestone Street, may know of annual rods to let. For Longford and Trafalgar Estates apply T Williams, Keeper's House, Charlton, nr Salisbury. Hotels: County, White Hart and Red Lion. Tackleists: Greenfield Ltd, 21a Milford Street; John Eadie, 20 Catherine Street. (RD licences.)

Netheravon (Wilts). Trout, grayling; strictly preserved. The 6m from **Enford** to **Bulford** is The Services Dry Fly FA (Salisbury Plain Area) water; members only. Brown trout average 1–1½ lb, annual bag 1,200–1,300, many grayling. Best time: mid-May to mid-June and mid-Sept to mid-Oct. Assn also has five ponds stocked with trout. Dt for members' private guests only.

AVON (Hampshire) tributaries

BOURNE: Enters near Salisbury. Trout, grayling, coarse fish. Salisbury AC has fishery near town. Fishing stations: **Porton** and **Salisbury** (Wilts).

EBBLE: Joins Avon below Salisbury; good trout fishing, but mostly private.

WYLYE: Trout, grayling.

Wishford (Wilts). Preserved by Wilton Fly-Fishing Club.

Stapleford (Wilts). Salisbury AC has fishing here; members only.

Codford St Mary and Bapton (Wilts). Privately preserved.

Warminster (Wilts). Warminster AC has water on Wylye, and coarse fishing on lakes and ponds; members only (membership restricted to rural area). **Longleat** Estate owns just over 2m of upper river. Excellent coarse fishing in three lakes in Longleat Park, carp included.

Tickets are issued by Bailiff, Rushpool Farmhouse, Longleat Estate. St £20, dt £1.25, night ticket £2.50. Major J C Walker, Sutton Veney House, lets rods and half-rods on 3½m of Wylye. Full rods not less than £200 per season. Enquiries to Estate Office for precise terms.

Heytesbury (Wilts). Privately preserved.

NADDER: Tributary of Wylye. Trout, grayling, roach, dace. Mostly preserved by landowners. Fishing stations: **Wilton, Tisbury.** Tisbury AC has about 4m; dt and wt from Arundell Arms, Beckford Arms and hon sec; exchanges with Warminster and Salisbury clubs. Club also has lake at Old Wardens Castle; carp, tench, etc. For stretch near **Salisbury** Salisbury AC issue dt for trout and coarse fishing; apply Mr Moore, Station Café, South Western Rd, Salisbury.

AXE

(For close seasons, licences, etc, S.W. Water Authority, p 38)

Rises in Dorset and flows south to the English Channel at Seaton. Trout, sea trout and salmon. Fishing difficult to come by, but one or two hotels can provide facilities.

Seaton (Devon). Trout, salmon. Some sea trout fishing may be available on ticket from White Hart Inn, Colyford. Axe estuary fishable (for bass, mullet, flounders, etc), on ticket from harbour master. Tackle and WA licenses: F Ackerman & Co Ltd, Fore Street *(see Sea Fishing Stations)*. Hotel: Pole Arms.

Axminster (Devon). Axe, Yarty; trout and salmon. Trouting good especially in April and May. Salmon fishing fair. Hotels: George, Old Bell (limited permits for Axe); Western, Shute Arms, and

Bear Inn, Colyton (trout tickets; fish on small side).

Crewkerne (Som). Axe (3m off); trout. Parret (1m off); trout, roach, dace. Stoke-sub-Hamdon AA has trout fishing on **Parret;** members only. Yeovil AA has trout and coarse fishing on **Yeo** and tributaries; st from hon sec and Yeovil tackleists: Trout fishing Sutton Bingham Reservoir, near Yeovil *(see Somerset (lakes and streams))*. Tackleists: Hagas Fishing Tackle, 29 Princes Street, Sports, and Doneys, Bond St; all Yeovil.

BLACKWATER

(For close seasons, licences, etc, see Thames Water Authority, p 42)

Rises in NW of county, flows by Braintree to Maldon and empties into North Sea through large estuary. Generous re-stocking following pollution in 1976 producing improved results. Coarse fish include pike, chub, rudd and some carp.

Maldon (Essex). Maldon AS has three fisheries on main river, seven on the canal and three on stillwater: Railway Pond, Totham Pit and Totham Grove Res. St £9, with concession for ladies, OAP and young anglers. No dt. Stretch from Langford to Beeleigh; Ilford PS; no tickets. Permits for Beeleigh Lock to Heybridge Basin Lock from bailiffs on bank; dt. Tackleists: Last Sports, High Street. Hotels: Swan, White Hart, King's Head.

Witham (Essex). Blackwater and **Brain.** Coarse fish. Kelvedon and Dist AA has 7½m from here to **Braintree;** members only.

Kelvedon (Essex). Kelvedon and Dist AC has various stretches as well as water on Suffolk **Stour, Rivenhall Lake,** nr Witham, a reservoir near Tiptree and gravel pits. Trout, tench, crucian carp, rudd, roach. Club organises sea-fishing boat trips. Maldon AS has water here and at **Feering** and **Braxted;** members only *(see Witham, Coggeshall and Maldon)*.

Coggeshall (Essex). Coarse fish, Kelvedon and Dist AC has water here and at Stisted; members only *(see Witham and Kelvedon)*.

Braintree (Essex). On **Brain** and Black-

water **(Pant).** Braintree and Bocking AS owns most of water, both banks, from Shalford to Bradwell Village. Well stocked with roach, perch, rudd, dace, and chub. St from local tackleist *(see below)* and hon sec. *For Gosfield and Sparrows Lakes see Essex (streams and lakes).* Tackle: E McDowell, 2 Rayne Rd. Hotels: Horne, White Horse, Nag's Head.

CHELMER AND CAN: Coarse fish; much restocking.

Chelmsford (Essex). River stocked with roach, dace and bream. Above Chelmsford waters are private, but most of those below are controlled by Chelmsford AA; dt 75p for towpath bank only from bailiff on bank. Dt for **Heybridge Canal** from Beeleigh to Hall Bridge from hon sec, Chelmsford AA, Maldon AC, Christy AA and Marconi AS. Fishing in Can through park and along river bank free to licence holders. Tackleists: Godfreys, 52 Moulham Street, Edwards Tackle, 7 Broomfield Road and R Crowe, Maldon Road, Gt Baddow. Hotel: County.

Hartford End. TWA has trout fishery here; dt 75p (strictly limited) from Amenity and Fisheries Manager.

BLYTH (Northumberland)

(For close seasons, licences, etc, see Northumbrian Water Authority, p 40)

Rises near Throckington and flows 20m to North Sea at Blyth. Trout and grayling, with coarse fish (especially roach) in lower reaches.

Bedlington (Northumberland). Brown trout and grayling (both average about 9 in) with roach in lower reaches. Seaton Burn and Bedlington and Blagdon Angling Associations have water; some dt (Mon–Fri only) for holiday visitors outside 50m radius for lower reaches from hon secs. Dt £1 from Hon Sec for small stretch above bridge. Tackleist: W Temple, 43 Ocean View, Whitley Bay.

BLYTHE (Suffolk)

(For close seasons, licences, etc, see Anglian Water Authority, p 40)

Short Suffolk river, about 20m long, rising in lakes in Heveningham Hall Park (pike, roach and rudd; tickets when Hall open), 4m SW from Halesworth. W and dt for coarse fishing in Henham Dairy Ponds, R **Wang** and new trout fishery at Peasenhall. Fishing in river negligible until below Holton, where there is good roach fishing to Blyford. Immediately downstream river is tidal to **Wenhaston** *(see under Sea Fishing Stations)*. Several hotels.

BRUE

(For close seasons, licences, etc, see Wessex Water Authority, p 39)

Rises in Mendips and flows to Bristol Channel at Burnham. Coarse fish, except in higher reaches, where there are trout. River has reputation for carp; grayling introduced recently. Fishes well from September onwards as a rule. Stretch from Westhay downstream was badly polluted by salt influx a few years ago but has recovered.

Highbridge (Som). Roach, bream, etc. North Somerset AA has some of best waters. St and dt. Best Sept onwards. Club also has Apex Pit, between Highbridge and Burnham, and Newtown Pond, Highbridge (carp to 20 lb). Tickets and licences from hon sec or tackleists: Pouncey & Hydon, Church Street. Also from Information Bureau, Victoria Street, Burnham-on-Sea. Further information from hon sec. Huntspill River is 2m; Bridgwater AA water *(see Bridgwater–Parret)* Bristol Amalgamated has water at **East Huntspill, Burtle, Tealham Moor, Westhay,** and **Lydford-on-Fosse.** St. £3.51 *(see Bristol)*. Hotels: Highbridge; The George (clubs accommodated).

Bason Bridge (Som). Area around milk factory noted for carp; fish run up to 16 lb or so. Also roach, chub, tench, perch and pike. Bristol Amal holds extensive stretches here *(see under Bristol Avon)* and Highbridge AA also has water.

Mark (Som). Carp, pike, perch, roach, chub, tench. N Somerset AA has 2½m on river and 3 to 4m on North Drain; dt and wt from hon sec *(see also Axe–Somerset streams)*. Highbridge AA also has water on North Drain. Inn: Pack Horse.

Edington (Som). Roach, bream, carp, perch, pike; free.

Glastonbury (Som). Roach, bream, chub, etc, in lower stretches of River Brue. Glaston Manor, Bristol Amal and N Somerset AA clubs have water. Dt from hon secs. Trout from **Baltonsborough** to **West Lydford.** Fishing extends from White House, Westhay, to Fosseway Bridge, West Lydford (trout av ½lb). No dt. Weekly tickets only from D Smith, 6 Barn Close, Street. Tackleist: G Miller, 22 Benedict St (club permits).

BUDE RIVER AND CANAL

(For close seasons, licences, etc, see S.W. Water Authority, p 38)

Two branches of River Neet from Week St Mary and Stratton (latter often referred to as Strat) converge at Hele Bridge, flow into Bude Canal and out again towards Bude. Trout fishing quite good in Neet and Strat. River itself tidal and not worth fishing, except at estuary. A few trout may be taken between estuary and canal. Canal is noted roach water; also perch, tench and carp.

Bude (Cornwall). Bass from beaches, breakwater and rocks; bass and mullet in estuary of Bude River. Bude AA has several stretches of water on Tamar including Moreton Mill, Kingford, Crowford Bridge and North Tamerton. Send 50p to Hon Sec for membership details and map/guide to fishings. St £7.50, mt £5, wt £3, dt £1 from Hon Sec and DIY Centre, The Square, Holsworthy. **Tamar Lake** and **Crowdy** (trout reservoir) controlled by SW Water Auth *(see Cornwall lakes etc)*. **Bude Canal** (roach, dace, rudd, perch, carp and tench) leased by Bude Canal AA; wt £1.50, dt 30p. Permits from Boathouse, The Wharf. RD licences and other permits from N Cornwall Pet supplies. Hotel: Penstowe Manor, Kilkhampton *(advt p 18)*.

BURE

(See Norfolk and Suffolk Broads, p 104)

CAMEL

(For close seasons, licences, etc, see South West Water Authority, p 38)

A spate river, rising on the moors near Davidstow, flowing about 30m to enter the Atlantic between Pentire and Steppar Points. Salmon, sea trout and small brown trout. Salmon enter from April; grilse from June, with the main runs in October, November and December. Sea trout from June to August. Best brown trout fishing in tributaries Allen, De Lank, Lanivet and Ruthern and in the topmost reaches of the main river. Rainfall influences salmon fishing to an exceptional extent.

Wadebridge (Cornwall). Trout, sea trout, salmon; good bass fishing in tidal reaches, with bass and pollack in estuary. Large stretches held by Wadebridge and Dist AA, Bodmin and Dist AA and riparian owners. Dt (salmon, sea trout) in tidal water (Wadebridge AC) from N E Lane, Little Orchard Rock. Tickets for Bodmin Association water *(see Bodmin)*. Fowey within reach, with tickets for both Liskeard and Lostwithiel AC waters. Of Camel tributaries, Allen now provides fair sea trout sport in lower reaches—permission from landowners—and Ruthern holds trout, sea trout and some salmon, while bass may be taken from Amble. Tackleist: Lenaghan's, 27 Molesworth Street (licences). Hotels: Molesworth Arms, Bridge-on-Wool, Swan and Lanarth Hotel and Country Club, St Kew, *(advt p 18)*. *(For sea fishing see Padstow)*.

Bodmin (Cornwall). A few miles to the Camel and Fowey where Bodmin AA issues permits (ten per day) on some of the best water including the De Lank. Dt £1.50, wt £6 from 1 April to 31 October, juniors under 16 at 50p per day or wt £2. Dt in Nov and Dec £6, juniors £3. No wt. Apply with SAE to A Cowl, Dunmere, Bodmin. Hotels: Garland Ox. Westberry, The White Hart. Riverside accommodation. Licensed guest house phone Bodmin 2797. Dunmere caravan site phone Bodmin 2032. Permits, free maps and SWWA licences also available from Hon Sec Lt Col H M Ervine-Andrews VC, The Old Barn, St Neot, Liskeard. Phone Dobwalls 20799. SAE PLEASE.

CHESHIRE (Lakes/Reservoirs)

BOLESWORTH LAKE, Tattenhall, Chester. Now let on a long lease by Bolesworth Estate Co, Tattenhall. No details disclosed.

BOSLEY RESERVOIR. Fishing station: **Bosley.** Roach (good), bream, pike, perch, carp, few trout. Dt 50p from J Arnold (bailiff), Lakeside Estate, Harington Arms, Bosley. St £5 from A Jones, 10 Purley Avenue, Northenden, Manchester.

CAPESTHORNE POOLS. Fishing station: **Siddington.** Park and Garden pools controlled by Stoke-on-Trent AS. Large carp, tench, bream, roach, rudd and pike. Dt for Park pool only £2 from A

Bradley, East Lodge (tel Chelford 584). Stock pond carp and tench. Dt £2.50, ½ day £1.25. Top pool controlled by Prince Albert AS. No tickets.

DOVE MERE, SAND MERE, WOODLANDS LAKE. Allostock, Knutsford. New Prince Albert AS waters, heavily stocked, including large carp.

GREAT BUDWORTH MERE. Nr Northwich, 50-acre lake holding good bream, pike, etc. Northwich AA; tickets from hon sec or local tackleist. St and dt. **Pickmere** is assn water nearby; members only for south bank; permission from farmers elsewhere.

LAKE REDESMERE. Fishing station: **Siddington**. Excellent roach and pike, with bream, carp, tench and some trout. Dt £1.50 from East Lodge, Capesthorne. Boats available. Prince Albert AS.

LANGLEY BOTTOMS and LAMALOAD RESERVOIRS. Nr Macclesfield. Good fly fishing for trout. Prince Albert AS. Limited dt from Ray Newton, tackleist, 5–7 Park Green, Macclesfield.

LEADBEATERS RESERVOIR, Macclesfield. Trout and coarse fish. Macclesfield Prince Albert AS water. Dt 50p from R Newton, Park Lane, Macclesfield.

MANCHESTER RESERVOIRS: Tintwistle (A628). Trout, perch. **Vale House;** fly fishing, for trout. **Bottoms:** bait fishing. **Cote Lodge** (Glossop): bait fishing. Dt from reservoirs; 3-month permit from Manager, NWWA, Eastern Division, Oakland House, Talbot Rd, Manchester M16 0QF, or reservoirs. Charges under review.

OULTON MILL POOL. Fishing station: **Tarporley.** Well stocked with good carp, bream, tench and pike. Dt from Mill Office.

ROMAN LAKES. Fishing station: **Marple.** Roach, perch, carp (up to 20lb) and brown trout. Dt from Lakeside Café.

TABLEY MERE. Fishing station: **Plumley.** Coarse fish, especially carp, tench and perch. No bank fishing; boats £2 per day, including fishing. Dt from Estate Office, Tabley.

THORNEYCROFT HALL LAKES. Gawsworth. Prince Albert AS water. Carp, tench, roach, pike.

TURNERS POOL, Nr Macclesfield. Macclesfield Prince Albert AS members only tench water. Membership restricted, £25 pa.

WOODS RESERVOIR. Prince Albert AS water. Carp, tench, roach.

COLNE (Essex)

(For close seasons, licences, etc, see Anglian Water Authority, p 40)

Rises in north of county and flows to North Sea via Colchester. Improving as coarse fishery.

Colchester (Essex). Colchester APS controls 3m, roach, chub, perch, pike, bream, dace; no tickets. The society has also **Layer Pits** (6m S; pike, perch, bream, roach, rudd, tench, carp) (members only, restricted to 20m radius). Society also has water on **Stour** and Chigborough Reservoir. Colchester Piscatorial Society has water on Langham Ponds, Stour and Colne; members only. Belmain AS has water on Stour at Little Horkesley; members only. Birch Hall Lake fished by Kelvedon AA. *(See also Essex streams, lakes and reservoirs).* Tackleists: Radcliffe, High Street; Wass, Long Wyre Street; Home & Sports Ltd, St Botolph Street. Hotels: George, Red Lion.

Halstead (Essex). Coarse fish, including tench; some trout. **Gosfield Hall Lake** (45 acres), well stocked carp, with perch, roach, tench, pike, rudd; boats available. Also **Sparrows Pond,** Gosfield; coarse fish including carp and tench; Halstead & Hedingham AC members only (St £10.50) but dt for **Gosfield,** £1.50 from club, café or patrolling bailiff. Tackleist: E McDowell, High Street. *(See Essex, streams and lakes.)*

COQUET

(For close seasons, licences, etc, see Northumbrian Water Authority, p 40)

Rises in Cheviots and enters North Sea near Warkworth. Salmon, sea trout and trout. Usually a late river. Sport with salmon and sea trout affected by abstraction at Warkworth, but trout fishing still very good. Facilities for visitors restricted.

WHITTON FARM HOUSE HOTEL,

Rothbury, Northumberland, Rothbury (0669) 20811

FREE PRIVATE GAME FISHING FOR RESIDENTS.

Whitton Farm is a nineteenth century farm house which has been tastefuly converted into an hotel of considerable character and warmth. Many of the bedrooms (some with private bath) and the lounges have splendid views of the Coquet Valley. We have 2 miles of the Coquet plus access to the estuary waters and many nearby lakes. Keen anglers are recommended to try the late run of salmon and sea trout in October. We also have our own horses and organise shooting holidays. *Please send for our colour brochure.*

Warkworth (Northumberland). Trout, sea trout; salmon from Feb onwards to late summer and autumn. Duke of Northumberland leases large part of his water to Northumbrian Anglers' Federation. Permits restricted to Northumberland residents, but inquiries to hon sec will receive helpful consideration.

Acklington (Northumberland). Trout, sea trout and salmon. Northumbrian AF water on Coquet and tributary, Thirston Burn *(see also Felton)*.

Felton (Northumberland). Salmon, sea trout (spring and autumn), trout. Northumbrian A Fedn; permits from Post Office *(see Warkworth)*.

Weldon Bridge (Northumberland). Nearest station: Morpeth, 9½m. Trout (sea trout and salmon, late summer and autumn). Hotel: Anglers' Arms (RD licences).

Rothbury (Northumberland). A late salmon run and excellent sea trout fishing in June and Oct. Brown trout, including fish to 3 lb. Northumbrian AF has 4m of Coquet and stretch of tributary, Forest Lee Burn *(see Warkworth)*. Whitton Farm House Hotel *(advt p 59)*, managed by a keen game fisher, offers 2½m to guests. Best months—trout, May, June and Sept; av wt ½lb but fish up to 1¾lb. Salmon and sea-trout, June and Sept/Oct. RD licences at Hotel. Other hotels: Queen's Head and Newcastle. Tackleists: J R Soulsby & Sons, from whom licences and Federation permits can be had.

Holystone (Northumberland). Salmon (late), trout; mostly private. Holystone Burn, trout; Grasslees Burn, trout. Inn: Salmon, where particulars can be had.

Harbottle (Northumberland). Good trout and some late salmon fishing on Coquet and Alwin. Upper Coquetdale AC has extensive parts of upper river; members only.

CORNWALL (streams, lakes, etc)

(For close seasons, licences, etc, see South West Water Authority, p 38)

The six reservoirs mentioned below are all now South West Water Authority waters. Fishing on all of them is by st, wt (from SWWA offices) and dt from self-service units on site.

ARGAL RESERVOIR. (3m W of Falmouth.) Brown and rainbow trout: fly only. Season April 1–Nov 2, dt £4. Boats £4 per day (£2.50 after 4 pm). Self-service ticket unit in car-park.

STITHIANS RESERVOIR. (3m S of Redruth.) Brown and rainbow trout. Season Mar 15–Oct 12. St £20, wt £2, dt £1.50. No boats. Permits from Golden Lion, Post Office and tackleists.

PORTH RESERVOIR. (4m E of Newquay.) Brown rainbow and brook trout: fly only. Season April 1–Oct 12. Dt £4. Boats £4 per day (£2.50 after 4 pm). Self-service ticket unit by keeper's bungalow.

CROWDY RESERVOIR. (2m E of Camelford.) Brown and rainbow trout: fly only. Season April 1–Oct 12. St £20, dt £1.50. Self-service ticket unit at dam car-park.

SIBLYBACK LAKE. (5m N of Liskeard.) Brown and rainbow trout: fly only. Season April 1–Oct 12. Dt £4. Boats £4 per day (£2.50 after 4 pm). Self-service ticket unit in car park. Light refreshments available. A public picnic site overlooks the reservoir. Tackleists: A B Harvey, Market Strand; Berks, Arwenack Street, both Falmouth. J Bray, Market Street, Penryn. Central Sports, 2 Crantock Street, Newquay. Botterel & Son, Fore Street, Liskeard. Hotels: Golden Lion, Menherion; Crellow House Hotel, Stithians; Pencubitt Hotel, Liskeard. Details of Falmouth hotels from Town Information Bureau.

BREAM. Fishing station: **Par.** Heavily polluted, but tributary **Redmoor River** has good head of trout. Sand-eels at Par sands, mackerel from the bay, pollack by Gribben Head and near harbour, and bass between harbour and Shorthorne Beach. Boats for hire at Par and Polkerris. Tackleists: Hambley Store, Eastcliffe Road, Par; Hotels: Royal, Par; Carlyon Bay, St Austell.

CONSTANTINE BROOK. Fishing station; **Constantine,** ns Penryn WR, 6m. Trout; free on permission of farmers. Constantine joins estuary of **Helford River** (few trout, permission of farmers). Sea fishing off Helford Mouth *(see Falmouth).*

DRIFT RESERVOIR. Near **Penzance** (3m) in quiet valley. Brown and rainbow trout (fly only). St, wt and dt from Chyandour Estate Office, Penzance (Penzance 3021).

GWITHIAN BROOK. Fishing station: **Camborne.** Brook fishes well for trout, especially from Roseworthy down to Red River, but fish run small ($\frac{1}{2}$-pounder would be a good one). Very good beach and rock fishing in area. Club: Camborne AA. Hotels: Golden Lion, Regal, Tyak's.

HAYLE. Fishing stations: **Relubbus, Hayle Causeway** and **Gwinear.** Trout and sea trout; rapidly improving. Good beach fishing near Hayle, and estuary fishing very good, particularly for bass, mullet and flats; plenty of natural bait.

LOOE. Fishing station: **Liskeard.** Looe River, 1m runs to Sand place and Looe town. Here West Looe River, 8m long, joins on right bank. Good trout fishing; sea trout in July. Liskeard and Dist AC has water on West Looe, East Looe and Inny *(see Lynher below).* For further information visitors should consult hon sec or J Bray, The Quay, East Looe. Hotels: Ship, Boscarn. Good sea fishing. A A & M Crocker, newsagents, Barras St, Liskeard, issues permits for Siblyback Lake *(see separate entry). (See also Sea Fishing Stations.)*

LYNHER. Fishing stations: **Liskeard, Callington,** ns Saltash. Lynher holds trout, salmon and peal. Trout run small; pounders now rare. Many stretches owned by Liskeard and District AC (Bathpool to Pillaton Mill); preserved lower down. Salmon and peal run right up. Permits for all Liskeard AC water (which includes fisheries on **Fowey, Camel, Seaton** and **Looe, Inny** and **Lynher** Rivers; 30m in all). Wt £7, dt £1.50 (50% reduction for jnrs.) from hon sec and tackleists (see below). At Sportsman's Arms, Notter Bridge, Saltash, permits for a small portion can be obtained at a small fee. Siblyback Lake is near. Hotel: Webb's, Liskeard. Tackleists: Godfreys Stores, Barn Street, Liskeard and Pine Lodge, Fore Street, Callington.

PETHERICK WATER. Fishing station: **Padstow.** Small trout, RD licences from Radford's, Duke St, Padstow (also tackle and bait). Boats available for estuary fishing, which can be excellent for bass, plaice, turbot, ray. Hotels: Dinas, Metropole.

POLPERRO BROOK. Fishing station: **Polperro.** Polperro Brook is 6m long; small trout; private. Good sea fishing for pollack, mackerel, whiting, conger and bream; use pilchard bait. Boats available *(see also Sea Fishing Stations).*

ST ALLEN RIVER. Fishing station: **Truro.** St Allen and Kenwyn Rivers at Truro; Tresillian River (3m from Truro on St Austell road); Kennel or Parranarworthal River (5m from Truro); free on farmer's permission; trout six to the pound; a few sea trout run into **Lower Tresillian** River. Good reservoir trout fishing at **Argal** and **Collage,** Penryn; and **Stithians,** Nr Redruth. Inquire tackleist John Langdon, 20 St Mary Street, Truro. Hotel: Royal, Lemon St *(see also Sea Fishing Stations).*

ST AUSTELL RIVER. Fishing station: **St Austell.** Salmon fishing until Dec 15 in Rivers Camel and Fowey. Good sport with bass in bay; boats for hire at Charlestown and Mevagissey. Roche AC has rights in disused china clay pits; trout, coarse fish; wt and dt. Inquiries to tackleists. Hotels: White Hart, Rashleigh Arms at Charlestown; Carylon Bay and Cliff Head at Carlyon Bay.

SEATON RIVER. Fishing station: **Menheniot.** Seaton rises N of Liskeard, runs 1m E of the town and to the sea in 9m. Good trout stream, though bushed over. Fishing by permission from landowners, although Liskeard and Dist AC has considerable stretch; St £14, wt £7, dt £3.50 on all waters. *(See previous page.)*

TAMAR LAKE. Fishing station: **Kilkhampton** (Bude 5m). Mixed fishery stocked with brown and rainbow trout, rudd, wild carp. A South West Water Authority water. St £20, dt (from self-service unit at reservoir) £1.50. No

boats. Tackleists: Weys of Bude, Queen Street.

UPPER TAMAR RESERVOIR. A new 81 acre fishery immediately above Tamar Lake. Brown and rainbow trout: fly only. Season April 1–Nov 30. SWWA water. Dt (from self-service unit at reservoir dam) £4. Boat: £4. Evening only; £2.50.

TIDDY. Fishing station: **St Germans.** Sea trout to Tideford, trout elsewhere; free on permission of farmers. Accommodation at Blue Cap Hotel.

VALENCY. Fishing station: **Boscastle.** Valency is 4m long; holds small trout and few sea trout. Hotels: Wellington, in Boscastle (RD licences); Eliot Arms, Tregadillet 15m. Sea fishing good for bass, mackerel, pollack, etc.

CUCKMERE

(For close seasons, licences, etc, see Southern Water Authority, p 38)

Formed by two tributaries, which join at Hellingly, and enters sea at Cuckmere Haven, west of Beachy Head. Mainly coarse fish, but trout in upper reaches. Trout fishing mostly with minnow and worm, as water is narrow and thickly bushed, with steep banks. River closely preserved where any good.

Alfriston (Sussex). St £6, wt £2 and dt 50p for both banks from Berwick to Alfriston from the Compleat Angler FC, or any Eastbourne tackle shop. Below Alfriston Lock the river is salt and tidal, being open to mouth at Cuckmere Haven. In summer grey mullet are plentiful near Exceat Bridge (Eastbourne–Seaford road); also bass and occasionally sea trout. Cuckmere is tidal to ½m upstream from Alfriston.

Berwick (Sussex). Water held by Compleat Angler FC *(see Alfriston).*

Hailsham (Sussex). Cuckmere 2m. Hailsham AA has several stretches containing roach, perch, pike, bream and tench. At Hempstead Farm, dace, chub and bream may be taken. Some trout at Broad Farm, **Hellingly.** Hailsham AA also has water on **Pevensey Haven, Wallers Haven** and **Chilley Stream** *(see Pevensey Levels).* Details of membership fee, guest tickets, from Hailsham AA hon sec.

CUMBRIA (lakes)

(See English Lake District, p 71)

CUMBRIA (streams)

(For close seasons, licences, etc, see North West Water Authority, p. 39, unless otherwise stated.)

ANNAS. Fishing station; **Bootle.** Small trout; good sea trout and salmon; late. Millom AA has fishing. Also water on **Esk, Lickle, Irt** and **Lazy.** RD licences from R H Fisher, Main Street, Silecroft Post Office, and Wadesons, Market Square, Millom. Accommodation at Close Cottage.

BLACK BECK. Fishing station: **Green Road.** This stream rises on Thwaites Fell, and in 7½m reaches Duddon Estuary. Millom AA has water; permission also from riparian Owners. (Lancashire RD.)

CALDER empties into Irish Sea some 150 yards from mouth of Ehen. Salmon, sea trout, brown trout. Sea trout run large; 10 lb and more. Best June onwards; salmon July–Oct. Brown trout sport improving.

Calderbridge (Cumbria). Calder AA owns Calder Abbey Estate waters and the whole of the Lord Egremont Estate water on the upper reaches of the Calder and **Wormgill**. Approx 5m in all. Visitor's st £15 (includes fishing on **Ennerdale Water**). Fifteen only issued pa. Sella Park no longer a hotel. Purchased for private use by British Nuclear Fuels. *(For tackleist see Egremont.)*

EHEN. Outflow of Ennerdale Water. Flows into Irish Sea on west coast of Cumberland. Salmon, sea trout (June to Oct) and brown trout. At **Egremont** the local anglers' assn has about 8m of good salmon and sea trout fishing; own hatchery; wt, no dt; May 1–Oct 31; apply hon sec. Hotels: Black Beck, Egremont and Sea Cote (St Bees); Scawfell, Seascale. Good fishing in upper reaches held by Wath Brow and Ennerdale AA; st £10, wt £7. Tackleist: W Holmes, Main Street, Egremont. *(For Ennerdale Water see English Lake District, Cumbria.)*

ELLEN. Rises on Great Lingy Hill and flows into the Solway Firth at Maryport. Salmon and sea trout runs increasing; best late July onwards. Good brown trout fishing (Mar–June best).

Maryport (Cumbria). Trout; sea trout, salmon. Local club: Ellen AA, which has water. Tickets and licences from R Thompson (tackleist), 127 Crosby Street (information on river and sea fishing; boats) and Scott's, Aspatria. Hotels: Golden Lion; Waverley.

Aspatria (Cumbria). Trout; sea trout. Club: Aspatria AC; permits from R & J Holt, Outgang Rd. St £5, wt £2. Hotels: Grapes, Sun.

ESK. Rises near Scawfell and flows into Irish Sea near Ravenglass. Good runs of salmon, sea trout, July onwards.

Ravenglass (Cumbria). Salmon, sea trout. Rivers Mite and Irt here join Esk estuary *(see also Irt)*. Limited dt £1.50 for Muncaster Estate fishery (and licences) can be had from Pennington Arms Hotel, Ravenglass; Millom AA has water on Esk. No permits. Outward Bound School, Eskdale Green, has brown and rainbow trout fishing in private tarn (also perch). Limited to specific days. Enquiries to Bursar (Eskdale 281). May and June are best for trout; June, July,

Aug for sea trout; Sept, Oct for salmon. *(See also Eskdale.)* Hotel: Pennington Arms.

Eskdale (Cumbria); ns Drigg, 5m—Trout, sea trout, salmon; various private owners. Inexpensive fishing on **Wastwater, Devoke Water** and **Burnmoor Tarn**. Good sea fishing (especially for bass) within five miles.

IRT. Outflow of Wastwater, joining Esk in tidal water. **Bleng** is main tributary. Good runs of salmon and sea trout July onwards, some heavy fish taken; brown trout.

Gosforth. Gosforth AC has 3m, mostly both banks; members only. Licences from A Jackson (tackleist).

Holmrook (Cumbria). Salmon, sea trout, brown trout. Lutwidge Arms has 2–3m reserved for guests; wt from £14, dt from £2.50. Salmon, sea trout run early May onwards; brown trout best Mar, Apr, May. Licences at hotel. Millom AA holds two stretches; members only *(see River Duddon)*. Tackleist: E W Mitchell & Son. RD licences also from Wadeson's (newsagent), Market Square, Millom.

Netherwastdale (Cumbria). On **Wastwater Lake**; trout, permits *(see English Lake District)*. RWA licence from YHA caravan site, Gosforth. Greendale Tarn and Low Tarn feed Wastwater. Sport is good in May and June.

MITE. Flows south for short course from slopes near Eskdale to join estuary of Irt and Esk at **Ravenglass**. A late river. Sea trout, good brown trout but small, occasional salmon later on, but few opportunities for visitors.

WAMPOOL. Fishing stations: **Wigton** and **Curthwaite**. Wampool, under the name of Chalk Beck, rises on Broad Moor. Sea trout in lower reaches mostly free. *(For licences see Waver.)*

WAVER. Trout stream, flowing into the Solway Firth. Some water free, but most subject to agreement by farmers and landowners. RWA licence may be obtained from L Saunderson (Ironmongers), King Street, **Wigton.** Waver has run of sea trout and herling, particularly in its lower reaches.

Abbey Town (Cumbria). Crummock Beck; some free, but local knowledge needed.

Wigton (Cumbria). Wiza Beck, Wampool, 2m N. Waver, 2m W. Ellen, 8m SW. Lakes: Moorhouse Tarn, 2m N (private). Tackleist: Saunderson (Ironmongers), King Street. Hotels: Royal Oak and Kildare.

CRUMMOCK BECK (tributary of Waver). Flows into Holm Dub, tributary of Waver. Free, but difficult to fish. *(For licences see Waver.)*

Leegate (Cumbria). Waver, 1m E.

WHICHAM BECK. Fishing station: **Silecroft.** After a course of 6m runs into Haverigg Pool, which joins Duddon estuary at Haverigg. (NWWA)

DARENT

(For close seasons, licences, etc, see Southern Water Authority, p 38)

Rises by Westerham and enters Thames estuary at Dartford. Small Kentish stream once famous for its trout. Fishing destroyed early in present century by pollution. River was restocked with trout by Kent RA and sport improving.

Dartford (Kent). Dartford and Dist A & PS have pits along river valley which hold coarse fish, including carp and tench. Hotel: Bull.

Otford (Kent). Trout, perch, roach, dace. Darent Valley Trout Fishers have good stretch of water nearly up to Shoreham; strictly private and members only (waiting list).

Shoreham (Kent). Trout, perch, roach, dace. Now strictly preserved.

Sevenoaks (Kent). River preserved.

Sundridge Lakes, nr Westerham, 5 and 15 acres, hold large trout *(advt p 17)*. Season tickets available; inquire Sundridge Tackle Ltd, Buttercrock Wharf, Vicarage Lane, Hoo, W. Rochester. **Longford Lake:** private water of Holmesdale AS. Day tickets issued only to members' friends. Bromley (Kent) and Dist AS has Kent Sand Pits, Sevenoaks, and trout water on Darent; members only. *(See also Kent lakes and streams.)*

Tributary of the Darent

CRAY: Coarse fish.

Crayford (Kent). Free fishing at Five Arches. Crayford Kingfishers APS has Cray; bream, roach, perch, rudd, pike; members only. They also have a lake at Swanley; rudd, perch, carp, tench,

roach; members only; no dt. **Ruxley Pits, Orpington:** coarse fish; Orpington AA has lakes in a Nature Reserve. No dt. Waiting-list for membership. Tackleist: Orpington Angling Suppliers, 304 High Street, St Mary Cray.

DART

(For close seasons, licences, etc, see South West Water Authority, p 38)

Rises in centre of Dartmoor and at once divides into two, the East and West Dart. East Dart runs to Postbridge and thence to Dartmeet, where it unites with West Dart, which flows through Two Bridges. The West Dart above Dartmeet and the East Dart above Walla Brook, including tributaries, belong to Duchy of Cornwall. The river has runs of salmon and peal (sea trout). Best months for salmon are April and May in the lower reaches and May to September higher up. For peal July to September are favoured.

Dartmouth (Devon). Sea fishing from boats and rocks; pollack, bass, mackerel, bream, plaice, brill, turbot, dabs, pouting, conger, whiting, wrasse. Excellent sport at The Skerries; large turbot. Club; Dartmouth & Dist AA, annual membership, £2. Salmon, peal and trout Fishing in Dart on Dart AA water *(see Totnes, Buckfastleigh)*. Lake: Slapton Ley; pike, rudd, etc, 8m *(see Devonshire, small streams and lakes)*. Tackleists: Sportsman's Rendezvous, 16 Fairfax Place, Sea Haven, Newcomen Road; Bosun's Locker, Bayard's Cove. Hotels:

Castle, Raleigh, Manor House, Seven Stars, etc.

Totnes (Devon). Salmon, peal, trout. Dart AA controls most of left bank from just above Totnes to ½m below Buckfastleigh. Tickets with maps of water, from Blake Sports, 73 Fore Street (who also caters for bass and mullet anglers in Totnes tidal reaches). 6-day tickets available from May 1, but only to visitors resident outside Devon. (No Sunday fishing) S £15; MT £10; NT £5; dt (S and MT) £5 (NT) £1.50. Dt for weir pool, £5. Salmon av 10 lb; peal 2½ lb in May–June and about 1 lb thereafter. 4 lb and 5 lb peal not rare. School peal run from late June to mid-Aug. Nearly all peal caught after dark in normal conditions; Aug usually best. Fly only for peal and trout (latter run 3 or 4 to lb) *Note UDN has marred sport.* Hotels: Seymour, Royal Seven Stars and Cott Inn (at Darlington). At Staverton, near Totnes, is the Sea Trout Inn, right by the river. Old Mill, Harberton, has ½m trout fishing on **River Harbourne.**

Buckfastleigh (Devon). Salmon, peal, trout. Dart AA has most of left bank from Austin's Bridge down. *(For ticket conditions and details of fish see under Totnes.)* Tickets and maps of water from The Sports Shop, High Street, Totnes, also from Percy Hodge Ltd, 104 Queen Street, Newton Abbot. Holne Chase Hotel, near Ashburton, has about 1m right bank upstream from bridge free to residents. Limited st, £50, and dt £5, to non-residents. Fishing on Duchy of Cornwall waters arranged for guests. Fly only for salmon above Holne Bridge; spinning allowed below. Five holding pools. Fly only for trout (reduced rates for when water is low). Permits also from Black Rock Guest House; Bossell Guest House (tuition available); Dart Bridge Farm.

Princetown (Devon). Permits for salmon and trout fishing on main river, **East and West Dart, Wallabrook, Swincombe** and **Cherrybrook** from secretary, Duchy of Cornwall Office, The Square, or local tackleists. Salmon best May–Sept. Charges: S and MT,, st £30, wt £12, dt £3, T, st £12, mt £2.50, wt 60p. Accommodation: Tavistock Inn, Poundsgate.

Hexworthy (Devon); ns Tavistock or Newton Abbot. Salmon, sea trout (peal), brown trout. Hotel: Forest Inn; tickets, d, w or s, at hotel, for Duchy of Cornwall water; good centre for E and W Dart and Cherrybrook.

DEBEN

(For close seasons, etc, see Anglian Water Authority, p 40)

Short Suffolk river (about 30 miles long) rising near Debenham and flowing to North Sea near Felixstowe. Coarse fishing.

Woodbridge (Suffolk). Tidal. Roach, pike, tench, perch above town wt £7 dt £1 for river and reservoirs. Club: Woodbridge and Dist AC. Tackleist: Rod & Gun Shop, Church St. Hotels: Bull, Crown.

Wickham Market (Suffolk). Roach, perch, pike. Woodbridge AC water; apply hon sec.

DERWENT (Cumbria)

(For close seasons, licences, etc, see North West Water Authority, p 39)

Rises on north side of Scawfell and flows through Borrowdale, Derwentwater and Bassenthwaite Lakes to the Solway Firth at Workington. Salmon and trout practically throughout length. A late river. Best months for salmon, July to October. Trout fishing on some stretches excellent. River also holds pike and perch.

Cockermouth to **Workington** (Cumbria). Salmon, sea trout, brown trout. Trout and salmon fishing at **Armathwaite** and **Hewthwaite** from Fishery Manager, Cockermouth Castle. Permit charges under review. Permits for **Cocker** also (limited). Waters through town can be fished on permit from Tourist Information Office by residents and visitors staying locally on weekly basis. Cockermouth AA has water on **Cocker** (members only) but issues tickets for **Cogra**

CHECK BEFORE YOU GO

While every effort has been made to ensure that the information given in "Where to Fish" is correct, the position is continually changing and anglers are urged, in their own interests, to make preliminary inquiries before travelling to selected venues. This is specially important with reference to prices quoted. Inevitably, the rate of inflation is affecting stability in this quarter. Anglers' attention is also drawn to the fact that the hotels mentioned under the various fishing stations do not necessarily have fishing of their own.

Moss (details below). **Mockerkin Tarn,** stocked with carp, in 1978. Wt and dt from The Gun Shop, Lorton St. Fishing within reach on Bassenthwaite, Loweswater, Crummock and Buttermere. Other tackleists: D Lothian, Main St (information re Cocker fishing) and N H Temple, 9 Station Street, Keswick; both issue licences and permits, and will give information. Workington tackleist: Simpson's Sports, 1 South William Street. Hotels: Trout, Globe, Pheasant Sun, Bassenthwaite Lake.

Brigham (Cumbria). Trout, sea trout, salmon. Broughton Working Men's AA has about 1m from here to Broughton Cross. Permits to local working men only.

Bassenthwaite (Cumbria). Derwent, 1m N; trout, salmon; private. Lakes: Bassenthwaite; pike, perch, trout, occasional salmon *(see English Lake District—Bassenthwaite)*. Hotels: Swan, Pheasant, Armathwaite Hall.

Keswick (Cumbria). For Derwent and Greta; salmon, trout (average $\frac{1}{4}$ lb); mid-August onwards for salmon. Permits for Keswick and Dist AA water (Threlkeld to Bassenthwaite), salmon, trout. Visitors S wt £12, dt £3, NT: wt £5, dt £1; lake permits st £8, wt £5, dt £1 (reductions for juniors on all fishings), from N H Temple, 9 Station Street, who issues tickets also for Derwentwater and Bassenthwaite and guide to fishing in the area *(see English Lake District)*. Hotels: Hazeldene, Queen's Royal Oak, Lake, George, County King's Arms. Derwentwater (Portinscale) sells permits for all Assn water. *(advt p 65)*

Borrowdale (Cumbria). Trout, salmon; gin-clear as a rule and best fished after dark. Lakes: Derwentwater; trout, perch, pike; small charge for fishing. Watendlath Tarn 2m S; Blea Tarn, 4m S; trout. Hotels: Scawfell; Borrowdale; Lodore Swiss.

Tributaries of the Derwent (Cumbria)

COCKER: Salmon, sea trout, trout. July to October best for migratory fish. Mostly private, but dt for Cockermouth AA water (and for **Loweswater, Buttermere** and **Crummock Water**) from The Gun Shop, Lorton Street, Cockermouth.

Scalehill (Cumbria). Cockermouth. 7m Cocker: Salmon, sea trout, trout. Private. National Trust lakes: **Crummock Water;** pike, trout, char. **Loweswater,** 2m W; pike, trout. **Buttermere,** 4m (see below). April, May best for trout in Loweswater; June and July in Crummock and Buttermere. St, dt and boats. For **Loweswater** and north end of Crummock and Buttermere. St from Shop, Loweswater. Hotel: Scale Hill.

Cogra Moss. 40 acre trout reservoir 8m S of Cockermouth. Browns and rainbows. Wt and dt. Season 1 April–30 Sept. Tickets from The Gun Shop, Lorton Street, Cockermouth.

Buttermere (Cumbria). National Trust property. Char, trout, pike; tickets, boats, as for Loweswater (above); for Buttermere and south end of Crummock apply Buttermere Stores. Trust permit covers all three lakes.

NEWLANDS BECK: Trout.

Braithwaite (Cumbria); ns Keswick, 2m. Beck; fishable above Braithwaite, ruined by dredging below.

GRETA: Trout (av $\frac{1}{4}$ lb); salmon.

Threlkeld (Cumbria). Keswick AA increased their holdings in 1980 *(tickets, see Keswick)*. Best months for salmon Sept and Oct; mostly spinning and worm fishing. St John's Beck from Thirlmere is best from lake for 1½m and from Wanthwaite Bridge to New Bridge; between is canalised; trout. Glenderamackin Beck; trout; fishable throughout length, but fish few and far between.

DEVONSHIRE (streams and lakes)

(For close seasons, etc. see SW Water Authority, p 38, unless otherwise stated)*

AVON. Rises on Dartmoor and flows 22m SE, entering English Channel near Thurlestone via long, twisting estuary. Tide flows to Aveton Gifford. Trout (3 or 4 lb), sea trout, salmon.

Thurlestone (Devon). Near mouth of Avon estuary. Capital bass fishing off Bantham Sands at mouth.

Aveton Gifford (Devon). About 6¼m of left bank and 8¼m of right bank controlled by Avon FA. Sea trout (end of May onwards), some salmon; good dry-fly trout water (3 to the lb). Banks heavily wooded; good wading. Tickets: st and wt, from hon sec at 3 Warren Rd, Kingsbridge, or post offices at Aveton Gifford, Diptford and Loddiswell; Blake Sports, Totnes; Perrott, 26 Fore Street, Kingsbridge. Hotels: Ebb Tide, South Efford House.

Kingsbridge (Devon). Avon, 2½m N at **Loddiswell;** trout, salmon, sea trout. Further information from hon sec Avon FA *(see also Aveton Gifford)*. Capital bass and pollack in Kingsbridge estuary. Tackleist: Perrott Bros, 26 Fore Street. Hotels: King's Arms; Buttville; Torcross (for Slapton Ley).

Brent (Devon). Salmon, trout, sea trout. Avon FA water below *(see Aveton Gifford)*. Mrs J Theobald, Little Aish Riding Stables, South Brent, issues dt for stretch of Aish Woods. Red Brook, 2m N; trout. Black Brook, 2m S; trout. Hotel: Anchor.

AVON RESERVOIR (8m NE of Totnes). Brown trout, zoned worm, spinning and fly fishing free to SWWA licenceholders. No boats. Season April 1–Oct

12. Reservoir is about 1½m beyond **Shipley Bridge,** car park available.

BURRATOR RESERVOIR Yelverton. Brown and rainbow trout. Dt £1.50, st £20 (concessions for OAP and Jun). Self-service ticket unit at Burrator Lodge, Sheepstor, Yelverton.

ERME. Rises on Dartmoor and flows 14m S to Bigbury Bay. Trout.

Ivybridge. Mrs B S Sparrow, Cleeve, grant free fishing to ACA members (membership-forms available). Furnished cottage sometimes available.

FERNWORTHY RESERVOIR, near **Chagford.** South West Water Authority. Trout, April 25–Nov 8. Dt £4 (evenings £2.50) boat £4 (evening £2.50) concessions to OAP and Jun. Self-service unit by hut on S side of reservoir.

GAMMATION, and **JENNETS RESERVOIRS. Bideford** *(see Bideford).*

MELDON RESERVOIR (3m SE of Okehampton). Brown and rainbow trout. Spinning, bait and fly fishing free to SWWA licence-holders. Season March 15–Sept 30.

LYN, near Lynmouth (Devon). Ns **Barnstaple** or **Minehead.** This beautiful river has good run of salmon, July onwards. Also sea trout and brown trout; latter small. Season March 1–Oct 31. Dt (S) £4.50 (NT) 70p from Warden, Combe Park Lodge, Hillsford Bridge, Lynton; Mr Hill, The Esplanade, Lynmouth and Anglers Corner, Imperial Buildings, Castle Hill, Lynton. Mr Burge, Glebe Farm, Oare, Brendon, issues dt £1 for 3m (both banks) of East Lyn. Tackleists, A J Holman, The Avenue Post Office. Francis Sully, Sports Outfitter, The Parade, Minehead. *(See also Sea Fishing Stations.)*

PLYM. Devon trout stream which enters English Channel at Plymouth. (Cornwall RD.)

Plymouth (Devon). On Plym and Tavy. Trout, sea trout and salmon in Tavy, but Plym now mainly a trout stream. Plymouth and Dist Freshwater AA has short stretch of Plym; two dt per day (Mon–Fri) for Plym Bridge upstream from D K Sports, 204 Exeter Street, Plymouth. (Tel. 663483), remainder of river private except for portion above Bickleigh Bridge, controlled by Tavy, Walkham and Plym FC. Club issues tickets (salmon, sea trout, brown trout) for its water *(see Tamar–Tavy).* Salmon, sea trout and trout fishing available by ticket on Wabreddon Fishery on Tavy and Walkham; tickets from Jefferys (see below). **Burrator Reservoir** (13m); trout; tickets *(see separate entry).* Sea fishing excellent *(see Sea Fishing Stations).* A R and H V Jeffery Ltd (tackleist), 19–21 Old Town Street, will provide information. *(See Cornwall, streams, lakes etc.)*

MEAVY (tributary of the Plym). Fishing stations: **Shaugh** and **Clearbrook.**

OAREWATER, Brendon. Trout. Dt and wt from W Burge, Oaremead.

SID. Sidmouth. Trout. For details, contact SW Water Authority.

SLADE RESERVOIRS. Ilfracombe. Brown and rainbow trout; st £20, dt £1.50; fly only. Dt self-service unit at reservoir, by dam.

SLAPTON LEY. ns **Dartmouth,** 7m; Kingsbridge, 8m. Good pike, roach eel and perch. Part of nature reserve, bank fishing prohibited. For boats (£2.50 day plus 75p per angler) apply Field Centre, Slapton Village (Torcross 466). Half-day rates also offered. Excellent sea fishing for bass, turbot, plaice, brill and large whiting. Hotels: The Torcross and (in Slapton) the Tower Inn. Many guest houses.

KENNICK and TOTTIFORD RESERVOIRS. (8m NE of Newton Abbot.) Brown and rainbow trout. Fly only. £4, evenings £2.50. Season: April 1–Oct 12. No boats. Tickets from South West Water Authority. Self-service on site.

Trenchford Reservoir, now closed.

WISTLANDPOUND RESERVOIR. Arlington. Brown and rainbow trout. April 1–Oct 12. Dt £4, evenings £2.50. Concessions to OAP and Jun (fly only); from self-service unit at reservoir.

YEALM. Rises on southern heights of Dartmoor and flows 12m south and west

---

POLLUTION

Anglers are united in deploring pollution. To combat it, urgent action may be called for at any time from any one of us. If numbers of fish are found dead, dying, or seriously distressed, take samples of both fish and water and contact the office of the Director of Scientific Services at the appropriate Regional Water Authority.

to English Channel, which it enters by a long estuary. Trout, sea trout (about 6–8 lb), occasional late salmon. Fishing private. Good bass and pollack in estuary (Cornwall RD).

Newton Ferrers (Devon). On estuary. One of finest deep-sea fishing stations in south-west. Hotel: River Yealm. *(See sea fishing section.)*

DORSET (streams)

(For close seasons, licences, etc, see Wessex Water Authority, p 39)

BRIT AND ASKER. Fishing station: **Bridport.** Trout. Rivers mostly private or overgrown, but Civil Service Sports Council has stretch of Brit for members only. Also **Radipole** Lakes; dt for latter; coarse fish. Tickets from Weymouth tackleists. Tackleist: Lawrie Rathbone (Tel 0308 23475), Tackle Shop, West Bay, Bridport *(see also Sea Fishing Stations)*.

CHAR. Fishing station: **Charmouth.** Char is some 7m long; trout, private, but leave may sometimes be obtained. General sea fishing. Tackleist: Childs & Son, High Road. Hotels: Coach and Horses, Queen's Arms, Hammons Mead.

CORFE. Rises 1m W of Corfe Castle (ns Wareham, 4½m), and runs into Poole Harbour 5m down. Coarse fishing sometimes available from landowners.

DURHAM (reservoirs)

DERWENT. Edmundbyers. May 1–Oct 14, 1,000 acre trout water run by Sunderland & South Shields Water Co, 29 John Street, Sunderland. Well stocked with 2-year-old brown and rainbow trout (av ¾ lb); fly only. St (from Company) £100. Dt £3, obtainable on site. Motor boats £13, rowing boats £6.50. RD licence required. Tel: Edmundbyers 55250 for boat bookings. Hotel: Lord Crewe Arms. **Note:** *Reservoir also partly in Northumberland.*

SMIDDY SHAW, and WASKERLEY. Good trouting, preserved by North-West Durham AA. Season April 1–Sept 30. Nearest towns: **Wolsingham, Consett** and **Stanhope**.

EDEN

(For close season, licences, etc, see North West Water Authority, p 39)

Rises south of Kirkby Stephen and empties into Solway Firth 5m NW of Carlisle. Salmon, sea trout, brown trout. Still some spring fish, but now more a back-end river. Sea trout in lower and middle reaches and tributaries from June onwards. Trouting best in middle and upper reaches, fish run to good average size for north. Chub and grayling in parts.

Carlisle (Cumbria). Salmon in spring and autumn, sea trout and herling in July and August, brown trout fair, some chub and dace. Carlisle AA has 7m on Eden. S, st (limited) £13, wt £6.50, dt £2. T, st £6, wt £1.50, dt 75p. Tickets (and RD licences) from tackleists: Raine, 21 Warwick Road; McHardy's, South Henry Street; Carlisle Angling Centre, 2 Globe Lane. Inquire Mrs Elwes, Warwick Hall, **Warwick-on-Eden,** for salmon and trout fishing. Hotels: Crown and Mitre, Central, Hilltop.

Wetheral (Cumbria). Salmon and sea trout preserved for 4m to 5m by the Yorkshire Fly-fishers' Club here and at Great Corby; Cairn Beck, 2m, Irthing, 3m N. Scotby Beck, 2m W at Scotby. Hotel: Crown.

Armathwaite (Cumbria). Salmon, trout, grayling. Croglin Waters, 3m E.

Lazonby (Cumbria). Salmon, trout and grayling. A private shooting and fishing lodge with restricted licence, Bracken Bank (Tel 241), has six good stretches on Eden for its guests (salmon and trout), comprising 3½m with some fine pools. Also good beck fishing and sport in moorland streams. Good shooting (especially grouse driving) may also be had by guests at Bracken Bank. Details sent on application to the proprietor, R N Burton. Limited wt S and NT for non-residents from £30 and £12 respectively.

Great Salkeld (Cumbria). Fetherston Arms Hotel, Kirkoswald, has 2½m (Lazonby 284). High Drove Inn has salmon and trout fishing; salmon 75p day, trout 50p.

Langwathby (Cumbria). Salmon, trout; preserved by Yorkshire FFC.

Culgaith (Cumbria). Trout; preserved by Yorkshire FFC from Culgaith to below Langwathby apart from vicinity of Watersmeet. Winderwath, left bank; now Penrith AA from Eden Bridge, Temple Sowerby *(see also Temple Sowerby)*; mt £4.50, from hon sec Eller Beck, 1m S Eamont, 4 m W Tees, 6m NE. Trout, private. Hotels: Black Swan, Culgaith; King's Arms, Temple Sowerby.

Temple Sowerby (Cumbria). Salmon, trout, grayling; preserved (with some miles of Eamont) by Yorkshire FFC; members only. Penrith AA has 1¼m down from Eden Bridge on left bank *(see also Culgaith)*. A £16 wt is issued, covering a number of waters. Eller Beck, 1m W. Lyvennet; trout, preserved as Eden. King's Arms Hotel has trout fishing for guests on 1½m of Eden; licences and tickets available at hotel; trout average 1 lb.

Kirkby Thore (Cumbria). Salmon, trout and grayling. Penrith AA preserves 2m on main river and Kirkby Thore Beck from road bridge 1m upstream.

Appleby (Cumbria). Eden trout are very free risers, averaging about three to pound with better fish to 3 and even 4 lb. Ample accommodation available at Tufton Arms *(advt p 16)*, also at White Hart, Glen, Royal Oak, Courtfield, Appleby Manor, Crown and Cushion Inn. Tickets for Upper Appleby fishings from John Pape *(see below)*. Wt £30 and £24, dt £5 and £4, according to date. Brown trout, fly only. Sedge fishing in evenings good May to August. Grayling provide good winter sport. 14m of Assn water; but membership full, no guest tickets. Licences and local flies from John Pape, Appleby Shoe & Sports Supplies, Market Place.

Kirkby Stephen (Cumbria). Kirkby Stephen and Dist AA has about 20m on main river and becks, fly only. *(See Belah and Scandal tributaries.)* Visitors' st £25 and dt £3.50 from hon sec or Robinson, Silver Street (waiting-list for membership). Thornaby AA has "Outhgill" (1½m), White Bracken (½m) and Stenkrith (½m) stretches; trout only (3 to lb); members only *(see Thornaby under Tess)*. Hotel: King's Arms. Licences from Newsagent, 46 Market St. Tackleist: H S Robinson.

Tributaries of the Eden

PETTERIL joins Eden at Carlisle. Good trout fishing, but lower half mostly private. Penrith AA has 3m of water on upper reaches.

Plumpton (Cumbria). Trout. Penrith AA preserves from Kettleside Farm to Boggle Hall Farm.

IRTHING. Rises on Grey Fell Common and joins Eden east of Carlisle. Salmon, trout, grayling and few sea trout.

Brampton (Cumbria). Irthing, 1m N; Gelt, 1m S; trout, grayling, chub. Brampton AA preserves; wt (£10) dt (£3) and RWA licence from Atkinsons Sports Shop, Front Street. Trout average ½ to ¾ lb; early months best. Kingwater, 2m N. Cambeck, 1½m N, Eden 5m W; salmon, trout; preserved. Lakes: Talkin Tarn, 2m SE; pike, perch. Tindale Tarn, 6m SE; pike, perch, trout. Hotels: White Lion, Scotch Arms, Sand House (temperance), Eden House (temperance), Howard Arms. Tackleist: Atkinsons, Front Street.

EAMONT flows from Ullswater Lake. A good grayling water. Penrith AA has some water. Lake Ullswater good trout fishing; free, but RWA licence required.

Penrith (Cumbria). Eamont, 1m S; salmon, trout. Upper portion (trout only) preserved by Penrith AA (fly only) from Pooley Bridge on left bank to Yanwath Viaduct, and on right bank from Pooley Bridge to Yanwath Wood. Also on **Eden, Lowther** and on becks. £16 wt covers a variety of fishings. Yorkshire Flyfishers preserve left bank of Eamont from Broughton Castle down to Barrack Bank and then on left bank only to below Udford; members only. Other water on Eamont private. Lakes: Ullswater, 5m S; trout; free to licence-holders. **Haweswater,** 10m SE; rights in hands of N West Water Authority, and guests at Haweswater Hotel, Mardale, Bampton, near Penrith, may obtain permits at hotel (see Westmorland lakes). Crown & Mitre Hotel, Bampton Grange, has 8m of salmon and trout fishing on Eden and tributaries available to residents. Other hotels: Crown, George, Gloucester Arms, Kings Arms, Edenhall, near Langwathby. Licences from tackleists: S Norris, 21 Victoria Road or C R Sykes, 4

It's never too young to start. The late Frank Swayer gives a six-year-old her first lesson. The scene – a Game Fair. Game Fairs, covering all field sports, do their round of the country year by year. *Photograph: John Tarlton.*

Great Dockray, both Penrith; or Langwathby PO.

Pooley Bridge (Cumbria). Eamont; salmon, trout. Penrith AA water *(see Penrith)*. Ullswater; good trout fishing; only RD licence needed; boats available *(see also Patterdale)*. Hotels: Sun, Crown.

Patterdale (Cumbria). The becks Goldrill, Grisdale, Deepdale and Hartsop; free. Aira Force below NT property (3m) free. N Hawes and Riggindale Becks, permits N West Water Authority. Blea Tarn and Smallwater, N West Water Authority, Hayeswater (Hayes Tarn) now belongs to Penrith Urban District Council; no permits. **Ullswater.** Trout numerous, average three to pound. Bank fishing free to licence holders, but some restrictions on access. Evening rise during May and June yields heavy baskets; six brace of trout in evening quite common. Day fishing also good, and heavier fish begin to move about middle of May. Use of maggot and ground bait banned during coarse fish close season. Numerous boats available. Angle Tarn, permits. Greenside Reservoir, Red Tarn, Grisdale Tarn, free. (Kepple Cove Tarn is dry). Hotels: Ullswater, Patterdale; White Lion, Brotherswater; Glenridding (boats); Royal, Dockray, 3m; Old Church, 5m; Brackenrigg, 6m; Rampsbeck, 6m; Howtown, 6m; Sharrow Bay, 6m; Waterfoot.

LOWTHER (tributary of Eamont.: Salmon and trout. Abstraction affecting salmon sport—autumn run now very late. Sport with trout remains good (av ¾ lb). Crown and Mitre Hotel, **Bampton** (via Penrith), has more than 3m fishing for guests (trout and late salmon) including Haweswater Beck; a good centre, only 100 yds from river. Penrith AA holds substantial stretches of good fly water on river; other assn water on Eden, Eamont and Petteril; £5. RD licences from hotel or Penrith tackleists.

LYVENNET: Good trout stream; runs in a few miles below Temple Sowerby. Leave from farmers in some parts. 1m preserved for Yorkshire Flyfishers' Club.

BELAH: Flows from Pennine fells to join Eden 2m below Kirkby Stephen. Lower reaches, from Brough Sowerby, rented by Kirkby Stephen and Dist AA; members only.

SCANDEL BECK: Smardale (Cumbria) and **Crosby Garrett** (Cumbria). Potts or Helmbeck 2m W; Eden 3m NE; trout; preserved Kirkby Stephen & Dist AA has water on Scandal Beck. *(See Kirkby Stephen under Eden.)*

ENGLISH LAKE DISTRICT

(For close seasons, licences, etc, see North West Water Authority, p 39)

BASSENTHWAITE, 5m Cockermouth; 8m Keswick. Long famous for its perch fishing, also a pike fishery. Salmon, too, occasionally caught on the troll. Now owned by Lake District Special Planning Board, Kendal. Hotels: Pheasant Inn, Swan, Armathwaite Hall.

BLEA TARN. About 2m above Watendlath Tarn; perch; some trout. Wt £1, dt 25p, from Mrs Myers, Blea Tarn Farmhouse.

BLELHAM TARN (in Lancashire). ns **Windermere.** Pike, perch, some trout, wt £1.20, dt 30p from National Trust Warden, Low Wray Campsite.

BROTHERSWATER. ns **Windermere** 10m; Ullswater is 2¾m; trout. National Trust property; excellent fishing; boats available.

BURNMOOR TARN. Boot (2m). Good trout and pike. National Trust; fishing free.

BUTTERMERE. National Trust lake. Char, trout, pike, perch. Permits (wt £4.50, dt £1) which cover Crummock and Loweswater, too, from Mrs Richardson, Gatesgarth Farm and The Gun Shop, Cockermouth. Hotels: Bridge, Fish. Guest Houses: Trevene, Wood House.

CODALE TARN, 4m from **Grasmere.** Perch, some trout; free. Hotels: *(see Grasmere).*

CONISTON. Trout, char, perch, pike. Free; RD licence needed only for trout and char. Boats from Coniston Power Boat Co, Bridge End Café, and café at boathouse. Tackle and licences from J D Fox, Yewdale Road, and W R Garner, Low House, Coniston. Local club: Coniston AA, which has fishing on tarns and becks. *(See Yew Tree Tarn).* Hotels: Sun, Black Bull, Crown, Ship Inn.

CRUMMOCKWATER. National Trust lake. Pike, trout, char; salmon and sea trout from Cocker sometimes caught by trolling. Fishes best June and July. Wt £4.50 and dt £1 (covering also Buttermere and Loweswater) from Mrs Beard, Rannerdale Farm or Gun Shop, Cockermouth. Best periods for Crummock, Buttermere and Loweswater are: Trout, late May and early June (good mayfly hatch); char, July and August (special technique required—trolling 60 to 90 feet down). *(For hotels see Buttermere.)*

DERWENTWATER. Keswick. Trout (best in mayfly season); good-sized perch and a fair head of pike (8–10 lb). Salmon present but rarely taken. Fishing rights leased to Keswick AA (dt £1.50, wt £7); permits also from N Temple, Station Street; boats at Lodore, Nicoll End, and Keswick landings. *(For Keswick hotels see Derwent (Cumbria)—Keswick.)* Other hotels are Swiss, at Lodore; Lodore, which has trout fishing in Lodore Falls in grounds; Scawfell and Borrowdale in Borrowdale.

DEVOKE WATER near **Ravenglass** (5m E). Moorland tarn offering sport with fair-sized trout. Millom AA holds rights. No tickets.

DRUNKEN DUCK TARN, Ambleside. Brown trout. Dt (£5) from Drunken Duck Hotel; four rods only, incl two for Grizedale AC (inquire Forestry Commission).

EASEDALE TARN, 3m from **Grasmere.** Good perch, few trout. Permits from Brimmer Head Farm, Grasmere. Hotels: *(See Grasmere).*

ELTERWATER, ns **Windermere.** Pike and perch, few trout.

ENNERDALE, ns **Whitehaven.** Trout,

char; controlled by Ennerdale Lake Fishery formed by Calder AA, Egremont Anglers, Wath Brow and Ennerdale Anglers; wt 50p, st £1 from W Hail, Hardware Shop, 48 South St, Egremont. Boats (limited). Licences and permits for **R Ehen** also available.

ESTHWAITE WATER (nr Hawkshead, Lancashire). ns Windermere, 3m. Good pike, perch and trout (av ¾ lb). Fishing by permit only (dt 60p, wt £2) from B & C Raistrick, Post Office, Hawkshead, near Ambleside (also daily boat permits tackle and licences). Boat and annual fishing permits from W Taylor, Esthwaite Howe Farm, Nr Sawrey, Ambleside (Tel Hawkshead 331). Nearest accommodation is in Hawkshead, Sawrey and Windermere.

FISHER TARN, ns **Kendal,** 3m. Kendal's water supply. Few trout of good average size; privately leased.

GRASMERE, ns **Windermere.** Pike, perch, few trout; free to RWA licence-holders. Boats available. For **Rydal Water** and **River Rothay** apply Windermere, Ambleside and Dist AA, c/o Musgroves Ltd, Lake Rd, Windermere. Wt £3, dt £2. *(See Lancashire and Westmorland small streams.)* Hotels: Swan, Red Lion, Rothay, Prince of Wales, Dale Lodge, Ben Place (private), Moss Grove (private).

GREAT RUNDALE TARN, ns **Long Marton,** 5m. Seamore Tarn and Little Rundale Tarn are in the vicinity. Small trout.

GRIZEDALE LEA RESERVOIR. Trout; hon sec, Kirkham and Dist FFC issues dt (limited), boat extra; fly only.

HAWESWATER, ns **Penrith** or **Shap.** Small stock of trout. Water Authority has rights. Permits available only to guests at Haweswater Hotel, Mardale, Bampton, nr Penrith.

HAYES WATER, ns **Penrith.** Trout (3 to lb) and perch. Penrith AA; members only.

KILLINGTON RESERVOIR, ns **Oxenholme,** 3m. Trout, pike, perch. Leased to Kent AA. St £8, wt £3, dt £1.20 from Kendal tackle shops or Keeper at reservoir. Parties should book in advance through Kent AA sec.

LOUGHRIGG TARN, ns **Windermere.** Pike, perch; wt £1.20, dt 30p, from Tarn Foot Farm.

LOWESWATER. National Trust lake. Pike, perch, trout (av 1½–2 lb but hard to catch; fly only up to June 10); Kirkstile

Inn, Loweswater. For wt £4.50 and dt £1 (covering also Buttermere and Crummockwater) apply at Gun Shop, Cockermouth, where RD licences are also obtainable. Other hotel: Scale Hill.

MOCKERKIN, near Loweswater. Tarn stocked with carp by Cockermouth AA. Wt and dt from The Gun Shop, Lorton Street, Cockermouth.

RED TARN, ns **Penrith.** Free (under Helvellyn). Abounds with gwyniad and trout; best late in season.

RYDAL WATER and **HIGH ARNSIDE TARN,** ns **Windermere.** Pike, perch and fair-sized trout; preserved by Windermere, Ambleside and Dist AA. Tickets from Musgrave's Ltd, Windermere (st £6, wt £4, dt £2, juniors ½ price).

SKELSMERGH, ns **Kendal,** 3m. Swarms with small roach and rudd, fishing free; bank treacherous.

SMALLWATER TARN, ns **Penrith.** Water Authority has rights. Trout; difficult of access and often disappointing. (Cumb RD.)

SPRINKLING TARN. Right up Stye Head Pass. Trout. Good on a favourable day until July.

STYE HEAD TARN. Same information as Sprinkling Tarn.

TARN HOWS. Hawkshead. National Trust, but fishing reserved. No permits.

THIRLMERE. Perch, pike, trout. Preserved by N West Water Authority, who issue privilege tickets only to employees.

ULLSWATER, ns **Penrith.** Covers 2,200 acres. Noted trout fishery. Also perch, char and gwyniad. Trout average 3 to lb but fish up to 8 lb taken. Free to licence-holders. Hotels: Ullswater, Patterdale, White Lion, Glenridding, Waterfoot, Waternook, Sharrow Bay, Rampsbeck, Brackenrigg, Howtown, Crown, Sun (last two Pooley Bridge). Good trout fishing; boats available. (NWWA).

WASTWATER. Trout, char; and pike. Wt £2.25, dt 50p from Warden, National Trust Campsite, Wasdale Head. No boats. Hotels: Lutwidge Arms Hotel, Holmrook, and Bridge Inn, Santon Bridge and Strands. Other tarns: Greendale, High Fell, Scoats; brown trout. *(See also Bassenthwaite and for river fishing in outflow see Irt.)*

WATENDLATH TARN. Keswick 6m. Good pike fishing. Many small trout. Free.

WHINFELL TARN, ns **Kendal,** 5m. Rudd,

perch and pike plentiful. Fishing prohibited by owner.

WINDERMERE, ns Windermere, Largest lake. 10½m long and nearly 1m wide. Good pike and perch, also eels, char and trout (trout best March–June). Fishing free, apart from RD licence. Big fish taken by trolling. Boats from Bowness Bay. Local club: Windermere, Ambleside & Dist AA, which issues dt £2, wt £3 for fishing on **Rydal Water, Rivers Rothay, Brothay** and **Troutbeck,** and two tarns *(see Grasmere and Lancashire and Cumbria small streams).* Tackleist: P

Musgrave & Sons Ltd, Lake Road. Hotels: Storrs, Old England, Royal, Crown, Belsfield, Hydro; Windermere Hotel (formerly Rigg's) is 1m from lake. Hotels at Ambleside: Lowood, Salutation, White Lion, Waterhead, Water Edge (facing Windermere Lake).

YEW TREE TARN, near **Coniston.** Now owned by National Trust and leased to Coniston and Torver Anglers. Brown trout only; Dt £4 and £2, according to date, from Shop 3, Lakeland House, Tilberthwaite House, Coniston.

ESK (Border)

(Esk in England is under North West Water Authority; close seasons, licences, etc, see p 39. Statutory close times apply to river in Scotland; no licences needed)

Rises in Dumfriesshire and flows into the Solway Firth and is now classed as an English river. Upper reaches of Esk and main tributary, Liddle, good for brown trout but rivers are primarily sea trout and salmon waters from Langholm and Newcastleton to the mouth. Heavy run of sea trout and herling from June to September. Salmon in spring and autumn, September and October being best months. Chub and dace in lower reaches provide good sport in winter.

Canonbie (Dumfries and Galloway). Salmon, sea trout, herling, trout; Esk and Liddle Fisheries Association issue permits: St £60, wt £12/24. No dt *(see Langholm).* Tackle obtainable from Kershope House Estate *(see Kershopefoot, under Liddle below).* Hotels: Cross Keys, Marchbank, Riverside Inn.

Langholm (Dumfries and Galloway). Salmon, sea trout, herling, trout. Certain stretches of Esk and its tributaries (the Liddle, White Esk, Ewes, Wauchope and Tarras) are under the control of the Esk and Liddle FA. Tickets from Secretary's office, Bank of Scotland,

Langholm; J I Wylie, river-watcher, Byreburnfoot, Canonbie; A Little, 48 High Street; J M White, Market Place; or (for the Liddle) from Mr Ewart, draper, Newcastleton. St £62, wt £12/25 according to season. "All waters" tickets as follows: St £180, wt (to end of May) £35, (from June 1) £70. No dt. Assn also has four boats on **Black Esk Reservoir** (20m); trout non-residents £6 day (including boat). Permits from R J B Hill, Bank of Scotland Buildings, Langholm, Dumfrieshire DG13 0AD. No RWA licence needed. Netherby Estate Offices, Longtown, issue permits for salmon and sea trout fishing at **Netherby.** No Sunday fishing and restricted night fishing. There are also restrictions on spinning and worm fishing. Full particulars from secretaries. Hotels: Crown, Eskdale

(advt p 73), or Cross Keys (Canonbie); Langholm Guest House. Holmwood House.

Westerkirk (Dumfries and Galloway). Salmon, sea trout, herling, trout.

Tributaries of the Border Esk

LIDDLE: Salmon, sea trout, herling, brown trout.

Kershopefoot (Cumbria). Kershope House, previously a hotel with fishing for guests, has recently reverted to private house status. The fishing is no longer available on dt or any other basis.

Newcastleton (Roxburgh). Salmon, sea trout, herling, brown trout. Esk and

Liddle Fisheries Association has much water. Tickets (st and wt) from Messrs Ewart (draper), South Hermitage Street. Hotels: Liddlesdale, Grapes (fishing arranged on Esk, Liddle and other local waters) *(see also Esk–Langholm)*.

LYNE: Lyne rises on Bewcastle Fells and joins Esk ½m above Metal Bridge. Salmon, sea trout, herling, trout. Riparian owners sometimes give permission.

Two small streams, Sark and Kirtle Water, form **Gretna Water** and are in reality Scottish streams, but are included here for convenience, as they come within watershed of Border Esk.

SARK: Trout stream about 10m long, forming for a short distance boundary between England and Scotland, and emptying into Solway at Gretna; has run of sea trout and herling (best July onwards).

Gretna (Dumfries and Galloway). Gretna AA has water *(see under Kirtle Water, below)*.

KIRTLE WATER: Stream which empties into the Solway at Kirtlefoot. Sea trout, herling, trout. About 3m from mouth controlled by Gretna AA. Association

controls also 5m on Sark; st £2, wt £1.50 and dt 80p (covering sea trout and salmon) from Central Cafe, Gretna. Humbers Lodge Hotel, Rigg Shop, Rigg and Kirtleside Farm, Rigg.

Kirtlebridge (Dumfries and Galloway). Sea trout and trout; short free length. Winterhope Burn. Penoben Burn. Annan, 3m SW. Well-stocked reservoir 3m off, **Middlebie Dam,** fishable by permit; trouting very good.

Kirkpatrick (Dumfries and Galloway). Trout.

ESK (Yorkshire)

(For close seasons, licences, etc, see Yorkshire Water Authority, p 40)

Rises on Westerdale Moor and runs into sea at Whitby. Salmon, trout and grayling. This stream, from which salmon had disappeared, was artificially restocked, and now holds good head of fish. Represents most successful effort at artificial restocking with salmon. Good runs of sea trout as a rule; brown trout plentiful but on small side. River largely controlled by Esk Fishery Association.

Whitby (Yorks). Salmon, sea trout, trout, grayling, eels; largely preserved by the Esk FA from Whitby to beyond Glaisdale. Applications for vacancies in association should be addressed to the hon sec. Visitors' tickets available only for tidal water below Ruswarp and between Ruswarp and Sleights. No maggot fishing is allowed. Price of tickets for fishing from Iburndale Beck down to Whitby Harbour. St £35, dt £1. Salmon, sea trout and brown trout. Tickets from boat-landing at Ruswarp. *(see also under Sea Fishing Stations.)*

Ruswarp (Yorks). Salmon, sea trout, trout, grayling, eels; preserved for 2m by Esk Fishery Association. Tickets from Yorkshire Water Authority.

Sleights (Yorks). Salmon, sea trout, trout, grayling, eels; preserved by Esk Fishery Association. Tickets from Yorkshire Water Authority.

Goathland (Yorks) Salmon, sea trout, trout, grayling. Murk Esk; trout. Goathland AC water; members only.

Grosmont (Yorks). Trout, salmon; preserved by the Esk FA above to Glaisdale, and below to Whitby.

Egton Bridge (Yorks). Salmon, trout; some water preserved by the Esk FA. Other water (1½m both banks) owned by Egton Estates Co. Tickets sometimes issued. Trout fishing in **Randymere Reservoir,** between here and Goathland and **Scaling Dam** (worm and fly). Hotels: Horse Shoe; Wheatsheaf Inn; Station.

Glaisdale (N Yorks). Salmon, sea trout, trout; preserved below by the Esk FA *(see Whitby)*. Hotel: Angler's Rest. Tackle and licences from Esk FA bailiff, D J Swales, 23 Priory Park, Grosmont. Dt from Yorkshire Water Authority.

Danby (N Yorks). Salmon, sea trout, brown trout, grayling, preserved by landowners and Danby AC. Danby AC has about 8m of water; st (limited) £6, dt £1.50 (£3 in Oct), from Duke of Wellington (Danby); Post Offices, Castleton and Danby; Ward Thompson, Borough Rd, Middlesbrough and F Farrow, Butcher, Danby. Spinning for trout with fixed-spool reel prohibited; fly only until June 1; maggot prohibited. Accommodation, licences, tickets, available at the Duke of Wellington; also "The Moorlands", Castleton.

Castleton (N Yorks). Trout: Danby AC water *(see Danby)*. Hotel: Moorlands.

Westerdale (N Yorks). Trout, grayling. Stokesley AC has about 3m above and below village. Members only.

Tributaries of the Esk (Yorkshire)

MURK ESK: Salmon and trout. Tributaries are: Little Beck, Brocka Beck, Eller Beck, Little Eller Beck. Fishing station: **Grosmont.**

COMMONDALE BROOK: Commondale (Yorks). Trout: preserved by the owners.

ESSEX (streams, lakes and reservoirs)

(For close seasons, licences, etc, see Anglian Water Authority, p 40)

AQUATELS LAKES, Basildon. 25 acre coarse fishery. Large bream and carp. Dt only, £1.50. Night fishing allowed; boats. Hotel, country club and tackle shop on site. Details from Aquatels Rec Centre, Cranes Farm Rd, Basildon (Tel 27278).

ARDLEIGH RESERVOIR, nr Colchester. 130 acre reservoir stocked with brown, brook and rainbow trout. Season: April 1 to Oct 29. Fly only to Oct 1. Full st £130. Mon–Fri st £96. Dt we & bh £5.60; other days from Apr 4, £4.40 (£3.40 after 5 pm). Concessions to jun. Boats: £7 p.d., £4.40 ½day. AWA licence req. Spinning and bait fishing for trout and coarse fish from Oct 1 dt £5. Fishing and fly-tying courses offered. Enq. to Fisheries & Est. Officer, Ardleigh Reservoir, Nr Colchester, Essex CO7 1BR, with sae. Tel Col 230642.

BERWICK PONDS. Rainham. Elm Park and Dist AS has lake and carrier; coarse fish; dt from bailiff.

BIRCH HALL LAKE. Near **Colchester;** coarse fish; Kelvedon AC; club also has Rivenhall Lake, near **Witham,** Silver End Pit, and stretches on Blackwater; all members only.

CONNAUGHT WATERS, Chingford. Roach, bream, carp; free.

CORRINGHAM LAKE, Corringham. Excellent coarse fishing; large bream and carp, and good tench and roach, etc. St only (limited) from C Wood, MBE, Culham House, Church Road, Corringham (Stanford-le-Hope 3799).

EPPING FOREST PONDS. Most notable is Wake Valley Pond, near Wake Arms on A11; roach and small carp. Ponds usually free but for Warren Pond at **Chingford** a dt 11p must be obtained from keeper; roach, bream, perch, carp, tench, pike. Ornamental Water and Perch Pond, Wanstead Park. Dt £1.40 and 70p. The office of Superintendent of Epping Forest is at The Warren, Loughton.

FISHERS GREEN: Waltham Abbey. Pike, tench, bream, roach. St. Apply Leisure Sport Ltd, RMC House, High St, Feltham, Middx TW13 4HP.

GOSFIELD LAKE. Halstead (Essex). 45 acres; well-stocked with carp, perch, roach, tench, pike; boats available. Inquire R P Dawney, Gosfield Lake Café. Dt £1, st £9.

HANNINGFIELD RESERVOIR. Near Chelmsford. Excellent brown and rainbow trout; restocked annually. Bank and boat fishing. Season: Apr 29–Oct 29. 300

full st at £230 rod; 170 Mon–Fri only £166.75 rod; no dt but guest tickets to permit holders at £7.50 day; one guest per permit per day. Rowing boats £7 day, £4 half-day all prices incl VAT. Bag limit 6 fish. Car parks and fishing lodge. Total catch around 27,000, averaging 1½lb. Permits from Essex Water Co, Hanningfield Works, South Hanningfield, Chelmsford, Essex (Tel: 0245 400381).

HATFIELD FOREST LAKE. Near Hatfield Broad Oak and Bishop's Stortford. National Trust property; good pike and tench, carp and bream; some roach and rudd. St and dt. Boats and punts. Full st, including night-fishing, £30. St (days only) £12.50 (nights only £18. Dt £1.25. For tickets and boats apply Head Ranger, 1 Takeley Hill Cottages, Bishop's Stortford, Herts, or Lake Warden, at Shell House Cottage (Tel. B Stort 870447). Restrictions on use of groundbait.

LAYER PITS. 6m S of **Colchester;** controlled by Colchester APS; coarse fish; members only. Colchester Piscatorial Society has **Langham Ponds;** no tickets.

STANFORD-LE-HOPE. Two "Leisure Sport" gravel pits. Carp, roach, tench. St from RMC House, Feltham, Middlesex.

MARDYKE. Fishing stations: **Purfleet** and **Ockendon.** Rises by East Horndon and flows 12m to Thames at Purfleet. Fishing formerly negligible, but Essex RD has restocked and there are some club lengths.

PANT. Bocking. Upper part of R. Blackwater *(see Blackwater in main list)*.

RODING. Rises near Dunmow and flows 30m south and south-west to enter the Thames in East London. Polluted in lower reaches, but higher up holds coarse fish.

Ongar. Coarse fish; good chub, roach, dace and perch. Practically whole of fishable Roding controlled by clubs, principally Ongar and Dist AS (members only; river and pit) Collier Row AS (st available from hon sec). Essex RD have from Gangbridge to Fyfield Bridge; dt. Fishing showing considerable improvement. Tackleists: Edko Sports,

Romford; Morris, Kings Road and Roblin, 114 High Street, both **Brentwood.**

Passingford Bridge. Roach, chub, pike, bream, carp, tench. Barkingside and Dist AS has 1½m downstream; bailiff on water. Dt from bailiffs on bank for ¾m upstream of bridge. Woodford AS has 1¼m north of bridge; members only (st for associates from hon sec), Elm Park AS has water; dt from bailiff. Tackleist: Edko Sports, North Street, **Romford.**

SCRUBBS LAKE. Hadleigh (Essex). Good perch, roach, rudd, etc; dt.

SHOEBURY PARK LAKE. Shoeburyness (Essex). Coarse fish; dt issued.

SOUTH WEALD LAKES. Two lakes near **Brentwood.** Elm Park, Hornchurch and Dist AS water; tench, carp, roach, pike, perch; dt for one lake only from bailiff; other lake, strictly members only.

THE CHASE. Dagenham (Essex). White Hart Anglers' water; gravel pit; roach, bream, tench (excellent), carp (common, mirror and crucian), rudd, pike, perch; no night fishing; hempseed banned; dt from bailiff; RD licences needed. Tackleists: Edko Sports, North Street, Romford; Ridge & Co, 277 Oxlow Lane.

HOLLAND BROOK. Roach, and bream. Kelvedon and Dist AA (members only). 1m from Holland-on-Sea.

WANSTEAD & WOODFORD LAKES AND PONDS. Eagle Pond, **Snaresbrook** (roach, perch, carp); Knighton Wood Pond, **Woodford; Hollow Pond, Whipps Cross;** all free.

OTHER TICKET WATERS. Priory Lakes, Priory Park, **Southend;** Eastwood Pit, **Rayleigh;** Essex Carp Fishery (crucian carp, bream) at Mollands Lane, **South Ockendon;** Old Hall Lake, **Herongate;** Moor Hall Farm Fishery, **Aveley;** Great Myles Lake, Langford Bridge, **Ongar;** Raphael Park Lake, **Romford; Danbury Park Lakes, near Chelmsford;** Harwood Hall at Corbets Tey, and Parklands Lake, both near **Upminster;** Warren Pond, **Chingford;** carp, bream. Tickets mostly available from bailiffs on site. Stanford-le-Hope. "Leisure Sport" gravel pit. See Fishery Agents.

For Walthamstow reservoirs see p 94

EXE

(For close seasons, licences, etc, see South West Water Authority, p 38)

Rises on Exmoor and runs south through Devon to Exmouth. Salmon and trout, with grayling and coarse fish in lower reaches. At several points on upper reaches trout fishing (moorland) and occasional salmon fishing may be had by hotel guests.

Exeter (Devon). Bream; mirror, king and common carp; dace, gudgeon, pike, perch, roach, rudd, tench and eels. **Exeter Ship** and **Tiverton Grand Western Canals** contain bream, carp, pike, perch, rudd, roach, tench, eels and odd dace. Better part of Exeter canal from Broadwater (lime Kilns) to Turf (where canal enters Exe estuary). Hotels on canal banks: Double Locks, Turf. Exeter & Dist AA (amalgamation of local clubs) has coarse fishing rights on R. Exe (eleven fishings) on **Clyst, Culm** and **Creedy,** from City Basin to Double Locks on Exeter Ship Canal, and on ponds at Kingsteignton, Sampford Peveril and Mamhead. Visitors wt £2.50, dt £1.50. For fishing on Tiverton Canal contact Estates Surveyor, County Hall, Exeter (tel. 77977) or tackle shops. SWWA has 3m of salmon fishing on lower Exe. Dt £2.50 from Feb 14 to June 15. Apply SWWA, 3–5 Barnfield Road, Exeter or Exeter AC, City Arcade, Fore St. Tickets for Exeter & Dist AA waters from hon sec or tackleists. 2m W of city, **Haldon Ponds** trout fishery, stocked with rb to 10 lb, b to 7 lb. Wt £35, dt £6, evening £3. Rods limited pd. Boats. Phone Exeter 32967. One permit a day available for salmon fishing (weekdays only) from hon sec, Countess Wear Salmon FA, and John Webber (Sports) Ltd, Queen Street. Other tackleists: Bennett Bros, New Bridge Street; Black's Sports Shop, Sidwell Street.

Brampford Speke (Devon). Salmon, trout, dace; preserved. Pynes Water, from here down to Cowley Weir (2½m) fished by local syndicate. Exeter & Dist AA water towards Stoke Canon *(see Culm)*.

Thorverton (Devon). Trout, salmon, dace; private hence up to within 1½m of Bickleigh. Fisherman's Cot has beat *(see Bickleigh)*.

Silverton (Devon). Trout, salmon, dace, pike, perch; preserved. Exeter & Dist AA has coarse fishing on Culm here *(see Exeter and Culm)*.

Bickleigh (Devon). Trout, salmon. Fisherman's Cot Hotel (W T Townsend) has ¾m both banks adjoining hotel for salmon and/or trout. Mr W Messer, Court View, Church Green, has salmon fishing. St £40, dt £3–£4 according to date. Inn: Trout Inn.

Tiverton (Devon). Exe, Lowman and Little Dart; trout, salmon. **Tiverton Canal;** pike, perch, roach, tench. Exe preserved for 2m both above and below town (trout and grayling) by Tiverton FFC, fly only; Dt £2 for ½m of Exe from Country Sports, 9 William Street (also licences). Hotels: Boar's Head and Bark House *(advt p 77)* at Oakford Bridge; Fisherman's Cot, Bickleigh (beat on Exe). At Tiverton Junction is Railway Hotel, where accommodation can be had by anglers fishing **Tiverton Canal;** tickets. Tackleist: Country Sports, 9 William St (permits, licences, etc) *(see Exeter)*.

Dulverton (Som). Salmon, trout, grayling.

Uually good run of salmon (May onwards and autumn) to Dulverton and beyond, depending on water conditions. Trout fishing good in Exe and **Barle** (four to lb). Grayling less plentiful. Guests at Carnarvon Arms may fish for more than 7m on Exe and Barle; individual beats and gillie. Dt (S) £7 (NT) £3. Anchor Hotel has ½m at **Exebridge;** trout; some salmon; dt from hotel. Some free fishing for guests at Lion Hotel. Dulverton AA has 1m of Barle; members only. Royal Oak, Winsford, issues permits. Exe Valley Fishery. Two small lakes stocked with browns and rainbows averaging 2 lbs +. Dt available March–

October. Limit: 2 brace. Licences from hotels. Tackleist: Lance Nicholson, High Street (permits, casting tuition)

Exford (Som). Trout. Crown Hotel can arrange fishing on Exe and instruction on stocked trout ponds. Trout fishing also available on Nutscale, Clatworthy and Wimbleball Reservoirs (rainbow and brown) and Badgeworthy Water and Oarewater (both banks) in Doone Valley on Exmoor.

Winsford (Som). Exe; trout. Hotels: Tarr Steps Hotel *(advt p 144)* has 2½m (both banks) on Barle. Dt (S)£11 (NT) £3.50; Royal Oak, which has four beats; fly only; tickets from hotel.

Tributaries of the Exe

CREEDY: Trout, coarse fish.

Cowley Bridge (Exeter). Coarse fish. Exeter and Dist AA has rights *(see Exeter)*.

Crediton (Devon). Trout; preserved by owners. Yeo 3m; trout; leave from farmers. Crediton FFC has about 5m on Creedy and Yeo. Limited wt (Mon–Fri only); fly only. Hotels: Ship, White Hart.

CULM: Trout, coarse fish, few grayling.

Stoke Canon, Rewe and Silverton (Devon). Dace, roach, perch and occasional grayling. Exeter and Dist AA has water *(see Exeter)*.

Cullompton (Devon). Trout. River mostly preserved. Kentisbere Brook, Ashford Brook, Fulford Water. Hotels: Railway and Cullompton.

Uffculme. Permits for stretch from here to Five Fords (about 1½m mostly both banks) issued by Lt Cdr T L Metters, The Old Parsonage Farmhouse; St £20, mt £10, wt £5, dt £1.

Hemyock (Devon). Trout. Upper Culm FA preserves about 4m both banks. Trout season begins April 1; fly only. Tickets from hon sec or the PO, Hemyock. St £8, mt £4, wt £2, dt £1. No Sunday

fishing. Lower water preserved, and no fishing obtainable between Hemyock and Culmstock. Hotel: Railway. Accommodation also at Sanders'.

Clayhidon (Devon). Upper Culm FA preserves about 4m in this district *(see Hemyock)*. No sunday fishing. Hotel: Half Moon.

Killerton (Devon). National Trust controls coarse fishing on Killerton Estate; tickets from hon sec, Exonian AA or City of Exeter AA *(see Exeter)*, for some water.

BARLE. Runs through beautifully wooded valley and holds salmon (av 7–10 lb) and trout (av 8–10 in).

Tarr Steps (Devon). Salmon, trout. Tarr Steps Hotel *(advt p 144)* has 2½m of Barle. Fishing free for residents. Dt (S) £11, (T) £3.50.

Withypool (Som). Trout; some salmon. Crown Hotel, Exford, can arrange fishing. Inn: Royal Oak.

Simonsbath (Som). Exmoor Forest Hotel has rights on 8m of Barle, free to hotel guests. Dt for non-residents, S £6, NT £2.50. RWA licences at hotel. Spinning for salmon allowed. Convenient for **Wimbleball Reservoir** *(see Exford)*.

FAL

(For close seasons, licences, etc, see South West Water Authority, p 38)

Rises near Roche and flows about 23 miles, due south, past Grampound and Tregony to the English Channel at Falmouth. Fair trouting.

Falmouth (Cornwall). Excellent trout fishing in South Cornwall Water Board reservoirs (College, and Stithians); *(see Cornwall streams, lakes etc)*. Trout in

many of the small streams flowing into creeks around Falmouth; free in most on permission of farmers. Coarse fish in stocked pond at Tory Farm,

Ponsanooth; permission from farmer. Tackleists: A B Harvey, Market Strand (RD licences; reservoir permits); Berks, Arwenack Street; Cunningham's, 10 Lower Market Street, Penryn. Further information from Falmouth and Penryn

AA. *(For sea fishing see Sea Fishing Stations.)*

Tregony (Cornwall), ns **Grampound Road,** 5m. Trout, 2m off runs Polglaze brook, 4m long; trout.

FOWEY

(For close seasons, licences, etc, see South West Water Authority, p 38)

Rises in east Cornwall and enters English Channel by estuary at Fowey. Noted sea-trout river, with salmon and many small brown trout. Restocked annually with salmon fry by SWWA.

Fowey (Cornwall). Trout, sea trout, salmon. Fishing for rod and line above Lostwithiel partly preserved; free below. July–August best time. Into east side of harbour, opposite town, flows Pont Brook, 4m long, holding small trout; free. Capital sea fishing *(see Sea Fishing section)*. Club: Fowey AC (sea only). Hotels: Fowey, Rockside, Riverside, Ship, Old Quay House, Greenbank. Tackleists: Gift and Sports Shop, 10 The Esplanade.

Lostwithiel (Cornwall). Salmon, sea trout, brown trout. Good salmon fishing now up to Dec 15. Fly fishing best, but minnow good in coloured water. Lostwithiel best centre for Fowey. Lostwithiel FA has about 1½m and issues tickets for salmon and trout season licence holders.

Fishing extends from just outside town to just above end of Whitmarsh Moor. Season tickets, £2.50, from M A North, Parade Square, Bodmin, J C Penhaligon, 15 Queen Street, Lostwithiel and R Johnson, The Tackle Box, 11 Trinity Street, St Austell. (Juniors £1) Hotels: Royal Talbot, Monmouth, King's Arms, Earl of Chatham, Royal Oak, Globe, Trevone Guest House and Carotel Ltd (flatlets).

Bodmin Road (Cornwall). Trout, sea trout, salmon. Liskeard and Dist AC has 6m water on middle and upper reaches; tickets available (£7 week, £1.50 day) from hon sec and tackleists *(see Looe River)*. Hotel: Royal, at Bodmin, where guests can obtain fishing on **Camel.**

FROME AND PIDDLE (Dorset)

(For close seasons, licences, etc, see Wessex Water Authority, p 39)

Frome rises in West Dorset and flows into the English Channel at Poole Harbour, near Wareham. Piddle rises in a mill pond 1 mile north of Piddletrenthide and enters Poole Harbour near mouth of Frome near Wareham. Both are chalk streams and closely preserved, but sport may sometimes be had. Some very good sea trout have been caught in the Frome, which also receives a run of heavy salmon. Trout in both rivers plentiful and good. Bass run up to where the river enters Poole Harbour. Piddle carries small stock of heavy salmon.

Wareham (Dorset). On Frome and Piddle; salmon, sea trout, trout, grayling, pike, roach and dace. Salmon and trout preserved, but leave sometimes from owners of waters. Morden Estate Office, Charborough Park, Wareham, sometimes has rods available for entire season (never per day or week) as follows: salmon, Frome and Piddle; trout, Piddle and Bere; River Stour. Avon and Dorset RD lets 14 rods for the season (on the basis of two per day) for fishery on Piddle; salmon, sea trout (details from Div Fisheries and Recreations officer).

Authority also has some free fishing for coarse fish on south bank below South Bridge on landowners' permission for access to banks. RD licence needed. By hiring a boat from Frome Boat Service, Wareham Quay, coarse fishing at Wareham on RD licence. Local society: Wareham and Dist AS, which has stretch of north bank and pond at Creech; members only. Hotels: Red Lion and Black Bear. Tackleist and bait: G Elmes & Son, St John's Hill.

Wool (Dorset). Frome: Salmon, sea trout. Woolbridge Manor Hotel (100 yards from river) has 1½m; fly and spinning. Salmon run large, fish over 30 lb not rare. Dt £10. RWA licence required.

Dorchester (Dorset). Frome: trout; preserved for 3m above and 2½m below town by the Dorchester FC of 36 members only (ann sub £80); dry fly only; no dt. Rest of river strictly preserved by landowners. RWA licences and one dt per day £3.50 (dry-fly only) for the Frome (5m away) from C Jeffery & Sons (see below); booking advised for April, May, June. Other society: Dorchester and Dist AS (coarse fishing only) who issue dt for short stretch of **Stour.** 1m of dt water at **Grimstone,** 4m upstream from Dorchester. Dry-fly only. Details from Dr J D W Peck, Bilboa House, Dulverton, Somerset, Tel: 23475. Tackleist: C Jeffery & Sons, 25 High East Street (Tel: 2332). Hotels: King's Arms, Antelope.

GIPPING (Orwell)

(For close seasons, licences, etc, see Anglian Water Authority, p 40)

Rises between Stowmarket and Bury St Edmunds, and flows into the North Sea by an estuary near Ipswich. Coarse fish.

Ipswich (Suffolk). Most coarse fish. Gipping APS (Annual mem £15) issues dt £1 for 1m of their water on river. New 350 acre coarse fish reservoir at Tattingstone, 5m SE of Ipswich. "**Alton Water**". Dt 50p from tackleists or Hon Sec Gipping APS. Flowton Brook (1m). Good codling, skate, whiting and flounder fishing below town. Tackleists: Aldridge's High Street; East Anglian Supplies, Upper Orwell Street; R Markham, Woodbridge Road East; Tackle Box, Bramford Road; Ipswich Angling Centre, Felixstowe Road; Peachy's Sports, Meredith Road.

Stowmarket (Suffolk). Stowmarket and Dist AA has short stretch of **Rattle;** members only.

GLOUCESTERSHIRE (streams)

BIDEFORD BROOK. Fishing station: **Awre.** Rises in Abbot's Wood and flows 7m to Severn estuary; coarse fish; preserved. **Blackpool Brook** enters at Awre; Forest of Dean AC; members only.

CONE. Fishing station: **Woolaston.** Cone rises by Hewelsfield, and is 5m long. Eels and flounders.

FROME. Rises near Cheltenham and flows into Severn estuary. Polluted by dye works. Coarse fish; a few trout higher up. Fishing stations: **Stonehouse** (Glos), **Brimscombe** (Glos), coarse fish, and **Stroud** (Glos), a few trout and coarse fish. Several brooks in vicinity. Pike and coarse fishing in Stroudwater Canal. Stroud tackleist: Batemans Sports, Kendrick Street, who issue st £2) for local club waters and tickets for small carp lakes.

NAILSWORTH BROOK (tributary of Frome). Fishing stations: **Nailsworth** (Glos) and **Woodchester** (Glos). Brook reported polluted in parts. Lakes: Longfords Lake, pike, carp. Woodchester Park lakes; pike, perch, roach, tench, brown and rainbow trout; now strictly preserved. **Coombe Lakes,** Wootton-under-Edge. Dt for trout (fly only) and coarse fishing. Boat available. Advance bookings. Tel: 3136. At Nailsworth is The Midland Fishery trout farm *(see list on pages 32/3).*

HOPE BROOK. Fishing station: **Westbury-on-Severn,** ns Grange Court, 1½m. Hope Brook rises 2m above Longhope, runs thence 5m to Westbury and Severn estuary (1m). Coarse fish, mostly preserved, farmers sometimes give leave. Inn: Red Lion.

LITTLE AVON: Small Gloucestershire stream flowing into Severn estuary. **Berkeley** (Glos). Coarse fish, trout, Waterley Brook. Fishing below Charfield preserved. Close by station rises Billow Brook, which runs thence 3m to estuary. Clubs have water on **Gloucester and Berkeley Canal;** 16m Sharpness to Gloucester.

LYD. Chub, roach, perch. Fishing station: **Lydney.** Lydney AA holds stretch from railway station to Tufts Junction. Club also has **Lydney Lake** (carp, roach and perch), **Lydney Canal** and a dam.

HAMPSHIRE (streams, lakes and canal)

(For close seasons, licences, etc, see Southern Water Authority, p 38)

BASINGSTOKE CANAL. Fishing stations: **Basingstoke, Greywell, North Warnborough, Odiham, Winchfield, Crookham, Fleet, Farnborough, Aldershot, Ash Vale, Brookwood, Woking** (Surrey), **Byfleet** (Surrey). Pike, carp, roach, good tench, perch; most of canal let to clubs; fishing from towpath only; boat fishing on flashes; dt from hon secs or New Inn, Odiham. Farnborough AS also has rights on **Whitewater** at **Heckfield, Loddon** at **Winnersh, Wey** at **Frensham** and gravel pits; (tickets from Raison's tackleists) *(see below)*. Five "Leisure Sport" gravel pits at **Frimley;** another at **Ash Vale.** Carp, tench, roach and perch. Large specimens recorded. St £6 from RMC House, Feltham, Middlesex. Tackleists: Cordings, 18 New Market Square, Basingstoke; Raison's, Park Road, Farnborough (permits for Farnborough AS waters); Fleet Sports Centre, 182 Fleet Road, Fleet; Hayes, 36 Station Road, Aldershot. **Ewhurst Lake** (6m N); pike, perch, roach; strictly limited permits; inquire of estate office. **Hollybush Lakes**, Farnborough. 20 acres of water stocked carp, pike and other coarse fish. Dt £1 from Lakewent Farm, Old Bury Hill, Dorking. Tel. 8836211.

BEAULIEU. The Beaulieu River is approx 14 miles long. The stretch above Beaulieu village north to the Estate boundary holds sea trout, brown and rainbow trout, but rights are let. Tickets for tidal stretch, Beaulieu to Needs Ore (bass, mullet, flounder) st £12, dt 75p. Access from Bailey's Hard, Buckler's Hard and Park Shore (Solent). Tickets from Harbour Master, Buckler's Hard (tel 200) or Resident Land Agent, John Montagu Building, Beaulieu (tel 612345). Coarse fishing on **Hatchett Pond** (Forestry Commission); bream, carp, tench and pike; tickets from Forestry Commission, Southampton Rd, Lyndhurst, or camping offices during camping season (st £16.50, mt £5, wt £2, dt 90p, VAT incl). Inquire also at Smiths Sports, Lymington, and tackleists in Christchurch. Hotels: Montagu Arms at Beaulieu; Master Builder's Arms at Buckler's Hard.

DAMERHAM TROUT LAKES, Fordingbridge (3m). Six lakes, and river for St holders. Rainbow trout. Open April 1 until October 31. St £235, ½st £130, dt £9.75, ½day £5.50. Advance booking recommended for peak periods. A justly famous fishery. Tel Rockbourne 446 (07253 446). Hotel: Compasses Inn. Tel. 07253231, *(advt p 16)*.

FLEET POND. Fishing station: **Fleet.** Cove AS water. No tickets. Tackleist: Fleet S C, 182 Fleet Road.

HAMBLE. Sea trout and trout. **Bishop's Waltham.** Fishing mostly private, but leave sometimes obtainable.

LADYWELL LAKES. Alresford. 3 lakes providing 900 yds of fishable bank. Brown, rainbow and American brook trout. St £180, ½ st £95. Dt, seasonal bookings permitting, £8.50, ½ day £5. Inquiries to B H Dening, Arle House, Ladywell Lane, Alresford. Tel (not permanently manned) Alresford 2317. Advance bookings only. Bag limits and method restrictions. One lake, brown trout only.

LYMINGTON RIVER. Fishing station: **Lymington.** Sea trout (2–11 lb), brown trout (¾ lb to 1 lb). Sea trout best June to Sept. Fishing improved by Brockenhurst Manor FFC; private.

MEON. Trout, with sea trout as far as Titchfield Mill. Fishing station: **East Meon;** Hants and Sussex Alliance has water; inquire hon sec. RD licence required.

SANDLEHEATH. Four lakes and chalk stream at **Allens Farm,** Sandleheath, Fordingbridge. Hotels: Victoria House, Sandleheath. Excellent fishing for Rb trout, fly only, various period-terms from dt £8 to st for one day per week £195. Tel. 07253 313 for full details, *(advt p 54)*.

SPRING LAKES, Aldershot. Brown and rainbow trout on 25-acre spring-fed lakes, fly only; members only at £145 per season. Inquiries to Springlakes Ltd, The Gold, Aldershot, Hants. (Aldershot 20434.)

TWO LAKES, near **Romsey.** Very large trout on dry fly (average over 2 lb). St only, £310.50 incl VAT. Apply Mr Alex Behrendt, Two Lakes, Crampmoor, nr Romsey, Hants.

WAGGONERS' WELLS, near **Hindhead.** Two lakes; one trout, one coarse fishing

(National Trust waters). Fly fishing for trout, April 1 to Sept 30, st £7, dt £1.50, restocked annually. Coarse fishing: carp, perch, tench, roach; st £2, dt 50p, plus 25p each extra rod. Permits on spot. Apply to The Ranger, Summerden, Waggoners' Wells, Grayshott, near Hindhead, Surrey. Hotels: Fox and Pelican, Grayshott; Spaniard's Inn, Bramshott.

WARBURN. Dace, trout, salmon; preserved; leave sometimes from landowners; joins sea at **Key Haven.**

HERTS AND GREATER LONDON
(reservoirs and lakes)

(see also London Reservoirs, p 93)

ALDENHAM (Herts). **Aldenham Reservoir,** near **Elstree.** Coarse fish. Dt from Senior Warden, No 1 Bungalow, Aldenham Country Park, Dagger Lane, Elstree. Dt (bank) 50p. Punt: £1.50 per day, £1 half-day. St available, £7.50. Water now property of Herts CC. Car parking.

BEDFONT (Middx). "Leisure Sport" lake well stocked with pike, carp, tench, perch, etc. Large specimens recorded. St £5 from RMC House, Feltham.

SHEPPERTON (Middx). **Ashmere;** two lakes stocked with rainbow trout. Boats available. Various terms available. Apply Mrs K Howman, Felix Lane, Shepperton (Tel Walton 25445).

STANSTEAD ABBOTS. "Leisure Sport" fishery consisting of 3 lakes, mill stream and part of R Lea. St £7 from RMC House, Feltham, Middlesex.

TRING (herts). Four large reservoirs: **Marsworth, Startops End,** and **Wilstone** (2m from Tring, 3½m from rly station) main feeders for Grand Union Canal. Fishing at times very good. Fourteen bream over 10 lbs in 1980, tench to 9½ lbs, pike to 26 lbs. British record catfish, 43½ lbs, taken at Tring. No Sunday fishing. St £32.20 (including right to nightfish) dt £1, evening 50p, jun 50p. Boats, £2 per occupant. Tickets obtainable on bank from bailiff, B C Double (Tel Tring 2379). The fourth reservoir is a private trout fishery. Hotels: Anglers' Retreat, Startops End, Rose & Crown.

HULL

(For close seasons, licences, etc, see Yorkshire Water Authority, p 40)

Tidal river (to Hempholme Lock) is free fishing to anyone holding current RD licence, but hit by pollution. From Beverley first-class sport may be had with roach, dace, pike, chub, bream etc. Higher up still, on West Beck, there is excellent but strictly preserved trout fishing of chalk-stream character.

Hull (North Humberside). River polluted. Drains giving good coarse fishing, available to holders of WA licences, include: **Marfleet Drain, Barmston Drain** (Hull to Hempholme), **Burstwick Drain, Holderness Drain, Fordyke Stream. Market Weighton Canal** also provides free fishing with WA licences. Twenty good ponds at **Brandesburton** controlled by Hull and Dist AA. Assn has water on **Trent, Derwent, Rye,** in **Hull Docks** and in drains. No dt. Memberships (£3.50 pa) from hon sec and local tackleists. Stone Creek and Patrington Haven hold flounders. Other club: Hull Rock AC. Good Sea fishing. Tackleist: G W Hutchinson & Co, 27 Anlaby Rd.

Beverley (N Humberside). River Hull and drains *(for latter see Hull).* River Hull gives good coarse fishing; from Hull Bridge upstream through **Arram, Aike Wilfholme, Baswicke** and **Hempholme** to Frodingham Beck: free to Yorkshire Water Authority licence-holders; weedy June to Nov. **Leven Canal** (6m): roach, bream, pike, tench and chub; dt 10p from Mrs Thurlow, Sandholme, Leven. Hotel: Beverley Arms.

Keep the banks clean

Several clubs have stopped issuing tickets to visitors because of the state of the banks after they have left. Spend a few moments clearing up.

Brandesburton (N Humberside). River Hull 3m W, excellent coarse fishing in gravel pits *(see Hull)*.

Wansford (N Humberside). River Hull (here known also as **West Beck**) and **Driffield Canal**. Restored as trout and grayling fishery by Yorkshire WA, which has established four sections with different stocking patterns and charges, ranging from dt £1.40 for trout, fly only, on Sec A, to free coarse fishing on Sec D. Permits and details from Wansford PO. 6m coarse fishing in **Market Weighton Canal** free to YWA licence-holders, but charge made for match-pegs. West Beck preserved by Holden Hill AS and West Beck PS; members only.

Driffield (N Humberside). Centre for noted Driffield Trout Stream and Driffield Beck; strictly preserved. See below.

Tributaries of the Hull

FOSTON BECK (or KELK or FRODINGHAM BECK):

North Frodingham, Foston-on-the-Wolds and Lowthorpe (N Humberside). Rises in Yorkshire Wolds; true chalk stream containing brown trout averaging well over the pound. Preserved from Bracey Bridge to Foston Mill by Foston FC (members only). For ¾m below Foston Mill water stocked with trout by Millhouse Beck AC; private.

DRIFFIELD BECK:

Driffield (N Humberside). Provides chalk stream fishing for trout and grayling of high order; strictly preserved. Controlled by Driffield AC, Golden Hill Club and West Beck PS. *(See Driffield on River Hull.)*

ISLE OF MAN

The geographical nature of the Isle of Man tends to dictate the type of river, fish and hence fishing one may encounter when angling in the Island. Being a relatively mountainous place, rivers and streams are small, swift flowing and very clear. There are no coarse fish on the Isle of Man but nevertheless excellent sport can be had in the numerous trout streams where the art of approach to the river bank and the gentle and accurate cast of the true angler becomes vital.

There are very few preserved stretches of river in the Island, a well chosen word with the land owner is often all that is required to enable an angler to fish in peace. Approximately a half mile of the River Douglas through the Nunnery Estate is exclusively reserved and small sections of the rivers Dhoo and Glass can only be fished under permit from the Douglas Angling Club—visitors membership is available from either Nods for Rods, Castle Street, Douglas, or the Angling Centre, Victoria Street, Douglas.

Natural baits (worms, bread, cheese) and artificials are allowed on the Island's rivers, ponds and streams but anglers are reminded that only artificials are allowed when reservoir fishing. Further details of reservoir fishing may be obtained from the Isle of Man Water & Gas Authority, Tromode Drill Hall, Tromode, Douglas. However, anglers must abide by the regulations wherever they fish. (1) Not to use or carry a gaff or tailer. (2) Not to use a line the diameter of which exceeds 0.013″, excepting that a fly line used solely for fly fishing may exceed 0.013″ diameter, provided the leader exceeds five feet in length and does at no point exceed 0.013″ in diameter. (0.013″ diameter is approximately equivalent to 10 lb breaking strain). (3) Not use more than one hook on a line unless (a) Pennel or Stewart tackles are being used for bait fishing; (b) a "point with two droppers" is being used for fly fishing only; (c) a spinner is being used for spinning only. (4) Not to use a hook larger than No 6 Redditch scale, unless the hook is comprised in an artificial fly. (5) Return to the water all fish foul hooked. (6) Return to the water unharmed any freshwater fish hooked which is less than 18 cm in length overall.

The freshwater fishing season commences on the 10 March, and finishes on the 30 September for trout and 20 November for salmon. A freshwater fishing licence is required to fish any river, pond or reservoir, and if one is contemplating reservoir fishing it should be noted that an additional permit is required from the Isle of Man Water and Gas Authority.

Salmon fishing takes place mainly in the Autumn as the Island does not enjoy a spring run of any size. Fish are small and rarely if ever exceed 20 lbs—a more reasonable average would be 5–10 lbs.

The Board of Agriculture and Fisheries pursues a continual stocking programme of rivers, ponds and reservoirs throughout the spring and early summer, with trout (brown and rainbow) of a takeable size i.e. in excess of 7″ and in the 1 lb to 2 lb range.

At present there are six reservoirs under the administration of the Isle of Man Water and Gas Authority, with a further one under construction at Tholt-y-Will. They are: (a) The West Baldwin Reservoir (300 mg) is near the centre of the Island. A main road goes past the end of the dam. There is an infrequent bus service to West Baldwin village 1¼ miles from the reservoir. (b) Clypse and Kerrowdhoo Reservoirs lie, one beyond the other, about 1½ miles north of Onchan Village. A private road runs, off the road to Grange Farm, to the Attendants house where there is room to park cars. (c) Ballure Reservoir is just south of Ramsey. Access is by a private road branching off the main road to Douglas, on the Douglas side of the MER crossing near the town boundary. (d) Block Eary Reservoir is on a tributary of the Sulby river and lies on the north slopes of Snaefell. Access is by a private road, leaving the Sulby to Tholt-y-Will road about ¾ mile from Tholt-y-Will. The private road is too rough for motor cars and they must not be taken on it. (e) Cringle Reservoir is just north of the road from Ronague to Foxdale and is on the south slopes of South Barrule. Cars can be parked on the reservoir land.

Fishing Licences
Freshwater fishing licences—needed before *any* fishing commences—cost: Season, adult £5.00; Season, child under 13 years £2.50; Fortnight, adult £2.00; Fortnight, child under 13 years £1.00.
They are available from: DOUGLAS—Nods for Rods, Castle Street, Douglas. The Angling Centre, Victoria Road, Douglas. RAMSEY—J Mead, 9 Parliament Street, Ramsey. Ramsey Pets, 1 Christian Street, Ramsey. CASTLETOWN—Castletown Sports, Arbory Street, Castletown. PEEL—The Tackle Box, Promenade, Peel. PORT ERIN—Port Erin Commissioners, Town Hall, Port Erin. LAXEY—Laxey Commissioners. SULBY GLEN—G. Caley, Railway Station, Sulby. BALLASALLA—Rushen Abbey Hotel.

Reservoir fishing permits: Season, adult £10.50; Season, junior under 17 years £6.25; Day ticket, adult 40p; Day ticket, junior under 17 yrs 25p available from: (a) The Reservoir Attendant's house at Baldwin Reservoir. (b) The Reservoir Attendant's house at Clypse Reservoir. (c) The filter Station, Ballure Glen, Ramsey. (d) The Authority's Showroom, Mill Road, Peel. (e) Filter Station, Sulby Glen. (f) Filter Station, Ballagawne, or at Head Offices, Tromode Drill Hall, Tromode, Douglas. No licence required for sea fishing, which from pier, rocks or boat is excellent, especially for pollack—locally called "callig"—mackerel, cod and codling, whiting and plaice. Chief bait for ground fish is herring, but lugworm, sand-eels and shellfish also found. Whiffing with white and coloured flies and india-rubber sand-eel for pollack, mackerel and cod is successful. Good centres for most species are Peel, Port Erin, Port St Mary and Ramsey. At Port Erin is sea-fish hatchery and aquarium under control of Liverpool University. Tourist Board, Douglas, issues useful booklet on sea and river fishing. Principal rivers as follows:

COLBY RIVER. Trout. This stream is 4m long; preserved in lower reaches.
DOUGLAS RIVER. Salmon, sea trout, trout. Douglas formed by junction of Dhoo and Glass, half a mile above the town of **Douglas.** Fishing on Glass River and lower part of Dhoo preserved, but free above **Union Mills.** Glass largely rented by Douglas AC; permits and licences from Nods for Rods, Castle Street and Angling Centre, Victoria St.
GLEN MOOR BURN, 3m long. Trout; fishing free, but not very good. Fishing station: **Kirk Michael.**
LAXEY RIVER. Trout; free but poor. This stream is 5m long. 1m above junction with sea at Laxey, Glen River (trout),

3m long, joins on right bank. Fishing station: **Laxey.** Licences from Commissioners Office, Laxey.
NEB. Trout; mostly free and good; salmon from Aug. Neb (sometimes called Peel River) rises above **Little London** and runs 3m to **Glen Helen** (Hotel: Glen Helen). Here Blaby joins. Neb runs 4m to **St John's.** Here **Foxdale River,** 6m long, joins on left bank. Hence to **Peel** is 3m. 3m S is **Glen Maye River** 4m long; sea trout below waterfall, trout above. Licences: E & J Roberts, 6a Douglas St, Peel.
SANTON BURN. 6m long; trout; mostly preserved, but poor; salmon from Aug. Fishing station: **Santon.**

SILVERBURN. Trout, sea trout; free. This stream rises on the slopes of South Barrule, runs 5m to **Ballasalla**, where Awin Ruy, 4m long, joins on left bank. Silver Burn runs 3m to the sea at **Castletown.** Best sport downstream for about 1m to Castletown. Licences from Castletown Sports, Arbory Street, Rushen Abbey Hotel, Ballasalla, and Commissioners Office, Station Rd, Port Erin.

SULBY. Salmon (from Aug), sea trout; free; good after spates. Sulby rises on western slopes of Snaefell and runs 7m to

Sulby Glen. Sulby is island's largest river and best for salmon and sea trout; brown trout poor. Five miles S is **Cornaa River,** 5m long, which runs into sea at Port Cornaa, the site of the Fishery Board's hatchery. Good for salmon and sea trout in lower portion (Sept, Oct). Fishing station: **Ramsey.** Excellent sea fishing; bass from beach, plaice and cod from pier. Hotels: Mitre, Prince of Wales. Licences from R Caley, Sulby Glen; J Mead, 9 Parliament St, Ramsey.

WYLLIN BURN. 4m long; trout; free; fishing poor. Near **Kirk Michael.**

For further information about sea fishing on the island, see p 201

ISLE OF WIGHT

(For close seasons, licences, etc, see Southern Water Authority, p 38)

Freshwater fishing on island has improved recently, due to considerable restocking by Isle of Wight Freshwater AA. Yar from St Helens, Bembridge to Alverstone now holds fair numbers of roach, dace and rudd, with perch, carp and bream in some stretches. Society also has excellent carp fishing at Gunville Pond, Carisbrooke, with perch, tench, rudd and pike. Somerton Reservoirs, Cowes, hold carp, tench, roach, perch and bream. Summer best for Gunville carp and perch, but roach and dace on Yar best in winter. Temporary membership tickets for all society waters (£3 week, £1 day) from hon sec W Kingswell, 12 Manor Road, Lake (Tel: Sandown 403994). Southern WA rod licence required, available from following tackleists: G C Young, The Sports Shop, 74 Regent Street, Shanklin; W Bates & Son, 5 Springhill, Ventnor; Don's Sports, 14 Cross St, Ryde; David's Food Market, Lane End Court, Bembridge; Sports & Pastimes, 140 High Street, Newport. Light sea fishing, for which freshwater tackle may be employed, available at Whippingham (River Medina), Fishbourne (Wootton Creek) and in Bembridge Harbour; mullet, bass, flatfish, etc. *(For boats, bait, etc, see Sea Fishing Stations.)*

ITCHEN

(For close seasons, licences, etc, see Southern Water Authority, p 38)

Rises some miles north-west of Petersfield and flows via Winchester into Southampton Water at Southampton. Famous Hampshire chalk stream. Trout fishing excellent, but strictly preserved for most part. Some salmon and sea trout lower down, but also preserved. Principal tributaries are **Alre** and **Candover Brook;** both strictly preserved.

Southampton (Hants). Itchen and Test estuaries. Pout, whiting and eels in Southampton Water; and whiting, bass, grey mullet from the piers and quays. Coarse fishing from public footpath between Woodmill and Mansbridge. Tackleist: Patstone & Cox Ltd, 25 High Street, who can generally give information as to any waters available in district. *(See also under Sea Fishing Stations.)*

Eastleigh (Hants). Trout, salmon and grayling; preserved. Here is Bishopstoke FC water, which affords excellent sport. Water holds large trout. Salmon run right up to Brambridge. Some sea trout also come up; private. Small stretch at

Bishopstoke and another at Woodmill (tidal) is public fishing.

Bishopstoke (Hants), ns Eastleigh. Salmon, trout and grayling; preserved by Bishopstoke FC and other owners.

Winchester (Hants). Trout above city; trout and grayling below. All fishing on the R Itchen strictly preserved other than water between Durngate Mill and Wharf Mill which runs through city embracing Water Lane and The Weirs. SWA licence required. Obtainable from tackleist The Rod Box, 52 St Georges St *(advt p 13)*. Col Eric Hay, the proprietor of this business, offers on a carefully discriminatory basis dt and other rods on celebrated private stretches of the Test and Itchen and lakes. Charges on request. Phone 0962 713458 for details of these and other fishings.

Itchen Abbas (Hants). Trout; preserved by riparian owners. **Avington Trout Fishery,** lakes fed by R. Itchen, provide remarkable trout fishing. British rainbow record broken there several times. St £280, dt £11.85 VAT incl. (Tel. Itchen Abbas 312)

Alresford (Hants). **Candover Brook, Alre,** Itchen; trout; strictly preserved by riparian owners. Grange Lakes, Alresford Pond; coarse fish; preserved.

A winter's day at Itchen Abbas. It is during the winter that rivers receive their maximum input of decomposing organic matter on which all future productivity depends. *Photograph: John Tarlton.*

KENT (lakes and streams)

(For close seasons, licences, etc, see Southern Water Authority, p 38)

BAYHAM LAKE TROUT FISHERY, nr **Tunbridge Wells.** Stocked with very large b and rb trout which anglers are encouraged to return alive. Removals charged extra. Variety of st (£400, unlimited access) and dt £8. Phone 0892 890276 for full details *(advt p 96).*

BEWL BRIDGE RESERVOIR, nr **Lamberhurst.** 770 acre SWA fly-only trout fishery. St (full week) £180: (Mon–Fri) £135. Dt £6 and £5. Single-seat and 2-seat pulling and motor boats £4–£10 a day. Evening only terms available, and concessions for juniors. 70,000 brown, brook and rainbow trout in 1981 stocking programme. Season Apr 15 to Oct 29. Pre-season enq to Lamberhurst 890661; in season, to 890352.

BROOKLANDS LAKE and HORTON KIRBY LAKES. Fishing station: **Dartford.** Dartford and Dist APS; Dt issued.

CHIDDINGSTONE CASTLE LAKE. Good coarse fishing; dt £4; apply The Secretary, Chiddingstone Castle, near **Edenbridge.** Tel. 870 347.

DARENTH, SUTTON-AT-HONE and **LARKFIELD LAKES.** Carp, pike and other coarse fish. St £12, £6 and £7 respectively. Apply Leisure Sport Ltd, RMC House, High St, Feltham, Middx.

HAWKHURST. Small stillwater fishery for rainbow trout. Fish to 3 lb. Phone 3457.

LONGFORD LAKE. Fishing station: **Sevenoaks.** Private water of Holmesdale AS; (mem fee £5 pa) dt for friends of members only. *(See also Darent.)*

LULLINGSTONE LAKE, near **Eynsford.** Trout. Kingfisher APS; no tickets.

MOTE PARK LAKE. Fishing station; **Maidstone** *(see Medway).* Coarse fish (including specimen bream, tench and pike): dt for non-residents £1.40 from Arts and Recreations Office. Old Palace, Mill Street, Maidstone, Kent. Concession for OAP.

MURSTON PITS. At **Murston,** 1½m N of **Sittingbourne,** Sittingbourne AC has three pits; coarse fish; no dt, enquiries to hon sec. Tackleist: Dean's, East Street.

OARE PITS. At Oare, 1½m N of **Faversham,** Faversham AC has large pool containing carp (30 lb plus), tench, bream, roach and pike. Also other pits holding coarse fish. Dt from waterside or hon sec. £1.50.

PETT POOLS. Fishing stations: **Winchelsea,** 2m; **Rye,** 4m. Coarse fish; dt (limited) from M Piddington, Market Stores, Pett Level. St (limited) from SWA, Miller House, Stone Street, Maidstone, Kent.

ROMNEY MARSH. Much good fishing on marsh, especially in main drains to Rother; best in summer (large bream shoals); water on low side in winter. Clubs with water here are: Ashford and Dist APS; Cinque Ports AS; Clive Vale AC; Clive Vale reservoirs (carp), Ecclesbourne Reservoir, Hastings, Bexhill and Dist AA (members only); Rye and Dist AS; Tenterden and Dist APS; Linesmen AC (also waters on **Medway, Beult** and **Stour;** details from hon sec).

ROYAL MILITARY CANAL. Summer fishing only; level partially lowered in winter for drainage, Stations: **Hythe and Ashford.** Cinque Ports AS has from Seabrook to West Hythe Dam; carp, bream, chub, roach, rudd, tench, dace, perch, pike; dt 50p, wt £1.50 from bailiff, from Light Railway Restaurant, J B Walker Ltd (both Hythe) and hon sec. Ashford and Dist A & PS has about 16m from West Hythe Dam to Iden Lock (south bank only from dam to Appledore Bridge) dt 20p, wt 75p; roach, rudd, chub, tench, perch, carp, bream, dace, pike. Tickets available from inns near canal at West Hythe, Ruckinge, Warehorne, Appledore, and from cottage at canal bridge. Hon sec Ashford and Dist APS will give further information. RD licences and tackle in Ashford *(see Medway and Hythe Sea fishing stations).*

SUNDRIDGE LAKES. Sevenoaks. These 5- and 15-acre lakes hold large brown and rainbow trout. St £150 (waiting-list) from Sundridge Tackle Ltd, Buttercrock Wharf, Vicarage Lane, Hoo, Nr Rochester, Kent. Tel. 01 6989088. (St only: no dt) *(advt p 17).*

LANCASHIRE AND CUMBRIA
(Westmorland) streams

(For close seasons, licences, etc, see North West Water Authority, p 39
unless otherwise stated)

BELA. Cumbrian trout stream, flowing from Lily Mere to estuary of Kent at Milnthorpe. Much of its course is through low-lying country with heavy water. Size of fish better than in some northern streams; many dry-fly reaches. Salmon and sea trout below Beetham Mills private. One of earliest of northern streams; trout fishing starts March 3.

Milnthorpe (Cumbria). Trout. Preserved by Milnthorpe AA and confined to members and guests. Association also preserves St Sunday's Beck from Deepthwaite Bridge and Peasey Beck from Farleton Beck downwards and thence, from confluence of these streams, to Beetham Mills, which is as far as salmon run. Fishing below mills private. Sport very good in March, April, May and Aug. RWA licences and tackle from Atkinson's. Stricklandgate, Kendal (also Kent AA tickets) *(see River Kent)* or Garsides, Stationers, The Square, Milnthorpe. Hotels at Milnthorpe: Cross Keys, Bull's Head, Coach and Horses; Wheatsheaf at Beetham.

Oxenholme (Cumbria). Bela, 2m E Beehive Beck, 1m E. Old Hutton Beck, 3m SE. Killington Reservoir; large sheet of water, 3m E. Pike, perch and some big trout. Leased to Kent AA *(see Kendal–Kent)*.

CONDOR. Fishing station: **Galgate.** Brown trout and sea trout. No tickets.

DUDDON. Fishing station: **Broughton-in-Furness.** Sea trout, salmon. Dt from E A Clark, solicitor, for river from Duddon Bridge to Greety Gate; both banks. Millom & Dist AA has rights; members only. Assn also has water on **Esk, Lickle, Annas, Irt, Lazy** and **Devoke Water** (salmon, sea trout, trout); members only. Close to Broughton-in-Furness, **River Lickle** joins Duddon on left bank. River rented by Millom AA. Members only. Applications for membership to hon sec.

Ulpha (Cumbria). Good sea trout and salmon, few brown trout. All river below down to Ulpha Bridge private. **Devoke Water** (large trout) may also be fished from here. Millom AA has rights, members only. Applications for membership to hon sec. *(See Cumberland—small*

streams). Below this point Duddon runs into estuary. Hotel: Old King's Head.

KENT. Fast-flowing salmon and trout stream running into Morecambe Bay. Fishing reported much improved following pollution and drainage schemes. Salmon, sea trout, trout.

Kendal (Cumbria). Salmon, sea trout, trout. A few spring salmon with main run and sea trout moving up about June; fairly plentiful Aug onwards. Kent below Burneside preserved (together with **Mint,** both banks, from Mealbank to junction with Kent. Also about ½m of **Sprint,** south bank). Thence for about 1m below Hawes Bridge (both banks) held by Kent AA, wt £2.50 until May 31, £7 thereafter. RWA licence necessary. Tickets and licences from Atkinson *(see below).* Below is Levens Park fishery, private. Dt from Low Levens Farm for good stretch. Stainton Beck 2m; trout. Kendal Corporation owns Fisher Tarn; now privately leased. **Killington Reservoir** (ns Oxenholme), is property of British Waterways; pike, perch and trout. Fishing rights leased to Kent AA; st £3, wt £3, dt £1.20. Tackleists: T Atkinson & Sons, Stricklandgate, who issue Kent AA tickets and RD licences. Kendal Sports, 28–30, Stramondgate (RD licences only). Hotels: County, Kendal, Woolpack, Seven Stars, Rainbow, Globe.

Burneside (Cumbria). Burneside AA water from a little below junction of Sprint up to Sandy Hill Farm near Staveley, including mill dams at Burneside, Bowston, and Cowan Head, which hold large trout (up to 1½ lb); salmon and sea trout from Aug. *(See Sprint below.)* Permits from Anglers Arms, Burneside. Lakes (not assn): Skelsmergh Tarn, 2m NE; Gurnal Dubs, 3m N.

Staveley (Cumbria). Kent; trout (small); salmon and sea trout in Sept and Oct. Staveley and Dist AA has rights on river, and on **River Gowan** and **Kentmere Tarn.** Wt £2 from Smith's garage, Main Street, Staveley (not available for tarn, fishable only by st £6.50) Hotels; Eagle and Child, Duke William, Railway.

MINT (tributary of Kent). Best fished from

Kendal. Joins Kent about 1m above town; holds good head of small trout. Kent AA has lowest water *(see Kendal)*.

SPRINT (tributary of Kent). Joins Kent at Burneside. Burneside AA *(see Burneside)* has about 1m of fishing from junction with Kent. Kent AA has ½m (east bank only). Salmon and sea trout from Aug; brown trout small; banks much wooded.

KEER. Rises 4m above Borwick, runs into Morecambe Bay 3m below **Carnforth.** Good sea trout and brown trout (no coarse fish). Carnforth AA has water; wt and dt (limited). Canal fishing for pike, perch, roach, bream.

LEVEN: Drains Windermere, and is joined by **River Crake** (from Coniston Water) at Greenodd, near Ulverston, before flowing into Morecambe Bay. Salmon, sea trout, trout. Both rivers strictly preserved.

Ulverston (Cumbria). Salmon, sea trout, trout. Ulverston AA has fishing on **Ulverston Canal,** 1¼m long, specimen tench, carp, etc; restocked; day and season tickets from Canal Tavern Inn and A Parker, Market St. St £5, dt 40p, concessions to OAP and jun. Match permits from AA sec. Lakes: **Urswick Tarn,** 3m S; very good coarse fishing. Apply Gen Burgoyne Inn, Urswick. Mere Tarn, 5m S (Furness FA; st only). Hotels: Armadale, Sun, Queen's, King's, Bay Horse, Lonsdale House. *Note: Guide book to fishing obtainable from Town Hall.*

Greenodd (Cumbria). Salmon, trout, sea trout; preserved by Lower Leven Fishery; waiting list closed. Crake: salmon, sea trout, trout *(see Crake)*. Colton Beck; sea trout, salmon; private. Hotel: Armadale.

Newby Bridge (Cumbria). Salmon, trout; preserved by Leven AA down to Greenodd railway bridge; members only. Swan Hotel issues dt. Lakes: Windermere, 1m N; Bawtry Tarn, 2m NE; pike, perch; preserved by Furness FA. High and Low Dam, Finsthwaite; brown trout, coarse fish; dt from the Manager, Stott Park, Bobbin Mill, Finsthwaite. 2m S, **Bigland Hall** Sporting Estate. 12 acre coarse fish lake. Dt £1.60: evening only 80p.

Lake Side (Cumbria). Salmon, trout. Some free fishing; other sections of the shore private. Inquire locally Pike, perch, trout. Lakes: Windermere; pike, perch, char, trout. Bawtry Tarn 2m W *(see*

Newby Bridge) (see Westmorland lakes for Windermere).

TORVER BECK (tributary of Coniston lake), **Torver** (Lancs). Lakes: Coniston, 1m E; pike, perch and trout, Goat's Water, 3m NE. Beacon Tarn, 5m S. Hotel: Church House Inn.

CRAKE (tributary of Leven):

Greenodd (Cumbria). Crake; salmon, sea trout, trout. Dt £1.15 for stretch at Lowick Bridge from W. Hall, Mill Farm, Lowick Bridge. **Rusland Pool River,** tributary of Leven; st £2 (jun £1) from Dr Hill, Haverthwaite and Black Beck caravan site. Clitheroe FA has water; members only. Forestry Commission, Satterthwaite issues tickets, as do some farmers and landowners.

Coniston (Cumbria). Yewdale Beck, Torver Beck, 2½m S. Crake; salmon, sea trout, trout. Duddon, 8m; salmon, sea trout. Lakes: Coniston; pike, perch, char and trout. Leven Water, 2m NW; Goat's Water, 2m W; Low Tarn, 3m NE. Esthwaite Lake, 4m; pike and perch *(see Hawkshead)*. Char fishing in **Coniston Lake** very good in May and June. Lake free to RD licence-holders. Licences from J D Fox (tackleist), Yewdale Road. Boats: Coniston Power Boat Co; Bridge End Café; and café at boathouse. Coniston AA gives permits for Yew Tree Tarn (rainbow and brown trout). Dt £4 and £2, according to date, from Tackle Shop, Tilberthwaite Ave, Coniston.

GRIZEDALE BECK (tributary of Leven):

Hawkshead (Cumbria). Forestry Commission, small brown trout; let to Grizedale AA; wt £3.50 and dt £1 from Fern Cottage, Camp Shop, or Forestry Office, Grizedale. Reduced rates preJune 30. Esthwaite Water; trout, pike, perch; preserved, but visitors can obtain tickets *(see English Lake District)*. Tackle and licences: J Haselhurst, Chemist. Hotel: Red Lion.

TROUTBECK (trib of Windermere):

Windermere (Cumbria). 1½m S; trout. Windermere, Ambleside and Dist AA has stretch; large lake trout run up after floods in August until end of season. Association also has School Knotts Tarn; 2m from Windermere Station; trout, fly only *(see Ambleside)*. Gowan, 2m NE. Lake Windermere, 1m W; pike, perch and large trout; best March to June. Hotels: Old England, Windermere, Stag's Head. Boats at Lakeside, Bowness, Millerground, Waterhead. Lake free to licence-holders *(see Cumbria Lakes)*.

Rothay (tributary of Windermere): Formed by confluence of four becks above Grasmere. Flows into Windermere via Grasmere and Rydal Water.

Ambleside (Cumbria) ns Windermere, 5m Windermere, Ambleside and Dist AA has water on Rothay (trout). **Brathay** (trout), **Rydal Water** (pike, perch, few trout) and **Troutbeck**. St £6, wt £4, dt £2 *(see Windermere)*. Other waters near Ambleside: Scandal Beck; trout; preserved. Rydale Rock, 2m N Windermere; pike, perch and trout; free. Belham Tarn, 3m S. Yew Tree Tarn; Coniston AA. Hotels: Salutation, White Lion, Waterhead (boats).

Grasmere (Cumbria). Rothay; trout, Easdale Beck; trout. Lakes: Grasmere; pike, perch and few trout. Rydal Water, 3m SE; perch, pike and few trout. Stream joining Grasmere with Rydal gives fair trouting. Easdale Tarn, 3m NW; good perch, trout. Codale Tarn, 4m NW; trout, perch. Hotels: Rothay, Prince of Wales (boats), Dale Lodge, Swan, Allonby (boats).

PILLING WATER. Some trout; permission of farmers.

WINSTER. Parallel with Windermere for 6m. Joins the sea by **Grange-over-Sands**. Salmon, sea trout, brown trout, coarse fish. Permits no longer issued for St Mary's College stretch. Brown trout and sea trout (late) may be taken in **River Eea**. Dt and wt from Commodore Hotel, Grange-over-Sands. Tackleist: B Mandsley, Kents Bank Road.

LANCASHIRE (lakes and reservoirs)

(see North West Water Authority, p 39, unless otherwise stated)

APPLETON RESERVOIR. Fishing station: **Warrington.** Coarse fish; Warrington Corporation, st and dt available from lodge near reservoir. At **Lymm,** near Warrington, is Lymm AC water; lake; good carp, etc. Dt from bank walker.

BARROW-IN-FURNESS RESERVOIRS. Barrow AA has trout fishing in five reservoirs. No tickets. Furness FA issues season and day tickets for all waters, coarse and game, stocked and unstocked. New rates not yet available. Details from Hannay's (tackleist), 50 Crellin Street. *(See also Sea Fishing Stations.)*

BARNSFOLD WATERS. 7m NE of Preston. Trout, fly only. St and limited dt. Tel Ribchester 202.

BRYAN HEY RESERVOIR. 3m NW of Bolton. Coarse fish and trout. St £8 and dt 80p (£1 Sundays) from Belmont Fisheries, Woodlands, Mill Lane, Aspull, nr Wigan.

BUCKLEY WOOD RESERVOIR, Rochdale. Leased by NWWA to Rochdale Walton AS. Inquire hon sec *(see also Mersey and Rochdale)*.

BROWNHILL RESERVOIR. Between **Colne** and **Foulridge.** Feeder for Leeds and Liverpool Canal. Holds brown trout; preserved by Colne AA, tickets for members' guests only.

DEAN and **SUNNYHURST HEY RESERVOIRS, Darwen.** NWWA (S Rivers Div). Trout, few perch. Darwen AA has rights on reservoir; good fly water; four dt per day at £2.10 from County Sports, Duckworth St, Darwen.

FOULRIDGE (LOWER) RESERVOIR. Colne 2m. Good brown trout and coarse fishing. Permits from Southworth, BW bungalow, Reedy Moor Lane, Foulridge, Colne.

HEAPEY LODGES. Chorley. Three reservoirs hold trout and coarse fish. St £5 from T Witter & Co, Water Street, Chorley. Dt 50p from Heapey Factory.

NORTH WEST WATER AUTH RESERVOIRS. Rivington. These reservoirs which include **Upper and Lower Rivington, Anglezarke, Rake Brook, Upper and Lower Roddlesworth** are about 35m north-east of Liverpool. Trout and coarse fish. March 15 to Sept 30. No maggots. Upper Roddlesworth and Upper Rivington Reservoirs reserved for fly-fishing only; size limit 10 in; bag limit. No wading; no dogs. Tickets from the Divisional Manager, NW Water Authority, Western Division, Merton House, Stanley Road Bootle, Merseyside L20 3NH (Tel 051 9227 260); Resident Engineer's Office, Rivington, Horwich, near Bolton BL6 7RN; A Leach, 78/80 Lee Lane, Horwich; R Wall, 10/12 Wigan Road, Hindley and Salmons (Caterers) Ltd, Rivington Hall, Horwich.

OLDHAM RESERVOIRS. Oldham United

AS leases six reservoirs from NWWA. **Lower Strinesdale, Castleshaw** and **Kitcliffe** (trout); **Upper Strinesdale, Ogden** and **Brushes Reservoirs,** pike, perch, bream, roach, carp, tench, chub; some trout in Brushes. Dt, except on Sundays. Tickets by post from sec or local tackleists.

ORMSGILL LOWER RESERVOIR. Barrow. Trout, tench, carp. Furness FA water. Inquiries to Hannays, 50 Crellin St, Barrow in Furness.

PENNINGTON FLASH. Leigh. Good coarse fishing. Pennington Flash AA issues st £2.50 and dt 50p. Inquiries to J Scotson, 26 Glover St, Leigh, Lancs.

SABDEN RESERVOIR. Whalley. Trout (av 10 in), carp. Accrington and Dist FC water. Dt from T Littler, 2 Pendle Street, West Sabden. Lancashire RD licence required.

LEA

(For close seasons, licences etc, see Thames Water Authority, p 42)

Walton's river; flows through Bedfordshire and Hertfordshire then along boundary between Essex and Middlesex to join Thames near Blackwall; 46m long. Building and canalisation have largely removed its charm, but still holds good coarse fish and occasional trout.

Tottenham (Middx). Roach and dace predominant; some chub and bream. Water cleaner than in past but barges midweek and boat traffic at weekends may disturb fishing. Best baits: hempseed, casters; free TWA reservoirs close to Tottenham Hale (roach, perch, bream, pike; one reservoir stocked with brown trout *(see under London)*. Tackleists: Farrer, Seven Sisters Rd, N15; Don's, 239–246 Fore Street, Edmonton.

Enfield Lock (Middx). Fair sport with roach, perch, few bream and pike, and occasional carp.

Waltham Abbey (Herts). Good coarse fishing on **Lea Relief Channel** from Fisher's Green to Waltham Abbey. TWA has fishery 1¼m long able to accommodate about 250 anglers. St £6.20 and dt 65p (concessions for OAP, regd disabled and juniors) from Div Manager, TW (Lea Division) The Grange, Crossbrook Street, Waltham Cross, Herts. EN8 8LX Tel. Waltham Cross 23611. *(For LAA water see Wormley.)* Tackleists: P & B Hall, Highbridge Street, Waltham Abbey and Abbey Angling, Sun Street, Waltham Abbey.

Cheshunt (Herts). **Coarse fishing.** Red Spinner AS has Cheshunt South Reservoir; carp and tench. Members only. Cheshunt AC has Friday Lake; members only.

Wormley (Herts.) London AA controls from below Aqueduct Lock up to King's Weir Fishery; coarse fishing; dt (towpath only). Private bank and new channel for members.

Broxbourne (Herts.) Leased by BT Committee from King's Weir Fishery boundary below Broxbourne bridge up to Dobbs' Lock above, including the Crown Fisheries *(advt. p 92)* and Carthagena weir. Tickets on water at modest charge. "Leisure Sport" has group of lakes here. St from RMC House, Feltham, Middlesex.

Hoddesdon (Herts), ns Rye House or Broxbourne. On Lea, Stort and New River Lea: London AA has rights of Dobbs' Weir Fishery; large dace, bream, roach, pike, chub and perch, and a few trout. Dt 20p. Tackleist: C J Ross, 2 Amwell Street. Hotel: Fish and Eels.

Rye House (Herts). Roach, chub, dace, bream, pike, perch, tench, few trout. Rye House Bridge to October Hole is London AA water and October Hole to Ware public. West Ham AS controls "Forty Guinea" water, just above Fielde's Weir Lock to about 300 yds above Fish and Eels footbridge, both banks. Dt 15p (towpath only) from bailiff. Hotel: Ye Olde Rye House.

St Margaret's (Herts). Old River Lea. Public fishing from towing-path.

Ware (Herts). Old River Lea. Fishing in Lea Navigation from towpath is public. There are roach, dace, bream and trout in the water, and "The Boom", where a side-stream comes in above the bridge, is a favourite place with anglers. This is a likely spot for a trout.

Hertford (Herts). For Lea, **Mimram, Beane, Rib** and **New River.** Lea is public from towing-path between Hertford and Old Ford Lock and Stort Navigation between Bishop's Stortford and Hoddesdon, excluding club waters, for which dt are obtainable (details on notice boards). London AA has stretch from Town Mill gate to junction with Lee Navigation (¾m); members only. Tackleists: Brown Bros, Castle Street; Mecca Angling, 31 Railway Street. Hotels: Salisbury Arms, Dimsdale Arms, White Hart, Station. Trout, jack, perch, chub, roach and dace.

Hatfield (Herts). Hatfield AS has rights on river from Mill Green to Essendon (about 2½m); including seven-acre broadwater (large carp and bream). Members only.

Luton (Beds). Tring Reservoirs (10m); Grand Union Canal (10m); Great Ouse (20m). Clubs: Luton AC, Leighton Buzzard AC, Ampthill & Dist A & FPS. Information from tackleists: Anglers Corner, 73 Austin Road, or Wilds, 8–10 Bute St.

Tributaries of the Lea

STORT:

Roydon (Essex). Roach, dace, perch, pike, chub, bream. Between Roydon Station bridge and Mill bridge is ticket water; permits from Green's Leisure Centre. Lychnobite AS leases Temple Farm Fishery, which begins at iron bridge just before mill down to Lower Lock (often called No-man's Lock), including Brick Lock, part of mill stream and back stream (about 2m of fishing). Dt from bailiff on water.

Burnt Mill (Essex). Stort. Controlled by London AA; strictly members only. Bishop's Stortford AS *(dt; see Harlow and Bishop's Stortford)* and Harlow AS (private) have water.

Harlow (Essex). Coarse fish. Harlow UDC has town waters. Inquiries to clerk of council. London AA has water here and at **Spellbrook** and **Thorley;** (available to associates—*see p 214*). LAA grants facilities for Harlow residents on its water. Inquiries to Sec.

Sawbridgeworth (Herts). Good head of all coarse fish with many large roach; fishes best Sept onwards. Sawbridgeworth AS has 1½m each side of railway station; dt from bailiffs; pike fishing (after Oct 1), limited number of st. Dt and tackle from The Pet Shop, Knight Street. Hotel: Queens Head (club HQ). Visiting parties welcome; apply hon sec for reservation.

Bishop's Stortford (Essex). Bishop's Stortford and Dist AS has coarse fishing to Spellbrook Lock (tickets) and has length at Harlow (members only). Tickets from tackleist: H & T C Godfrey Ltd, 3 South Street, or hon sec. Hotels: Foxley, George, Hatfield Forest Lake (National Trust) *(see Essex (small streams and lakes))*.

ASH. Fishing stations: **Widford** (Herts) and **Hadham** (Essex); a few trout, pike, etc; preserved.

RIB: Trout, coarse fish. "Leisure Sport" fishery for st holders, inquires to RMC House, Feltham, Middlesex. Fishing stations: **Standon, Braughing, Westmill,** all Hertfordshire. Abbey Cross AS has a stretch from Hertford to Watton Rd, nr Ware; strictly members only. Entrance fee £22.50, annual sub £15, waiting list.

BEANE: This once-excellent trout stream has been largely ruined by abstraction. Some stretches still hold good fish, however.

Stevenage (Herts). Water abstraction has ruined trout fishing. Club: Stevenage AS; no water. Tackleist in district: Oliver's of Knebworth.

MIMRAM: Trout, preserved.

LINCOLNSHIRE (small streams)

(For close seasons, licences, etc, see Anglian Water Authority, p 40)

GREAT EAU or WITHERN. Rises above Aby and flows some 12m to sea at Saltfleet; coarse fish; much free water; fishes best in autumn.

Saltfleet (Lincs), ns Saltfleet, 3m. Grayfleet, South Eau, and Mar Dyke; coarse fish; some free water. At Saltfleetby St Peters is pond on which fishing is available; dt, at shop near pond; no Sunday fishing. Sea trout in Haven in Sept; also flounders.

Louth (Lincs). Great Eau private above bridge on main Louth—**Mablethorpe** road, including Calceby Beck, Aby and South Ormesby Park; free below to licence-holders as far as Gayton lugs, thence ½m private to members of Mablethorpe, Sutton-on-Sea Dist AC (also another ¾m stretch), thence free to ½m above Cloves Bridge, **Theddlethorpe** (Mablethorpe Dist AC), and free below Cloves Bridge. Altogether 10m free fishing to RD licence holders; coarse fish, including good roach, bream, perch, pike, rainbow trout (few and mostly small) and grayling. **Lud** generally free below Louth to outfall at Tetney. Coarse fishing in ponds at **Grainthorpe, North and South Somercotes, Fulstow, Saltfleetby** and brick pits, Alfred Rd, **Sutton-on-Sea;** dt at adjacent houses. **Louth Canal** free to licence-holders from Louth to sea outlet at **Tetney;** coarse fish; some private access; permission from farmers. Tackleists: Lincolnshire Gun Co, 27 Upgate; Clarke's Stores, High Street, Mablethorpe. Pet Shop, opposite Mablethorpe Station; Epsleys, High Street, Sutton-on-Sea.

STEEPING. Rises 5m above **Spilsby** (1m off on left bank), runs thence to **Wainfleet** and joins the sea 4m below near **Skegness** *(see also Sea Fishing Stations)*; coarse fish; largely free to RD licence-holders; applications for match lengths to RD after Jan 1. Croft AC has stretch at Haven House; tickets. Spilsby AA has **Eresby Canal;** good bream, tench, perch, etc; members only; confined to 13m radius; st and dt from hon sec or Higgs Bros (tackleists), Spilsby, who also issue licences.

LONDON (MWD reservoirs, etc)

Most of the waters referred to below under **'MWD Reservoirs'** are in the area termed Greater London. They are all administered by the Metropolitan Division of the Thames Water Authority; all are easily accessible from Central London. A number are rented by angling clubs and reserved for members, but at others fishing is available to the general public at modest charges on season or day ticket basis.

It seems appropriate to mention here two important angling bodies—first, the **London Anglers' Association,** which has water on several reservoirs as well as scores of miles on rivers, streams and lakes (125 fisheries in all). The Association now has about 25,000 full members through 550 affiliated clubs. It has offices at 183 Hoe Street, Walthamstow,

London E17 3AP (telephone number: 01-520 7477). The current subscription for full members is £8 per season (including NFA subscriptions) and day tickets at 60p are issued for a number of fisheries (concessions to ladies, Old Age Pensioners and juniors under 16). For a brochure and application form please send a stamped addressed envelope to General Secretary, 183 Hoe Street, Walthamstow, E17 3AP.

The Central Association of London and Provincial Angling Clubs (HQ The Lord Raglan, St Martin Le Grand, EC2) has about 120 affiliated clubs and fisheries on rivers, canals and lakes in the South of England. Day tickets issued for many fisheries. Full details from hon sec.

Among tackleists in Central London are: Hardy Bros, of 61 Pall Mall; C Farlow & Co Ltd, 5b Pall Mall *(adv p 1)*; and Milwards *(advt p 24)*. At 19 Piccadilly, are Cording & Co Ltd, specialists in fishing clothing. The British Association of Fishing Tackle Makers and Distributors is at 145 Oxford Street. W1R 1TB (Tel: 01-437 7281) and Stablers is at 350 Barratt Lane, SW18 *(advt p 14)*.

(Tackleists in Metropolitan area listed under individual centres.)

MWD Reservoirs where *fishing rights are let to clubs* include the following:
King George's, Chingford; Queen Mary, Staines (North); Lambeth (No 4). All to London AA.
Banbury, Staines (South); Lambeth (Nos 2 and 3) to Civil Service Sports Council.
Cheshunt (South) to Red Spinner AS.
Chelsea (Hurst Road, Walton) to Kingston PS.

Reservoirs open to the public for game fishing (stocked with rainbow, or brown and rainbow trout)

Walthamstow Nos 4 & 5. E Warwick, Barn Elms Nos 6, 7 & 8. Kempton Park West, Queen Mother. Boat fishing only on Queen Mother Reservoir, at a price still to be determined when we went to press, possibly with a percapita reduction if two or three anglers share a boat. Bank fishing only on the other waters, at a basic charge of £5 (surcharged Sat, Sun and BH). Comprehensive leaflet issued by TWA, supplied on request. See p 42 for addresses.

Reservoirs open to the public for coarse fishing.
Walthamstow Nos 1, 2 & 3, W Warwick, High and Low Maynard, Coppermill Stream, Barn Elms Pond. St, where issued, £8, dt 90p. Comprehensive leaflet issued by TWA, supplied on request. See p 42 for addresses.

Rivers belonging to the Metropolitan Water Division

MOLE and EMBER (Surrey). Let to clubs. Thames is near.
NEW RIVER (Middx and Herts). An artificial cut. Coarse fish; private except for a length at Hertford, let to Palmers Green AS; lengths near Ware, let to Lychnobite AS and Swan and Pike AS; and lengths either side of Amwell Hill PS to London Specimen Hunters' Club and Myddelton AS.

LUNE

(For close seasons, licences, etc, see North West Water Authority, p 39)

Rises on Ravenstonedale Common (Westmorland) and flows through beautiful valley into Irish Sea near Lancaster. Excellent sport with salmon, sea trout and brown trout. Lower reaches also well-stocked with coarse fish. August and September best for salmon and sea trout.

Lancaster (Lancs). Salmon, sea trout, trout. NWWA has Skerton Fisheries. (Beaumont Beck to Scaleford—both banks.) Limited dt for salmon £3.50 (to 31 July), £5.00 (to end of season), night permits for sea trout £2.50, trout £1.00. Above weir limited tickets for coarse fishing 50p. Matches can be booked on Sundays. NWWA licences and tickets from Darwen and Gough (Tackle Shop), 6 Moor Lane, Lancaster.
Halton (Lancs). Lune; salmon, sea trout, trout, coarse fish. NWWA has water above and below weir; day permits for salmon £3.50 (up to 31 July) and £5.00 (1 August to end of season). Sea trout

£2.50 per night, trout £1.00, Coarse Fishing (above weir) 50p. Tickets from Darwen and Gough (Tackle Shop), 6 Moor Lane, Lancaster. Sea trout after 6 pm, Mrs Curwen, Greenup Cottage, Hornby Road, Caton, nr Lancaster (Lancaster 770078).

Caton (Lancs). Lancaster and Dist AA has fishing over 6 bank miles divided into three sections. Waiting list for membership. Wt £24; dt (pre-July 1) £3 (post July 1) £6, from H W Darwen, 6 Moor Lane, Lancaster and Greenop Cottage, Caton. No dt Saturdays and Sundays, though Sunday fishing is allowed to members. Fly only when water level 1 ft 3 in or below. Worm prohibited in October. No maggot or grub fishing. Restrictions on threadline.

Hornby (Lancs). Salmon, sea trout, trout. Lancaster AA has Claughton stretch *(see Caton)*. No dt.

Whittington (Lancs). Salmon, sea trout ($\frac{1}{2}$ lb to 2 lb). Dt 75p from H G Mackereth, Whittington Farm.

Kirkby Lonsdale (West'land). Salmon, sea trout, trout. Trout fishing is good; average $1\frac{1}{2}$ lb; sea trout up to 8 lb. Kirkby Lonsdale AA has about $2\frac{1}{2}$m of water. Visitors' tickets (Mon–Fri £15) to persons staying locally only (not caravanners or campers), from the Tackle Box, 67 Main Street. Clitheroe AA has 1m. Limited dt. Hotels: Royal, can arrange salmon and trout fishing. Red Dragon, King's Arms, Sun, Fleece Inn. Casterton Hotel at Casterton, 1m upstream, is convenient for association waters. Salmon (best August, September); sea trout (June onward), trout.

Barbon (Cumbria). Lune, 1m W Barbon Beck. Barbon is good centre for Kirkby Lonsdale AA water. Hotels: Barbon Inn.

Tributaries of the Lune

Sedbergh (Yorks). Sedbergh AA has about 2m on Lune and about 10m of tributaries **Rawthey, Dee** and **Clough.** Brown trout; salmon and sea trout from July. Tickets (£10 week) from The Sports Shop, Main Street. Manchester AA has stretch at **Firbank;** members only. Tickets for 9m on **Clough** from The Hive Garage, The Street, Garsdale.

Low Gill (Cumbria). Trout, sea trout and salmon (salmon and sea trout best at back end); about $2\frac{1}{2}$m both banks preserved by Manchester AA, which has water at Low Gill and Firbank; no tickets. Membership: £120 pa. Blackburn AA also has water.

Tebay (Cumbria). Salmon and sea trout (August onwards best), trout (average 3 to lb). Tebay and Dist has 17m of good water; wt £15 (April 1–Sept 15) but visitors must stay locally. Tickets from Tebay club secretary and hotels. Hotels: Cross Keys, Black Swan and Junction, Tebay.

Orton (Cumbria) ns Tebay. Trout (all season), salmon, sea trout. Accommodation at George Hotel. RWA licences: Davies, 8 North Terrace, Tebay.

RAWTHEY. Trout, with sea trout and occasional salmon late in season. Sedbergh AA has good stretch on river and tributary **Dee** wt £10 *(see Sedbergh on main river)*.

WENNING. Sea trout (good), brown trout,

few salmon (late). Best latter part of season. Fishing stations: **Clapham** and **Bentham** (Yorks). Day tickets for Hornby Castle Estate water were available when previous edition was published. Recent enquiries having proved unfruitful, anglers are advised to make their own investigations locally. Bentham AA has about $3\frac{1}{2}$m of water; fast stream, good sport; visitors' tickets: st £27.50, wt £10, dt £2 from Punch Bowl Hotel, Lower Bentham, or Mottram, Station Rd, Bentham. Spinning prohibited. Ingleborough Estate holds 5m. Wt (limited); apply Estate Office, Clapham; trout run 3 to lb. Blackburn AA has water; members only. Hotels: Royal Oak, Brown Cow, Black Bull. Punch Bowl Hotel also has $\frac{3}{4}$m private trout and sea trout fishing and issues dt. D Burns, tackleist, Station Road, Bentham, issues licences and permits, and will supply further information. Note: NWWA licence required at Clapham.

GRETA. Trout (4 to lb) and late run of salmon and sea trout. Fishing stations: **Ingleton** and **Burton-in-Lonsdale** (Yorks). Trout. Ingleton AA controls 6m of unbroken water on Greta and Doe; st, wt and dt from Wells (newsagent), Main St, Ingleton, and hon sec. No Sunday fishing. Accrington FC has Clifford Hall length at Burton; no dt. Hotel: Punch Bowl, Burton-in-Lonsdale (WA licences).

MEDWAY

(For close seasons, licences, etc, see Thames Water Authority, p 42)

Kentish river joining estuary of Thames at Sheerness through estuary of its own. Coarse fish (abundant bream) with few trout in upper reaches.

Maidstone (Kent). Free from towpath from Maidstone bridge to midway between East Farleigh and Barming bridges. Maidstone Victory Angling and Medway PS have water at Barming, Teston, Wateringbury and Yalding. Permits from hon sec and local tackleists. **Pooh Corner trout fishery** apply Mr J Thompson, Pooh Corner, Rolvenden, Cranbrook, Kent. **Mote Park Lake** (coarse fish); dt £1.40 (non-residents) from A Sanders, 85 Bank Street; Pettitts, 18 Market Building (tickets and licences). Inns: Medway; West Kent; Rose and Crown; Queen's Head.

East Farleigh (Kent). Free on towpath side from Maidstone to notice-board midway between East Farleigh and Barming; thence mostly Maidstone Victory Angling and Medway Pres Soc water; tickets *(see Maidstone)*. Inn: Victory.

Barming (Kent). Maidstone Victory Angling and Medway Pres Soc *(see East Farleigh and Maidstone)* has water. Dt from C J Ralph, Riverdale, St Helen's Lane, East Farleigh, for CALPAC water upstream and downstream of bridge. Inn: The Bull (no accommodation).

Wateringbury (Kent). Maidstone Victory Angling and Medway Pres Soc has most of towpath bank here and at **Teston;** tickets *(see East Farleigh and Maidstone)*. Medway Wharf Ltd, Riverside Cafe, issue dt for about 2½m; boats available, summer. Barking AS has a meadow; members only but open to visiting clubs. Inn: King's Head.

Yalding (Kent). Kent RD has about 200 yds upstream of Yalding Sluices, towpath side; no charge to licence-holders. Maidstone Victory Angling and Medway Pres Soc has towpath bank downstream of Railway Inn; tickets *(see East Farleigh and Maidstone)*. Yalding AS has water; dt (weekdays only). New Studio AS has short length. Central Assoc of London and Prov AC has ¾m and one meadow at junction of Medway and **Beult;** dt from

Bailiff. Inns: Railway (tackle, but no accommodation); George; Anchor (boats).

Tonbridge (Kent). Tonbridge and Dist A & FPS has 9m of Medway, 1½m of Eden and lakes. Dt for parts of Medway only at 50p; from water bailiffs. Vacancies for membership; g'men £5.50, ladies £3.50, concessions for OAP, from Mrs P Wolfe, 59 Hunt Road.

Tunbridge Wells (Kent). Royal Tunbridge Wells AS has coarse fishery at **Ashurst** and **Fordcombe,** trout waters on **Medway** near **Marefield, Teise** at **Lamberhurst** and **Rother** at **Stonegate** and two ponds, membership limited; entrance fee, £1.50; annual subscription £10, concessions for

ladies and juvs. Dt £1 to friends of members only. **Bartley Mill Stream** holds trout. Dt 50p (juv. 25p) from Forge Garage, Little Bayham, Lamberhurst. Tackleist: S E Haward, 14/33 Goods Station Road.

Ashurst (Kent). Coarse fish, some trout and grayling. Tunbridge Wells AS has water (see above). Edenbridge AS has about 5m; trout, grayling, coarse fish (stocked with barbel, which are thriving). Guest tickets for members' friends only.

Fordcombe (Kent). Trout, coarse fish. Tunbridge Wells AS has water (see above).

Tributaries of the Medway

BEULT: Excellent coarse fishing; lower reaches noted for chub, bream and tench; trout higher. Gravesend Kingfisher A & PA (stretches at **Smarden, Hunton, Headcorn** and **Staplehurst;** members only); London AA has water at **Hunton** and **Linton;** members only. Lewisham Piscatorials and Dartford AA has fishing. CALPAC has water at Headcorn for members only.

EDEN: Coarse fish.

Penshurst (Kent). On Eden and Medway; coarse fish. Croydon AS has water on Eden and fishes CALPAC waters. Penshurst AS has rights from Ensfield to Pounds Bridge and from The Point on Medway to weir on Eden; members only. Dt at Salmans Farm for trout, grayling, chub, dace, etc. Hotel: Leicester Arms.

Edenbridge (Kent). Coarse fish. 8m controlled by Edenbridge AS (members

only) also a mile at Penshurst. Short stretches rented by Holland AS.

TEISE: Joins Medway at Yalding. Trout, coarse fish.

Laddingford (Kent). London AA has water for members only at Mileham and Manor Farms. Another fishery for members only at Moors Farm.

Goudhurst (Kent). Teise Anglers and Owners' Association holds 5m of river; brown and rainbow trout; some sections fly only. Members only (£40 entrance fee, £30 sub). Season, April 1 to Sept 30. Strictly limited visitors dt £4 from hon sec, for anglers on holiday in district. Enquire well in advance.

Lamberhurst (Kent). Tunbridge Wells AS has trout water; members and friends only *(see Tunbridge Wells).* **Bayham Lake** trout fishery near here. *(For details, see Kent Lakes, p 87.)*

MERSEY

(For close seasons, licences, etc, see North West Water Authority, p 39)

Forms Liverpool Channel and seaport. Main river polluted and of no account for fishing except in higher reaches. Some tributaries contain trout.

Liverpool (Merseyside). Liverpool and Dist AA has extensive fisheries on **Shropshire Union Canal** and **Rufford Canal,** and sole rights on **Leeds and Liverpool Canal** from Liverpool to Halsall, rights held jointly with Northern AA on **Rufford Canal,** permission to fish waters of **River Dee and Cwyd** FA and the **Dee** at Berwyn. Also fishings on

Severn at Leighton, **Vyrnwy** at Llansantffraid and Houghton, **Banwy** at Llanerfyl and Rhydarwwydd, **Dee** at Holt and Lower Hall, **Mule** at Newton and Rhiew. Membership cards £4 from hon sec. Tickets for NWWA reservoirs from Div Manager, Merton House, Stanley Road, Bootle, Merseyside L20 3NH *(see Lancashire lakes and reservoirs).* Tackleists:

Heslop and Dukinfield, 32 Smithdown
Road; Whitty's, 15 Basnett Street; Skin-
ners, 469 Rice Lane; Bob Thomas, 183
Breckfield Rd North, and 202 Walton
Breck Rd; Wm Hitchell & Son, 47 Oxton Rd, Birkenhead; Frank Price, 42
Bridge Road, Litherland. **Stockport**
(Cheshire). Stockport County Anglers
have private water at Davenport; four
pools; carp up to 10 lb. Stockport Waltonians AA also has private waters; coarse
fish and trout. Tackleist: Edgeley Sports
and Fishing Depot, 45 Greek Street,
Edgeley.

Whaley Bridge (Derbyshire). River here
known as Goyt; polluted. Dt (not Sundays), for one bank only. **Todd Brook
Reservoir,** Whaley Bridge, has been
emptied and its future, as we go to press,
uncertain. Dt 40p for **Bosley Reservoir,**
near Macclesfield, from Harrington
Arms on Macclesfield–Leek Road, and
Mr J Arnold at 1 Lakeside Estate, Bosley. Both waters hold roach, perch,
bream, carp, pike, gudgeon *(see also
Weaver)*. **Peak Forest Canal** starts here;
coarse, sport patchy. Lock pools at **Marple** stocked with carp and tench. Canal to
Ashton Junction being opened and
dredged. County Palatine AA has water
on canal.

Tributaries of the Mersey

NEWTON BROOK (tributary of Sankey
Brook):
St Helens (Merseyside). All brooks polluted. Lakes: **Eccleston Mill Dam,
Eccleston Mere** and other local dams
preserved by two works' clubs; members
only. Dt for **Carr Mill Dam** from lodge;
perch, pike, bream, roach. St Helens
AA has waters in dams and canals and
on the **Dee** and **Calder.** Limited st and wt
from hon sec. Good carp, roach, chub,
tench and dace in **St Helen's Canal**
(Church Street length) and grayling in
Blackbrook stretch; canal fishable all
season.

BOLLIN:
Heatley (Cheshire). Occasional trout,
roach, dace, pike. **Arden Brook,** 1m SE
Mersey, 1m N.
Ashley (Cheshire). Bollin, 1m N; trout,
roach, dace, pike; Bollin and Birkin AA;
private.
BIRKIN (tributary of Bollin):
Knutsford (Cheshire). Birkin, 4m; Bollin
and Birkin AA has water; private. **Mere
Hall Lake,** 3m; reserved for members of
Mere Golf and Country Club. **Tabley
Mere,** 3m. Boat fishing only; no Sunday
fishing; carp, tench, bream, roach, pike,
perch, etc; apply Tabley Estate Office
for dt, £2. Toft Hall Pool, 1½m S; occasional permits. Small Lane Pool, 3m E;
Altrincham AA water. **Redesmere** and
Capesthorne Lakes (6m S of Wilmslow
on A34 road); large roach, bream,
tench, king carp, pike; dt £2.50, £2 &
£1.50 from A Bradley, Bailiff, East
Lodge, Capesthorne (Tel. Chelford
861584). Tackleist: H Whittaker, Princess Street, Knutsford.

IRWELL:
Manchester. River polluted, but fair fishing
(trout and perch) in three **Water Authority reservoirs** at Tintwistle, Hadfield,
18m. Half-season permits and dt from
offices and permit points on reservoirs.
Charges under review. At **Poynton,** 10m
out, there is coarse fishing in pool; dt
costs 15p. 18m from Manchester, at
Northwich, is coarse fishing in Weaver
(see Weaver). Northern AA issues st
covering all its canals. Assn has about
40m in district, including parts of
**Bridgewater, Macclesfield, Peak Forest,
Bury** and **Bolton Canals.** A little river
and some reservoir fishing *(see Chapel-
en-le-Frith)*. Dt 10p for many waters.
Warrington AA has 16½m of **Bridgewater Canal** as well as water on **Dee,
Ribble, Severn** and tributaries, **Dane**
and 100m of **Shropshire Union Canal,**
reservoirs, pits, etc. No dt, but visiting
anglers accommodated, if due notice
given. Apply hon sec. Macclesfield
Prince Albert AS has rights on canal
from Buxton road bridge to Bosley
Aqueduct (about 6m). Tickets from hon
sec. Assn also controls **Turks Head Reservoir,** members only. Moss Side AS
has water *(see Whaley Bridge)*. Tackleists: Arrowsmiths, la Gorton Lane,
West Gorton; Buckleys, 957 Oldham
Road, Newton Heath.
ROCH:
Bury (G. Manchester). Brooks polluted.
Accrington and Dist AA has water on
Ribble, Lune, Wenning and **Hodder;** dt
£2 for reservoir trout fishing, £1 for
coarse fishing. Bury and Dist AS fish
Bury and Bolton Canal and has several

small ponds and reservoirs; mostly coarse fishing, but some sport with trout on Northern AA waters. Tackleists: Fisherman's Way, Boundary Street; Compleat Angler, 64 Bolton Street; Angling Centre, 83 Rochdale Road, Belbeck Pet Supplies, 59 Belbeck Street; all Bury. Also Wood, Penny Street, Blackburn; Sports Shop, Blackburn Road, and Fisherman's Haunt, both **Accrington.**

Rochdale (G. Manchester). Rochdale Walton AS. **Buckley Wood,** 1m N (coarse and trout), dt only on application to hon sec. Rochdale and Dist AS has trout and coarse fishing at Castleton (dt 50p; visitors must be accompanied by member), and coarse fishing on **Rochdale Canal,** 3m from town; st £1, dt 12½p from tackleists (see below). Length of canal also held by Dunlop Cotton Mill Social Club; tickets from local tackleists. **Hollings-** **worth Lakes,** Littleborough; coarse fish; dt from tackleists: J Towers, 52 Whitworth Road; F Kay, 18 St Marys Gate; W Pennine Angling Supplies, 204 Yorkshire Street, who issues tickets for fly-only trout fishery (fish to 12 lbs) and for coarse fishing in **Calderbrook Dam.** *For Rochdale Canal see also Calder (Yorks)– Hebden.*

TAME:

Ashton-under-Lyne (G. Manchester). River polluted. Water Authority reservoirs **Knott Hill** and **Walker Wood,** 2m NE; trout; st and dt; local residents only. Tackleist: The Petman, 142 Stamford Street.

COMBS RESERVOIR:

Chapel-en-le-Frith (Derby). **Combs Reservoir,** 2m W; a variety of coarse fish and some trout; dt £1; enquiries to C N Farley, Lakeside.

MIDLANDS (reservoirs and lakes)

ARLESEY LAKE. Church End, **Arlesey,** Beds. Specimen carp, pike, perch, tench, bream, roach and rudd, lake restocked by Hitchin AC; members only. Annual membership: £7.

BLENHEIM LAKE. Woodstock, Oxon; excellent tench, perch, roach in summer; pike winter. Boat fishing only for visitors. Apply by letter to Estate Office for details of current charges.

BODDINGTON RESERVOIR. Byfield (Northants); **Banbury,** 7m. 65 acres. Pike, perch, roach, carp, tench; st £9 from Fisheries Officer, BWB, Willow Grange, Church Road, Watford, Herts WD1 3QA (British Waterways Board). Long waiting list. Phone before applying.

BURLEY FISH PONDS. Oakham (Rutland). Anglian Water Authority fishery. Previously rented by Oakham AS, which also has water on **Welland, Chater, Glen, Bourne Eau, Oakham Canal;** pike, perch, roach; no tickets. Tackleist: Rutland Sports, Sport & Leather. Hotels: Crown, George.

CLUMBER PARK LAKE. National Trust property, 4½m from **Worksop;** coarse fish (including pike); st £15, dt £1 from bailiff on bank. Licences and tackle from W Egley, Gateford Road, Worksop. Mr Egley also issues tickets for other lakes in area.

CASTLE ASHBY LAKES. Northampton 7m. Coarse fishing in four lakes totalling 19 acres. Pike and perch, roach to 2 lb, tench to 6 lb, bream to 6 lb, and carp to 8 lb. St £20, dt £1; £10 and 50p jun, OAP and disabled. Fishing dawn till dusk, enquiries to Water Bailiff tel Yardley Hastings (0601 29) 302. One hitherto unfished lake to be opened as a match venue and another as a season ticket only specimen carp water. Details from Estate Office, Castle Ashby, Northampton, NN7 1LJ (tel 0601 29 223). Welland and Nene RD licence required. *(See also Nene).*

CLAYDON LAKES. Buckingham, 6m. Upper and Middle Lakes at Middle Claydon, near Winslow, are Leighton Buzzard AC water; Danubian catfish, pike-perch, big carp, all from the lakes at Woburn; members only. *(See also Ouse (Great)).*

COSGROVE PITS. Stony Stratford, 2m (Bucks); **Northampton** 12m. Coarse fish; dt at waterside. Great Ouse RD.

CRANFLEET CANAL. Roach, perch, gudgeon. Whole length from Trent Lock to Cranfleet Lock held by Long Eaton Victoria AS. Dt 50p on bank and from Bridge Tackle Shop. St £4 from hon sec. *(See also Erewash Canal).*

CRANSLEY RESERVOIR. Kettering (Northants) 2½m; **Northampton** 13m. Roach, perch and tench. Anglian Water Authority, Northampton, Welland and

Nene RD. Tickets from Authority at Cliftonville, Northampton, or from reservoir. St and dt.

DENTON RESERVOIR. Denton (Lincs). Excellent coarse fishing; held by Grantham AA; dt £1 from hon sec and tackleists.

DERWENT AND LADYBOWER RESERVOIRS, Bamford (Derbyshire). Trout; fly only; April 15–Oct 8. Severn-Trent Water Authority, Derwent Division, Bamford, near Sheffield (Bamford 424). Dt £4 from Fishery Warden at reservoirs; st from £78 from Bamford Office. Boats: £4. Reductions for evenings, OAP, juvs and disabled. Limited permits at £1.18 day from Fishery Warden for fly fishing on River Derwent below Ladybower Dam. All prices include VAT.

DRAYCOTE WATER, near **Rugby** (Warks) 600 acre reservoir, brown and rainbow trout. Season April 19–Oct 12. Dt £5.20 (£3.10 after 4 pm) bank anglers limited to 300. St £138. Boats: pulling £3.80; petrol ob £9.50. (£5 after 3 pm.) Advance bookings and st applications to Senior Fishery Officer, Draycote Water, Kites Hardwick, Rugby. Dt and boats from Fishing Lodge (Tel: Rugby 811107)

before 10 am. Concessions for juvs, OAP and registered disabled.

DUKERIES LAKES. Worksop Welbeck and Thoresby private. Dt £1 on site for **Clumber Lake;** trout and coarse fish. National Trust property. **Sandhill Lake.** Worksop. Dt on site 55p. Same for Quarry Pond. Worksop & Dist AAA properties.

EYE BROOK RESERVOIR. Caldecott (Rutland), 400 acres; good trout fishing (20,000 averaging over 1 lb caught annually); fly only; dt £4, boats £5 day extra; concessions after 5 pm, season April 1–Sept 30. Anglian Water Authority, licence required; tickets at reservoir hut (Rockingham 264). Inquiries to Corby (Northants) and District Water Co, Stanion Lane, Corby, Northants NN1 8ES (Tel: Corby 2331).

FAWSLEY PARK LAKES. Daventry (Northants) 3½m; Northampton 12m. Two lakes; coarse fish; Northampton Nene AC water; dt at waterside. Anglian WA licence required.

FOREMARK RESERVOIR. Melbourne 1m. Large new water opened for trout fishing by Severn-Trent WA in 1981. Brown, brook and rainbow trout. Season: April 22–Oct 15. St (limited) £125, dt (also limited) £4.20–£4.60. R boat only, £3.80. Permits from Bendall Farm Shop, by main entrance. No permits by post.

GRAFHAM WATER. St Neots (Hunts). 1,570-acre reservoir holds brown and rainbow trout including many large fish. Dt £4.80 (bank); boats (outboard or inboard motors) £11.60 a day for two or three anglers. Rowing boats £6.30 a day, half-price for evening sessions (after 5 pm) if available. St £124 (incl 6 guest tickets) st (Mon–Fri) £90 (incl 3 guest tickets). Limit: 8 trout. Dt only from Fishing Lodge at reservoir. St and boat bookings from Area Manager, Anglian Water Authority, Grafham Water Area, W Perry, Huntingdon (Tel Huntingdon 810247). Note: rod licence required. *(Advt p 100.)*

HARLESTHORPE DAM. Clowne, Derbys. Trout, coarse fish. Dt on site; also tackle and bait. Tel Chesterfield 810231.

LINACRE RESERVOIR, Near Chesterfield. 43 acres. Severn-Trent WA *(advt p 129).* Trout. St £69, dt (limited) £4 (£2 OAP, juv, dis), from div office, Derwent div STWA, 43 Dimple Road, Matlock.

NASEBY RESERVOIR, Naseby. Carp, bream, rudd. St £10, from BWB, Willow Grange, Church Road, Watford, Herts. Long waiting list.

OGSTON RESERVOIR, near Chesterfield, Derbyshire. 206-acre water owned by Severn-Trent Water Authority. Large trout. Dt £3.40 (limited): Div Manager, Derwent Div, STWA, Raynesway, Derby DE2 7JA.

PACKINGTON FISHERIES, Meriden (Warks). Excellent brown and rainbow trout fishing on 120 acres of pool, 4m of river. Dt £6, boats £3. Members' fees £80 to £210, which includes boat charges. Season March 18–November 15. Fishing on Somers fishery for carp, tench, roach, perch, bream and rudd. St £25, dt £1.50. Concessions for juniors and OAP. Reduced rates for evenings. Details from Packington Fisheries, Broadwater, Meriden, nr Coventry CV7 7HR (Meriden 22754). *(Advt. p 7.)*

PITSFORD RESERVOIR, Northampton 5m. Anglian Water Authority, Cliftonville, Northampton. Trout; fly only. Dt £2.80 (bank); st £74 (covers Ravensthorpe too); boats additional £3.30 per person. All prices VAT inclusive. Season April 1–Sept 30. Permits from Fishing Lodge (Tel. Walgrave St Peter 350) and from Cliftonville (Northampton 21321).

PATSHULL POOLS

Pattingham, nr Wolverhampton. Gt pool: fly-only trout fishing until June 16. Coarse fishing thereafter. Two smaller trout pools. Dt on site, but advance booking for smaller pools after June 16.

RAVENSTHORPE RESERVOIR, Northampton 8m. Anglian Water Authority, Cliftonville, Northampton. Trout; fly only. Dt £2.80; st £74 (covers Pitsford too), limited permits. Boats additional £3.30 per person. Season April 1–Sept 30. Permits from Pumping Station and from Cliftonville (Northampton 21321).

RUTLAND WATER. (Empingham) 3m E of Stamford, Lincs. 3,000 acres+. With 17m of fishable bank, the largest manmade lake in Britain and the largest trout fishery in Europe. Browns, brook trout and rainbows, fly only. Full st £168, week-day only st £126, dt £4.80. Mb £13.70, rb £6.30 per day. Dt self-service from Lodge, other bookings to Recreations Officer, Rutland Water, Oakham, Leics, Tel 9686 321. Season opens April 24.

SHELSWELL LAKE. Buckingham 7m. Tench, perch, roach and pike, winter best; st only from hon sec, Bicester AS and Allmonds Sports, Market Square, Bicester; boat available at no extra charge. Bicester AS also has two stretches on **River Ray;** coarse fish; no tickets.

SHUSTOKE RESERVOIR. Shustoke; Coleshill 3m (both Warwicks). Tame Division of Severn-Trent Water Authority. Trout (av 1 lb), fly only. April 17–Oct 15. St (comprehensive) £95. St (Mon–Fri) £65. St (Mon–Fri; excluding evenings) £39. Boats £3.80. Details from 156/170 Newhall St, Birmingham B3 1SE.

STOWE LAKES. Buckingham, 4m. Carp, tench, pike, roach, rudd and perch. Limited dt £1 by post (SAE) from C Hawkins, hon sec Stowe AC. Advance notice and alternative dates required *(see also Ouse (Great).)*

SULBY RESERVOIR. Welford (Northants) 1m; **Northampton** 14m. Coarse fish; st only, (£10) from BWB, HQ Watford. S-TWA licence required. **Welford Canal** (Grand Union) also holds coarse fish.

STAUNTON HAROLD RESERVOIR, near **Melbourne,** Derbys. Severn-Trent WA coarse fishery. Limited st, and dt (60p) from local tackleists. St inquiries to

Leicester Water Centre, Gorse Hill, Anstey.

SYWELL RESERVOIR. Northampton 6m. Large tench (6 lb or over), pike (over 20 lb), perch, roach and carp; members of Wellingborough and Dist AC only; apply hon sec for details.

THORNTON RESERVOIR. Leicester 3m S of junction 22 on the M1. 76 acres. Trout, fly only. Severn-Trent WA fishery. Limited st £75 from Leicester Water Centre, Gorse Hill, Anstey. Dt £3, boat £3, from agent, Thompson, 50 Main Street, Markfield. Hotel: Bulls Head.

TITTESWORTH RESERVOIR, near **Leek,** (Staffs). 109-acre trout water. Easter–Oct 15. Dt £4 (limited); st £95 (limited).

Tickets from Upper Trent Div, Severn-Trent WA, Westport Road, Burslem, Stoke-on-Trent (Tel 85601). Dt also from Fishing Lodge at reservoir. Boats (2 anglers) £3.80 extra, (1 angler) £3.20 extra. RWA licence.

TRIMPLEY RESERVOIR, near **Bewdley,** Worcs. Trout, fly only, from April 17–July 31. Aug 1–Oct 15, mixed fishery; then coarse fishing until Feb 28. Four classes of season ticket £54–£15. No dt write for details to S-TWA, 156/70 Newhall St, Birmingham.

WELFORD RESERVOIR, near **Welford,** Leics, 20-acre coarse fishery. Pike, carp, tench, bream, rudd and roach. St only £8 from BWB, Willow Grange, Church Rd, Watford. Waiting list.

NENE

(For close seasons, licences, etc, see Anglian Water Authority, p 40)

Rises in West Northamptonshire and flows to Wash. Good, all-round coarse fishery, slow-running for most part. Roach and bream predominate, the bream in particular running to a good average size. Excellent sport with carp in Peterborough and Northampton areas. Trout fishery in upper reaches.

Wisbech (Cambs). Centre of intricate system of rivers and drains; all waters well stocked with pike, bream, roach, perch and some good tench. Sheffield and District AA has water in **North Level Drain** at Tydd (jointly with Sheffield AAS), **Middle Level** (good bream), **Popham's Eau,** 10m on **Sixteen Foot,** 6m on **Forty Foot,** 3m on **Delph,** and 6m on **Old Bedford;** st from hon sec. Wisbech and Dist AA sub-hires some waters. RD licence and Assn wt required. Concession price for locals. **Great Ouse Relief Channel** provides 11m of good fishing from Downham to King's Lynn *(see p 113)*.

Peterborough. Excellent centre for roach, bream, chub, tench, carp, dace and pike; electricity cut in town centre has produced some large carp. Peterborough AA has rights on south bank of electricity cut (north bank private) and on Nene from Peterborough to Wansford Bridge and downstream to "Dog-in-a-Doublet" (south bank) and Middleholme (north bank). Dt 50p and st £3. The north bank from "Dog-in-a-Doublet" sluice to Middleholme is available to RD licence-holders (waters restocked). **Wansford** AC waters now members only. Brotherhoods Sports Club issue dt for their water on the Nene at **Warmington,** where Warmington AC also has stretch

for members only (membership restricted). Apply John Bradshaw, New Lane, Stibbington, for dt on Nene. First-class sport in fen drains and brick pits, but many pits being filled in. Information and RD licences from tackleists: Webb. 196 Newark Avenue; Nene Sports, New Bridge; Gallyon, 3 Cumbergate.

Cotterstock (Northants). Excellent fishing for roach, chub, bream, perch, tench, dace and pike held by Cotterstock AA here and at Tansor. St £2.50 and dt 50p from B Wing, Church Farm and Tackle Shop, Oundle.

Elton (Northants). Leicester and Dist Amal Soc of Anglers has extensive stretches here and at **Nassington** and **Fotheringhay.** Dt and st from hon sec or bailiffs.

Oundle (Northants). Roach, bream, tench, dace, etc. Oundle AA has water; limited dt and st. Coventry AA has stretch at Stoke Doyle; members only. Wellingborough Nene AC has 3m at Barnwell, just upstream of Oundle and 2-acre gravel pit (tench, pike, perch and rudd). Members only *(see Wellingborough).* **Elinor Trout Fishers,** Aldwincle. 36 acre lake stocked B and Rb, limited to 30 rods at £60 per season. Dt £3, punts £2 extra. Inquiries to 40 North St, Oundle. Tel 3671 after 6.0 pm. Hotels: Talbot, Ship, Riverside (Oundle HQ).

Thrapston (Northants). Roach, dace, perch. Kettering, Thrapston & Dist AA no longer issue guest tickets. Dt for gravel pits and adjacent river-bank £1.30 from Coventry bailiff and tackleists.

Rushden, Higham Ferrers and **Irthlingborough** (Northants). Coarse fish. With new sewage works completed, fishing now showing marked improvement. Information, tackle and Rushden club cards (membership £3 pa) from Jack Leach, 26 High St, Rushden and Webster, Corn merchant, Irthlingborough. **Ditchford Lakes** heavily re-stocked in 1976 and bank-improvement programme begun. Dt on several gravel pits incl 40 acre trout fishery at **Ringstead.**

Wellingborough (Northants). Pike, perch, bream, tench, chub, roach, dace; strictly preserved by Wellingborough Nene AC from Ditchford Weir to one meadow below Hardwater Mill and water on **Great Ouse.** Club also has **Ditchford Reservoir** in conjunction with Rushden AA (coarse fish) and parts of **Ise Brook.** St from hon sec. Northampton Nene AC has from Doddington up to paper mills, excluding Earls Barton AC water (1m) and water at Billing *(see Castle Ashby, Billing and Northampton).* Tackleists: Cove's Fishing Tackle, 26a Knox Road; Watts and Reynolds, 4 Herriots Lane.

Castle Ashby (Northants). Pike, perch, bream, tench, roach; preserved for most part by Northampton Nene AC, which issues dt. Lakes on **CA Estate** (1¼m S); pike, bream, tench, perch, roach; dt from bailiff at waterside or estate office. *(See also Midlands Reservoirs.)*

Billing (Northants). Pike, roach, perch, bream, tench, chub; preserved by Northampton Nene AC, which issues dt for 1½m on both banks of river. Good coarse fishing at Billing Aquadrome (Northampton 890-849).

Northampton (Northants). Pike, perch, bream, chub, roach, carp, etc; Nene AC controls north bank from Weston Mill to Clifford Hill Lock. Details of membership charges and visitor's tickets not decided when we went to press. Northampton good centre for lake and reservoir fishing in Ravensthorpe, Sywell, Pitsford, Grafham Water *(advt p 100)* and Draycote Reservoirs, Abington Park and Overstone Park Lakes and Mackaness Gravel Pits *(see Midlands Reservoirs and Lakes).* Hotels: Plough, Grand, Angel. Tackleists: Sportman's Lodge, 44 Kingsthorpe Road, Kingsthorpe Hollow *(advt p 14).* Gilders, 148 Wellingborough Road; T H Thursby, Sheep Street.

Weedon (Northants). Pike, perch, bream, roach. **Grand Union Canal.** Northampton Nene AC has rights from Weedon to Yardley Gobion (16m); dt *(see Grand Union Canal).* Lakes: **Fawsley Park** (two lakes); coarse fish (pike, roach, rudd, etc); dt from Nene AC. Nene and Ouse licences needed for canal. Welland and Nene RD has stocked **Bugbrooke** reaches with trout (3½m in all between Heyford Mill and Harpole Mill); limited dt from Fisheries Officer.

Tributaries of the Nene

OLD RIVER NENE:
March (Cambs). Pike, perch, bream, rudd, roach, tench. Fen drains. **Old River Nene** mostly free to licence-holders. **Reed Fen** (south bank) controlled by March and Dist AA. **Twenty Foot** controlled by March Working Men's AC (tickets). **Popham's Eau, Forty Foot** and **Middle Main** fished by Sheffield and Dist AS. Tackleist (and licence-seller): A Crowson (March) Ltd, Bridge House, who will give further information. Hotels: Griffen, Wades, Temperance.

Ramsey (Hunts). Pike, perch, bream, etc. Holme Brook. Wiston Brook. Lake: Ramsey Mere, 3m NE. Club: Ramsey AA.

WILLOW BROOK: Trout, coarse fish; preserved.

King's Cliffe (Northants). Willow Brook. Welland, 3m NW.

ISE:
Kettering (Northants). **Cransley Reservoir;** roach, perch and tench *(see Midlands Reservoirs and Lakes).* **Wicksteed Lake,** also preserved water on Nene at Thrapston, apply Kettering, AA for st and dt. Licences, tickets, tackle and information from N Spring, 117 Wellington Street; Franks, 38 Wellington Street; Sports Stores, Gold Street. Hotels: Royal, George.

Geddington (Northants). Preserved by Duke of Buccleuch to Warkton. Barford Bridge to Geddington is association water *(see Kettering).*

STRECK:
Crick (Northants). Streck, 2m S. Lakes: Dunsland Reservoirs (pike, perch, etc), 3m SW; private.

Daventry (Northants). Lakes: New Reservoir, 1½m W; pike, perch, etc; private. Old Reservoir, Ashby Road; rights belong to British Timken Ltd. Canal waters held by Coventry AC.

NORFOLK AND SUFFOLK BROADS

(Rivers Bure, Waveney and Yare)

(For close seasons, licences, etc, see Anglian Water Authority—Norfolk and Suffolk RD, p 40)

Rivers Bure, Waveney and Yare, their tributaries and Broads are among the finest coarse fisheries in England. They contain pike, perch, roach, rudd, tench, gudgeon and bream. Anglian Water Authority—Norfolk and Suffolk River Division has rights on about 27 miles of tidal rivers which can be fished free and 15 miles on non-tidal rivers and some lakes etc for which a permit in addition to the licence is required. Permits obtainable from the Authority and certain tackle dealers. Some Broads are preserved and can be fished on payment. Rivers and most Broads very busy in summer, so early morning and late evening fishing advised. Best sport in autumn and winter. Boat essential for Broads.

BURE

Notable coarse fishing river, mostly free on tidal stretches but permit required on certain non-tidal stretches, particularly those controlled by Anglian Water Authority. Strong current from Yarmouth to little above Acle; upper reaches gentle and ideal for float fishing. The river contains a good head of coarse fish for its entire length. Excellent roach, bream, perch, etc. at Thurne Mouth, St Benet's, Horning, Wroxham and beyond. Several Broads are connected and can be fished, as well as tributaries Thurne and Ant. Water Authority controls stretches from Oxnead to Buxton (permit required), at Woodbastwick, South Walsham, Upton and Acle.

Stokesby (Norfolk). Bream, roach, pike, perch. Strong tides and sometimes brackish; legering best; free.

Acle (Norfolk). Bream, roach, pike, perch. Tides often strong. River traffic heavy in summer. Fishing free to licence-holders. Inns: Queen's Head and King's Head, both 1m from river; Bridge Inn (close to river); Hermitage and the Thurne Lion at Thurne Mouth.

Horning (Norfolk); ns Wroxham, 3½m. Good coarse fishing; free to licence-holders; boat almost essential; roach, rudd, bream, perch, pike, tench; river very busy in summer and early morning and late evening fishing gives best results. At **Woodbastwick** RD has about ½m of right bank, tidal; free to licence-holders. Broads: **Ranworth** (tickets for Inner Ranworth from store on Staithe); **Decoy** (club water), **Salhouse** (dt issued); and **Wroxham** (small charge—*see Wroxham*) upstream. Tackle, licences and bait at post office. Several boat yards. Hotels: Swan, New Inn and Petersfield House Hotel.

Wroxham (Norfolk). Roach, rudd, bream, pike, perch, tench; good pike and bream in winter; boats only. Much river traffic, summer. Broads; **Bridge Broad**, right bank; permission and boats from C R Chamberlain, Hoveton. **Salhouse Broad,** right bank, 2m SE dt issued. Hotels: King's Head, Broads, Horse Shoes. Tackleists: Haylett's Tackle Shop, Station Road.

Coltishall (Norfolk). Roach, bream, perch, pike. Hotels: King's Head, Rising Sun.

Buxton Lamas (Norfolk). Pike, good bream and roach, perch. Norfolk and Suffolk RD control water from here to Oxnead. Inquiries to and permits from Fisheries Officer, A.W.A., Norwich and Clarke's of Market Place, Aylsham. St £3.90, wt £1.30, dt 65p.

Aylsham (Norfolk). Trout, roach, rudd, dace and pike. Heavily weeded in summer; best Oct onwards. Above town are Aylsham and Dist AS preserves; apply hon sec. Tackle and bait from C Clarke, Market Place (also permits for local residents). Hotels: Ship, Black Boys, Plough and Shuttle, Marsham.

Blickling (Norfolk). Trout upstream from Ingworth Bridge. Controlled by Blickling Flyfishers; permits for members'

Black a Winner!

John Player Special
KING SIZE

New

John Player Special King Size

JPS 53WF

friends only. Part of river between Ingworth Bridge and Aylsham is trout
fishing only; dt from E Suffolk and Norfolk RD. **Blickling Lake** (good coarse

fishing) also controlled by RD. Permits
from RD or bailiff, 1 Park Gate Cottages, Blickling. Dt only from C Clarke,
ironmonger, Market Place, Aylsham.

Tributaries of the Bure

THURNE: Slow-flowing, typical Broad-
land river; tidal below Potter Heigham.
Coarse fish, good bream and roach. RD
water at **Potter Heigham, Martham,
Thurne Marshes.**
Thurne Mouth (Norfolk). Good roach,
bream, perch. Hotel: Thurne Lion.
Potter Heigham (Norfolk). Popular centre;
good roach and bream; fair-sized eels.
Bure. 3m S. Broads: **Womack,** 1½m;
Hickling Broad and **Heigham Sound**
(good bream, roach, pike; free). Hotels:
Bridge, Broads-Haven, Cringles, Broad-
land House. Boats from Herbert Woods;
Bridge Hotel; Whispering Reeds
Boatyard, Hickling; Arthur Walch,
Nurses House, Martham. Licences, tack-
le, etc. from Ken Latham, Potter
Heigham (Tel 388).
Martham (Norfolk). Rudd, tench, bream,
roach, perch, pike; good bank fishing;
free. **Heigham Sounds** free: good pike,
bream, etc. **Horsey Mere:** dt for pike and
other coarse fish from millman; closed
Oct 1–Jan 31. Boats and licences: Mar-
tham Boat Co. Inn: King's Arms *(see
also Hickling).*
ANT:
Irstead and Neatishead (Norfolk). Ant and
Barton Broad. Good bream, perch,
rudd, pike; also tench and small roach.
Fishing free. Hotel: Barton Angler
(boats). Boats also from Cox, Barton
Turf.
Stalham (Norfolk). River clear, slow-
running and weedy in summer; roach,
rudd, bream, perch, pike and few tench.
Broads: **Barton,** 1m; rudd, bream and
big pike; free fishing. **Hickling,** 3m by
road; good pike, bream, etc. Sutton
Broad overgrown. Tackle, bait, RD
licences and information from Sam's
Sports Shop. Hotel: Sutton Staithe Hotel
and Country Club. Inns: Swan, Grebe,
Maid's Head, Harnser, Wood Farm.

Wayford Bridge (Norfolk). Upper Ant;
head of navigation; fishing free to
licence-holders; roach, rudd, perch,
pike, tench, bream; boat advisable; river
is narrow and fairly busy at times in
summer; weedy and clear. Boats from
Wayford Marina and Mixons Ltd, Catfield. Bait and tackle from Stalham.
Good fishing also above the head of Ant
Navigation in Dilham and North Wal-
sham Canal, navigable to rowing boats
as far as Honing Lock. Accommodation:
Wayford Wood Farm (also licences).
North Walsham (Norfolk). Ant, 1m E.
Gunton Beck, 4m W. Lakes: **Wolerton
Lake** 8m NW, **Hevingham Lake,** 9m W.
Details from tackleist: Barry's, 28 Mar-
ket Place, who can advise on fishing in a
number of waters in the district. Hotels:
Beechwood, Black Swan, Scarborough
Hill.
SAW MILL LAKE: Fishing station: **Gun-
ton** (Norfolk). 16-acre lake in Gunton
Park, 3m; coarse fish; dt £1.20, from
bailiff, on bank.
Horning (Norfolk), ns Wroxham. **Salhouse
Broad;** too much traffic in summer, but
good fishing in early mornings and from
Oct to March. Dt issued. **Ranworth
Broad** (tickets for Inner Ranworth from
store on Staithe). **Malthouse Broad;** free.
Rollesby Broad; free. **Decoy Broad;** now
open only to clubs. Tackle, licences, bait
at post office *(see also Bure).*
Ormesby, Rollesby and **Filby.** Fishing by
boat only, boats available by the day or
hour. These Broads are connected and
undisturbed by motor cruisers and
yachts; fishing good everywhere. Excellent pike in winter. Inn: Eel's Foot
(boats and accommodation), Ormesby.
Boats also from W Tennant (Filby) and
G Skoyles (Ormesby).
Salhouse (Norfolk). Salhouse Broad, 1m
NE; few pike in winter.

Broads connected with the Bure

Wroxham Broad, 1m N; dt *(see Wroxham);*
good for bream in summer, fair pike
fishing in winter. **Decoy** or **Woodbastwick Broad,** 2m NE; fishing on payment.

Little Ranworth Broad, 3m E; good for
bream. South Walsham Broad, 5m E;
private; good bream and pike fishing;
leave from owner.

Wroxham (Norfolk). **Wroxham Broad,** boat fishing only. **Bridge Broad,** boats and permission from C R Chamberlain, Hoveton. **Salhouse Broad,** right bank, 2m, SE; 12½p day. Tackleist: Haylett's Tackle

Shop, Station Road, permits for **Alderfen Broad,** tench, pike, bream, rudd, roach; dt issued, boat only, limited, £2.50. Hotels: King's Head, Broads, Horse Shoes.

Broads connected with the Thurne and Ant (arranged under "Fishing Stations")

Potter Heigham (Norfolk). **Hickling Broad** *(see Hickling)*. **Heigham Sounds;** fine rudd fishing in summer; pike fishing excellent in winter (free). Pike fishing on **Horsey** (no live-baiting). **Womack Broad** dredged and cleared of weed, and may be fished from quay below. *(For hotels, boats, etc, see entry under Thurne.)*
Hickling (Norfolk). Heigham Sounds, **Horsey, Barton** and **Hickling Broads,** rudd, tench, bream, roach, pike, perch. All free except Horsey dt from keepers.

Licences from Post Office and stores; boats available. Accommodation: Pleasure Boat Inn; guest houses.
Martham (Norfolk). R Thurne and Martham Pits. Bream and tench. Dt on bank.

Broads connected with the Ant:

Catfield (Norfolk). **Barton Broad,** 1m W; excellent rudd and bream fishing and noted for big pike. Hotel: Barton Angler, Irstead. Hickling Broad, 2m. Catfield Broad; overgrown.

WAVENEY

Flows along Norfolk-Suffolk border. Beccles is noted centre for roach and bream fishing, and reach between Geldeston Lock and St Olaves gives some wonderful sport with bream in most seasons.

Lowestoft (Suffolk). Oulton Broad and Waveney, which connects with Broad; bream, perch, roach, pike, etc; boats at Broad. Flounders and smelts in harbour. Railway and Claremont Piers. Good sea-fishing in Oct, Nov and Dec from boats, piers and beach for whiting, cod and flatfish. Several Broads within easy reach as are following fishing stations: Beccles, Geldeston, Bungay, Somerleyton, Haddiscoe, Reedham, Cantley, Buckenham, Brundall. At **Kessingland** (5m S) visitors to wildlife, Country Park may have free river fishing. Hotels: Royal Harbour and Suffolk. Tackleists: S G Hook, 132 Bevan Street; A A Collen, Commodore Road. **Oulton Broad** (Suffolk). Broad gives good sport with bream, roach, perch, pike, etc, but crowded with boats in summer. Waveney near; free fishing. (Anglian WA licence required); best from boat. Good perch and pike (best Oct, Nov); roach (good all season, best Jan, Feb, Mar), bream (moderate, best Sept, Oct); dace. **Oulton Dyke** (north side only); bream (excellent Aug, Sept, Oct); perch; roach. Club. Oulton Broad Piscatorial Society. Fritton Lake, 2½m N *(see Haddiscoe)*. Lake at The Villa, 2½m N. Fishing free to licence-holders. Map of best fishing areas on Oulton from

Publicity Manager, 7 Esplanade, Lowestoft, and S Hook, 132 Bevan Street. Hotels: Wherry, George Borrow, Golden Galleon.
Haddiscoe (Norfolk). **New Cut:** good coarse fishing; free. Lakes: **Fritton:** perch, pike, roach, rudd, tench; dt for bank fishing; accommodation and boats at Fritton Old Hall. Other hotels: Crown, Queen's Head.
Burgh St Peter (Norfolk). Lakes: Fritton *(see Haddiscoe)*. Hotel: Waveney House; licences, boats.
Beccles (Suffolk). Good roach, bream, pike, etc; best early or late in summer but especially good Oct onwards, when river traffic eases off. Boats may be hired at several places. Hotels: King's Head, Waveney House. Tackle and information: Crack Sports, 7 Blyburgate (licences).
Geldeston (Norfolk). Good pike, roach, perch, bream, etc; free. Inns: Wherry (RD licences) and Geldeston Lock. Tackleist in Beccles (3m).
Bungay (Suffolk). Good roach, chub, bream, perch, pike and tench; fishes best at back end. Cherry Tree AC has several stretches and pit at **Ditchingham;** restocked with good tench and carp; members only; subs £5 pa. (Ladies, OAP and juvs £1.25, wt £2.) Accommodation at

Bungay Angling Centre, where membership cards may be obtained.

Homersfield (Suffolk). Pike, perch, roach (large), dace, tench. Licences from landlord, Black Swan Hotel. "Leisure Sport" gravel pit. See Fishery Agents.

Harleston (Norfolk). Waveney, 1m S; coarse fish. Harleston, Wortwell and Dist AC has about 5m on Waveney; st £4 from hon sec; private pits stocked with tench, carp, perch, roach; visitors' tickets st £8, wt £3.20, dt 80p, from G Denny (tackleist), Market Place, and The Dairy, Shotford Bridge. Hotel: Magpie.

Eye (Suffolk). **Dove Brook;** large dace. Fishing in Waveney at Hoxne, 3m.

Diss (Norfolk). Good sport in **Waveney** and **Dove. Diss Mere** improving; mainly carp. Tackleist: E Nunn, Mere Street (tickets for club waters £2.50 pa). Hotels: King's Head, Park.

Broads connected with the Waveney (arranged under "Fishing Stations")

Lowestoft (Suffolk). **Flixton Decoy,** 3m W. Large bream stocks (to 7 lb); also roach, rudd, tench, crucian carp, perch, pike and large eels. Boats available from South Lodge, Flixton. Tackleists: Ted Bean, 175 London Rd North. Hotels: Royal Harbour, Suffolk. Oulton Broad. Hotel: Wherry.

Belton (Suffolk). **Breydon Water;** salt estuary; no fishing. Fritton Lake, 2m S *(see Haddiscoe).*

YARE

Rises few miles from East Dereham and flows through Norwich to Yarmouth. Still one of the best Broads rivers for roach and bream; specially good for roach in middle reaches; bream in lower. Some trout stocking in upper reaches by River Authority which has water (some tidal) at Easton, Bawburgh, Buckenham Ferry and Postwick, Rockland and Langley. Permit required.

Great Yarmouth (Norfolk). Broads and rivers. Rivers Yare, Bure and Waveney fall into Breydon Water (Bure joined in upper reaches by Thurne and Ant). In all, some 200 miles of rivers well suited to boat and bank angling are within easy reach; some Broads are landlocked, strictly reserved for angling and free from river traffic; others connected to rivers, but mostly best fished from boat. Within 6m are Filby, Rollesby and Ormesby Broads (136, 240 and 207 acres, respectively) forming part of the Ormesby group; also Fritton Lake (163 acres). Many other Broads easily accessible; also rivers Bure, Thurne, Ant and Waveney. Trout in Bure. Most water in Yarmouth district is free to holders of RD licence. Other waters on AWA permit. Apply for details to office at Thorpe Rd, Norwich. Also good sea fishing. Tackle, baits and further information from: King Street Tackle Shop, 123a King Street; J Markham, 43 South Market Road.

Reedham (Norfolk). Strong tide; legering best; roach, perch, bream, eels; free. Chet near, upstream. Hotel: Ship.

Cantley (Norfolk). Roach, bream, perch; bream and roach plentiful; fishing free; mostly by leger. Inn: Red House.

Buckenham (Norfolk). Bream, roach,

Check before you go

While every effort has been made to ensure that the information given in "Where to Fish" is correct, the position is continually changing and anglers are urged, in their own interests, to make preliminary inquiries before travelling to selected venues. This is especially important with reference to prices quoted. Inevitably, the rate of inflation is affecting stability in this quarter. Anglers' attention is also drawn to the fact that the hotels mentioned under the various fishing stations do not necessarily have water of their own. Any amendments or further data for inclusion in subsequent editions, and any criticism, will be welcome.

perch, pike; boats at Beauchamp Arms; fishing free. Mouth of Hassingham Dyke is good spot. Lakes: Strumpshaw Broad, 1m NW. Buckenham Broad and Hassingham Broad, 1m SE; preserved. Rockland Broad, 1½m SW on other bank of river; free.

Brundall (Norfolk). Roach, bream, perch in Yare; fishing mostly by leger; dt from Riverside Estate gives access to river and new dyke; fish plentiful. Several reaches between Coldham Hall and Surlingham Ferry can be fished by boat. **Surlingham Broad** belongs to National Trust; fishing only fair in summer; water shallow and weedy; pike in winter.

Norwich (Norfolk). Good centre for Broads fishing. Roach and bream in vicinity. **Wensum** above city holds fine roach, perch, dace, grayling and pike. Good roach and bream fishing at **Rockland Broad**; 7m from Norwich; but poor access to banks. No boats now. Norwich AA has water on **Bure, Thurne, Ant** and **Yare, Ranworth Inner Broad** and **Woodbastwick Decoy** (fishing by boat only on last two waters); dt from hon sec and tackleists. 6m NW, at **Taverham,** seven lakes known as the Ringland Pits, carp, tench, bream etc. St £10 from "Leisure Sport", RMC House, Feltham, Middlesex, dt £1 from bailiff at lakes. Bait, licences and tackle from Gallyon, 7 Bedford St; C F Browne, Timberhill; John's Tackle Den, 16 Bridewell Alley. Hotels: Royal, Maid's Head, Bell and many others.

Bawburgh (Norfolk). Centre for Upper Yare; much free fishing. Badly weeded in summer, but good autumn onwards. Mostly controlled by River Division from Cringelford to Bawburgh. London AA has about 1m, members only. Trout and grayling as well as coarse fish, but most have gone downstream into stretch controlled by River Division.

Tributaries of the Yare

CHET:

Loddon (Norfolk); ns Norwich, 12m. Free coarse fishing in Chet from Loddon down to Reedham on Yare; roach, dace, bream, perch, occasional trout; this water now navigable and fishes best in autumn and winter when traffic finishes; licences, river and sea bait and tackle from W H Rager Ltd, Post Office, Loddon, and at Chedgrave. Hotels: Swan, and Angel Inn, Loddon; White Horse, Chedgrave.

WENSUM: Coarse fish (good roach), some trout. Tidal through Norwich. RD water upstream of **Bintree Mill, North Elmham, Swanton Morley, Elsing Costessey** and **Hellesdon** (excellent fishing at mill).

Costessey (Norfolk). Coarse fish. RD has stretch here st £3.90, wt £1.30, dt 65p. "Leisure Sport" have pits here. See Fishery Agents.

Drayton (Norfolk). Free on permission of landowners; otherwise strictly preserved. Spixworth Beck, 2½m NE; free adjoining Crostwick Common; also free fishing in Bure. Hotel: Red Lion.

Attlebridge (Norfolk). Good trout fishing here, some miles of water being preserved. Tud, 4m S; private. Lakes: Haveringland, 3½m N; private. Hopground Lake, Honingham 4m S; private.

Lenwade (Norfolk). London AA has good water on river and pits. Dt for latter from Bridge Farm or Roberts, Common Lane, who also offers accommodation. Carp, tench. bream, roach, rudd, perch and pike. LAA bailiff: G A Fisher, Memorial Cottages, Mousehold Lane, Norwich.

Hellesdon (Norfolk). Roach, chub, grayling, some tench. Good stretch of open water to New Mills, Norwich. RD controls fishery here and on River Tud upstream of mill; no permit required.

Lyng (Norfolk). Fine roach, dace and some trout. Dereham and Dist AC has water; excellent roach fishing; also **Wensum Pit;** good tench, pike, perch and bream; dt from Fanthorpe's Tackle Shop, Norwich Street, **Dereham.** Dereham and Dist AC also has lake (roach and perch) at **East Bilney;** dt from Bilney Hall; good trout, perch and roach. RD has about ⅓m of left-hand (Spatham) bank downstream of Lyng Bridge. London AA has water for members only. River and 3 lakes at **Swanton Morley** stocked trout and coarse fish. St £5, dt 50p from house by lake.

Elsing (Norfolk). RD has 1,270 yards of right bank.

North Elmham (Norfolk). Fishing in Wensum for pike, roach, perch, dace and few trout. RD has water; dt 12½p. from Railway Hotel (permits for other RD stretches). London AA has 1½m in three sections; members only. The Lake, Elmham Park, holds carp, large tench, rudd, roach and pike.

Fakenham (Norfolk). Good trout and dace, some roach, grayling and pike. Fakenham AC has 4m. Tackle, bait, licences and London AA permits from Len Bryer, 4–6 Bridge St (inc membership cards and London AA permits). Hotels: Crown, Red Lion.

TASS or TAES:

Swainsthorpe (Norfolk). Yare, 3m N. Lakes: Bracon Hall and Carlton Lodge, 2m W. All private.

BASS:

Wymondham (Norfolk). Yare, 4m N at Barford and 6m N at Marlingford; roach. Club: Wymondham AC. Tickets from the Horse Shoes Inn, Shropham. Lakes: Ketteringham Hall lake, 4m E; private. Shropham, 8m S; bream, tench. Tackleist: F W Myhill & Son, Fairland St (branches at Swaffham, Dereham and Thetford). Hotel: Abbey.

BLACKWATER: Trout; preserved.

Booton (Norfolk). Clay pits here hold carp (common, mirror and crucian), tench, perch, roach and pike; Aylsham and Dist AS has rights. St £2 and dt 50p from A Clarke, tackle dealer, Aylsham, Fairfields Stores, Cawston, or bailiff on bank.

Broads connected with the Yare (arranged under "Fishing Stations")

Buckenham. Rockland Broad, 1½m SW; good roach fishing and pike fishing in winter. No boats at present, but R Dye, The Kilns Boatyard, expected to resume eventually.

Brundall. Belongs to National Trust; shallow water grown up in summer, but good for pike in winter.

NORFOLK (small streams)

(For close seasons, licences, etc, see Anglian Water Authority, p 40, unless otherwise stated)

BABINGLEY RIVER. Fishing station: **Castle Rising,** ns North Wootton, 2m. Rises in the lake at Hillington Hall, and is 9m long. King's Lynn AA has water; no tickets. *See King's Lynn—Ouse (Great).*

GLAVEN. Rises 3m E of **Holt** and joins sea at **Cley,** 6m down, where RD has about 1m of right bank. Access via Wiveton Bridge. Trout: dt £2.80 from Anglian WA, Yare House, 62–64 Thorpe Road, Norwich, NR1 1SA or Mr P Suckling, The Old Manor, Cley.

OTTER

(For close seasons, licences, etc, see South West Water Authority, p 38)

Noted Devonshire trout stream flowing into English Channel immediately east of Exe. Mullet in estuary and some sea trout, with brown trout of good average size for West Country higher up, where hotels have some excellent dry-fly water.

Budleigh Salterton (Devon). Tidal. Free fishing from river mouth to Clamour Bridge (about 1½m, both banks) to visitors staying in East Budleigh or Budleigh Salterton; RD licence necessary. Sea trout, brown trout, grey mullet. Fishing on both banks from Clamour Bridge to Newton Poppleford; private. Excellent sea fishing; bass, flatfish, etc *(see Sea Fishing Stations).*

Ottery St Mary (Devon). Some good trout water in vicinity. Venn Ottery Barton Hotel *(adv p 110)* has ⅔m, both banks, S of **Gosford Bridge.** Fly only: trout to

3 lb. Dt for non-residents, when available, £3.50. Special rate for residents: fishing chalet available.

Honiton (Devon). Deer Park Hotel has 2½m (both banks) of first-class trout fishing; trout up to 2 lb, average 1 lb; rods limited to six daily. Licences at hotel. Dt for non-residents (£3.75) when available. Combe House Hotel, **Gittisham,** has 1½m, south bank, from Weston Bridge downstream; dt sometimes available for non-residents; dry-fly only; £4. Monkton Court Hotel has 1m (both banks) available to visitors and guests;

fly only. Dt for ½m (both banks) from Cotterson Farm, **Awliscombe** and for ¾m (right bank) from Tracey House, Hon- iton. Mr Brimmicombe, c/o Ford's Shoe Shop, High Street, issues dts.

OUSE (Great)

(For close seasons, licences, etc, see Anglian Water Authority, p 40)

Rises in Buckinghamshire and flows north-east through Northamptonshire, Bedfordshire, Cambridgeshire, Huntingdonshire and Norfolk, entering the North Sea by The Wash. Coarse fishing throughout. Slow, winding river for most part. Lower reaches provide particularly good sport.

King's Lynn (Norfolk). Coarse fish of all kinds except barbel. King's Lynn AA has water on the Ouse from Ten Mile Bank to Denver Sluice; on the Wissey at Hilgay; on the **Middle Level** drain at St Germans (st £7, wt £3, dt 60p; from hon sec, tackleists or bailiffs.) **Relief Channel** from King's Lynn to Denver Sluice (11m) is RD water; excellent coarse fishing *(see separate entry on p 113)*. Tackleists: Colin Stevens, London Road, F Harker, Railway Road, Downham Market. Hotels: Globe, East Anglian, Duke's Head.

Downham Market (Norfolk). Coarse fish, sea trout; tidal.

Hilgay (Norfolk). King's Lynn AA water on Ouse and **Wissey** *(see King's Lynn)*. London AA has water on Ouse; dt from bailiffs.

Littleport (Cambs). Ouse and **Lark;** coarse fish, except barbel; good pike and bream, with roach and tench in parts. Preserved from Littleport Bridge to Ely (5m) by Ely Beet Sugar Factory and Littleport AC; permits for individuals and clubs. Black Horse Inn at Sandhill Bridge, Littleport, has ½m of bank and issues dts. London AA controls 14m of water from Littleport Bridge to Southery (Norfolk), both banks. Dt from bailiffs.

Ely (Cambs). Free fishing from Lincoln Boatyard upsteam to Newmarket Railway Bridge. Cooper's Arms Club hire

stretch from Carmuckle Bridge to AWA works (known as "The Cresswells"). Ely Highflyers have about 5m downstream from this and last mile of River Lark ("Queen Adelaide" stretch); dt and club-cards from T & J Chapman. Rosewell pits hired by Ely Beet Sugar Factory FC; dt (limited). Hotels: Lamb, Cutter Inn, Castle Lodge. Tackleists: T & J Chapman, Fore Hill; Thornton's, Broad Street.

Earith (Hunts). **Old West River.** Earith Bridge to Pope's Corner (Cambs); mostly hired by Histon AC, Cambridge Albion AS; good coarse fishing. **Old Bedford River** at Earith, Sutton Gault, Mepal Bridge and Manea, and **New Bedford Level** or **Hundred Foot** (tidal) at Sutton Gault and Mepal Bridge controlled by Cambridge Albion AS and Shefford AS; members only but dt issued by hon sec for Ivel. Ploughman's Pit (good carp, bream, pike; dt also from Airman public house) and lake at Oldfield Farm. St obtainable at local inns near the waters and Cambridge tackleists. The **Hundred Foot** (Earith to Sutton Gault), rented by Cambridge FPS; tidal; practically all coarse fish, except barbel; dt from hon sec or local inns for Cambridge FPS water. London AA has 6¾m on Hundred Foot from Adventurers' Drove, Oxlode, to ¼m above Welney on Hundred Foot and from Stokes Bridge to Welney on **River Delph;** members only. Hitchin AC and Letchworth AC share stretch of Old Bedford from Purls Bridge to Welches Dam, both banks; dt on water. Great Ouse Fishery Consultative Association rents water on **Counterwash Drain, Old Bedford River, Pingles Pit** (Mepal) and the **Hundred Foot.** Affiliated clubs have rights. Members of Sheffield AAS may fish these waters, the **Delph** at Manea (Manea AC water) and the **Bedford River** from Purls Bridge to **Welches Dam** (Letchworth AA).

Over and Swavesey (Cambs.). Bream, perch, chub, rudd, tench, pike, dace and zander. Over and Swavesey Dist AS has water. St £3. No competitions. Punts for hire. Tickets from all Cambridge tackleists and Over P.O.

Holywell Ferry (Hunts). Hotel: Ferry Boat. Pike, bream, roach, rudd, chub, etc; free; boats available; good fishing, especially roach. Over and Swavesey Dist AS has water downstream on Cambridgeshire bank *(see Over and Swavesey)*.

St Ives (Hunts). All coarse fish, but barbel rare; bream and roach predominant with dace, perch, rudd, chub in quantity; tench increasing. Ample bank fishing, but boats available. St Ives FP & AS has water; st £5, wt £1.50, dt 70p. Adjoining water held by LAA, Houghton and Wyton and Hemingfords AS. Tackleist: Handicrafts, Bridge Street. Hotels: Golden Lion, Cromwell. Accommodation also at 10 Station Road (Mr and Mrs W Dick).

Godmanchester (Hunts). Good bream, roach, chub. Chance of carp and barbel. Godmanchester A & FPS has about 5m. Tickets from hon sec. St £3, dt 50p. London AA has Portholme Meadow (dt) and Berry Lane Meadows (members only). Boats from Huntingdon; no free fishing. Hotels: Black Bull, Exhibition, Bridge and George.

Huntingdon (Hunts). Chub, bream, roach and tench; good when boat traffic declines. Huntingdon AS has water below town. Dt and wt 50p and £1.50 from tackleists. London AA *(see p 214)* has 4½m of Ouse, stretch of **Alconbury Brook, Brampton Mill Pool** and millstream, and other water at **Brampton;** members only. Tickets issued for some waters; inquire hon sec. Tackleists: Sports and Fashions, County Angling & Sports, both High Street, Ken Bradshaw, Old School Building, Walden Road.

Offord Cluny (Hunts). Chub, roach, bream, tench. Offord and Buckden AS has 4m of Great Ouse between Offord and Buckden; dt 75p from car park; coach-party enquiries (40p per peg) to E Blowfield, 4 Monks Cottages, Huntingdon. Hitchin AC has short stretch; no dt. Letchworth AC also has meadow.

St Neots (Hunts). St Neots and Dist AS has extensive fishing from Barford Power Station with some gaps down to pumping stn, Diddington, incl part of gravel pit; good tench, chub, bream, roach and carp to 30 lb. Dt 60p, wt £1.80, st £6 from hon sec and bailiffs. London AA has water at **Tempsford** and **Blunham** *(see Ivel).* **Grafham Water,** noted trout reservoir, is nearby *(advt p 100).*

Biggleswade (Beds). Ouse, Ivel, Biggleswade AC has water on Tempsford Estate. Arlesey Lake (4m S); Hitchin AC; members only.

Bedford (Beds). Some 4m water above town centre free to RD licence-holders. Bedford AC controls most other fishing and issues limited dt at £1, st £6.50, concessions for OAP and juniors. Sunday fishing allowed; sport excellent. Hotels: Embankment, Swan, Lion. Tackleists: R B Dixon, 95 Tavistock Street.

Sharnbrook (Beds). Wellingborough and Dist. Nene AC has ¾m upstream of **Harrold** and one field at **Pavenham.** Leighton Buzzard AC has water on left bank here and on river at Dairy Farm. **Renhold.** Tickets *(see Olney)*. St £5 for Leisure Sport **Harrold** fishery. Apply RMC House, Feltham, Middlesex.

Newton Blossomville (Bucks). Coarse fish. Northampton Nene AC has water; strictly limited dt from Old Mill, Newton Blossomville.

Olney (Bucks). Coarse fish, good bream. Leighton Buzzard AC has ¾m stretch at **Stoke Goldington,** from Gayhurst Spinney to brook, short stretch (right bank) below bridge and at **Clifton Reynes.** Dt for two stretches. Hitchin AC has water, members only.

Newport Pagnell (Bucks). Good roach, bream, etc. Stretch fishes well in winter. Newport Pagnell FA has about 10m of river and nine gravel pits. St £7, dt for members' guests only. At **Gt Linford** there is a complex of gravel pits holding bream, roach, tench and pike on which the fishing rights are now held by the Birmingham AA. There are arrangements for Luton & Dist AA members to fish, also on 5m of main river and another gravel pit. Inquire hon sec. Club has vacancies. St £5. Tackleist: Willetts, High St. Hotel: Bull Inn (club HQ).

Stony Stratford (Bucks). Stony Stratford AS has 2m of Ouse following on 3m held by Deanshanger AS (members only; limit, 5m radius). Galleon AA has water on **Grand Union Canal.** Dt from hon secs. Cosgrove Lodge lakes at Cosgrove (Northants); noted for roach, tench, bream, pike; dt on water.

Buckingham (Bucks). Coarse fish. Buckingham and Dist AA has water; some dt £1 from tackleist J Wilkins 62, Nelson St. Claydon Lakes, 6m; Leighton Buzzard AA; no dt.

Tributaries of the Ouse (Great)

NAR: Trout, coarse fish (good dace) 5m, Buckingham AA; members only. Tackleist: Herring & Son (assn tickets), Bull Ring.

Narborough (Norfolk). Good trouting; preserved; London AA has water at **Wormegay;** members only.

WISSEY:

Hilgay (Norfolk). King's Lynn AA have 2m of both banks down to Ouse. St £7,

wt £3, dt 60p. London AA issues dt for Five Mile House Farm.

LITTLE OUSE: Good bream, roach, etc; dace run large in some stretches.

Brandon (Suffolk). Bream (good), roach, dace, perch, pike (good) a few chub and zander. Water below bridge held by Brandon and Dist AC; limited number of visitors admitted. Licences and dt (10p) from T Edwards, tobacconist,

Check before you go

While every effort has been made to ensure that the information given in "Where to Fish" is correct, the position is continually changing and anglers are urged, in their own interests, to make preliminary inquires before travelling to selected venues. This is especially important with reference to prices quoted. Inevitably, the rate of inflation is affecting stability in this quarter. Anglers' attention is also drawn to the fact that the hotels mentioned under the various fishing stations do not necessarily have water of their own. Any amendments or further data for inclusion in subsequent editions, and any criticism, will be welcome.

High Street. Thetford and Breckland AC has water above bridge, and London AA has a fishery here; members only. Hotel:The Ram.

Thetford (Norfolk). Little Ouse and Thet. Roach, rudd, tench, chub and pike; and dace to specimen size. Fishing free from Barnham Common to first staunch. Thetford Breckland AC has several stretches and **Barnham Pit.**

LARK: Trout, grayling and coarse fish. **Mildenhall** (Suffolk). From Bury St Edmunds to Lackford controlled by Bury St Edmund's AA; trout water; no permits. Lark APS has good water here. Tackleists: W T Reeve, Ferry Lane, West Row; E Morley & Sons.

Bury St Edmunds (Suffolk). Coarse fish. Club: Bury St Edmunds AA. Tackleist: R Nunn, 49a St John's Street.

CAM: Coarse fish, mostly roach and bream.

Upware (Cambs). Bream, roach, perch, rudd, dace. Cambridge FP & AS has water *(see Cambridge).*

Cambridge. Bream, roach, chub. Cambridge FP & AS leases west bank of Cam from Pike & Eel, Chesterton to Clayhithe; st £4, dt £1 from local tackle shop or on bank. Society also has about 4m of the **Hundred Foot River** from Earith Bridge to Sutton Gault and sole rights on whole of **Burwell Lode** and **Reach Lode,** plus 1m of **Gt Ouse** at **Barway** and 1m of **Lark** below **Prickwillow Bridge;** inquire hon sec for permits. London AA has water for members only at **Swaffham Prior. Cam** and **Granta** offer some free fishing to licenceholders. Cambridge tackleists: Gallyon & Sons Ltd, 66 Bridge Street, P A Anderson, 243 Newmarket Road; Thorntons, 46 Burleigh Street.

OLD WEST RIVER: Good stock of coarse fish; burbot taken on Histon AS stretch. St for rivers £3, dt for **Milton Lake** £1.50 Large carp and other coarse fish.

Cottenham (Cambs). Willingham and Smithy Fen controlled by Histon and Dist AS. Waters also on **Cam** and **Lark.** No dt, except for parties of ten at £5.

IVEL: Dace, roach and perch.

Tempsford (Beds). Ouse and Ivel. Biggleswade AC has some water on both rivers. *(See also Blunham).* London AA has several miles on Ouse here and at Blunham; members only.

Blunham (Beds). Ouse (1m W). Tickets from hon sec, Blunham FC for Ivel.

Below Blunham Bridge to Ouse held by Biggleswade and District AC. Club also has right bank of Ivel from Langford Mill to Broom Mill; no dt. Shefford AC has left bank.

HIZ (tributary of Ivel). Ruined as trout stream by land drainage, abstraction. **Arlesey Lake:** controlled by Hitchin AC; specimen perch, etc. *(See Midlands reservoirs, lakes.)* Club also has water on **Ouse, River Oughton** (trout, few chub, restocking under consideration; members only), and fishes waters of Great Ouse FCA and Ivel Protection Assn. Well-stocked trout lake at **Oughton.** Big fish. Dt £6.80; evening only £4.60. Tackleist: Alan Brown, Nightingale Road, **Hitchin.** Accommodation: Railway Hotel, Hitchin (club HQ).

OUZEL: Coarse fish.

Leighton Buzzard (Beds). Leighton Buzzard AC preserves various stretches above Leighton Buzzard and at Stoke Hammond, Water Eaton, Bletchley, Woolstone-Willen and Newport Pagnell but some stretches will be temporarily lost by Milton Keynes development. Club also has several stretches on **Gt Ouse** (three at **Emberton** and others at **Clifton Reynes, Stoke Goldington, Renhold** and **Sharnbrook),** five on **Thame–Shabbington** and **Worminghall**— and 3m of **Grand Union Canal.** Also **Claydon Lakes, Tiddenfoot** (trout, coarse fish) and other pits. Fen drains and **River Cam.** No dt but members may buy guest tickets for most waters. *(See Midlands, reservoirs and lakes.)* Tackleists: Tom Lindars, 82 North Street; S L Pedder, 112 Victoria Street, both **Dunstable;** S G Walters, 12 Kingsbury, **Aylesbury** (licences, assn permits, specialists in reservoir flies).

RELIEF CHANNEL: not strictly a tributary but included here because of the status traditionally enjoyed as an excellent coarse fishery in its own right. Now dominated by zander, though, and of little other interest to anglers until remedial measures take effect. Channel controlled by Great Ouse RD. Dt 55p, ft £1.60, st £3.20; all incl VAT. From distributors near access points to channel or from Fisheries Officer.

TOVE: Coarse fish.

Towcester (Northants). Towcester and Dist AA has water on river and three ponds; members only.

OUSE (Sussex)

(For close seasons, licences, etc, see Southern Water Authority, p 38)

Rises few miles south-east of Horsham and flows for 33 miles to enter English Channel at Newhaven. Tidal for 12 miles from mouth to point 4m upstream of Lewes. Coarse fish and trout, but notable for run of big sea trout.

Lewes and Barcombe Mills (Sussex). Sea trout (good), perch, bream, roach, dace, chub. Ouse APS has west bank to Barcombe Mills (about 4m) and east bank for 1m north of Lewes. Certain stretches also available above mills. Limited st only at £11. Sea trout all time from May, but June–August best provided there is rain. Barcombe Mills Pool and side streams reserved entirely for sea-trout fishing and available to st holders at £2 a day (two rods daily) bookable in advance from hon sec. Trout fishing also available on 40-acre **Barcombe Reservoir** to st holders on payment of £3.50 day or £3 from 4 pm. Charges subject to review for 1981. Full details from hon sec, Ouse APS. Hotels: Shelleys; White Hart; Crown (all Lewes). For Barcombe Mills: Angler's Rest, Anchor Inn. Tackleists: Rice Bros, High Street, Lewes.

Isfield (Sussex). Coarse fish, trout and sea trout. Isfield and Dist AC has about 12m of river between **Newick** and **Lewes.** Club also has a stretch of **Uck.** Licences from hon sec (sae please). Exchange ticket system with other clubs. Hotels: Laughing Fish, Isfield (club HQ), and Maiden's Head, Uckfield. *(For tackle see Lewes.)*

Haywards Heath (Sussex). Coarse fish and trout. Haywards Heath AS has 12m of Ouse from **Ardingly** down to **Newick** (excluding stretch below **Fletching Mill**) and two lakes (**Balcombe Lake** and **Vale Bridge Mill Pond**). No dt but wt £2 for holiday visitors. Membership open to approved applicants £10 pa. Tackleists: Penfold's, High Street, Cuckfield.

UCK:

Isfield (Sussex). Coarse fish and trout. Isfield and Dist AC has water from here to **Uckfield** (members only). Several lakes in Sussex, Kent and Surrey.

OUSE (Yorkshire)

(For close seasons, licences, etc, see Yorkshire Water Authority, p 40)

Forms with Trent the estuary of the Humber. Coarse fish, with some trout. Dunsforth, Beningbrough and Poppleton reaches noted for barbel and chub. Large bream present but difficult to catch. Most water held by Leeds and York clubs. Tributaries give excellent trout and coarse fishing.

Goole (S Humberside). Don enters Ouse here. Goole AA has stretch of **Derwent** near Sutton Bridge; good roach, chub, pike, dace, few trout. No dt. Memberships (£5 pa) from Barry's Fishing Tackle, Westfield Avenue. Club has other waters on Trent, Derwent, and three ponds.

Acaster (N Yorks). Coarse fishing. Controlled by the Leeds Amalgamation. Tickets at Blacksmith's Arms, Naburn, and Manor Guest House, Acaster Malbis. Fishing mostly free below dam (tidal); fish include barbel; above dam, trout and coarse fish. Accommodation: Manor Guest House.

Naburn (N Yorks). On opposite bank to Acaster. Between ferry and dam (Leeds Amal); dt from Garage, Naburn, and Manor Guest House, Acaster. York Amal also has water; dt from Ebor Hotel. Below dam fishing free and water tidal.

York (N Yorks). Coarse fish; some free fishing on public waters. On left bank nearly all free except 8m from Rawcliffe Ings and Clifton Ings up to Aldwark. York Amalgamation has fishing on Ouse and tributaries. Assn issues dt via local tackleists for lower **Nidd.** Also controls 4m on Rivers **Rye** and **Seven**; very good grayling and trout; members only. York Tradesmen's AA has rights on several becks, members only. Tackleists: Hookes Ltd, 28–30 Coppergate; G E Hill, 40 Clarence Street; Bulmers, 1–7 Lord Mayor's Walk; Holgate, 84–86 Holgate Road.

Poppleton, Beningbrough and Newton (N Yorks). Good barbel, pike, etc. York and Leeds Amalgamations have extensive stretches. Dt from Fox Inn, Nether Poppleton, and post office *(see York)*.

Aldwark (N Yorks). Coarse fish. York Amal have privileges for 2½m above and ½m below Aldwark Bridge *(see York)* with exception of short stretch. Hotels: Three Horseshoes and Crown, Great Ouseburn; Bay Horse, Aldwark.

Low Dunsforth. From Low Dunsforth to Aldwark Bridge (about 4m right bank) fishing is in hands of Leeds Amal. Dt from Anchor Inn, Low Dunsforth; Anchor Inn, Whixley (Little Ouseburn); Crown, Three Horseshoes and Bay Horse (Great Ouseburn). Leeds Amal also has good length at **Hunterslodge** on opposite side below Aldwark bridge (left bank). Tickets as above.

Tributaries of the Ouse (Yorkshire)

DON (tributary of Ouse). Rises on Wike Head and flows through Sheffield and Doncaster to the estuary of the Ouse; much polluted in its lower reaches but efforts of water authority beginning to bear fruit. Elsewhere holds coarse fish. Some tributaries hold trout.

Doncaster (S Yorks). River polluted. **Thrybergh Reservoir,** about 8m. Now disposed of by YWA to Rotherham Borough Council for general amenity use. Doncaster & Dist AA has water on the **Idle** at Misson (10m) the **Torne** at Rossington Bridge to Pilfrey Bridge (18m) the **Trent** at Marton and Littleborough, the **S Yorkshire Navigation Canal,** lakes and drains. St £3.50 from Assn HQ and tackleists. Tackleists: M Potter, The Gables, Church Street, Armthorpe; F G Gale & Son, 26 Copley Road; W Argyll, 81 Call House Road; and Anglers Supplies, 148 High Street, Bentley.

Sheffield (S Yorks). Don polluted. **Damflask,** YWA reservoir, 5m W; trout. **Underbank,** corporation reservoir, 10m W; coarse fishing and odd large trout. Tickets from attendant's office. For further information, see *"Yorkshire Lakes".* Sheffield Amal AS (membership books from Lansdowne Hotel) has waters on **Trent, Delph** (Manea) and certain drains. Sheffield and Dist AA has water on Rivers **Delph, Trent, Till, Don, Witham** and **Old Bedford River, Dearne and Dove Canal** at **Barnsley** (14m), **Stockwith and Chesterfield Canal** at **Staveley** (3m) and **Stockwith** (8m), **Idle** at **Haxey** (4m), and drains at **Keadby**

in Wisbech district (Nene) and near **Chatteris.** Dt issued for most waters. **Stainforth and Keadby Canal** controlled by joint committee including Rotherham, Doncaster, Sheffield Amal, Sheffield and Dist and British Railways clubs. At **Staveley** urban district council have five-acre lake stocked annually with coarse fish; dt and st. Also Foxtone Dam; dt. Tackleists: Arthur Turner, 33–35 West Bar; Bennett's, 38–40 Howard Street, Sheffield; Ernest Stamford, 419 Attercliffe Common; W G Dawson, 70 Holme Lane.

DEARNE tributary of Don):

Barnsley (S Yorks). Dearne; Barnsley Fitzwilliam AC; dt Sheffield and Dist AA has water on **Dearne and Dove Canal.** Barnsley Trout Club fishes **Scout Dike Reservoir;** trout av ¾ lb; limited dt. **Wintersett Reservoir;** coarse fish; dt from bailiff. **Worsbrough Reservoir;** dt from Reservoir House, Red Lion Hotel, Ship Inn (good roach, bream, tench and pike). Other club: Barnsley and Dist AA. Tackleists: Tony Briggs and Field Sports Supplies, Pitt St.

Claycross (Derby). Lakes: Williamthorpe Ponds, 2m NE. Wingerworth Hall Lakes (two), 2½m NW. Great Dam, 3½m NW.

ROTHER (tributary of Don):

Killamarsh (Derby). Short Brook. Lakes: Woodhall Moor Dams, 2m E. Barlborough Hall Lake, 3m SE. Pebley Dam, 3m SE. Harthill Reservoir, 3m E. Woodhall Pond, 3m E.

AIRE: Issues from ground at Aire Head, half a mile south of Malham village. Its

---

Keep the banks clean and tidy

None of us, presumably, would choose to fish from a rubbish-heap. We should therefore at the end of the day remove our own rubbish and any other present. Fisheries have been closed to the public because of litter.

upper reaches contain quality trout and grayling, which give place to coarse fish between Steeton and Keighley; heavy stocking by Yorkshire River Authority. Lower reaches and others near large towns polluted. *(For Malham Tarn—see Ribble—Settle.)*

Leeds (W Yorks). Polluted. Adel Beck and Dam (private). **Roundhay Park Lakes,** 4m NE. Leeds and Dist ASA have fishing; dt from local tackleists. Larger lake (Waterloo) contains pike, perch, roach, tench, carp, etc; small lake stocked with carp, bream and roach. Leeds Amal has extensive fishing on Ouse and tributaries, canals and lakes, dt for many waters; full details from hon sec. Also trout at Pool and Arthington *(see Ouse (Yorks)—Wharfe)*. At Swinsty and Fewston, 7m from Otley, are YWA reservoirs, containing trout; visitors' dt can be had at Reservoir Lodge, Fewston; no Sunday fishing. Minnow and fly only. Tackleists: S M Wainwright, Leeds Bridge; Linsley Bros, 137 Albion Street; Ritz Angling Centre, Vicar Lane; Gledhills, 60 The Headrow.

Bradford (W Yorks). Aire, 7m N. Bradford City AA has extensive rights. Other water on the canals at **Apperley Bridge** and near Skipton; on **Wharfe, Ure** and **Swale,** reservoirs and lakes. Bradford No 1 AA has water on **Wharfe, Aire, Swale, Ure, Leeds and Liverpool Canal,** and reservoirs (no dt). Bradford Waltonians have water on **Wharfe** (Addingham, 1½m; Denton and Ben Rhydding, 2½m; trout and grayling) and three reservoirs holding trout and perch; members only st £50. Waiting list. Tackleists: W Carter, 15 Bridge Street; Knuttons, Barry Street; D Richmond, 110 Morley Street.

Bingley, Saltaire (W Yorks). Trout, coarse fish; Bingley AC has good coarse fishery; restocked annually. St £4.50, dt 50p. Club also has good trout fishing on **Sunnydale Reservoir** (dt £1 from hon sec or Cullimores of Bingley); also two dams and beck. Trout waters are for members only. Excellent trout preserve in Myrtle Park; water restocked; dt. Saltaire AA has water (being restocked); dt. From Bankfield Hotel downstream to Baildon Bridge (both Banks, except Roberts Park) is Bradford No 1 water. Dt £1.50 for 1m of **Harden Beck** which enters Aire at Bingley. Advance booking by letter to G R Reynolds, Goit Stock Estate, Har-den, or by phone, Cullingworth 3810. Fly only.

Keighley (W Yorks). Trout, grayling, coarse fish. Sport improved after restocking. Keighley AC has 11m; dt 60p from hon sec. Trout to 1¼ lb; best May-June and Sept. Club also has the **Leeds-Liverpool Canal** from Office Lock, Leeds, to Banknewton, **Whitefields Reservoir,** stocked with carp, tench, roach and perch, and, for members only, **Roberts Pond** (large tench, carp, pike) and the **R Worth,** trout. *(See also Yorkshire lakes, reservoirs, etc.)*

Cononley (W Yorks). Trout, perch, chub, roach, dace, bream, grayling; dt after June 1, for Bradford City AA water st £10, concessions for ladies, juniors and OAP. Bradford No 1 AA also has water. Dt 50p from tackleists.

Skipton (N Yorks). Trout, grayling, pike, chub, roach. At Skipton, Skipton AA has four miles of fishing, both banks; st £15 (entrance fee £15), wt £8, dt £2.50 (wt & dt, reduction for grayling only), issued on recommendation of member. Association also has rights on **Embsay Reservoir** (trout), **Whinnygill and Jennygill Reservoirs** (trout and coarse fish) dt and wt. Bradford City AA water begins on both banks below Skipton water; about 7m in all. Assn also has canal near here. Tackleist: Norman Goodwin, Water Street, issues dt, wt and st for Aire below Skipton and Leeds & Liverpool Canal. Bradford No 1 AA has Bradley Fishery; roach, pike, chub, trout. St from hon sec. Tickets also for **Leeds and Liverpool Canal;** trout, coarse fish. For **Earby Beck** (6½m SW), trout; applications for st to hon sec, Marsden Star AS. Licences, tackle from H Slinger, 17 Otley Street. Hotels: Devonshire Arms, Midland, Hole in the Wall (both latter can advise anglers).

Gargrave (N Yorks). Trout; preserved hence down to Colne Railway Bridge by Aire Fishing Club. Members can obtain tickets under certain conditions for their friends. Eshton Beck, Mell Beck, 2m NE.

Bellbusk (N Yorks). Trout; preserved by private owners. Lakes: **Coniston House;** trout. **Eshton Tarn,** 2m NE; pike. **Malham Tarn,** 8m N; trout and perch; tickets *(see Ribble—Settle).*

CALDER (tributary of Aire): Good coarse

fishing from Brighouse to Sowerby Bridge.

Halifax (W Yorks). Calder 2m S. Clubs: Halifax and Dist AC (dams); Dean Clough AC (canal at Copley); Greater Elland AA (dams); Halifax Flyfishers'; no water. Ripponden Flyfishers'; good trout fishing in **Ryburn Reservoir**, Ripponden. Hebden Bridge AS; coarse fishing in canal; trout in beck. Brighouse AA and Bradford No 1 AA control 14m on Calder above and below **Brighouse**; heavily restocked and now provides sport with good-quality roach. St (no dt) from D B Arnett, 49 Templars Way, Bradford but 3-year waiting list. Brighouse AA also has water on canal and gravel pits. Ryburn AS; lakes near **Sowerby Bridge**; coarse, trout; tickets. Tackleist: A J Jewson, 1 Westgate.

Sowerby Bridge (W Yorks). Ryburn AS, st £3, has water on Calder and local dams and reservoirs. Top Willow Hall Dam and Lower Willow Hall Dam on dt from G Riley, 35 Leigh Street.

Hebden (W Yorks). Hebden Bridge AS has water on Calder and **Rochdale Canal** (Callis Lock No 13 to junction with Calder and Hebble Navigation Sowerby Bridge) and on **Rivers Ryburn** and **Elphin,** and **Hardcastle Crags Stream.** Dt for stream only of which club has several miles; being restocked. Membership open to Alderdale residents only. Canal also restocked. At **Todmorden** (Lancs) (4m away) the Todmorden AS (annual membership, £5) has about 6m of the **Rochdale Canal** and **New Mill Dams** (trout); members only. Dt for **Calderbrook Dams, Littleborough,** only (two trout, one coarse fish), Steve's Tackle Shop, Rochdale.

COLNE (tributary of Calder):

Huddersfield (W Yorks). **Longwood Compensation Reservoir.** This, as its name implies, is compensation water known locally as **Oak Scar Reservoir.** Preserved and stocked by Huddersfield AA. It has good head of pike, perch, roach and gudgeon. Angling restricted to members of the association along with special annual permit-holders accepted by association up to 50 per season. No river fishing.

Slaithwaite (W Yorks). Slaithwaite and Dist AC (st £6) has rights on **Trent** at Sutton and Dunham, on **Rye** at Butterwick and on Rivers **Calder, Colne** and **Holme,** as well as several miles of canal and reservoir fishing; trout, coarse fish; dt (for canal) from hon sec. No dt between Feb 28 and May 31. Dt 40p some waters June 1–Feb 28. Apply hon sec for details.

HOLME (tributary of Colne):

Holmfirth (W Yorks). Lakes: **Holmstyes Reservoir;** trout (Huddersfield 8m) preserved by Huddersfield AA. St £35. **Boshaw Reservoir** (Huddersfield 8m); preserved as above.

DERWENT: Rises in high moors and flows almost to coast near Scarborough where it turns south and enters estuary of Ouse. Its upper reaches, most easily reached from Scarborough, are trout and grayling waters *(see Ayton).* Lower down coarse fish predominate: barbel in lower stretches.

Wressle (N Humberside). Coarse fish, mostly free.

Breighton (N Humberside); ns Wressle 1m. Bubwith 1m. Chub, dace, pike, etc; fishing free. Inquire Half Moon Inn.

Bubwith (N Humberside). Coarse fish; Howden & Dist AC has 4m of good mixed fishing on left bank to **Ellerton;** roach, perch, dace, bream, chub, eels and pike; flatfish lower down. Dt and st from White Swan Inn. Match bookings to hon sec.

Wheldrake (N Yorks). Tidal. Coarse fish. York AA has 1½m right bank; dt from the Alice Hawthorne Inn.

Sutton-on-Derwent (N Yorks). Coarse fish. Cross Keys Inn; 2m tidal, 2m non-tidal; coarse fish below dam, trout above; dt and st. Further information from inn.

East Cottingwith (N Yorks); ns High Field, 4m. Coarse fish (pike and chub very good). York AA controls East Cottingwith Water (2m) and 10m of good coarse fishing on **Pocklington Canal.** Dt from secretary or Blue Bell Inn. At **Thorganby,** on other side of Derwent, Ferry Boat Inn can give permission for about 3m of river.

Pocklington (N Yorks). **Pocklington Canal.** Well stocked with bream, roach, perch, pike, etc *(see East Cottingwith).* York AA water. Dt from Wellington Oak, Canal Head; College Arms, Beilby; Melbourne Arms, Melbourne; and The cottage at Coats Bridge.

Ellerton Landing (N Yorks). Mixed fishing. Hotel: White Swan, Bubwith.

Kexby (N Yorks); ns Fangfoss, 3m. Pike, chub, etc. York and Leeds Amalgamated Societies have water; members only. *(See also Stamford Bridge and Low Catton.)*

Low Catton (N Yorks). Coarse fish. Leeds and Dist AS has good length of water on left bank; members only. *(See also Kexby and Stamford Bridge.)*

Stamford Bridge (N Yorks). Excellent for roach, pike, chub, dace. York and Dist Amal has fishing on good length down to Kexby Brickworks; also pits. Dt at cafés in Stamford Bridge. *(See also Kexby and Low Catton.)*

Howsham (N Yorks). Coarse fishing. York and Dist AA has water on Derwent and Barton Hill Beck; dt on beck (trout) from the Blacksmith Arms, Barton-le-Willows. Bradford No 1 AA has water; members only.

Kirkham Abbey (N Yorks). Coarse fish. Leeds and York Amalgamations have water; members only.

Castle Howard (N Yorks). **Castle Howard Great Lake** contains specimen coarse fish, including pike, perch, tench, bream, roach and dace; bank fishing only. For further details, see *"Yorkshire Lakes"*.

Huttons Ambo (Yorks). Roach, pike, dace, grayling, perch and few trout. Barbel introduced 1973. South bank held by Malton and Norton AC *(see Malton)* for 1m down and 1m up; no dt. North bank held by Huttons Ambo AC for 2m down and 2m up; membership, for people resident within 10m Malton, £3 pa.

Malton (Yorks). Coarse fish (mainly roach). Malton and Norton AC. Waters extend to 1m below Huttons Ambo. No dt. Membership restricted to local residents. Club also has water on **Rye** (no dt). Tickets from Malton Estate Office, Old Maltongate, for 3m of Derwent and Rye (trout and coarse fish). Slaithwaite and Dist AC has 2½m on Derwent and Rye above Old Malton; shared with Castleford AC. Dt at farm. Costa Beck, 3m NE. Lakes: Castle Howard Park Lake, 5m W *(see Castle Howard)*. Good deal of free water on Derwent and Rye. Tackleists: J Anderson & Son, Market Place (tickets for Malton AC waters); and C Swift, Castlegate. Hotel: Green Man.

Riddlington (Yorks). Derwent, 1m N. Coarse fish; Leeds Amal water. Scampston Beck, 1m E, private. Rye, 2m N. Costa Beck, 3m N.

Yedingham (Yorks). Coarse fish. Construction of new bridge and removal of

dam has changed conditions and affected fishing. Scarborough Mere AC has water; members only, who must reside in Scarborough area. Dt 75p at Providence Inn for Leeds Amal waters. Inn also has private stretch. Foul Bridge Farm issue dt.

Ganton (Yorks). Chub, pike, dace, grayling; dt for 1m each way from Hay Bridge, from farm at railway crossing. Ruston Beck, 2m W.

Ayton (Yorks). Some good trout water. Scarborough Mere AC has **Scarborough Mere**, just outside town; coarse fish; dt 75p; mere restocked regularly. About 2m trout fishing from Ayton towards Ganton controlled by Leeds Amal; no tickets.

Hackness (Yorks). Derwent AC (sub £100; entrance £60) controls 10m of trout (brown and rainbow) and grayling fishing down to **East Ayton**, for part of which dt at £5 are available on main club water (from East Ayton to Hilla Green bridge on the Troutsdale Road) from July 1 to Sept 30. Farther up, above Langdale End bridge (3m both banks), dt available at £3 from April 1 to Sept 30, Fishing one fly only, wet or dry, is club rule on all water. Tickets from Scarborough tackleists: Pritchards, Eastborough (WA licences and club tickets, dt on lower water and dt on upper water), and Grange Hotel, Hackness Grange Hotel (rods for residents on 8m of Derwent) *(advt p 10)*. Sunday fishing reserved for members and guests on lower club water, and all fishing between Hilla Green bridge and Langdale End bridge exclusively reserved to members and guests. Size limit for trout 10 in; limit three brace per day. No limit to size or number of grayling. Wading allowed.

FOSS BECK (tributary of Derwent). Fishing station: **Fangfoss** (Yorks); fishing private.

SPITTLE BECK (tributary of Derwent):

Barton Hill (Yorks). Derwent, 2m E. Whitecarr Beck, 4m SE. Loppington Beck, 4m SE. Swallowpits Beck, 5m SE at Scrayingham.

RYE (tributary of Derwent): Trout, grayling, other coarse fish.

Nunnington (Yorks). Rye, 2m. Trout fishing; limited number of dt £3.50. Coarse fishing (grayling, chub, some trout) on lower water; dt £1.50. Tickets from Estate Office, Nunnington Hall, and gamekeeper. Permits for Holbeck

Fishery 25p day from Worsley Arms, Hovingham.

Butterwick (Yorks). Trout. Slaithwaite AC has water; members only. St £6 + £2 entry fee from F Siswick, 30 Cliff End Road, Quarry, Huddersfield. Hull & Dist AA water for ¾m below bridge. Dt 40p from local tackleists.

Helmsley (Yorks). Trout, grayling; preserved above from Helmsley (road) bridge to Tylas Farm boundary and below to Nunnington (railway) bridge by Ryedale Anglers' Club; no tickets. Tackleist: Cooper & Son (ironmongers), Bridge Street. Hotels: Black Swan, Feversham Arms, Crown.

Hawnby (Yorks); ns Helmsley, 6½m; Thirsk, 10m. Hawnby Hotel has 12m private fishing in Rye and **Seph;** trout; fly only; thigh waders and shortish rods advised; dt for non-residents £1.50; £2 weekends and holidays.

PICKERING BECK (tributary of Rye) and Costa Beck (chalk stream). Trout, grayling.

Pickering (Yorks). About 1m of free fishing in town; private above, preserved below (3m) by Pickering FA; fly only; membership limited to 70 (st £30, entrance free £75). Permits issued to members' guests only, but hon sec would be pleased to help prospective visitors. **Costa Beck;** large trout and grayling. Club HQ, Bay Horse Hotel. Pickering FA also has fishing on **Oxfolds Beck** (chalk stream; trout, grayling) and trout lake with boat. Also 3m on Thornton-le-Dale beck. Dt on lower Costa, **Rye, Dove** and **Seven** from farmers; 3–7m from Pickering, mainly coarse fishing. Hotels: Forest and Vale, Crossways.

SEVEN (tributary of Rye): Trout, grayling; some coarse fish.

Newsham Bridge (Yorks). York and Dist AA has water on Seven and Rye; no dt.

Marton (Yorks). Private from mill to Marton; below Marton some free water; grayling, pike, chub, dace and a few trout. Tackleist in Malton, 12m.

Sinnington (Yorks). Seven AC has 2½m downstream; trout and grayling; members only. Coarse fishing mainly below large weir and bottom farm. Upstream Sinnington AC has water; inquire hon sec. Waiting list for membership.

WATH BECK (tributary of Rye):

Slingsby (Yorks). Trout; preserved. Rye, 2m NE.

DOVE-IN-FARNDALE (tributary of Rye):

Kirby Moorside (N Yorks). Dove-in-Farndale, 1m E; trout; private. Dt for stretches downstream of Kirby Moorside available from some of the farms. Hodge Beck, in Sleightholme Dale, 1m W, trout only. Hotel: King's Head.

THORNTON BECK (tributary of Derwent):

Thornton-le-Dale (N Yorks). Trout and grayling; preserved. Pickering Beck, 3m W. Derwent, 3m S. Hotels: The Hall; The Buck; all Thornton-le-Dale.

WHARFE: Rises on Cam Fell and flows 60m south-east to join Ouse near Cawood. Trout in upper reaches, with coarse fish in increasing numbers downstream.

Ryther (N Yorks); ns Ulleskelf, 3m. Castleford and Dis ASA has water; mainly coarse fish. Ryther Arms will give further information. Ouse 1m N.

Ulleskelf (N Yorks). Coarse fish; preserved by Leeds Amal: dt 70p from Ulleskelf Arms.

Tadcaster (N Yorks). Coarse fish (mainly chub and dace, but good head of barbel, perch and bream); trout (restocked); preserved by Tadcaster Angling and Preservation Association on both banks downstream, from road bridge to Sewage Farm (1m) and from road bridge to Grimston Park (2m); st and dt. Tickets from Britannia Hotel (also dt for Leeds Amal waters) *(see also Ulleskelf)*. Other hotels: White Swan, Bay Horse Inn, Commercial Street, (Tadcaster HQ).

Boston Spa (W Yorks). Trout, grayling, other coarse fish (chub, barbel and pike good; bream introduced). Most rights held by Boston Spa AC. Dt 65p from Spa Baths. South bank from river bridge to Wharfedale Hall belongs to Spa Baths, who issue day tickets, 75p. Club members (who must live within 3m of Boston Spa post office) allowed 12 guests a yeat at current cost of dt and guest must fish with member on non-ticket waters. Club stocks water with trout and grayling of 12 in or over. Limit two trout, one grayling, or vice versa; trout 12 in. June best month for trout and August for barbel and chub.

Wetherby (W Yorks). Wetherby and Dist AC water (stocked with trout and coarse fish) extends from Collingham Beck to Wetherby Weir, south bank (about 350 yards in Collingham Wood, south bank is private). Club also has four fields between golf course and playing fields, north bank. This water is open for visitors at £4 st (above weir), and 50p dt. Members only below and on weir, but visitors may fish if accompanied by a member. Same charge as above. Tickets from: T Cockayne, George and Dragon, Wetherby; and F T Buckley, Star Filling Station, Collingham. No legitimate bait or lure barred. Trout limit 11 in. Hotels: Angel, Wetherby Turnpike.

Collingham (W Yorks). Wetherby AC has water here; trout and coarse fish (including barbel, grayling and good dace). Permits (50p day) for part of these preserves from George and Dragon, Wetherby and Star Garage, Collingham.

Arthington (W Yorks). Trout; left bank and much of right bank leased to Leeds and Dist Amal; rest preserved

Pool (W Yorks). Trout, few chub; preserved by the Leeds Amal which has 5m of fishing from River Washburn to Castley Beck on left bank and about 3m on right bank. Dt from Leeds tackleists. Members of Leeds AA, small private club, can fish Harewood Estate preserves, 3m right bank 2m left bank.

Otley (W Yorks). Otley AC hold 2m left bank and 2½m right bank below Otley Bridge. Trout, with occasional chub and dace; trout av 10–12 oz; best months March–August. Application for membership to hon sec. Club also has **Knotford Lagoons;** excellent roach, chub and tench to 4 lb and carp to 28 lb; dt from tackleists. Bradford No 1 AA has water here. At Yeadon (6m) Airboro' and Dist AA has **Yeadon Tarn;** roach, perch, carp, tench; boats available. Tackleists in Otley: A Agar, Cross Green; The Pet Shop, Kirkgate Arcade. Hotels: Black Horse, Royal White Horse.

Burley and Askwith (W York). Trout, grayling, chub, dace; Bradford clubs have rights for members only.

Addingham (W Yorks). Trout, grayling; Bradford City AA has water here; no dt obtainable. Bradford Waltonians have 1½m here and water at **Denton** and **Ben Rhydding;** also **Chelker Reservoir** near here. No tickets. Keighley AC has water; dt from hon sec.

Ilkley (W Yorks). Ilkley and Dist AC and Myddleton AC have water. Ilkley membership restricted to ratepayers. Wt £12, dt £2, (April 15–Sept 30 inc) from Crees Pet Stores and Chandlers', newsagents, all Leeds Road. Good trout, grayling and dace fishing (restocked annually) from Brook Street Bridge to Stepping Stones, both banks (abt 2m); worm and fly only; no Sunday fishing. Hotels: Ilkley Moor, Troutbeck, Craiglands, Crescent (Club HQ).

Bolton Abbey (N Yorks). Trout and grayling. Dt from Estate Office, Bolton Abbey for 5 miles stretch (both banks) from Barden Bridge to Kex Beck below Bolton Bridge. Fly only. Trout April 1–September 30. Grayling can be taken from 15 June. Grayling only Oct 1–Dec 31. Limit 4 trout of not less than 10 in. Grayling no limit. Some interference on Sundays and Bank Holidays due to public access. Furnished holiday cottages also available for fishermen. Fishing facilities available at the Devonshire Arms Hotel.

Burnsall (N Yorks); ns Skipton, 12½m. Trout (av ½ lb–1 lb; many large fish), grayling; preserved by Appletreewick, Barden and Burnsall AC from Linton Stepping Stones, below Grassington, to Barden Bridge, 7m. Dt for trout, June–Sept (excluding June week-ends) £5; wt £20 to guests at Red Lion Hotel; fly only during trout season; limit 3 brace; grayling dt £3 Nov to Jan (upstream worm allowed but no spinning or maggot fishing). Waters restocked annually with trout from ½ to 1 lb. Tickets from Red Lion Hotel, or from river watcher, J Smith, Gable End Cottage, Linton Falls, PO, Burnsall, N Goodwin, tackleist, Skipton, Grassington. Bradford City AA has water at **Appletreewick;** members only. Dt for stretch at Appletreewick from New Inn (left bank only).

Grassington (N Yorks); ns Skipton, 10m. Trout (av ½ lb), grayling (av ¾ lb); preserved by Linton, Threshfield and Grassington AC for 2½m both banks (also in Captain Beck and Linton and Threshfield Becks until August 31); wt £10, dt £2.50 for fly-fishing only. No night or Sunday fishing. Trout season: April 1 to Sept 30 inclusive. Grayling only from Oct 1 to Feb 28; st £12, dt £1.50; fly only during Oct. Tickets from post office, Grassington. Saltaire AA also has water at Linton and Threshfield: st. fishing best in May. Eller Beck, Hebden Beck, 2m E. Lakes: Blea Beck dams 4m NE. Hotels: Black Horse (Saltaire AA HQ), Wilson Arms and others.

Kilnsey (N Yorks); ns Skipton-in-Craven, 13m. Trout. Preserved by Kilnsey AC of 50 members, from 1m above Starbotton down to Netherside 2m below Kilnsey; dt £5 from C Pettinger, Kilnsey (number limited, and none on Sundays or Bank Holidays). **Skirfare,** 1m N; trout; preserved as Wharfe up to 1m below Arncliffe. Hotels: Tennant Arms, Falcon *(advt p 19).*

Buckden (N Yorks); ns Skipton, 19m. Trout. Bradford City AA has 2m; members only (st £10 + entry fee of £5). Other fishing for guests at Buck Inn (dt 50p).

SKIRFARE (tributary of Wharfe); Well stocked with trout (3 to lb).

Arncliffe (N Yorks); ns Skipton-in-Craven, 16m. 2½m on Skirfare and 1½m on **Cowside Beck** available to guests at Falcon Inn *(advt p 19).* Dt £2.75. Fishing on Skirfare and Wharfe held by Kilnsey AC. *(See "Kilnsey", previous page.)*

FOSS (tributary of Ouse): Trout.

Earswick (N Yorks). Free fishing on right bank. Owners are Joseph Rowntree Trust.

Strensall (N Yorks). Foss Navigation Cut, 1m NE. Whitecar Beck, 1m NE. York and Dist Amal has fishing here and at **Towthorpe** (ns Haxby); members only.

NIDD: Trout and grayling, with coarse fish from Birstwith downstream in increasing numbers.

Nun Monkton (N Yorks). Coarse fish. Bradford No 1 has 1½m reserved for members only.

Kirk Hammerton (N Yorks). Coarse fish. Following on Harrogate AA water *(see Goldsborough),* almost all fishing downstream to where Nidd joins the Ouse controlled by the Leeds and York Amalgamations. York Amal holds York side of river from Skip Bridge on Boroughbridge Road upstream for about 2m and also for about 1m above Hammerton Mill dam. Tickets from York tackleists; York Road Service Station, Mrs Abel, Crown Inn, Kirk Hammerton and Myers, Skip Bridge Filling Station.

Cowthorpe (N Yorks). Coarse fish, Harrogate AA water *(see Goldsborough).* Stretch of 1m, one bank, belongs to Old Oak Inn, tickets issued; Sunday fishing. Licences and tackle available in Wetherby.

Goldsborough (N Yorks). Trout, grayling and mixed coarse fishing, including pike and barbel. From Little Ribston downstream through Walshford Bridge to first meadow below Cattall Bridge belongs to Harrogate AA. Association also has

both banks of **Crimple Beck** from confluence with Nidd above Walshford Bridge up to Spofforth. Waiting list for membership. Dt issued by hon sec to members' guests only. Water otherwise strictly preserved.

Knaresborough (N Yorks). Trout, grayling and coarse fish, including barbel. Practically all fishing in vicinity controlled by Knaresborough AC and Knaresborough Piscatorials. Former issues st to visitors from ½m below Goldsborough Dam to Little Ribston village. Knaresborough Piscatorials provides st, wt and dt for visitors. York Amal has good stretches here. Tickets from P H & J R Smith (tacklesists), 28 High Street.

Ripley, Nidd Bridge (N Yorks). Trout, grayling and coarse fish. On right bank from about 300 yds below Harrogate–Ripon road bridge to Killinghall and downstream to Sewerage Works, about 2½m, held by Harrogate and Claro Anglers, who have full membership and long waiting list. Downstream for 2m river privately owned and includes Knaresborough Sanatorium. At Killinghall both banks above and below Harrogate–Ripon road bridge held by Knaresborough AC, whose water continues about 2m up left bank; tickets for members' friends only.

Birstwith (N Yorks). Trout and grayling above Birstwith Dam upstream to upper reaches of Nidd. Below Dam there are also coarse fish. Knaresborough Anglers have length above Killinghall Bridge. Birstwith Private AC has some water on both banks between Hampsthwaite Bridge and about 1m above Birstwith Bridge, where their water joins that of Harrogate FFC. Two small stretches private. Club confined to small number of members; waiting list. No dt.

Darley (N Yorks). Trout and grayling water, strictly preserved by Harrogate Fly Fishers and Birstwith Clubs. No tickets. *(See Harrogate.)*

Pateley Bridge (N Yorks). Trout and grayling. From 1½m above Pateley Bridge down to **Dacre,** owned and rented by Nidderdale AC, who hold nearly all water, both banks, except short pieces here and there which are private; dt and wt. Ticket distr: Royal Oak, Dacre; PO Summerbridge; The Shop, Low Laithe; PO Glasshouses and Shoe Shop, Pateley Bridge.

Gouthwaite (N Yorks). River enters

Gouthwaite Reservoir, fine sheet of water 2m long, well stocked with large trout and numerous grayling. Privately owned and fished; no permits. Below reservoir Nidd private.

CRIMPLE (tributary of Nidd). This river is about 12m long, very narrow and joins Nidd near Walshford Bridge, where for short distance there is reasonably good fishing. Harrogate AA has water *(see Nidd–Goldsborough).* Permission to fish other water may be obtained from adjoining farmers. **Plumpton Lake:** coarse fish; recently stocked with rainbow trout. Permission from lodge house at Plumpton for small charge.

Harrogate (N Yorks). Trout and coarse fishing; within easy reach of town in Nidd, Wharfe and Ure. Details from Information Bureau, Royal Baths. Harrogate Flyfishers preserve excellent trout and grayling water at Darley. Membership details from hon sec. Hotels: Crown, Majestic, Old Swan, St George, Cairn, Prospect.

KYLE: Coarse fish.

Alne (N Yorks). Coarse fishing in Kyle up to Tollerton; York Dist AA has use.

Tollerton (N Yorks). Coarse fishing free down to Alne. Ouse at Aldwark, 4m W, and Linton Lock, 3m S and 7m NE, at Stillington.

URE (or YORE): Noted for grayling, but also holds good trout. Coarse fish from Middleham downstream.

Boroughbridge (N Yorks). Fine coarse fishing (especially chub and roach, bream increasing); few trout and grayling; taken by clubs. Numerous inns in town and at **Langthorpe, Aldborough** and **Roecliffe** where Bradford City AA has 6m (roach, perch, dace, pike, chub); no dt, limited privilege tickets for members only. Boroughbridge and Dist AC has HQ at Black Bull, Boroughbridge. Club issues dt (75p) (weekdays only) from June 1–Feb 27; available from Post Office. Harrogate and Claro AC issue dt for water on north bank after June 1. Tickets from Three Horseshoes. Other hotel: Black Lion.

Ripon (N Yorks). Trout, grayling, pike, perch, chub, barbel, roach; preserved for 6m by Ripon Piscatorial Assn (¾m fly only), for membership of which there is a waiting list. Wt £5, dt 75p. Association also has 2m **Ripon Canal** (carp, tench, bream); dt. **Skell** and **Laver;** trout, preserved for 7m by Ripon AC; fly only; dt.

Club also has 1m on **Ure** (trout, coarse fish; dt from Hodgson; *see below*) and **Lumley Moor Reservoir;** trout fly only; no dt. Lakes: Queen Mary's Ponds; coarse fish; Bradford No 1 AA. Hotels: Spa, Unicorn, Studley Royal, Station, South Lodge. Tackleist: R C Hodgson, 7 Queen Street, who can give information.

Tanfield (N Yorks). Trout, grayling; preserved for about 5m, mostly both banks, by Tanfield AC. Guests must be accompanied by member. Full time bailiff employed. Long waiting list.

Masham (N Yorks); ns Ripon. Trout, grayling. 6½m west bank belongs to Countess of Swinton's estate. A 2m stretch has been put at the disposal of Masham AC and is for members only. Rods limited on remaining waters; always waiting list. Yorkshire Flyfishers hold Clifton Castle water (about 2m left bank) above Masham. No tickets. Hotel: King's Head.

Cover Bridge (N Yorks); ns Ripon or Northallerton. Trout, grayling. East Witton Estate issue dt on R Cover from Hallo Bridge to mouth. Mostly both banks. Fly only, £1. Tickets from Smiths Gore, Estate Office, Leyburn; Blue Lion, E Witton; Pheasant, Harmby; Cover Bridge Inn, Middleham.

Middleham (N Yorks). Fishing may be had in Middleham Deeps by dt from Old Horn Inn, Spennithorne. Leeds Amal water; excellent barbel, chub and grayling; Few large trout; odd salmon. Dt from Cover Bridge Inn for trout and grayling fishing on Cover. Hotel: White Swan.

Leyburn (N Yorks). Grayling, trout, coarse fish. Two dt (£3) available from Blue Lion, E Witton, for E Witton Estate water on Ure from Ulshaw Bridge to Harker Beck. 1¾m S bank. Fly only. Bolton FA and Thornaby AA have "members only" water here. Hotels: Bolton Arms, Golden Lion. Tackleists: Wray Bros, Town Hall (also licences).

Redmire (N Yorks). Trout, grayling; preserved by Lord Bolton. Restocked; fly only. All fishing now by st only (£50); numbers limited; apply Bolton Estate Office, Wensley, Leyburn. Trout best April, May and June; grayling Oct and Nov. Hotels: King's Arms, Redmire; White Swan, Middleham; Rose and Crown, Bainbridge; Wensleydale Heifer, Westwittom.

Aysgarth (N Yorks). Trout, grayling.

North bank preserved above by Wensleydale AA *(see Bainbridge)*. Palmer Flatt Hotel has short stretch; dt from hotel. Bradford City AA has 3m (st £3, no dt). Skipton AA has ½m above town.

Askrigg (N Yorks). Trout, grayling; preserved by Wensleydale AA. Tickets *(see Bainbridge)* from King's Arms or Victoria Arms, Worton. Hotel: King's Arms.

Bainbridge (N Yorks); ns Askrigg. Hotel: Rose and Crown (HQ of Wensleydale AA). Wensleydale AA water includes 6m on Yore, 2m of Bain, flowing from **Lake Semerwater,** north and west shores of lakes (bream, rudd, eels) and 2m trout water above lake; st £10, wt £4, dt £2. Fly only before June 16. Grayling only, st £2, dt 50p (Oct 1 to Feb 28). All maggot fishing prohibited in streams. Tickets from: Rose and Crown (also WA licences), Bainbridge; King's Arms, Askrigg; Victoria Arms, Worton. Bradford City AA has ¾m left bank and 1m right bank of Bain leaving lake; dt and wt, from C Peacock, The White House, Countersett. Other accommodation at Greenways Guest House; Victoria Arms, Worton.

Hawes (N Yorks). Trout, grayling; preserved with tributaries, from source of river downward about 8m (stock of big trout) by Hawes and High Abbotside AA; wt (no dt) from hon sec. Below Hawes preserves Wensleydale AA has several miles of excellent water *(see Bainbridge)*. Hotels: Crown, White Hart, Fountain, Board.

SWALE: Good chub and barbel water. Trouting best in upper reaches.

Helperby (N Yorks). Coarse fish; right bank from Swing Bridge to Myton Plantation controlled by Leeds Amal; dt from Golden Lion, Helperby. Dun Royal Hotel also issues tickets. Thornton Beck, 2m Sun Beck.

Topcliffe (N Yorks). Noted coarse fishing centre; especially good for club and barbel. Thirsk AC and Bradford clubs have much water in this area; inquire hon secs. Assn of Teesside and Dist ACs has 1½m at **Sand Hutton;** members only. Hotels: Angel, Black Bull, which have water and issue dt. **Cod Beck;** trout; perserved by Bradford City AA; apply hon sec for permits.

Pickhill (N Yorks). Coarse fish; trout. Thornaby AA has two fields (about 500 yds); members only *(see Thornaby*

under Tees). Leeds Amalgamation has a ¾m stretch at **Ainderby.**

Morton-on-Swale (N Yorks). Trout, grayling, pike, perch, roach, chub, dace, barbel, eels. Restocked with trout; fishing good. Northallerton AC has 4m both banks upstream of Morton Bridge reserved for members and 5m on east bank downstream for which wt £5 and dt £1 can be had from Mr J Grainger, Morton, and tackleist Metcalfe, Northallerton. Stockton AA has short stretch near here *(see Stockton-on-Tees)*.

Langton (N Yorks). Trout, grayling, coarse fish; trout to 5 lb taken; Kirkby Fleetham AA has both banks downstream, linking up with Northallerton AC's water at Bramper Farm; fly only; no tickets. Darlington Brown Trout Club's water begins above Kirkby Fleetham stretch.

Catterick (N Yorks). Good mixed fishing: trout, grayling, dace, chub, barbel, few roach and pike. Trout from 8 oz to 1 lb; fast takers. Richmond & Dist AS has water on both banks (1m south bank, ½m north bank) near Brompton-on-Swale. Wt £6, dt £2 from hon sec; visitors to be accompanied by member. Hon members admitted at £8. Darlington Brown Trout AA has fishing downstream to Ellerton (north bank). Dt 25p to visitors accompanying member. Thornaby AA has Thornbrough Farm 1m upstream from railway bridge above Catterick Bridge; noted grayling, trout and barbel stretch; members only. Also other fishings on Swale, **Ure, Tees** and **Eden.** Annual membership: £10. Hotels: Farmers' Arms; Angel Inn. Licences and permits: E & B Langstaff, Parkgate, Darlington, who is also tackleist.

Richmond (N Yorks). Above town, trout; below, trout, grayling, chub, dace and barbel. Richmond and Dist AS preserves several miles: 6m above town and 4m below; mixed trout, grayling and coarse fishing below; dt. Guest tickets Oct 1 to Feb 28. St £8, wt £6, dt £2 (limited) from W Metcalfe (tackleist), Market Place, The Bungalow, Easby; and F Carter, Caravan Site. Richmond AS also controls waters of Richmond Town Council Dt Sunday above town during trout season, 50p. Spinning prohibited. Sand Beck, 1m S. Ash Beck, 1m N. Gilling Beck, 3m N. Colburn and Hipswell Becks, 2m S. Clapgate Beck, 4m W. Ravensworth Beck, 5m NW. Smelt Mill

Beck, 4m N. Marske Beck, 5m W. Eller or Marrick Beck, 6m W; all trout. Skeeby Beck, 2½m NE; trout and grayling; preserved. Aske Hall Park lake, 2½m N; Forcett Park, 8m N; pike and perch, Calt Hole Tarn, 4m S.

Grinton (N Yorks); ns Richmond, 9m. Trout. Thornaby AA has whole south bank and part of north bank, from Isles Bridge to Grinton Bridge (about 5½m); trout three to the lb. No tickets, but help given by hon sec to visiting anglers who write with SAE. Tackleists: F Fynn, 12 Varo Terrace, Stockton; or J W Wright & Son, 107 Park Gate, Darlington. *(See Thornaby under Tees.)*

Reeth (N Yorks). Swale; trout; Grinton (Bridge Hotel); Bridge East, N bank only; fly only; Black Bull Hotel has water, free to guests; non-residents £1 day. Inn: Buck.

Muker (N Yorks); ns Askrigg, 8m. Trout; strictly preserved. Muker Beck; trout; Thwaite Beck, 1m W; trout; free. Summer Lodge Beck, 5m E; trout; preserved.

Keld (N Yorks); ns Kirkby Stephen, 12m. Trout; plentiful but small; preserved. *(See also Muker.)*

GUN BECK (tributary of Swale):

Husthwaite (N Yorks). Centre for good trouting on **Husthwaite Beck;** preserved by York and Dist Amal; dt from York tackleists, hon sec.

Coxwold (N Yorks). Pond Head Reservoirs (two), 3m SE; perch and pike. Hole Beck and Gun Beck preserved.

BEDALE BECK (tributary of Swale):

Leeming (N Yorks). Swale, 2m NE; preserved by Black Ox AC; trout and coarse fish. Club also has 3m on Swale at **Gatenby,** 14m N of Boroughbridge.

Bedale (N Yorks). Trout, grayling; private. Tackleists: Wrights Ltd, Market Place *(see also Leyburn).*

COD BECK (tributary of Swale); good trout water, but recent pollution of lower reaches has affected sport.

North Kilvington (N Yorks). Trout; preserved by Thirsk AC *(see Thirsk).*

Thirsk (N Yorks). Thirsk AC has water on beck; limited permits; trout restocked and coarse fish removed. Tackleists and licences: J Moss, Finkle Street. Hotels: Royal Oak, Three Tuns.

Sessay (N Yorks). Cod Beck, 2m W; Thirsk AC, Swale, 2m SW; Bradford club now has fishing on P J Till's farm (The Heights). Inn: Railway, Dalton.

Brawith (N Yorks). Trout; preserved. *For Cod Beck Reservoir see Northallerton.*

WISKE (tributary of Swale): Good coarse fishing ruined by pollution. Recovery expected to be slow.

Otterington (N Yorks). Cod Beck, 2m E. Broad Beck. Sorrow Beck, 4m E.

Northallerton (N Yorks). Roach, dace, chub, pike; preserved: fishing good. Northallerton AC has several miles of water on the Swale at Morton Bridge; wt £5, dt £1 from Grainger, Morton on Swale, and Metcalfe. At Osmotherley is **Cod Beck Reservoir;** trout; fly only; fair fishing; one dt available from Hambleton DC offices. Tackleists: R Metcalfe, The Arcade.

PARRET

(For close seasons, licences, etc, see Wessex Water Authority, p 39)

Rises in hills on border of Somerset and Dorset, and flows into Bristol Channel near Bridgwater. Roach, bream and dace predominate. Thorney-Middle Chinnock stretch and some of tributaries hold trout. Occasional salmon and sea trout run through into Tone.

Bridgwater (Som). Parret tidal. Bridgwater AA preserves fishing in Bridgwater Docks, ½m from town centre. Docks sluiced off from main river. Good roach, rudd, bream; some tench and carp. **King's Sedgemoor Drain** is also preserved by Bridgwater AA which has fishing from about ¾m above Greylake Bridge, where 18 ft rhine enters main and wider water, to Old Salt Works at Dunball. Good roach, rudd and pike; few tench, but chance of a 5-pdr. Bream, carp and perch being introduced to this water. St £4.50, wt £1.50, dt 50p. Other Bridgwater AA fisheries: **Huntspill River, Cripps River, North Drain, South Drain, 18 ft Rhine, Bridgwater and Taunton Canal, Dunwear, Screech Owl** and **Combwich Ponds** (mainly carp), and **Ashford Reservoir;** other ponds and drains. Season, weekly and day tickets, with concessions for jun, ladies, OAP. Permits cover all waters. Pocket maps from hon sec (see list of clubs at end of section). Bathampton AA has ponds near here; details from hon sec. Wessex

WA reservoir at Durleigh, 1½m from Bridgwater; trout; fly only *(see Somerset lakes, etc)*. For tickets, licences, tackle, apply Bridge Sports, 24 Eastover; Homemakers, 129 Taunton Road.

Langport (Som). Parret and Yeo; pike, perch, carp, bream, roach, dace. South, East and West Wessex Fed hold large section from **Oath** to **Thorney,** and also has water on **Isle;** open to affiliated clubs. Langport AA issues st £2.50, wt £1.75 and dt 50p, obtainable from A W Rule, Parrett Close, Langport, tackleist.

Crewkerne (Som). Trout, coarse fish. Stoke-sub-Hamdon AA has trout fishing from Bow Mills to Hurdle Pool (trout av ¾ lb); members only (st £2); coarse fishing from Hurdle Pool to Thorney Mill; tickets from hon sec during coarse fishing season only; 50p day, £1 week.

TONE: Trout above Taunton, coarse fish. Weedy in summer below Taunton but provides first-class coarse fishing in winter.

Taunton (Som). Fishing free at French weir and through Taunton. Taunton Fly Fishing Club has water on the Tone from Roughmoor to Wellisford (not continuous) which is mainly fly only but other baits and lures allowed in certain areas on a day ticket basis.

Hillfarrance Brook (a Tone tributary—Hillfarrance to confluence with Tone). Trout, grayling—fly only—Members only. **Axe** (Chard Junction) ¾m single bank fishing below the village, fly only—Members only. Axe (Axminster) ½m double bank fishing, Town Weir to Cloakham Bridge. Fly only—Members only. Entrance fee £20. Annual subscription £17. Day tickets for restricted areas available from Hinton's, Bridge Street; Bridge Sports, Bridge Street and Topp Tackle, Station Road, Taunton. A A Woodbury, High Street, Wellington. St £5, wt £2, dt 50p (OAP's and juniors half price). Coarse fishing waters in area controlled by Taunton AA. **Taunton-Bridgwater Canal** from Taunton to Durston—roach, rudd, tench, pike: a few bream and carp; weed in summer; **West Sedgemoor Drain** from Stoke St Gregory to Stathe (mainly bream and tench, but also roach, pike, perch, eels and carp); several long stretches on Lower Tone between Taunton and Athelney. Map of club waters, tackle, tickets and RD licences from George Hinton & Sons, Bridge Street. Hotels: Castle (dt for Clatworthy Reservoir); County; George.

Wellington (Som). Trout, roach, dace; trout average ½ lb. Wellington AA has water from Fox Bros' works 2m upstream; mt £2 and dt 50p from hon sec. Thereafter preserved by owners through Bradford to Taunton FFC water. RD licences from tacklists, A A Woodbury and Son, High Street.

Wiveliscombe (Som). Tone, Milverton Brook and Norton Brook; trout; leave from owners; banks bushed. Tackleists: Arthur Twigger, The Square; issues dt (bank only) for Clatworthy Reservoir and Wessex WA licences.

NORTON BROOK (tributary of Tone):

Bishops Lydeard (Som). Norton Brook and Bishops Lydeard Brook; trout; leave from owners; banks overgrown.

MILVERTON BROOK (tributary of Tone):

Milverton (Som). Trout; private; leave from owners; banks bushed. Taunton FFC has well-stocked stretch of **Hillfarrance Brook.** Members only.

YEO: Coarse fish, some trout.

Long Lode (Som). Good coarse fishing; permission from farmers.

Ilchester (Som). Mainly roach, dace, eels and some trout. Dt and st from A D Coles, greengrocer. Club: Ilchester AC. Hotel: Ivelchester.

Yeovil (Som). Trout (av 12 in), roach, chub, dace. Yeovil club waters on Yeo & Parret; trout and coarse fish (restocked). St from hon sec. **Sutton Bingham Reservoir,** 3m S; tickets; fly only *(see Somerset (lakes and small streams))*. Tackle, licences, permits and further information from E & H Doney, 5 Bond Street; Sports of Bond Street. Hotels: Mermaid; Manor; The Choughs.

ISLE: Prolific chub water; also roach, dace, etc.

Midelney (Som). Water down to junction with Parret held by South, East and West Wessex Fed of Anglers *(see also Langport)*.

Isle Brewers (Som). Roach, chub, dace, some trout from Fivehead Road to Hambridge; private.

Ilminster (Som). Roach, chub, dace, trout. Ilminster AA water; dt and wt from hon sec or tacklists (see below). Bathampton AA also has water here; inquire hon sec. Tackleists: T Clapp, West Street.

RIBBLE

(For close seasons, licence, etc, see North West Water Authority, p 39)

Rises in the Pennines and flows 56 miles into the Irish Sea between St Anne's and Southport. Good coarse fishing lower down, between Great Mitton and Preston. Also coarse fishing in Long Preston Deeps. Best salmon, sea trout, brown trout and grayling fishing is between Settle and Great Mitton. Above Settle there are only brown trout. Tributary Hodder has good salmon, sea trout and brown trout fishing throughout length but much affected by water abstraction. Upper waters impounded in Stocks Reservoirs. Its main tributary, the Loud, also provides good trout and sea trout fishing.

Preston (Lancs). Coarse fish, few salmon and sea trout. 2m Northern AA (Preston Centre) water through town; st issued, including other waters on Ribble and **Wyre,** and **Lancaster Canal** (Preston to Natland). Further information from tackleists in Preston; C Calderbank, 33 Moor Lane; James Lynch, 81 New Hall Lane; Richard Marsden & Son Ltd and Ted Carter, both Church Street.

Samlesbury (Lancs). Coarse fish, few salmon and sea trout. Coarse fishing tickets for 2m from Samlesbury Hall, Ribchester. Several miles preserved by Northern AA (Preston Centre) and Ribble and Wyre FA, dt from hon sec.

Longridge (Lancs). Ribble, 3m SE. Hodder, 5m NE. Salmon, sea trout and trout. Loud 2m N. Most of right bank preserved by Loud and Hodder AA. Visitors' tickets issued if accompanied by member. Dt for stretch from Ribchester Bridge to Marlswood (about 2m) from S Hargreaves, Samlesbury Hall, **Ribchester.**

Mitton (Yorks); ns Whalley, 2m. Salmon, sea trout, trout and coarse fish. Lancashire RD has much water on Ribble and **Calder.** Dt from J Hoyle, Filling Station, Hill Crest. Dt for Mitton Hall water from The Keeper, Mitton Hall Cottages. Hotel: Aspinall Arms, where tickets can be obtained for CWS water on Yorkshire banks of both rivers *(see Clitheroe).*

Clitheroe (Lancs). Clitheroe AS fishes 3m of Ribble, 4m of **Hodder** and 1m of **Lune.** Visitors must be accompanied by member. Much of right bank from Edisford Bridge to Mitton Bridge held by CWS Ltd. St £15. Tickets include 2½m on Hodder at Higher Hodder Bridge; available from J Hoyle, Filling Station, Mitton; The Fisherman's Haunt, 161 Blackburn Road (also Northern AA permits, RD licences); John Hoyle (tackleists), 31 Larkhill, Blackburn and E Harrison, 67 Castle View, Clitheroe.

Lancashire FFA have 4m; tickets only to members' friends. **Blackburn** (10m SW) and Dist AA has several miles on Ribble and other fisheries on **Lune, Wenning, Aire, Gilpin** and reservoirs. Some dt; apply hon sec, Blackburn tackleists (J Hoyle, 31 Larkhill) and Fisherman's Haunt (as above). Two rods on Hodder for residents of Red Pump Hotel, Bashall Eaves; dt issued. Some permits from Rectory, Stoneyhurst College. Clitheroe Corporation issue dt for water below Edisford Bridge. Other Tackleists: Ken Varey, 32a King Street; Harry Le-Moine, 22 Accrington Road, Blackburn. Hotels: "Inn at Whitewell" *(advt p 17)* and Roefield (free fishing for guests; non-residents 50p day).

Chatburn (Lancs). Ribble, 1m W; good trout, occasional salmon and sea trout. Several miles of river preserved by Clitheroe AA; limited visitors' tickets through members only.

Sawley (N Yorks). On Ribble; ns Chatburn, 2m. Salmon, sea trout, trout and grayling. Trout and salmon fishing good. Several miles preserved by Yorkshire FFC (visitors' tickets through members only). Inn: Spread Eagle.

Gisburn (N Yorks). Trout, salmon. Stocks Beck: Gisburn AA.

Long Preston (N Yorks). Ribble, 1m W. Trout, grayling, odd salmon, coarse fish. Long Preston AC issues dt £1.50 for 1m; apply Maypole Hotel. Several miles of water preserved by Blackburn and District AA; visitors' tickets through members only. Settle AA also has water *(see Settle).* Malham Tarn, 3½m NE. Hotels: Boar's Head (fishing for residents), Maypole.

Settle (N Yorks). Settle AA has 7½m of good trout fishing in Ribble between Langcliffe, Settle and vicinity of Long Preston. Tickets at Royal Oak Hotel. Fly only; limit 2½ brace. Water stocked yearly. Good coarse fishing in waters below Settle. Hotel: Royal Oak, from which

Settle AA tickets are obtainable during licencing hours. **Malham Tarn** is 6m from Settle and holds large trout. Dt available *(see Yorkshire Lakes, reservoirs, etc)*. Further north are Manchester AA's waters. Other hotels at Settle: Falcon and Golden Lion.

Horton-in-Ribblesdale (N Yorks). Trout; preserved from source to Helwith Bridge, including all tributaries, by Manchester AA. Fish passes erected at Settle Weir, but few fish ascending. Assn also has **Newhouses Tarn** (fly only); trout and stretch on **Lune** at Firbank, near Sedbergh. No tickets. Annual membership: £100. Hotel: Crown Inn.

Tributaries of the Ribble

HODDER: Good salmon and trout water.

Higher Hodder Bridge (Lancs and Yorks). Salmon, sea trout, trout, grayling and coarse fish *(see Clitheroe on Ribble)*.

Caldermouth (Lancs). Dunkenhalgh Estate water for which st previously available now rented to a fishing club. No details available as we go to press.

Chipping (Lancs). Hodder, 1½m E. Salmon, sea trout, trout and grayling. Loud, 1m SE. Trout and sea trout. About ½m of Hodder below Doeford Bridge on right bank and several miles of **River Loud** are preserved by Loud and Hodder AA; tickets if accompanied by member. Hotel: Derby Arms.

Whitewell (Lancs). Salmon, sea trout, trout, grayling. Two rods on Assn water for residents at Red Pump Hotel, Bashall Eaves.

Slaidburn (N Yorks); ns Clitheroe, 8½m. Hodder; salmon, sea trout and trout; all preserved. Hotel: Bounty.

CALDER: Mostly polluted but RD issues dt (limited) for stretch from Mitton Wood to Calder Foot, north bank. Some club water.

Whalley (Lancs). West Calder. Ribble, 2m W; salmon, sea trout and coarse fish. Marsden Star AS has Morton Hall Farm stretch *(see Colne)*. Hodder, 2m W; salmon, sea trout and trout. Sabden Brook, 2m E. Park Brook, 3m SW. Dean Brook, 4m W. Crowshaw Reservoir, 5m NW.

Barrowford (Lancs). Pendle Water; trout. Colne Water (polluted) and Pendle join near Barrowford to form Calder (polluted). **Leeds and Liverpool Canal** runs through district *(see Colne)*.

Burnley (Lancs). Local waters mostly polluted. Burnley AS leases **Lea Green Reservoir,** but tickets available only to local ratepayers; trout. Reservoir at **Hapton** stocked with rainbow trout; dt from Trevor Hughes, Egerton Road, Fallowfield, Manchester 14. Tickets for **Leeds and Liverpool Canal** from Northern AA and local tackeists: Littlewoods, Parker Lane; Mack's, 33a Parliament Street; H McLoughlan, 33a Parliament Street.

COLNE (tributary of Calder). Much pollution but holds some trout and coarse fish.

Colne (Lancs). Colne; trout. Water held by Colne Water AS. **Leeds and Liverpool Canal** held by Northern AA (Lancashire side of Mile Tunnel) and Marsden Star AS (Yorkshire side of Mile Tunnel); pike, trout, tench, bream, roach, rudd, perch; st and dt for waters held by both clubs. Northern AA: st £2.50, dt 50p. Marsden Star AS: (other waters on **Calder, Aire, Earby Beck** and **Greenfield Reservoir**) st £6, dt 30p from Fodens *(see below)*. For Colne AS and reservoirs see *Foulridge*. Tackleists: D W & D Foden. Post Office Buildings, Barnoldswick; Boyces, 44 Manchester Road, and Wally's Tackle Shop, Forest Street, both **Nelson.**

Foulridge (Lancs). Four British Waterways Board reservoirs: **Lower (or Burwains), Upper, Slipperhill, White Moor.** Only Lower fishable by ticket; match bookings from J Sutton, Western Electric, Foulridge, dt from bailiff on bank; trout, pike, roach, perch, bream, gudgeon. Other reservoirs let to clubs: members only. *(See also Colne)*.

ROTHER

(For close seasons, licences, etc, see Southern Water Authority, p 38)

Rises near Rotherfield and reaches sea at Rye Bay. Mostly coarse fish, with trout in upper reaches and tributaries but runs of sea trout increasing. Mullet and bass in estuary. Mullet also abound in lower reaches of Tillingham and Brede in season.

Rye (Sussex). Near mouth of Rother; coarse fish. Rye and Dist AS has 3½m upstream from Starlock to Wittersham. Club also has water on **Brede, Tillingham** and various drains on Romney Marsh. Memberships (£9.50), wt £3, dt £1 from hon sec. Ashford and Dist APS have water on **Royal Military Canal;** dt £1. Romney Marsh *(see Kent—small streams)* is close by. Several clubs have water, including Hastings, Bexhill and Dist (Freshwater) AA (12m to Robertsbridge, membership limited). List of accommodation from Adams of Rye Ltd and hon sec. Tackleists: C A Robins, 22/23 Landgate.

Wittersham (Sussex). Clive Vale AC have good stretch at Blackwall Bridge. Dt £1 from hon sec.

Newenden (Sussex). Large bream, chub and roach; preserved by Rother FA which controls about 12m from Robertsbridge to Iden, except Bodiam AC waters *(see Bodiam)*. Tickets: B Hart, Riverside Cottages, Newenden.

Bodiam (Sussex). Trout (small), coarse fish. Bodiam AC preserves N bank from Bodiam Bridge to Udiam rly bridge and part of S bank. Signed. Dt 50p from bailiff on bank. Fishes best Sept onwards. Rother FA has 12m. No individ dt, but applications from clubs may be accepted. Bookings from W S Rudd, 25 Streampit Lane, Sandhurst, Kent. Rye AS has water from Iden downstream; dt issued. Visiting clubs should apply in advance to hon sec. Kent RD has stretch from Iden Bridge to Scots Float (right bank only). Hotels: Castle, Justins. Anglers catered for.

Etchingham (Sussex). Hastings, Bexhill and Dist AA has water; trout and coarse fish; dt from Mrs V Becker, 5 Oxenbridge Cottages.

Stonegate (Sussex). Tunbridge Wells AS has trout water; dt to members' friends only. Hotel: Bridge.

Tenterden (Kent). River now improving after decline due to dredging. Tenterden and Dist AA has many miles on Rother and tributaries; no day or period tickets. Tackleists: N Warwick.

BREDE: Rother tributary. Coarse fish, a few small trout; controlled by Rye and Clive Vale clubs. No tickets. Fishing stations: **Rye, Winchelsea.**

SEVERN

(For close seasons, licences, etc, see Severn-Trent Water Authority, p 41)

Longest river in England. Rises in Wales (N Powys) and flows 180m into Bristol Channel. Fair salmon river, with commercial fisheries near mouth; spring salmon in January/April and May. Average size good. Some trout and grayling in upper reaches, but river notable chiefly for coarse fishing, expecially for chub in the upper reaches and barbel in the middle river. Shad run up river in May and are taken on rod and line, principally at Tewkesbury Weir. *(Soc advts p 129 and facing p 141)*.

Sharpness (Glos). Coarse fishing in the **Gloucester and Berkeley Canal** from Severn Bridge to Hempstead Bridge, Gloucester (about 16m); bank licence 50p from any bridge house; rod licence 25p.

Gloucester (Glos). Gloucester United AA controls several miles of Severn from Haw Bridge to Ashleworth, st £5, dt 65p, from tackleists *(see below)*, Haw Farmhouse, Boat Inn (Ashleworth). Assn also has water at **Deerhurst** and on gravel pit at **Saul.** Gloucester AC has trout water on **Leadon** (preserved). **Gloucester and Berkeley Canal** provides 15m of good coarse fishing; st 50p, dt 15p from bridge keepers. Tackleists: F Harvey & Co, 13 Barton Street; Allsports, 86 Barton Street (dt for Wye salmon fishing); D Caldwell, 45 Bristol Road; Jeff Aston, 78 High Street; Rod & Gun Room, Alvin Street. Hotels: New County, Fleece, New Inn.

Tewkesbury (Glos). Salmon, twaite and coarse fish. Avon: coarse fish. Birmingham AA has stretches at Bushley, Uckinghall, Ripple, Lower Lode, Deerhurst, Chaceley, Apperley and Maisemore. Tewkesbury AA water on Severn (400 yds above weir to Lower Lode—Ham bank), **Avon** (Healings mill to Abbey Mill) and **Mill Avon** (Abbey Mill to Lower Lode—both banks); membership limited to 3m radius of Tewkesbury Cross; dt and st from bailiffs. Hotels: Swan (Trust House), Bell, Hop Pole. Tackleist: J Wilkins, Barton Street.

Ripple (Worcs). Bream, pike, perch, chub,

TAKE CARE

you owe it to yourself and those who might risk their life trying to rescue you.

Don't take risks. Follow local advice and heed warning notices. Discretion is the better part of safety.

Always make sure that someone knows where you are going and what time you expect to be back.

Never let children go fishing alone or unsupervised. Make sure that you know where they are going, who they are with and that they can all swim.

Walk with special care at the water's edge. Banks can be slippery or suddenly collapse; undergrowth or hidden obstructions can trip you.

Wear the lightest clothing which will keep you warm and dry. Boots or waders should have non-slip soles.

On steep banks anchor yourself to something firm before starting to fish, especially if you are alone. Carry a small stake and line for this purpose.

Secure your keepnet strongly – it could be your lifeline if you were to fall in.

Wear a buoyancy aid when wading or in a boat or at all times if you cannot swim. They are comfortable and almost unnoticeable in use.

When wading always move upstream and prod the ground ahead with the handle of your landing net or a strong stick.

In a boat, fish sitting down; do not move about unnecessarily; when you do move, keep low and hold onto the boat; do not wear waders or wellingtons; do not overload the boat; check that your anchor, ropes, oars, rowlocks etc. are sound.

Watch how far you are drifting and move away from danger in good time.

On the sea, take sufficient fuel and carry flares; if bad weather threatens, head for harbour in good time.

Make the effort to **learn to swim;** it is well worthwhile whatever your age.

Learn basic rescue – you might be able to save someone from drowning.

ISSUED BY THE SEVERN-TRENT WATER AUTHORITY ON BEHALF OF THE SEVERN STANDING CONFERENCE ON WATER SAFETY AND THE TRENT WATER SAFETY COMMITTEE.

If you have any comments or questions contact the Severn-Trent Water Authority – we are always happy to discuss water safety! (See p. 41 for address.)

dace, roach. Ripple Brook. Avon 2m E; chub, dace, roach, pike, perch. Birmingham AA has 3m.

Upton-on-Severn (Worcs). Chub, barbel, bream, roach, dace, perch and pike. Upton-upon- Severn AA has right bank above town road bridge, and below, half-way to railway bridge. Free parking. St £6, dt 50p from G S Hinn, tackleist, 21 Old Street. Birmingham AA has two stretches, about 3m in all; members only. Other tackleists: V J Herbert, Church Street. Hotels: King's Head, Swan, The Inn, Star (Assn HQ).

Worcester (Worcs). Pike, chub, dace, bream, roach, salmon, trout, etc. S-T WA rents water above Kempsey and above Diglis Weir. Worcester & Dist United AS has more than 5m in four stretches; no dt but limited number honorary members' books issued by hon sec or through tackleists (below); society also has stretch of **Worcester–Birmingham Canal**, from Blackpole Bridge to Diglis Basin, 1½m on **Avon** and two meadows on **Teme** at Powick. Teme, 2m S; coarse fish, trout, salmon. Birmingham AA has stretches at Severn Stoke, Hallow, Grimely and Holt Fleet, rights on Worcester and Birmingham Canal from King's Norton to Blackpole (near Worcester); bream, roach, perch, pike. Hotels: Bridge (anglers' meeting centre), Star, Great Western, Diglis, Pack Horse. Tackleists: S F Dyer, New Street; W Richardson, St John's; F Durrant & Sons, Mealcheapen Street.

Lincombe and Holt (Worcs). Holt, Fleet and Wharf Hotels issue dt for water below bridge. Good perch at Lincombe.

Stourport-on-Severn (Worcs). At confluence of Severn and Stour; also **Staffordshire and Worcestershire Canal;** coarse fish. Lyttelton AA has 1½m; dt 60p from hon sec. Birmingham AA has water. Hampstall Cider House, Astley Burf, issues dt. Tackleist: J White, Raven Street. Hotel: Showman; where Lyttelton AA tickets are sold during opening hours.

Bewdley (Worcs). Salmon, trout, excellent head of coarse fish in general, barbel exceptional. Kidderminster AA has 2m, ½m of water free to licence-holders in town. Birmingham AA waters in vicinity. Cards for both clubs from S R Lewis, tackleist, 2 Severnside South, who runs own riverside guest-house and issues tickets for private pool; carp, pike, etc.

Upper Arley (Worcs). Salmon, trout, grayling, chub, dace, pike, etc. Dowles Brook, 3m S. Birmingham AA has stretch. Hotels: Valentia, Harbour and Unicorn (last two issue dt).

Hampton Loade (Salop). Pike, perch, chub, dace, trout, salmon; licences issued at Unicorn Inn. Birmingham AA water.

Bridgnorth (Salop). Salmon, trout, barbel (good), chub, pike, etc. Whitmore Reans AA rents a stretch here of about 1m. Bridgnorth AS has water and Birmingham AA has stretches at Bridgnorth, Knowle Sands, Danery, Quatford and Eardington. Salopian Fly FA has good stretches on **Worfe** at **Worfield** (3m NE); trout; members only. **Willey Park Pools** at **Broseley** (5m) and pools at **Ticklerton** are also on club card; rainbow, brown and some American brook trout. Membership limited. Tackleists: D H Foxall, Underhill Street; Jeffries, Whitburn Street; Hardwicks, Northgate. Hotels: Falcon, Fosters' Arms (both Low Town); Ball, King's Head (both High Town).

Coalport (Salop). Chub, barbel, pike, etc, fewer roach and dace than are found farther downstream. Some free water. Rowley Regis and Dist AS has stretch on right bank. No tickets.

Iron Bridge (Salop). Fish species—as Coalport; good fishing on association waters by permit; free fishing on Severn-Trent WA water by licence. Hotel: Tontine.

Buildwas (Salop). Coarse fish, grayling, salmon. Birmingham AA has fishing on both sides of river, 3m. Between here and Upper Arley *(see above)* the association has water at Quatford, 3m (The Danery); Eardington, 3m (The Crown); Hampton Loade, 3m (the Unicorn); Highley, 3m (The Ship).

Berrington (Salop). Severn, 1m N; chub, dace, pike, trout, salmon. Birmingham AA has Cotons Farm waters and former Cound Lodge Inn fishery (salmon as well as coarse fish) and downstream from Buildwas. Cound Brook, 1½m SW; trout; private. Tern, 2½m N; two pools; private. Hotels: Fox; The Bell.

Atcham (Salop). S-TWA has 3½m of right bank below the bridge available to licence holders. Prince Albert AS has members only fisheries here, at Bicton, Melverley, Longnor, Royal Hill, The Isle, Welshpool and Newton. Also fishings on the rivers **Gam, Vyrnwy** and **Banwy.**

Shrewsbury (Salop). Chub, pike, perch, roach, barbel, dace, a few trout; fishing free or by ticket. Excellent spring salmon fishing; annual local catch about 200 fish; steadily improving; best months Mar, Apr and May. Extensive fishery above and below weir mostly controlled by council. Permits from local authority. Wt for Ditherington AS water, 1m below weir, from Ebrall Bros *(see end of entry)*. Sabrina AC has 5m above town; members only; apply hon sec. Birmingham AA has stretches at Underdale, Bicton, Montford Bridge, Alberbury, Crewe Green, Pool Quay, Criggion and Buttington Bridge. Coventry AA has salmon and trout water on the Vyrnwy at **Meiford;** no tickets. Condover, Onny, Stapleton and Sheinton Brooks all private. **Marton Pool,** Chirbury, 16m SW; well stocked with coarse fish; boats from Sun Inn, Marton, Chirbury. Wingfield Arms Hotel controls ¾m of ticket water at Montford Bridge. Tackleists: Ebrall Bros, Smithfield Road; J H Holyoake, Mardol; Philipps, Abbey Foregate; Gordon Forrest, 12 Baker Street, who will supply information.

Pentre (Salop); ns Shrewsbury, 2m NW. Good coarse fishing. Hotel: Royal Hill.

Llandrinio (Montgomery). Chub, dace, trout, salmon; leave from farmers. Liverpool and Dist AA has water on main river at Leighton Bridge and on tributaries **Vyrnwy, Banwy** and **Rhiew;** dt from J Johnson, 97 L'pool Road N, Maghull, nr L'pool. Canal; coarse fish, tickets *(see Welshpool)*. Maerdy Brook, 2m SW. Arddleen Brook, excellent trout, dace and chub. Hotel: Golden Lion.

Welshpool (Montgomery). Salmon, trout, coarse fish (inc grayling). Trout small in streams, few but big in river. Welshpool and Dist AC now in Montgomeryshire AA which has 60m of coarse and game fishing in Severn, **Camlad, Vyrnwy, Banwy/Twrch.** Also **Llyn Tarw** (17 acres; clear; mostly fly only). **Shropshire Union Canal** (coarse fishing). Ticket 50p *(see under Newtown)*. The Leighton Estate waters (leased to Crewe AA; (annual memb £4.50) members only) adjoin those held by S-TWA below Kilkewydd Bridge. Sylfaen Brook is preserved. Some permits are available for **Maesmawr Pool** (5m NW). Other wa-

ters: Marton (coarse fish); boats from Sun Hotel, Marton (5m). Tackle and WA licences from A E Bond, Hall Street, and C D Millington, 3 Church Street. Hotels: Westwood Park, Welshpool; Bear, Newton; Black Lion, Llanfair Caereinion.

Forden (Montgomery). Montgomery, 3m. Trout, salmon, chub, dace, etc. Birmingham AA has extensive stretch. **Camlad;** trout, grayling. Montgomeryshire AA has water on river; tickets *(see Welshpool)*.

Montgomery (Montgomery). Severn, 2m; trout, salmon, grayling, chub, pike and perch. Lion Hotel, Caerhowell, has 400 yards of Severn; dt. **Camlad,** 2m N; good trout, grayling, chub. Mongomeryshire AA has water; tickets *(see Welshpool and Newtown)*. Warrington AA has ¾m and other waters at Caersws, Dolwen, Fron and Llanidloes. Also **Vyrnwy, Dee,** canals and pools. Herbert Arms, Cherbury, has 1½m; dt. Tackleists in Welshpool and Newtown.

Abermule (Montgomery). Severn and **Mule;** salmon, trout, grayling, coarse fish; mostly private, but dt for some lengths and free fishing for guests at Dolforwyn Hall (AA and RAC) on short length. Water not always fishable in summer. Montgomeryshire AA has 1½m of Severn and water on **Mule;** dt 60p from hon sec. *(See Welshpool.)*

Newtown (Montgomery). Salmon, trout, grayling, pike, chub, dace. Trout up to 3 lb 8 oz, chub to 7 lb 14 oz (excellent). Newtown and Dist FC, Llanfair Caerinion FC and Welshpool AC have joined to form Montgomershire AA, covering some 60m of coarse and game fishing on Severn and tributaries, brooks, canal and lakes. Dt for all waters 50p. St and wt available. Apply hon sec and local tackleists *(see also Welshpool)*. Birmingham AA and Prince Albert AS have two stretches here. Tackleists: L Bebb, Short Bridge Street. Hotels: Bear, Elephant and Castle.

Caersws (Montgomery). Maesmawr Hall Hotel has 3½m on Severn free to guests. Trout, coarse fish, some salmon. Mongomershire AA has waters on Severn and brooks: dt 50p from hon sec. Limited dt for club's trout pool (Fachwen Pool, Aberhafesp) £2. Birmingham AA water here, above at Llanidloes, below at Newtown and Aberbechan.

Llanidloes (Montgomery). Trout, salmon, pike, chub, dace, grayling. Llanidloes AA has about 20m fishing on upper Severn, **Afon Clywedog** and other tributaries. St, wt and dt from hon sec, Montgomeryshire Fedn of Angling Assns (address in Welsh section) or tackleists. **Llyn Clywedog** provides first-class sport with brown and rainbow trout; dt £2.80, wt £15, st £30 *(see Powys Lakes in Welsh*

section for further details). Warrington AA has water downstream. Red Lion Inn has 2m trout fishing at Llandinam; dt 50p. At **Trefeglwys** (4m N) is caravan park with 40m of fishing (trout and coarse) on **Trannon,** Severn and **Dulas.** Best months for trout: April–July. Nantgeifr Reservoir, 3m NE; trout. Hotels: Lloyds, Unicorn, Queen's Head, Angel, Temperance, Royal Oak, Red Lion.

Tributaries of the Severn

LEADON: Trout, coarse fish (some barbel introduced).

Upleadon (Glos). Trout; preserved from Upleadon Church to M50 motorway by Gloucester AC.

Ledbury (Hereford). Ledbury AA has trout water, no dt. Castlemorton Lake; coarse fishing; free, but RD licence necessary.

AVON: The principal tributary of the lower Severn. Roach, chub, dace and perch dominate higher reaches; bream and pike, the latter patchily distributed, below Evesham. Barbel beginning to appear.

Cheltenham (Glos). Cheltenham AC controls 9 or 10m of Avon from **Bredon** up. Good coarse fishing (perch, pike and chub and bream mostly). Dt 65p, wt £2.50 (Mon–Sat only) from secretary or country headquarters, the Bell Inn, Eckington *(see Twyning).*

Twyning (Glos). Chub, dace, roach, pike, perch, bream. White Swan Piscatorials preserve left bank of river from near Bredon Church to four meadows below Twyning lane. Club also has water on Severn at **Bewdley; Mease** at Harlaston; **Tern** near Wellington (Salop); and **Lugg** near Hereford; members only. Birmingham AA has stretches at Mythe Farm, Twyning, Bredon, Eckington. Cheltenham AC has about 10m of the **Avon** running through Bredon, Strensham, Eckington and Birlingham. Coarse fish, wt £2.50, dt 65p for part only, Mon–Sat only, from Bell Inn, Eckington. Other water for members only.

Pershore (Worcs). Pike, perch, roach, dace, chub, bream. Severn-Trent WA has stretch here, 2m on one bank, 1m on the other; for licence-holders. Worcester United AS has water nearby *(see Worcester)*. Birmingham AA has water here, at Nafford, Birlingham, Pensham, Fladbury and Cropthorne. Some free water in recreation ground. Tackleists: W L Brown, 3 High Street; H Heritage, 17 Boat Lane. Hotel: Angel.

Evesham (Worcs). Pike, perch, bream, roach, dace, chub. Evesham AA has water in town, dt 60p from bailiff on bank; E Huxley has stretch at Hampton Ferry accommodatiing 159 anglers. Dt 40p from cafe; matches booked at 60p per peg. BAA *(see Birmingham)* has several fisheries in vicinity. Hampton Playing Field and Workman Gardens (night fishing only) reserved for local anglers, permits from Council. Tackleists: J Heritage, Boat Lane; Daniels, Avonside; Evesham Sports Centre, 60a Bridge St. Details of accommodation from Town Guide.

Stratford-upon-Avon (Warwick). Recently dredged. A stretch of the Avon preserved by Corporation. Birmingham AA has "Seven Meadows" downstream of Stratford and stretches at Bidford, Barton, Milcote and Hampton Lucy; good chub and dace and also water on **Stour** (2m S). **Stratford Canal** provides good coarse fishing; Birmingham AA has water. Stour, 1m (trout); other trout fishing at Alcester on Arrow (8m). Dene, 5m NE. Tackleist: Coopers, 37 Greenhill Street. Permits for a number of waters in the district; RWA licences. Hotel: Salmon Tail, Evesham Road.

Leamington (Warwick). Bream, chub, dace, roach, pike, perch. Avon at **Barford, Wasperton** and **Guy's Cliffe** preserved by Royal Leamington Spa AA; annual membership, £3. **Leam;** roach, dace, chub, pike, perch, carp; association and Corporation water; dt 15p, st 85p for latter from Parks Director, Jephson Gardens. Association also has 12½m in **Warwick Canal;** coarse fish (good carp and tench in June, July, Aug); st £1.50. For canal only, st 85p, dt 40p. Tackleists: F Cooper, Clarendon Street;

Cartwright, Regent Place; Rook's, Clemens Street; Norris, 24 Russell Terrace.

Rugby (Warwick). Centre for **Draycote Water** (trout). *(See Midlands Reservoirs.)* Rugby Fed of Anglers has water on **Avon, Grand Union** and **Oxford canals,** on **Barby** and **Sulby lakes,** on part of **Stanford Reservoir.** Good general coarse fishing. Memberships, tickets for **Newbold Quarry** (tench, pike and roach) and Coventry AA water on **Grand Union canal** from tackleists and Rugby FA hon sec. Tackleists: Banks & Burr, 27 Claremont Road; C Donald, 155a Bilton Road. Hotels: Three Horseshoes, Rugby; Dun Cow, Dunchurch; Albany, Crick.

ARROW joined by the **Alne** at Alcester; flows into Avon at Salford Priors: Coarse fish, some trout.

Salford Priors (Worcs). Arrow and Avon; coarse fish.

Wixford (Warwick). Pike, perch, roach, dace, chub and bream; dt 30p for about 1m of water from Fish Hotel. Lakes: Ragley Park, 1m NW; permits for local residents only.

Redditch (Worcs). Redditch AC has water at **Fladbury, Binton** and **Wood Norton.** Inquire hon sec. Good fishing in **Lodge Pool,** tench and carp, and **Arrow Valley Lake,** a local authority leisure park. Dt on site. Tackleists: Powells, 28 Mount Pleasant. Hotels: Royal, Southcrest.

Alvechurch (Worcs). Barnt Green FC has rights on **Upper and Lower Bittell Reservoirs, Arrow Pools** and **Canal feeder. Lower Bittell** and **Mill Shrub** trout (fly only) remainder coarse fish. Guest tickets for **Upper Bittell** only issued by members to their friends. *(See also Salwarpe-Bromsgrove.)*

STOUR (tributary of Avon): Coarse fish, trout.

Shipston (Warwick). Shipston-on-Stour AC has about 12m; members only. Tickets (limited), for High Furze from E Draper, 37 Station Rd, Shipston-on-Stour. Stocked with trout by Severn RD. Birmingham AA has six stretches between Crimscote and the confluence with the Avon at Milcote. Knee Brook (2½m S); landowner issues ticket. Hotel: George.

LEAM (tributary of Avon): Coarse fish.

Eathorpe (Warwick). Coventry Godiva AS has fishery here; coarse fish. Good winter fishing; st.

HAM BROOK (tributary of Leam): Coarse

fish.

Fenny Compton (Warwick). Good pike, bream, tench, roach in **Oxford Canal.** London AA has 3m from here to **Claydon.** Dt from George and Dragon, Fenny Compton. Itchen, 3m N. Lake; Stoneton House Lake, 2½m NE. Farnborough Hall Lake; fishing good, but by invitation only.

SOWE (tributary of Avon):

Coventry (W Midlands). Excellent trout and coarse fishing on **Packington Estate, Meriden** *(advt p 7)* (5½m NW; S-TWA licence required). Over 5m of river fishing and 160 acres of lakes. Rainbow and brown trout; also coarse fishery 2m off. *For details see Midlands (reservoirs and lakes).* Coventry AA has extensive fishing on rivers, canals and reservoirs including fly-fishing on **River Vyrnwy** at **Meiford** and coarse fishing in **Trent, Nene, Thames** and **Warwickshire Avon.** Rivers are for members only, but dt 60p for canals and reservoirs may be had from tackleists in Coventry area or hon sec. Canal waters include stretches on **Coventry Canal, Grand Union, Ashby Canal** and **Oxford Canal.** Dt from bailiffs for Assn's **Napton Reservoirs,** noted bream, carp, tench and roach water; S-TWA licence needed. Tackleists: W H Lane & Son Ltd, 31/33 London Road.

BRAUNSTON CANAL: Coarse fish; sport only fair.

Braunston (Northants). Tickets for canal from Coventry AA. S-TWA licence also needed; obtainable from Coventry tackleists. Hotel: Old Ship Inn.

TEME: Trout and coarse fish, with a few salmon; has acquired reputation for grayling.

Worcester (Worcs). Worcester St John's AS has some water. Worcester and Dist UAS has two meadows *(see R Severn).*

Broadwas (Worcs). Trout, grayling, chub, dace. Birmingham AA has stretch of left bank.

Leigh Court (Worcs). Trout, chub, dace, grayling, pike, perch, salmon. Bransford AS and local clubs rent Leigh to Powick; members only.

Tenbury (Worcs). Good trout, grayling, coarse fish. Salmon run from Feb to end of season, following removal of obstructions at Worcester (April, May, June best). Peacock Inn has ½m one bank (mainly bottom and spinning water). Limited dt for Tenbury FA water; fly only; tickets from hon sec. Dt for ¾m at **Ashford Bowdler** (near Ludlow) from Mrs Wall. Birmingham AA has water here, near Ludlow, below Eastham Bridge, and on **Ledwyche Brook.** For **Kyre** carp pool, apply S Lewis, 2 Severside S, Bewdley. Tackleist: W E Bunce, 61 Teme Street. Hotels: Royal Oak, Swan, Crow.

Ludlow (Salop). Trout, grayling, chub, dace, roach, perch, pike. Ludlow AC has ¾m both banks above town, also about ¼m of **Corve.** Flyfishing on upper part of Teme water; dt (limited) available to visitors resident in the area. Trout water restocked annually. Best months: June and July. Excellent grayling. Birmingham AA has fishing here and on several other stretches of Teme. **Ledwyche Brook,** 1½m E; trout, grayling, chub, etc; Birmingham AA has ¾m; landowners sometimes give permission elsewhere. Hotels: The Feathers *(advt p 134)*, Angel, Bull, Bull Ring Tavern, Charlton Arms, and Exchange.

Bromfield (Salop). Trout, grayling, chub, pike; all water strictly preserved by Earl of Plymouth Estates, who also own some 5m of the **Corve.**

Leintwardine (Hereford). Birmingham AA has water on **Clun** here and at Aston and Broadward; members only.

Bucknell (Salop). Trout, grayling, chub; preserved by landowners. **Redlake Brook;** trout and eels. Licence to fish Redlake from Messrs Prince & Pugh *(see Knighton).*

Knighton (Powys). Trout; strictly preserved except for 1m free to licenceholders. Tackle, licences from Messrs Prince & Pugh. Hotels: Swan, Norton Arms.

ONNY: Good trout, grayling, chub, etc.

Plowden (Salop). Trout, chub; strictly private. Plowden Club has 4m running through Plowden Estate.

Craven Arms (Salop). Grove Estate water, N of Craven Arms, 1½m. Onny, 3½m. Quinney and Byne Brooks, preserved and strictly keepered by Midland Flyfishers; trout, grayling; members only; no tickets; club also has water from Stokesay Castle Bridge to Bromfield. Stokesay Pool; pike, chub. Bache Pool, Bache Farm; carp; dt 25p from farm. Dt £2 for trout and grayling fishing on 150 yards of Onny from Mrs Maund, 1 Onny Cottage, The Grove. Tackleist: W H Miller, Market Street.

SALWARPE: Trout, coarse fish, but much of river fishless through pollution.

Droitwich (Worcs). Trout above, coarse fish below; leave from landowners. Severn 6m W. Droitwich and District AS has water at **Holt Fleet;** dt from hon sec to members' guests only. Noted chub waters. Society also has **Heriotts Pool** (large carp). Dt (open to all) from Talbot Hotel, High Street. Some coarse fishing in canal; Birmingham AA members only (association also has water on **Salwarpe** at Claines and Porters Mill). **Westwood Park Lake** excellent coarse fishing. Dt. Enquire of tackleist: D Walsh, Queen Street. Other hotels: Worcestershire Brine Baths; Raven; Chateau Impney.

Bromsgrove (Worcs). Tardebigge Reservoir privately rented. Upper and Lower Bittel Reservoirs owned by Barnt Green FC; members only *(see also Arrow—Alvechurch)*. Hewell Grange Lake; permits from local clubs. *(See also Worcester and Birmingham Canal.)*

STOUR: Polluted and fishless.

Stourbridge (Worcs). **Staffordshire and Worcestershire Canal;** coarse fish. Tackleist: Riley's, Lower High Street *(see also canal)*.

Brierley Hill (W Midlands). Stour, 3m S, polluted. **Himley Park Lake;** coarse fish; Dudley Corpn issues dt. WA licenceholders may fish Fenn's Pools, Middle Pools and Grove Pools. Other clubs: Brierley Hill AC (no water) and various works clubs. Tackleist: Maybury, Church Street (tickets and WA licences).

Dudley (W Midlands). Lakes: Pennsett-Grove Pool, Middle Pool, Fenns Pool, 3m SW *(see Brierley Hill)*. Himley Park Lakes and Common Pool, 4m W. Dudley AS has 3m between **Bewdley** and **Stourport** (Severn). Plenty of fishing in canals within 6m radius. Lodge Farm Reservoir; Dudley Corporation. At Parkes Hall, Coseley, 2½m away, is good pool for which dt can be had; coarse fish (Dudley Corporation). Tackleist: Peter Gordon, 84 High Street.

SMESTOW (tributary of Stour): Polluted.

Wolverhampton (W Midlands). Smestow, 2m W; polluted. Some fishing in Penk at Penkridge. Whitmore Reans AS (hon annual membership £4) preserves water on **Penk, Tern, Roden** and **Severn.** Most local water on Severn held by Birmingham AA; permits from tackleists, Patshull Pool, Pool Hall (2m away) and

Tong Mere and Castle Pool (10m away). Further information from local tackleist: Fenwicks, Pitt Street.

TERN: Coarse fish, some trout.

Crudgington (Salop). A few trout and coarse fish. White Swan Piscatorials *(see Twyning—Avon, Severn)* have a fishery here.

Hodnet (Salop). Tern, 1m E; a few trout and coarse fish. Strine Brook, 2m E. Lakes: Rose Hill Ponds, 4m NE. **Hawkstone Park Lake,** 3½m; excellent tench and carp water (40 lb bags not uncommon) and large roach, rudd, pike and eels. Dt from hon sec, Wem AC or bailiff and D Wolltton, High Street, Wem; boats available.

Market Drayton (Salop). Trout, pike, roach, dace; private. Several private lakes and ponds in neighbourhood. At Great Sowdley, 7m SE, are canal reservoirs; Stoke AS; perch, pike, roach, tench, carp.

MEESE (tributary of Tern): Trout, coarse fish.

Newport (Salop). Meese, 1m N; trout; private. Lakes: Chetwynd Park Pond, 1m N. Minton's, Limekiln and Wildmoor Pools. 3m S. Moss Pool, 1½m NE. Dt for pools and canal from tackleist: H Tucker, The Square.

REA: Trout, grayling; preserved but leave sometimes given.

Minsterley (Salop). Trout, grayling, Minsterley Brook. Habberley Brook, 3m SE. Lake: Marton Pool, 7m SW. Hotel: Miner's Arms, Minsterley.

SHELL BROOK (tributary of Roden):

Ellesmere (Salop). Shell Brook, 2m NW; preserved. Halghton Brook, 4m N. Roden, 6m SE. Lakes: **Ellesmere Meres,** noted for bream (12 lb plus). Ellesmere AC issue dt £1 for **Whitemere** and **Blakemere** (bank fishing only). Sunday fishing is allowed. Boats available on most assn waters for members only. Ellesmere AC members may fish 4m stretch of **Shropshire Union Canal;** coarse fish. Tackleist: Clay & Sons, 51 Scotland Street (for club tickets'. Hotels: Black Lion, Bridgewater, Red Lion (Ellesmere AC HQ); tickets *(see also Shropshire Lakes)*.

PERRY: Trout, preserved.

Baschurch (Salop). Perry, 1m W; trout; some leave from landowners. Birmingham AA have two stretches. Severn, 5m S; chub, dace, pike, trout, salmon. Lakes: Birch Grove Pool, 1½m NE.

Berth Pool, 1m NE. Fennymere Pool, 2m E. Marton Pool, 2m NE.

VYRNWY: Provides sport with trout, grayling, coarse fish and salmon.

Llanymynech (Salop). Trout, salmon, grayling, roach, perch, pike, chub, etc. For Lord Bradford's water at Lower House Farm inquire of agent, Llanymynech. Vrynwy Angling Committee has length. S-TWA rents a short length, about four fields, on which fishing free to holder of WA licences. Warrington AA and Coventry AA have short stretches; members only. Hotels: Bradford Arms, Cross Keys, Lion and the Dolphin. Also The Willows boarding house and Central Cafe. Good trout fishing at **Lake Vyrnwy** *(see Montgomeryshire Lakes in Welsh section)*.

Llansantffraid (Powys). Bryn Tanat Hall and Lion Hotel have fishing for guests.

Meiford (Powys). Montgomeryshire AA has water; here and at **Maesbrook;** restricted to 12 rods; dt 60p from hon sec. Birmingham AA have water here and at Dolanog.

MORDA (tributary of Vyrnwy):

Oswestry (Salop). Severn, **Vyrnwy, Tanat, Dee, Ceiriog, Perry, Morlas, Morda, Clywedog Reservoir.** Many good trout lakes and carp pools, and excellent fishing in **Shropshire Union Canal,** all within easy reach. Most river fishing preserved, but Oswestry AS has good water game and coarse (including carp). St £4; no dt. Lakes: Meres at Ellesmere give good coarse fishing. Lake Vyrnwy (18m), good trout; proprietor of Lake Vyrnwy Hotel will give particulars *(see also Powys Lakes in Welsh section)*. Tackleist (and WA licences): J Ellis,

Regal Sports Stores. Hotels: Bear, Queen's, Wynnstay. Morton Lodge Hotel, Morton, can arrange fishing on Tanat, Vyrnwy and local pools.

TANAT (tributary of Vyrnwy): Trout (good average size), chub, and grayling, but fewer than there used to be.

Llan-y-Blodwell (Salop). Horseshoe Inn has 1½m and Green Inn, Llangedwyn, has short stretch; dt issued (3 rods only); fly only.

Llanrhaiadr-y-Mochnant (Powys). ns Llanfyllin, 7m—Moch; trout; free. Tanat, 1m; trout, grayling, chub, etc; 6m from Llangedwyn to Llangynog preserved by Upper Tanat FC, strictly members only.

CAIN (tributary of Vyrnwy): Trout, coarse fish.

Lanfyllin (Powys). Trout. Hotel: Bodfach Hall, which caters for fishermen and has 200 yds. Guests may fish adjoining ¼m free of extra charge. Hotel also has boat on Lake Vyrnwy (10m); trout.

BANWY (tributary of Vyrnwy): Trout, grayling, chub, pike, dace and chance of salmon here and there.

Llanfair-Caereinion (Powys). Montgomeryshire AA has about 4m trout fishing on Banwy and Twrch *(see under Welshpool on main river for permit details)*. Permits from Wynnstay Hotel or hon sec. No maggot fishing; some Sunday fishing for st holders. Birmingham AA have stetch here and at Foel. April–June fly only on upper reaches. **Maesmawr Pool** lies 5m NE; strictly limited permits from Maesmawr Hall; 50p day. Hotel: Wynnstay Arms.

Llangadfan (Powys). Trout; Montgomershire AA has good stretch; dt 50p from hon sec.

SHROPSHIRE LAKES

ELLESMERE LAKES. Fishing station: **Ellesmere.** Excellent coarse fishing in Ellesmere (noted for Bream), **Crosemere, Newton Mere, Kettel Mere, Blakemere, Whitemere** (bream of 12 lb 4oz taken) and **Colemere.** Controlled by Ellesmere AC who issue dt, bank fishing only, on **Whitemere, Blakemere** and **Colemere.** Boats for members only. Dt also for **Hardwick Pool** (1m) noted tench water.

PEATSWOOD LAKE. Market Drayton 1m. Brown and rainbow trout av 1 lb 6 oz. Two lakes, 5½ and 2 acres approx. St £125, dt £7. Phone Market Drayton 4505 for details.

WALCOT LAKES. Lydbury North, 3m NE of Clun. Two extensive lakes, one controlled by Birmingham Anglers' Assn. Tench, pike and other coarse fish. *For membership details, see "Birmingham", under Rea (tributary of Trent)*.

SOMERSET (streams, lakes and reservoirs)

(For close seasons, licences, etc, see Wessex Water Authority, p 39)

AXE. Rises on Mendips and flows 25m NW to Bristol Channel near Weston-super-Mare. A few trout in upper reaches and tributaries, but essentially a coarse fish river, containing a mixture of the usual species, with roach now predominating.

Weston-super-Mare and Bleadon (Som). Weston-super-Mare AA has 8½m of Axe, 4m of **Brue** at Mark, near Highbridge, stretches of **Old Glastonbury Canal, Old Bridge River, Congresbury Yeo** and **North Drain,** and two ponds (good carp), with trout and chub fishing in tributaries **Spring River** (Cheddar Yeo) and **Crooked River.** Club also has rights on 8–10m of fishing on **Parret** and **Isle** as members of SE and W Wessex Federation of Anglers. St £4, wt £1.50, dt 50p. Cheddar AC has 6m stretch upstream of **Clewer.** Inquire hon sec. Tackle, tickets, licences from Maroli Pet Shop, 19 Orchard Street; Weston Decorators' Supply Ltd, 22 The Boulevard. Tickets also from hon sec. Many hotels *(See Sea Fishing Stations)*.

Brinscombe (Som). Bristol Amalgamated has three fields here and further waters at **Clewer** and **Weare.** St from hon sec and tackleists *(see Bristol)*.

BRICKYARD PONDS: Pawlett. Bristol Amalgamated tench fishery. St from hon sec or tackleists *(see Bristol)*.

BRISTOL RESERVOIRS *(advt p 12)* Chew Valley, Blagdon and Barrow Reservoirs provide some of the best lake trout fishing in Europe, with a total annual catch which may exceed 40,000 fish of high average size. Season and day tickets available. Details as follows:

Barrow Reservoirs—Barrow Gurney. Open mid-April to Oct 15; Brown and rainbow trout; dt (bank) £3.20, st £70 (concessionary £35), fly only.

Bladgon Lake—Blagdon. Open mid-April to Oct 15; noted brown and rainbow trout water; dt £9.25 (pulling boat) or £4.50 (bank) per rod per day; st £180 (concessionary £100), fly only.

Chew Valley Lake—Chew Stoke. Open mid-April to Oct 15; noted brown and rainbow trout water where fish run large; dt £10.50 (motor boat) or £4.50 (bank) per rod per day; st £180 (concessionary £100), fly only. For all waters apply to: Bristol Waterworks Company, Recreations Department, Woodford Lodge,

Chew Stoke, Bristol BS18 8XH (Chew Magna 2339). Bank dt from self-service kiosks at all waters. Reduced charges for boats after 3.0 pm. Concessions for juvs (under 17), OAP and registered disabled. All prices incl VAT.

Cheddar Reservoir—Cheddar. Opened as general coarse fishery in 1974. Bank fishing £1, tickets from self-service kiosks at Cheddar and Axbridge entrances. St £15.

WESSEX WATER AUTHORITY RESERVOIRS, managed by the Fisheries and Recreations Dept, King Square, Bridgwater. Licence-fee included in permit charge: concessions for jun and OAP.

Clatworthy Reservoir. 12m from **Taunton** in Brendon Hills; 130 acres brown and rainbow trout; fly only; 2¼m bank fishing. St £78; dt £4. Boats (limited) £7, incl fishing permit. Season April 4–Oct 15. Dt from keeper and self-service. Concessions for juvs.

Durleigh Reservoir. 2m W of **Bridgwater.** 77 acres; brown and rainbow trout; fly only. St £78. Dt £4. Boats £7 incl fishing permit. Dt at reservoir from ranger or self-service. Season March 28–Oct 15 inclusive.

Hawkridge Reservoir. 7m W of **Bridgwater.** 32 acres. Brown and rainbow trout; fly only. St £30, dt £2.50. Season April 4–Oct 15. No boats.

Otterhead Lakes. About 1m from **Churchingford** nr Taunton. Two lakes of 2¾ and 2 acres; brown and rainbow trout; fly only; no boats. St £50, dt £4. Season April 4–Oct 15. Concession for juveniles.

Sutton Bingham Reservoir. 3m S of Yeovil. 142 acres. Brown and rainbow trout; average 1¼ lb; fly only; st £92; dt £4. Boats £7 incl fishing permit. Season March 28–Oct 15.

CHARGOT WATER, Luxborough. 3 ponds. Trout; fly only. Dt from Mr Cattley, Ponds Cottage, or Sir Ed Malet, Chargot House. Dt £1.60.

DONIFORD STREAM (Swill River at Doniford) and **WASHFORD RIVER, Taunton.** Trout; strictly preserved.

HORNER WATER. On National Trust Holnicote Estate; upstream from Newbridge to Pool Bridge (4m) excluding Nutscale Reservoir; fly fishing, trout. Dt 50p, wt £2. Licences, tickets and tackle from John Lynn & Co. **Porlock.** (Tel 862427)

WIMBLEBALL RESERVOIR. 4m NE of Dulverton. Brown, rainbow and tiger trout. 340 acres. Fly only. Season: May 1–Oct 12. SWWA water. Dt £4, evening £2.50, boats £4 (£2.50 half day). Conces-sions jun and OAP. Tackleist: L Nichol-son, High St, Dulverton. Hotel: Carnar-von Arms.

YEO. Fishing station: **Congresbury.** Tidal. Good fly water for trout; a few coarse fish. Bristol Amalgamated have water here and at **Wrington.**

STOUR (Dorset)

(For close seasons, licences, etc. see Wessex Water Authority, p 39)

Rises in Wiltshire Downs and flows through Dorset, joining Hampshire Avon at its mouth at Christchurch. Noted coarse fishery (roach especially good), salmon up to Wimborne, trout and grayling patchily distributed. Salmon not numerous but large. River best for coarse fish in winter.

Christchurch (Dorset). Avon and Stour. Salmon, pike, perch, chub, roach, tench, dace. Very strictly preserved. Limited number of dt and wt on stretch between Iford Bridge and Wick Ferry. Wt £4, dt 80p, juvs half-price. From Hales, tack-leists (address below). Coarse fishing can be had on Royalty Fishery waters *(see Avon)*. Sea fishing from Mudeford in Christchurch Bay is fair. Tackleists: Davis (Bargates) Ltd, 75 Bargates; Hales Tackle, 258 Barrack Road, both of whom sell tickets for various fisheries in the district. Wt £4 and dt £1.50 for Stour from Hales. Hotel: King's Arms, Christ-church.

Throop (Dorset). Throop fisheries (Christ-church station 2½m); 5½m of salmon, trout, sea trout and coarse fishing. Best salmon, 48 lb; some brown trout; sea trout up to 10 lb. Stretch also contains excellent chub (best 8½ lb) and barbel (including fish of 13 lb, 14 lb and 16¼ lb), salmon and trout fishing rates on ap-plication. Coarse fishing: st £24, wt £7, ft £10, dt £2.40 (reduced rates for pension-ers and for juveniles; special rates for clubs; booking essential); for tickets, RD licences and all inquiries apply to Ernest Leah (manager), South Lodge, Hol-denhurst, Bournemouth BH8 0EF (Tel Bournemouth 35532). Coarse fishing tickets, licences and information also from tackleist: Hales, 258 Barrack Rd, Christchurch.

Hurn Bridge (Dorset). Stour and Moors; pike, perch, chub, roach, barbel. Christ-church AC has water on Moors; mem-bers only.

STOUR (Dorset)—Tributaries

Wimborne (Dorset). Coarse fish, trout, odd salmon. Trout average 1 lb and are taken on minnow or spinner. Roach run to good size. Red Spinner AS has water at Barford and Eyebridge; about 7m in all; members only. Boat fishing good from Nov; information from W H G Newman, Boat House, Canford Bridge, Wimborne (who will give details of river conditions; ring Wimborne 3443). Hon sec, Wimborne and Dist AC will also be glad to give information. Wimborne Club has about 8m in Wimborne, Lon-gham and Charlton Marshall areas; five coarse fish and two trout lakes, also 2m of trout-stream. Membership £10 pa (en-trance-fee £5) dt to friends of members only. The Old Mill, Corfe Mullen, issues tickets for about 1m (one bank only) and has accommodation. Tackleist: Minster Sports, 8 West Street, Wimborne BH21 1JP (information). Hotels: Griffen, King's Head, Three Lions, Greyhound.

Sturminster Marshall (Dorset). South-ampton PS has about 2m here. Coarse, a few trout; no tickets. The Old Mill Guest House, Corfe Mullen, issues dt: free fishing for residents.

Shapwick (Dorset). Coarse fish. South-ampton PS has several miles of fishing here; no tickets issued. Durweston AS has fishing. Strictly limited issue of dt from Post Office, when open. No matches.

Blandford Forum (Dorset). Fine roach, chub, dace, perch and pike; best Oct onwards. Blandford and Dist AC have most fishing from **Durweston** Bridge to **Crawford** Bridge. Tickets from hon sec or A Conyers (tackleist), West Street. Also club membership forms and RD licences (Tel Blandford 2307).

Sturminster Newton (Dorset). Chub, roach, dace, pike, perch, tench; fishing good. Sturminster and Hinton AA has 7m above and below town. For st £6, wt £3 and dt £1 apply club secretary. Hotels: Crown, Marnhull; White Hart; Swan Hotel, Fiddleford Inn; Cottage Guest House, Sturminster Newton, Romaynes, Lydlinch.

Stalbridge (Dorset). Stalbridge AA (membership £5 pa) has 3m of Stour and 1m on **Lydden**. Wt £3, dt £1.

Gillingham (Dorset). Trout and coarse fish; Gillingham and Dist AA; wt £2.50 and dt 75p for coarse fishing only from Hussey, Station Road, Gillingham.

Stourton (Wilts). **Stourhead New Lake** on Stourhead (western) Estate at Stourton, near Mere. Coarse fishing; June 16 to March 14; dt issued. Apply M Bullen, The Laundry, Gasper, Stourton. Hotel: Spread Eagle.

ALLEN:

Wimborne (Dorset). Trout, grayling and coarse fish. Bull Inn guests can have trout fishing on 2½m; brochure from Estate Office, Wimborne St Giles. Some trout rods from Shaftesbury Estates, Wimborne.

MOORS: As Allen.

Verwood (Dorset). Allen and Moors. Moors trout in parts, otherwise mainly roach; Ringwood club has water; *(See Ringwood under "Avon".)*

STOUR (Kent)

(For close seasons, licences, etc, see Thames Water Authority, p 42)

Rises in two arms north-west and south-east of Ashford, where they join. From junction river flows about 30m north-east and east to sea beyond Sandwich. Good coarse fishing lower down. Trout fishing restricted to club members in upper reaches.

Sandwich (Kent). River fast-running from Minster to Sandwich (Vigo Sluice); good fishing for bream and roach; few perch and tench; sea trout and grey mullet. Fishing free between Sluice and Richborough Road. Sandwich and Dist AA has 1m; dt from hon sec. Sandwich AA also has **Reed Pond** (coarse fish; dt). **Stonar Lake** (flats, bass, rudd, eels) and North and South Streams, **Lyden** (coarse fish; dt). Tackleists: Francis, The Butchery. Hotels: Red Lion, Ramsgate Road (dt for mullet); Bell; Haven Guest House. *(See also Sea Fishing Stations.)*

Grove Ferry. Stour and Little Stour. Bet-teshanger Colliery Welfare AS has 6m on Stour from **Plucks' Gutter** to **Stonar.** Roach, bream and mullet (Red Lion stretch, June–Aug). Society also has stretch at **Minster.** Tickets from hon sec, Red Lion r bailiff on bank Canterbury AA has water on Stour *(see Canterbury).*

Canterbury (Kent). Trout, coarse fish. Free within city boundary, except for municipal gardens stretch. River from city boundary to **Grove Ferry** private for members of Canterbury & Dist AA. Tickets (to be applied for in advance) for stretch from Grove Ferry Bridge to **Plucks' Gutter. Westbere, Fordwich** and

Vauxhall lakes, members only. Hotels in Canterbury: County, Falstaff, George and Dragon, Chaucer, Abbots Barton. Hotels on water: George and Dragon, Fordwich, Fordwich Arms, Grove Ferry, Dog and Duck, Stourmouth. Permits from bailiff on bank, tackleists or hon sec at headquarters, "Riversdale", 14 Mill Road, Sturry, nr Canterbury. Tackleists: Greenfield's Rod and Gun Store, 4–5 Upper Bridge Street (bait, licences).

Wye (Kent). Pike, roach, etc; private but some permission from owners. Hotel: King's Head.

Ashford (Kent). Ashford AS holds **River Stour** between **Ashford** and **Wye** (members only) and **Royal Military Canal;**

16m between **Iden Lock** and **West Hythe Dam.** Coarse fish; wt £4 dt £1. Water level fluctuates during winter due to land drainage, thus making fishing at times difficult. Cinque Ports AS has water, dt and wt. Tickets from J B Walker and Light Railway Restaurant, Hythe *(see Kent small streams, etc).* Ashford Working Men's Club has a pit; good tench, carp, rudd; members only; no dt. Tackle and licences from Ashford Sports, North St, and Ironmongers' Stores, Beaver Road. Hotels: County, Kent Arms.

LITTLE STOUR: Same fish as main river, but overgrown in places.

Pluck's Gutter (Kent). Dog and Duck Inn issues dt; also from bailiffs on bank.

STOUR (Suffolk)

(For close seasons, etc, see Anglian Water Authority, p 40)

Coarse fish river forming border between Suffolk and Essex, Some sea trout in semi-tidal waters below Flatford. Experimental restocking with salmon and sea trout was carried out by Essex RA.

Manningtree (Essex). Tidal; roach, dace, perch, pike and occasional sea trout (fish of 9 lb caught). Sea trout and coarse fish between RD notices at **Flatford Mill.** (Elm Park, Hornchurch and Dist AS waters). Club: Lawford and Manningtree AC. Hotel: White Hart.

Dedham (Essex). Coarse fish, fine bream and dace in mill pool. St for **Clovers Mill waters** (£4) from Clovers Ltd, Flour Mills, Dedham, Colchester, Essex. Tackleist in Colchester: K D Radcliffe, High Street.

Nayland (Suffolk). Bream, chub, dace, perch, pike, roach, tench. Colchester APS has water here and at **Wormingford, Wiston, Boxted, Langham, Stratford St Mary** and **Flatford;** no tickets. Colchester PS has rights at **Boxted;** no tickets. Colnes AS has stretches at **Little Horkesley** and other fisheries in area. Dt 50p. Mill pools private. Essex RD has trout fishery on tributary **Box:** dt from

River Conservator (limited to three rods daily). **Hadleigh** and Dist AS has water on tributary **Brett:** coarse fish; no dt. Brett fishes best in winter.

Bures (Essex). London AA controls a good deal of water here and in **Clare, Cavendish** and **Sudbury** areas. Also **Bures Lake;** members only, but some waters available to associates at Bures. Dt from F Staples, 25 Nayland Rd. Elm Park, Hornchurch & Dist AS has stretch, members only. Moor Hall and Belhus AS has excellent 5 acre lake at **S Ockenden.** members only (£8 st + £5 entrance.) Hotels: One Bell; Eight Bells; Horseshoes.

Sudbury (Suffolk). Sudbury AA has water here and at **Long Melford;** dt from hon sec or R Nunn, 49 North Street. St £4.50, dt 75p. RD issues dt for stretch at **Wixoe.** Tickets also from W Coote, The Swan, Great Henny, for stretch there.

SURREY (lakes)

ENTON LAKES. Witley. Enton Fly Fishers' Club has four lakes stocked with trout; members only; no tickets; apply secretary for membership details.

FRENSHAM PONDS. Farnham (4m). Farnham AS has rights on Great Pond and Little Pond, leased from Hambledon Rural District Council; coarse

fishing; permits from hon sec and bailiff. "Leisure Sport" gravel pits at Yateley. Coarse fish. *See Fishery Agents.*

OLD BURY HILL LAKE. Nr. Dorking. Coarse fish, especially tench and pike. Dt (June–Oct) £1.50 (Nov–March) £1. Boat: £1 extra.

RIPLEY. Papercourt fishery, Sendmarsh.

LOW TAR

with

Middle Tar Taste

JOHN PLAYER

Vanguard

KING SIZE

80% of Vanguard smokers
previously smoked middle tar brands.

NOW'S THE TIME TO SWITCH!

Vanguard

JKV11WF

SSSH.......

....man fishing

All Severn-Trent trout fisheries
are pleasant, inviting and regularly
stocked with good, healthy fish.

A day permit will put you in the picture.

Pike, bream, tench etc. St £5 from "Leisure Sport", RMC House, Feltham, Middlesex.

STILLWATER FISHERIES. Ash Vale. Brown and rainbow trout lakes; apply Stillwater Fisheries Ltd, 2 Park Road, Farnborough. St £150, guest tickets for members' friends, £6.50. Various coarse fishings offered.

TRI-LAKES. Sandhurst. Now mixed fishery; well stocked with tench, carp (common and crucian), bream, rudd, roach, perch, pike, eels, trout. Dt £1.50 and £1.10, from fishing hut. Limited st at £15 from Fishery Manager, Yateley Road, Sandhurst, Berks. Boat for hire, car park, toilets, hot snacks (Tel 0252 873191).

VIRGINIA WATER. Virginia Water, Johnson Pond and Obelisk Pond, Windsor Great Park fishable by ticket only; coarse fish; st £6.90, dt £3. Early application advised in writing, to Crown Estate Office, Windsor Great Park (sae).

WEY FARM LAKE. Ottershaw. Coarse fishing. St £12, dt £1 from manager, 88 Beech Road, Brookwood.

WINKWORTH LAKES. Winkworth, nr Godalming. National Trust property. Trout fishery (fly only) managed by Godalming AS. St £60 + £15 entrance. Details from Hon Sec of AS.

WIREMILL POOL. Nr Lingfield. Coarse fish include tench up to 5 lb, bream up to 7 lb, roach up to 2½ lb, carp up to 4½ lb, pike up to 21 lb. Dt from bailiff.

YATELEY. Nr Camberley. Fourteen "Leisure Sport" lakes stocked with pike, carp, tench, roach and perch. Large specimens recorded. St from RMC House, Feltham, Middlesex.

SUSSEX (lakes and streams)

Ardingley Reservoir. Ardingley, nr. Haywards Heath. 180 acre SWA fly-only trout water; brown trout and rainbows. Full st £160: weekdays only, £120. Dt £5 and £4.50. Pulling boats. 2-seat, £5.50, single-seat, £4. Evening only rates available.

BLACKDOWN. Haslemere 2m. Two small lakes stocked brown and rainbow trout av 1¼ lbs. Fly only. St (1 day per week) from £70 from King & Chasemore, Estate Agents, Petworth who have two other lakes in same area. Stocked rainbows, brown and brook trout. St (1 day per week) £102.

CHICHESTER LAKES. Chichester (Sussex). Chichester and Dist AS has three gravel pits; roach, rudd, carp, tench, bream, chub, perch, pike; members only except for wt from hon sec or treasurer or local tackleists (see below). Society also shares stretch of **Rother;** members only. Tackleists: North End Tackle Shop, 59a Chicester Road; Russell Hillsdon Ltd, South Street; W Goodridge, Eastgate Square.

DARWELL RESERVOIR. At Mountfield, **Robertsbridge** (Tel: Robertsbridge 880 407); brown and rainbow trout averaging 1 lb; 180 acres; leased from Southern Water Authority by Hastings Flyfishers Club; membership limited (waiting list). Visitors' dt £4 from bailiff at fishing hut; boats £3 day extra, to be booked 48 hrs in advance from bailiff. Fly only; limit, three brace over 10 in; season May 1– Oct 31.

FARTHINGS LAKE. Nr Battle. Trout and coarse fish. St £10, dt £1 from house by the lake.

FEN PLACE MILL. 2m SW of E Grinstead. 14 acres of stillwater trout fishing on three developed hammer ponds. Brown and rainbow trout av 2½ lb weight. All amenities. St and dt for members' guests'. Tel 01 4307105. *(Advt. p 19).*

GREAT SANDERS RESERVOIR. At Sedlescombe (Tel: Sedlescombe 248); 57-acre water containing brown and rainbow trout; av 1 lb. (Details as for Darwell Reservoir.)

MILTON MOUNT LAKE. Three Bridges (Sussex). **Crawley** AS water; mostly carp; dt. Crawley AS also has Tittermus Lake (pike, tench, carp, roach, perch) and **Sandford Brook** (trout; fly only) in Tilgate Forest; Roffey Park Lake, near Colgate (carp, roach, tench, perch, gudgeon); New Pond, Pease Pottage (carp and crucian carp, tench), the Mill Pond, Gossops Green, and Furnace Lake, Felbridge (carp and crucian carp). These are for members and friends only. At **Buchan Park** nr Crawley, Buchan Park AA has lakes; permits from hon sec, carp, pike etc.

CLIVE VALE RESERVOIRS; ECCLES-

BOURNE RESERVOIR. Hastings. Good carp, tench, roach, bream and rudd. Tickets issued by Hastings Clive Vale AC. Dt **(Clive Vale)** £1; **(Eccles-bourne)** £1.50 from Owens corner shop above. Clive Vale Reservoir.

PEVENSEY LEVELS. Marshland drained by various streams into **Pevensey Haven** and **Wallers Haven;** good coarse fishing on large streams (pike, roach, rudd, perch, bream, carp and tench), most of best waters rented by clubs. Fishing stations: **Eastbourne, Hailsham, Pevensey.** Compleat Angler FC has substantial stretches on both banks of **Wallers Haven,** good fisheries on both banks of **Pevensey Haven** and water on **Langney Haven** and **R Cuckmere.** Tickets (50p) and RD licences from bailiff: Mr Miller, 17 Bridge End, Pevensey and The Eastbourne Tackle Shop, 183b Langney Road. Club cards and tickets from Compleat Angler, 22 Pevensey Road, East-bourne. Good coarse fishing on Old Haven (3½m) controlled by Hailsham AA *(see also Cuckmere)*; dt from hon sec. **Lydd** AC also has water; dt from bailiff on bank.

POSSINGWORTH PARK LAKE. Nr **Heathfield.** Like **Wiston Park Lake,** nr. **Steyning,** a Sussex Piscatorial Soc. trout fishery. Club has coarse fishing at **Ansty, Bolney, Islefield** etc. All members only. Trout £40 pa from J Baker, 48 Forest Fields Horsham: coarse fishing membership, £12 pa from hon sec.

WEIR WOOD RESERVOIR. Forest Row (Sussex), 1½m; **East Grinstead,** 4m; 280 acres. Hitherto a fly-only trout fishery, Weir Wood was re-opened for coarse fishing on June 16th 1979. Dt (bank) £1 extra for boat £1.50. St £26.60. Enq. to Recreations Officer at reservoir, Tel. Forest Row 731. Hotels: Brambletye, Ashdown Forest, Dorset Arms, Roebuck, within 2m.

TAMAR

(For close seasons, licences, etc, see South West Water Authority, p 38)

Rises in Cornwall and follows boundary between Devon and Cornwall for good part of course, emptying finally into Plymouth Sound. Holds salmon, sea trout, brown trout of fair size—pounders not uncommon—and grayling.

Milton Abbot (Devon). Endsleigh FC has 9m. Limited wt (S) for guests at historic Endsleigh House. Fly only after April. 234 fish taken in 1980. Apply Manager, Endsleigh House.

Lifton (Devon). Tamar, **Lyd, Threshel, Carey, Wolf;** trout (3 to lb), sea trout (mid-June to end Sept), salmon (May, to mid-October). Hotel: Arundell Arms, which has 20m of excellent water in lovely surroundings; 23 individual beats, also 4-acre trout lake. Licences and tackle at hotel, fly fishing courses (beginners and semi-advanced) by two resident instructors. Dt (when there are vacancies) for S & MT £7.50 and £6, according to date; for brown trout, £4. *(advt p 145).*

Launceston (Cornwall). Salmon, sea trout, trout. Permits can be obtained for some parts of Tamar, **Ottery, Kensey, Inney** and **Carey** from Launceston AA, which has 12½m and 2m on **R Inney.** Wt (S) £25, dt (S) £7, wt (T) £15, dt (T) £4. Tackleists: Raddalls of Launceston, Westgate Street, who issue permits for Launceston AA fisheries, **Dutson Water** (carp and tench) and other fishing in the area. Also RD licences. Other hotels: White Hart (RD licences), Eagle House, Race Horse Inn, North Hill. Launceston Publicity Committee issue booklet listing accommodation.

Bridgerule (Devon). Bude AA no longer has water here. Farmers may give permission. **Tamar Lakes** here: SWWA waters for which tickets are issued. *(See p 38)* Hotel: Court Barn, Clawton, Holsworthy.

Tributaries of the Tamar

TAVY: Rises in Cranmere Pool on Dartmoor and flows about 17m before forming estuary below Buckland Abbey. Excellent salmon and sea-trout river.

Tavistock (Devon). Tavy, Walkham and Plym FC; limited membership. Salmon, sea trout and brown trout permits for visitors on Bridge; main river and on **Meavy, Plym** and **Walkham.** Comprehensive: st £12, wt £4, dt £3. Brown trout only; st £6, wt £3, dt £2.75. Fly only. Available from tackleists Barkells, 15

Duke Street, Tavistock. Hotel: Bedford (salmon and trout fishing on Tamar and Tavy).

Mary Tavy (Devon). Brown trout; late run of salmon and sea trout. Fishing mostly privately owned; riparian owners sometimes give permission. Plymouth & Dist Freshwater AA has rights at **Peter Tavy** (members only).

Yelverton (Devon). Good centre for Tavy, Walkham and Plym FC waters. Hotels: Rock, Devon Tors and Dartmoor Inn (last two issue RD licences).

WALKHAM (tributary of Tavy): Upper reaches rocky and overhung, but down-stream from Horrabridge there are many nice pools. Peal run from July onwards.

Horrabridge (Devon). Salmon, sea trout, trout. A good centre for Tavy, Walkham and Plym FC waters.

INNEY: Trout.

Launceston. Farmers give permission *(see Launceston under Tamar).*

LYD: Trout, sea trout, some salmon.

Coryton (Devon). Arundell Arms, Lifton *(advt p 145)* has fishing for salmon, sea trout and brown trout. *See "Lifton", p 142),* for details. 4½m. Marystow Brook, 3m; trout.

TAW

(For close seasons, licences, etc, see South West Water Authority, p 38)

Rises on Dartmoor and flows 50m to Barnstaple Bay, where it joins estuary of Torridge. Salmon (best March–May) with sea trout (peal) from July onwards. Brown trout and good coarse fishing in places.

Barnstaple (Devon). Bass and mullet in estuary. Salmon, trout, peal, roach and dace. Salmon best March, April, May; peal July, August. Barnstaple and Dist AA has water immediately below New Bridge (some free water below this), on **Yeo** (trout and sea trout), and on ponds at **Lake Venn** and **Swimbridge** (carp, tench, bream, rudd, perch). Visitors' tickets for salmon, trout and coarse fisheries from local tackleists (see below) or hon sec. Coarse fishing in ponds: visitors may become assn members which entitles them to fish ponds (Mon–Fri only). Tickets limited and not weekends or Bank Holidays. Cdr R H Dean, Little Bray House, **Brayford,** has about 1m (both banks) of Taw and **Bray;** dt issued. For other trout fishing see tributary Yeo. East and West Lyns, Badgeworthy Water and Heddon are accessible, as well as fishing on Wistlandpound and Slade Reservoirs. Tackleists: E Gale & Son, 59 High Street, who produce a useful booklet on fishing in the area; E Stacey, Bear Street.

Chapelton (Devon). Salmon, peal, trout, dace. Taw mostly private down to New Bridge. Barnstaple and Dist AC water below *(see Barnstaple).*

Umberleigh (Devon). Salmon, peal, trout; preserved. Rising Sun *(advt p 17)* has 3½m of water (seven beats, including first fishing above tidal water) for which dt are issued when not required for residents; fly only after April 30. Sunday fishing is allowed; salmon best March, April, May and September; peal July, August and September. Brochure, giving charges, etc, on request. Wt £42 and £36, dt £7 and £6. Other hotel: Northcote Manor, Burrington *(advt p 156).*

South Molton (Devon). Taw and Mole; salmon, trout, peal. South Molton AC has water on Taw and **Mole** (¾m both banks); fly only; dt issued. Permits from hon sec. Rumbos, 6, The Square, issue permits for several stretches. Occasional dt for 1¼m at **Alswear** from J D W Peck, Bilboa House, Dulverton, Somerset. Tel. 23475. Fortesque Arms, South Molton Rd, Umberleigh, has 2½m (salmon and trout), including best bank of pool at junction of Mole and Taw, for guests. In March, April and May there are salmon throughout water, and occasional fish in Sept. Sea trout July on. Occasional permits to other than hotel guests in latter half of season. Wt £40, dt £8. Licences and tackle at hotel.

Eggesford, Chulmleigh (Devon). Fox and Hounds Hotel *(advt p 145)* has 7m good private salmon, sea trout and brown trout fishing on Taw and **Little Dart.** Salmon from March, sea trout from April. Fly and spinning. Tickets (limited) for non-residents. Wt and dt from £25 and £5. Full details from hotel.

Coldridge (Devon). Taw Fishing Club has water from Taw Bridge to Hawkridge Bridge; very good trout fishing; wt may be issued to visitor introduced by

member; wading advisable.

North Tawton (Devon). Trout. Burton Hall Hotel has about 4m of water here; trout; occasional sea trout and salmon. Free to guests; dt issued subject to hotel bookings. K Dunn, The Barton, also issues dt for about 1m.

Sticklepath (Devon). Trout. Dt from Mr French, Davencourt, for ½m downstream. Accommodation and RD licences: Taw River Inn.

YEO (Barnstaple): Sea and brown trout.

Barnstaple and Dist AA has water on Yeo; wt and dt from Barnstaple tackleists. *(See Barnstaple)*

MOLE:

South Molton (Devon). Sea and brown trout, some salmon. Hotel: George.

BRAY (tributary of Mole):

North Molton (Devon). Trout, sea trout, few salmon; ns South Molton, 2m. Poltimore Arms Hotel has 2m of fishing on Bray; fishing good. Cdr R H Dean, Little Bray House, **Brayford**, issues dt for about 1m of river.

TEES

(For close seasons, licences, etc, see Northumbrian Water Authority, p 40)

Rises below Cross Fell in Pennines, flows eastwards between Durham and Yorkshire, and empties into North Sea near Middlesbrough. Once notable salmon river, but destroyed by pollution. Trout up to 4½ lb in upper reaches and large shoals of grayling, chub and dace in Wycliffe to Darlington stretch.

Middlesbrough (Cleveland). River polluted. NWWA reservoirs **Lockwood** and **Scaling Dam** in vicinity. Stocked with trout dt £3.50 on site. Local tackleist: Anglers Corner, 121 Victoria Road. *(See Yorkshire lakes, streams, etc.)*

Stockton (Cleveland). Trout, grayling, coarse fish on one of best stretches of river. Stockton AA has over 10m at **Gainford, Winston, Dinsdale, Middleton-on-Row,** nr Darlington, **Aislaby,** nr Yarm, and on **Swale,** nr **Ainderby** (Moreton-on-Swale); no tickets. For reservoirs see Middlesbrough. Tackleist: F and K Flynn, 12 Varo Terrace.

Thornaby (Cleveland). Trout, grayling and coarse fish. Thornaby AA has 1½m below Leven Beck mouth at **Ingleby Barwick** (coarse fish; tidal), 6m at Croft (trout, grayling, dace, chub, roach, perch, pike, gudgeon), and stretches on **Eden, Swale** and **Ure.** Annual membership: £10. No tickets but applications to secretary will be sympathetically considered. Tackleists: F & K Flynn, 12 Varo Terrace, Stockton; J W Wright, 107 Parkgate, Darlington.

Yarm (Cleveland). Tees is tidal; good coarse fishing; occasional trout. Two clubs have water; Yarm AC (5½–6m tidal water; limited dt 50p from A L Adams, tackleist, Stockton).

Croft (Durham). Fair head of trout, grayling and coarse fish. Darlington AC water upstream *(see Darlington)*. Thornaby AA has water downstream; back to nor-

mal following pollution; restocked *(see Thornaby)*.

Darlington (Durham). Trout, grayling, coarse fish. Darlington AC (limited membership) has water; tickets only to bona fide visitors sponsored by member as a rule. Darlington Brown Trout AA has water between Middleton and Croft, also on **Swale.** Dt for members' guests only. Stockton AA has water at **Winston** *(see Stockton)*. At **Whorlton**, 4m T J Richardson, Whorlton Farm, issues strictly limited permits for a stretch. Tackleists (and licences): E & B Langstaff, Parkgate; Adams, Duke Street.

Piercebridge (Durham). Trout, grayling, dace, chub, gudgeon. Tickets available for Raby Estates water *(see Darlington)*; otherwise preserved, Clow Beck, 3m S of Darlington; part is Darlington AC water; otherwise preserved. Forcett Park Lake, 8m SW; pike, perch; private; occasional winter permits.

Gainford (Durham). Trout, grayling, coarse fish *(see Darlington, Raby Estates)*. Alwent Beck, 1m W; trout; private. Langton Beck, 2m N.

Barnard Castle (Durham). Trout, grayling. Barnard Castle FFC has from Tees Viaduct to Baxton Gill, near Cotherstone; private club water. Barnard Castle AS has from a point above Abbey Bridge to Tees Viaduct; private club water, but some dt to visitors staying locally. Darlington FFC has 2m above and below Abbey Bridge (1m below Barnard Castle). Water holds some big grayling; members only. Other fishing on permission from riparian owners. Grassholme, Selset, Balderhead, Blackton and Hury reservoirs, 5m NW; dt obtainable *(see Tees Valley Reservoirs)*. Tackleists: W G Richardson, 17 Calgate. Hotel: King's Head, Market Place.

Mickleton (Durham). Trout. St, dt for S bank between Cronkley Bridge and Lune Fort from Turnbull & Parkinson, 152 Front Street, Chester-le-Street;

Cleveland Arms; J Raine & Son, Horsemarket; both Middleton-in-Teesdale.

Middleton-in-Teesdale (Durham). Trout (plentiful but small); Turnbull & Parkinson, 152 Front Street, Chester-le-Street, issues limited st £12 (or pro rata) each for about 9m of Upper Tees; fly only. Wt £5, dt £2.50.

GRETA: Trout.

Bowes (Durham). Mostly private, but inquire of Richardson's Tackle Depot, Barnard Castle, for possibilities.

TEIGN

(For close seasons, licences, etc, see South West Water Authority, p 38)

Rises on Dartmoor, 5m south-west of Chagford, and flows 30m south-east to the sea through an estuary beginning below Newton Abbot. Principal tributary is Bovey. Salmon, sea trout (peal) and brown trout. A spring river. Teign usually fishes best from late March to early June.

Newton Abbot (Devon). Salmon, sea trout, trout; preserved by Lower Teign FA hence up to Sowton Bridge, Dunsford. Three separate beats; some private water between. Dt (three per beat) from May 1. Assn also has 3m on Bovey *(see below)*. Tickets for **Lower Teign** from Percy Hodge (Sports) Ltd, 104 Queen Street. Newton Abbot FA has five lakes at Rackerhayes and six at Preston; coarse fish, including carp and tench. Dt and st. Tackleists: Percy Hodge (Sports) Ltd, 104 Queen Street; Drum Sports, 47a Courtenay Street, Newton Abbot; Doel Sports, Bank Street, Teignmouth. Hotels: Globe, Queen's, Tavistock Inn (RD licences).

Chudleigh (Devon). Salmon, sea trout,

trout; Lower Teign FA has water *(see Newton Abbot)*.

Moretonhampstead. Manor House Hotel has 6m salmon and sea trout fishing on upper Teign. Trout streams and pools in grounds wt (S) £6.50, (T) £1.60, dt (S) £1.60, (T) 60p. (Tel: Moretonhampstead 355).

Chagford (Devon). Trout, sea trout, Upper Teign FA preserves about 12m in all, fly only before June 1 on some parts and for whole season elsewhere; size limit 8 in. Tickets, trout only: st, wt and dt. (Concession for juvs) from Percy Hodge (Sports) Ltd, 104 Queen Street, Newton Abbot; Gidleigh Park, Country House Hotel, has 1m of river. Fernworthy Reservoir, 3½m (trout) *(see Devon lakes, streams, etc)*.

Tributary of the Teign

BOVEY: Salmon, sea trout, trout.

Bovey (Devon). On Bovey and Teign. Fishing above Bovey preserved by landowners and below by Lower Teign FA. Tickets from Percy Hodge (Sports) Ltd, 104 Queen Street, Newton Abbot.

Lakes: Tottiford and Kennick Reservoirs; trout *(see Devon lakes, streams, etc)*. Hotels: Manor House, one mile from North Bovey (water on Bovey and Bowden, and salmon and trout fisheries on Teign); Glebe house, North Bovey.

TEST

(For close seasons, licences, etc, see Southern Water Authority, p 38)

England's most famous trout stream and also excellent for salmon up to Romsey. Rises from springs in chalk near Overton, above Whitchurch, and flows into Southampton Water. Almost entirely privately owned, fisheries fetching very high prices whenever they come on to market.* Tributaries of Test are excellent trout and grayling streams.

River Test, Leckford Estate. The class of parent stock from which ova are stripped to be hatched, grown on, and used to restock this world-famous river. *Photograph: John Tarlton.*

Romsey (Hants). Trout and grayling fishing good; salmon fishing good below the town, all preserved by the different landowners. Broadlands Estate has excellent stillwater coarse fishery. St £27.50, wt £9, dt £2. Golden orfe a special feature. Tel. Rownhams 733167; opportunities infrequent. Dt for residents from Council Offices, Duttons Road, for Romsey Memorial Park; limited to two rods daily. Salmon, few small trout, grayling, coarse fish. Good trout fishing at **Two Lakes,** near Romsey *(see Hampshire streams, lakes, etc).*

Stockbridge (Hants). Greyhound Hotel has water; (fish average 3 lb). Houghton

Club's preserves are above and below the town.

Houghton (Hants). Bossington Estate lets rods by season. (Tel King's Somborne 265; waiting list.)

Fullerton Bridge (Hants). Trout (av 2 lb 8 oz). Season mid-April to end of Sept. Leckford Estate controls 7m of main stream and carriers from Fullerton Bridge to Longstock Grange. Dry fly only. Waiting list. Inquires to Leckford Estate Ltd, Stockbridge (Stockbridge 634).

Whitchurch (Hants). Trout; strictly preserved. No tickets are granted. Fish numerous, but not so large as farther down. Hotel: White Hart.

Tributaries of the Test

ANTON: Trout, grayling.

Andover (Hants). Anton joins Test at Testcombe Bridge. Trout and grayling; all strictly preserved, but Rooksbury Mill Estate, Andover, lets rods on seasonal basis only (Tel 2921). Andover AA preserve worked-out gravel pits at **Charlton**, 1m NW, flooded by Anton; king carp, common carp, dace, perch, roach, rudd, tench. Dt. Tackleists: Hammond Bros, 11 Union Street. Hotels: Star and Garter, White Hart, Junction, George, Anton Arms, Globe Central.

PILL HILL BROOK: Trout, grayling.

Amport and Monxton (Hants). Trout and grayling. Nearly as long as Anton, but pure chalk-stream. Monxton Mill reach greatly improved and contains full head of locally bred brown trout averaging 14 oz, with occasional heavier fish. Fishing preserved by landowners who occasionally give permits. Dry-fly only.

DEVER: Trout, grayling.

Sutton Scotney (Hants). All strictly preserved. Dever joins Test at Newton Stacey.

BOURNE:

St Mary Bourne (Hants). All strictly preserved. Bourne joins Test above Longparish.

Test and Itchen Fishery Association compiles register of rods to let; inquire hon sec; address in club lists

THAMES

(For close seasons, licences, etc, see Thames Water Authority, p 42)

Second longest river in England. Tidal reaches recovering from pollution and fish returning in considerable numbers. Barbel, flounders, smelt and even odd trout taken at various points. River may now be worth fishing from Vauxhall Bridge upstream. Boat traffic largely spoils sport in summer, except in weir pools, but fishing can be good early and late. River fishes well from October to March. Holds good stocks of coarse fish, with excellent bream and barbel in some stretches. Large trout found in weir pools, but catching them ("Thames trouting") is separate and difficult art. Among famous tributaries are Kennet, which comes in at Reading and is one of best mixed fisheries in England. Trout and coarse fish run large. Higher up, Coln, Evenlode and Windrush are noted trout streams, but for most part are very strictly preserved and fishing difficult to obtain. Fishing on Thames open up to City Stone at Staines. Above, permission often necessary and lock-keepers and local tackleists should be consulted. Weir permits at £1 per season issued by Thames WA. Thames Angling Preservation Society, founded in 1838, has restocked seven tributaries—now keeps close watch on water quality and fish stocks in whole Thames basin. Not a fishing club; a fishery preservation society supported by anglers, membership details from treasurer, C Cargill, 14 Camden Passage, London N1, London Anglers Association (LAA) HQ, 183 Hoe St, Walthamstow E17, has numerous fishings on Thames and elsewhere. St £8. Dt 60p issued for some waters. Several Metropolitan Water Division reservoirs in which fishing is allowed (coarse fish and trout). *(See London—Reservoirs, etc.)*

Isleworth (G London). Tidal. Dace, roach, bream, perch, eels, etc; free from towpath or boats. Fly-fishing for dace on shallows when tide is down. Reach down past Chiswick Eyot can be good for roach, dace; towpath only; free. *Note: Many gravel pits and streams in Thames Valley and elsewhere are available on season ticket from George Bennet, secretary,* **Leisure Sport,** *53–55 High Street, Feltham, Middx TW13 4HA (01-890-1313).* Tackleists: Hounslow Angling Centre, Bath Road *(see also Colne-Wraysbury).*

Richmond (G London). Half-tidal. Down to Isleworth is fishing for roach, dace, bleak, bream, perch; free from towpath or boats (boatmen on towpath). Notable recent catches include two trout by members of Barnes and Mortlake AS. In Richmond Park **Pen Ponds** hold perch, carp, bream, roach and pike. Permit (£1) from park superintendent at his office in Richmond Park (enclose sae). Tackleist: Edgar Thurston & Co Ltd, 360 Richmond Road, Twickenham. Hotels: Castle, Bird's Nest, Pigeons, White Cross.

Twickenham (G London). Coarse fishing; free from boats and towpath. Deeps hold barbel, roach, bream, carp. Corporation allow fishing from Radnor, Orleans and Terrace Gardens. Club: Twickenham Piscatorial Society which has stretch of **Kennet** at Newbury, **Thame** at Thame, several gravel pits and three-acre lake at Newbury (tench, crucian carp and rudd). Dt from bailiffs. New members welcomed (apply hon sec). Dt for **Kennet** at Newbury, from White House Inn and bailiff. Tackleist: Guns and Tackle, 81 High Street, Whitton. Hotels: Bird's Nest, White Swan.

Teddington (G London). Thames holds barbel, dace, chub, roach, bream, pike, perch; fishable from boats but none available on spot; free fishing from towpath. Hotels: Anglers', Clarence, Railway.

Kingston (G London). Canbury Gardens, where warm water comes in from Kingston Power Station, is very popular stretch and has yielded large carp, bream, perch and roach. Tackleists: Morgan's, 17 High Street, Hampton Wick; Whitewoods, 103 Brighton Road, Surbiton.

Hampton Court (G London). Thames, Mole; coarse fish. Good roach, chub, barbel, etc, in Molesey Weir. Much free fishing from towpath; for RWA licence-holders. Several boatmen near bridge. **Bushey Park Ponds;** roach, tench, pike. **Home Park Ponds** and **Long Water,** Hampton Court, hold eels and tench; permission from park superintendent (send sae if apply by post). St £1, ½ price for OAP and young people 10–17. Tackleists: G W Oldham & Son, 8 Tudor Road, Hampton; E C Cheeseman, 11 Bridge Road, East Molesey.

Hampton (G London). Hampton Deeps hold bream, pike, perch and sometimes a good trout; free fishing from towpath and boats. Inns: Ye Old Red Lion, Bell.

Sunbury (Surrey). Excellent for all-round angling; free. Fine weir and weir shallows, barbel, chub, dace, bream and occasional trout may be taken. Tackleist: Wilson Webbs, Thames Street. Hotel: Magpie.

Walton-on-Thames (Surrey). Bream, barbel, perch, dace, chub, carp and pike; perch and pike in backwater; free; boats available. Clubs: Walton AS (water on **Mole,** Cobham). Boats: Rosewell's, River Bank. Tackleist: Walton Cycle Shop, Bridge Street. Hotels: Anglers',

Riverside; Weir, Riverside; Swan, Manor Road.

Shepperton (Surrey). Pike, barbel, perch, bream and carp; free; boats available. Ashmere Club has wellstocked trout lake; members only. Hotel: Anchor.

Weybridge (Surrey). Thames, **Wey** and **Bourne Brook;** pike, trout, bream, perch, barbel, roach, etc; free fishing in Thames only. Byfleet AA has six stretches of Wey; pike, dace, roach, chub, carp, barbel, bream, perch; no dt. Six local clubs have rights on **Wey Navigation Canal** from Thames Lock to Walsham Lock and have formed Wey Navigation Angling Amalgamation; dt from W Taylor (head bailiff), 1 Common Lane, New Haw. Hotels: Ship, Thames Street; Lincoln Arms, Thames Street; Oatlands Parks; Blue Anchor. For fishing in Basingstoke Canal *see Hampshire (streams, etc)*.

Chertsey (Surrey). Pike, perch, chub, roach, bream, occasional trout; free fishing from boats and towpath. Gravel pits available in area under "Leisure Sport" Angling Scheme *(see Isleworth)*. Club: Addlestone AA, which has water at **New Haw** (**Wey** and **Bourne**) and a gravel pit at Laleham; dt to members' friends only. Tackleist: J Isles Ltd, 93 Guildford Street, Chertsey. Several boat yards. Hotels: Cricketers, Bridge.

Staines (Surrey). Good coarse fishing; free from boats and towpath. Penton Hook good for barbel and chub. "Leisure Sport" gravel pits, pike, carp, tench, etc, at **Kingsmead** and **Longfield.** St from RMC House, Feltham, Middlesex. Others at **Yeoveny.** Clubs: Staines AS (stretch opposite Runnymede; members only). Tackleist: Tackle Dept Johnson & Clark, High Street. Hotels: Packhorse (Middlesex bank); Swan (Surrey bank). *See also "London Reservoirs".*

Laleham (Surrey); ns Staines. Barbel, dace, roach, pike, perch. Inn: Three Horseshoes.

Wraysbury (Bucks). Coarse fish, as above. Hounslow Piscatorials have stretch of **Wraysbury River.** "Leisure Sport" gravel pits. *See Fishery Agents.*

Windsor (Berks). Fishing from south bank below Windsor Bridge and north bank to Eton–Windsor road bridge, by TWA licence only. Dt issued for club waters near Maidenhead; inquire tackleists. Old Windsor AC issues dt from Romney Lock and stream. Much river traffic in summer. Punts available. Council offers fishing on one meadow. Fishing can be had in Windsor Great Park ponds and Virginia Water *(see Surrey Lakes)*. New TWA trout fishery on **Datchett Reservoir.** Details from controller on site. Tackleists: Stan Eldon (Sports), 6 St Leonard's Road.

Boveney (Bucks); ns Windsor, 2m. Coarse fish. Backwater good for pike, and weir pool for trout and barbel. Towpath free. LAA Eton Wíck fishery here.

Bray (Berks); ns Maidenhead, 1½m. Weir pool good for trout, and free from boat or punt. Bray Mill tail from 1m above lock to lock cut private. Towpath free. Hotel: Hinds Head.

Maidenhead (Berks). Roach, pike, perch, chub, barbel, dace, chance of trout. Some free fishing from My Lady Ferry down to Boulter's Lock cut. Clubs with water include Maidenhead and District AS, dt for Downey. Boveney reaches from bailiff. Boats: Andrew Bros; Bushnell Ltd. Tackleists: Jack Smith, 4 High Street; Angling Services, 41 Clare Road. Hotels: Skindles, Thames, Bell, Bear, Riviera.

Cookham (Berks). Cookham & Dist AC has all water from Odney weir pool to London AA water at Spade Oak ferry *(see Bourne End)*; no tickets; members only. Hotels: Ferry, Royal Exchange, King's Arms, Bell and Dragon, Crown.

Bourne End (Bucks). Wide, open water with some shallow streches, good for fly fishing. London AA has water here; dt from bailiffs. Stretch also available to associates.

Marlow (Bucks). Usual coarse fish, including barbel; good spot for Thames trout. Marlow AC has water; no tickets but open for competitions. Little free water. Hotel: The Compleat Angler, which has fishing for guests; boats.

Hurley (Berks). London AA has fisheries at Frogmill Farm and Hurley Flats. Dt issued for 1½m. Other water at Hambleden; members and associates only.

Henley (Oxon). Pike, roach, perch, tench, bream, eels. Good roach swims by Hambleden Lock. Barbel and trout at Hambleden Weir. Chub fly-fishing below weir and at Marsh Lock (upstream). Remenham AS has fishing from Henley Bridge downstream on Berks bank to within ¾m of Hambleden Lock. Tickets from bailiff. On Oxon and Bucks bank

water controlled by society for members only. Also from end of Henley Promenade upstream to Marsh Lock, bridges and meadows upstream from Marsh Lock. London AA has streches for members. Free water from Henley Bridge up to end of Promenade only (north bank), and on Marsh Lock bridges only (not weir). Tackleist: Parrots Riverside. Boats: Hobbs, Parrott. Good accommodation for anglers at Anchor Hotel, Friday Street. Other hotels: Catherine Wheel, Little White Hart.

Wargrave (Berks). Thames and Loddon; good coarse fishing and some trout in **Loddon.** London AA has Loddon Bridge meadow and Loddon Marsh fishery above Sindlesham Mill; members only.

Sonning (Berks); ns Twyford. Bank and boat fishing. Good strech for Thames trout, especially Shiplake Hole. Much fishing from **Shiplake** to Sonning Bridge on Oxfordshire bank controlled by Shiplake and Binfield Heath AS; members only. Mill Tails preserved by Lord Phillimore. Guests at White Hart can fish private stretch of ½m on Berkshire bank towards Shiplake. London AA has water for members only at Sonning. Lowfield and Mapledurham. Reading & Dist AA has Sonning Eye fishery (lake and river); dt from bailiff, Lake View.

Reading (Berks). Most coarse fish. Free to RWA licence-holders from towpath from Sonning Bridge up to Horseshoe Bridge; thence Huntley and Palmer AC water to Kings Meadow (members only). Reading Borough Council controls the fishing on Kings Meadow, Christchurch Meadow and Thames-Side Promendade. The fishing from Thames-Side Promenade to Scours Lane is controlled by Thames Water Authority. There is some free water on the **Kennet** from Horseshoe Bridge to County Weir (adjacent to Inner Distribution Road). Fishing upstream of County Weir is controlled by Reading and District AA. No dt for any Reading and District AA waters. Farnborough AS has good trout and coarse fishing on **Whitewater** at Heckfield (8m). **Countryside Club,** 109 Upper Woodcote Road, Caversham Heights, Reading, has trout and carp fishing let on a family st basis; woodlands in Home Counties. Leisure Sport Ltd, RMC House, High Street, Feltham, Middx TW13 4HA, has coarse fisheries available on permit at **Twyford** and

Theale. Tackleists: G R Cooke, North-umberland Avenue; T Turner & Son Ltd, 21 Whitley Street; Tulls Tackle, 258 Kentwood Hill (Tilehurst) and Wyers. 497 Oxford Road.

Tilehurst (Berks). Elthorne Alliance and Reading and District AA control the fishing on the Oxfordshire bank. Free fishing from towpath to Caversham (see restrictions under Reading). Roebuck Hotel has private stretch on the south bank.

Goring (Oxon). Pike, bream, roach, chub, perch and (in weir pool especially) barbel and a few trout; best fish taken from weir pool, fishing from weir (permits £1 pa) or boat. Other fishing can be had from towpath above and below lock. London AA has R bank from Beetle & Wedge Hotel to Cleeve Lock; Gatehampton Farm and Hartslock Wood fisheries on L bank. Members only, but ¾m available to associates. Hotel: Leathern Bottle.

Pangbourne and Whitchurch (Berks). Thames and **Pang**. Trout, perch, pike, roach, bream, chub, dace. River fishes well in winter; free fishing 1½m above and below Whitchurch Bridge; good coarse fishing; boats available. Weir pool private. Pang holds trout, especially near Tidmarsh, but is strictly preserved; trout at its mouth. Pangbourne and Whitchurch AS has local fisheries. Trout in pits at **Theale** (2m); dt issued. Carp and tench in local ponds.

Moulsford (Berks). All coarse fish. London AA has water here; members only. Hotel: Beetle.

South Stoke (Oxon). London AA controls the water from footbridge above railway bridge down to Beetle and Wedge ferry and second meadow below the ferry down to Runsford Hole; members only.

Wallingford (Berks). Usual coarse fish. Local club: Jolly Anglers, who have water (good bream in summer, chub in winter); wt £1.50 and dt 50p from B A Castle, 45 St Mary's Street and Wallingford Sports Shop, High Street. Boats at town landing stage. Other tackleists: B A Castle, 45 St Mary's Street.

Cleeve (Oxon). Usual coarse fish. Landlord of Leathern Bottle issues dt for 1m upstream of Cleeve Lock, including ferry.

Benson (Oxon); ns Wallingford. Usual coarse fish. Club: Benson AA. Dt 25p from Peter Aldridge, The Garage, Crown Square.

Shillingford (Berks). Dorchester AA has water upstream; dt from hon sec. Shillingford Bridge Hotel has good pike fishing on ¼m (both banks) free to guests; boats available.

Little Wittenham (Berks). Thame comes in here.

Clifton Hampden (Berks). Clifton AA has water. Tickets for holidaymakers from hon sec, Abingdon & Oxford AA. Oxford and Dist AA also has water. Inn: The Barley Mow.

Appleford (Berks). London AA controls from just above the railway bridge down to beginning of Clifton Hampden cutting; both banks then a short stretch on R bank only: members only.

Culham (Oxon). All water except weir pools controlled by Abingdon & Dist ARA. Other clubs: Culham AC and Sutton Courtenay AC. Sutton Courtenay AC has pits. No day tickets.

Abingdon (Berks). Bream, chub, pike and barbel good. Tickets from Town Clerk's office for 1½m controlled by Council. Details from Stratton House, Bath Street, Abingdon. Fishery includes weir, but must be fished from bank. Abingdon and Dist ARA has water. Abingdon & Dist ARA now member of Abingdon & Oxford Anglers Alliance. Annual subscription of £6 covers three clubs. Wt £1. 50 well-stocked river and lake fishings. Permits from M Ponting, 4 Holyoake Road, Headington, Oxford. Tackleists: Beadles, Ock Street; Knight, Bath Street; Haines, Stert Street; J Hayden, The Vineyard. Hotel: The Upper Reaches.

Sandford-on-Thames (Oxon). Pike, bream, roach, perch, etc. Oxford and Dist AA has water here; members only.

Iffley (Oxon); ns Oxford. Thames and Isis. From here to Folly Bridge is Oxford and Dist AS water; no tickets. Inn: Isis Tavern.

Oxford (Oxon). Thames (Isis), **Cherwell** and **Oxford Canal**. All coarse fish. Oxford A and PS has water on Thames, Cherwell, **Evenlode** and a carp pool at **Cassington.** Holiday visitors should apply for permits to hon sec. Oxford Alliance controls about 70m of riverbank, plus gravel pits. Oxford and Dist AA has fishing in **Clifton Hampden, Iffley, Sandford** and **Godstow** areas; members only. North Oxford AS has water on **Oxford Canal** (tench, roach, bream, perch; permits for clubs), stretch of Thames (no tickets) and Seacourt

Stream (no tickets). Good Thames backwater sport near Oxford available in season on day basis from David Corke, Frenches Cottage, Long Wittenham. London AA issues dt for 3½m from **Claydon** to **Fenny Compton**. Boats for Thames from Salter's Folly Bridge. Birmingham AA have water at Wolvercote and Kings Weir. For limited dt for private trout lake, contact J C Bonham, Dorchester Road, Drayton St Leonards, 4½m W of Oxford, **Farmoor Reservoir,** TW fly-only trout fishery. No boats. Dt (limited) £4.80 and £5.50. Phone Cumnor 3033 for advance bookings. Further information from A W Smith (tackleist), 86 Magdalen Road. Hotels: Cherwell, Oxford; Swan, Islip; Prince of Wales, Cowley Road (Oxford APS HQ).

Eynsham (Oxon). Good coarse fishing; large bream. Good centre for Thames trout. Hotels: Ye Talbot Inn, Railway, Red Lion. Oxford Angling and Pres Soc has water *(see Oxford)*. Eynsham Weir fishing available to holders of Thames Conservancy weir permits; likely place for trout.

Bablock Hythe (Oxon). Chequers Hotel issues dt for 1½m on north bank downstream. Water upstream on north bank (and some on south bank) is Appleton and Tubney AS as far as Oxford APS water. Car ferry.

Newbridge (Oxon). Near Witney. Good coarse fishing (bream increasing), few

trout in the **Windrush.** Birmingham AA has five meadows on right bank of Thames. Hotels: Rose Revived (¾m water on Thames and Windrush; good coarse fish, some trout) and May Bush (½m water on Thames). Other fishing preserved by Abingdon AA and Witney AS (members only). Tackleist: R Bridgman, 76 High Street, Witney, who can give further information.

Tadpole Bridge, Buckland (Berks). Coventry & Dist AA has water here. Good chub and barbel; good pike in weir-pool. Trout Inn issues dt for own stretch. Accommodation at Trout Inn (caravans, camp sites).

Radcot (Berks). Thames trout; bream, chub, barbel and roach. Radcot AC has 5m. St £1.50, mt and wt 50p, dt 25p. Apply Swan Hotel. Clubs catered for. Tents and caravans. (Tel. Clanfield 220). Anchor Inn, Eaton, Hastings has 3m of fishing. Dt and st. Clubs welcome; tents and caravans. (Tel Faringdon 20630).

Lechlade (Glos). For Thames, Coln and Leach. Dt for coarse fishing on about 10m of river and well-stocked gravel pits from Riverside Lechlade has Park End Wharf (tackleists). LAA has extensive fishery at **Buscot.** Dt issued. Trout fishing from hotels, including Trout Inn, St John's Bridge.

Cricklade (Wilts). Thames known here as Isis. Isis AC has water on main river, tributaries **Ray** and **Churn** and several lakes. St £8.50, wt £2, dt 50p.

Tributaries of the Thames

MOLE: Coarse fish, some trout.

Esher (Surrey). Chub, roach, dace, gudgeon. Epsom AS has 1½m on Garson Farm (no dt) and ½m on Wey at **Weybridge;** ann sub £5. Other club: Banstead AS (¾m at Hersham; members only). Tackleists: Angling Plus, Central Road, Worcester Park, Surrey.

Cobham (Surrey). Walton-on-Thames AS has 1¾m of Mole (good chub water); and two lakes holding roach, tench and bream. In the larger, pike to 30 lbs. Tickets to members' friends only.

Leatherhead (Surrey). Dace, chub, roach and perch. Tackleist: Bridge Sport Shop, 35 Bridge Street. Hotel: New Bull.

Dorking (Surrey). Coarse fish. Dorking SA has about 4½m; chub, roach, perch, dace; dt (part of water only) or st from S C

Fuller (tackleist), South Street. Dt also available for **Old Bury Hill Lake.** Good pike; boats; *(see Surrey Lakes, p 140).* Hotels: White Horse, Bell, Arundel.

Betchworth (Surrey). Coarse fish. Carshalton and Dist AS has water; strictly members only.

WEY: Coarse fish, trout higher up.

Weybridge (Surrey). Wey Amalgamation have water here *(see Thames).* Weybridge AC (st £3, dt 50p) and Addlestone AS have stretches.

Woking (Surrey). Roach, chub, pike, etc. Woking and Dist AS has rights on 23 miles of river bank and two ponds (perch, carp and tench) at Send; dt for members' guests only. New members welcome; details from hon sec. Tackleist: Surrey Anglers Supplies, Station Road, Addlestone.

Wisley (Surrey); ns Ripley. Woking AA has a stretch. Ponds: Wisley Mere, Hut Pond, and several other ponds on Ripley and Ockham Commons; carp, pike, perch, roach.

Guildford (Surrey). Guildford AS has about 9½m; inquire hon sec of club HQ, Guildford Trades and Labour Club, Mount Street. At Clandon Park are some lakes, also on Broad Street and Whitmoor Common (good carp in Britton Pond). At **Shamley Green** (6m) dt issued for trout fishing on private lakes, apply J G St G Syms, QC, Willinghurst, Shamley Green. Tackleist: S R Jeffery & Son, 134 High Street *(advt p 8)*. Hotel: Angel.

Shalford (Surrey). Wey; bream, roach, pike, etc. **Tillingbourne;** trout; strictly preserved. Inns: Parrot, Victoria, Sea Horse, Percy Arms, Chilworth.

Godalming (Surrey). Godalming AS has Wey from Eashing Bridge (Stag Inn) to Broadfield Bridge (about 8m); grayling, coarse fish and trout; society also has Broadwater Lake (11 acres) which holds good carp, tench and perch; (no boats or camping) and limited fishing on Busbridge Lake. St and dt for accompanied guests. Dt for river from tackleist Allchorne, also guest tickets for assn water. At Milford, Enton Flyfishers' Club has four trout lakes *(see Surrey Lakes)*. Peper Harow Flyfishers have about 2m of Wey and two ponds (brown and rainbow trout); rods limited; no dt. Tackleists in Farncombe: Patrick's, St John Street; F J Goodman & Sons, Silo Road. Tackleists in Godalming: A & G Allchorne, 10 Bridge Street; Atkinson, New Road, Milford. Hotels: Broadwater, Farncombe Manor, Lake, King's Arms (Godalming AS HQ).

Frensham (Surrey). Farnham AS has trout water below Frensham Mill. **Frensham, Great and Little Ponds,** roach, perch, carp, etc; dt from cafe at Little Pond, hon sec, Farnham AA and bailiff.

Haslemere (Surrey). Coarse fish. Surrey Trout Farm is here.

Farnham (Surrey). Farnham AS provides sport for trout and coarse angler. Trout at **Frensham;** stocked, but only open to members' guests. Coarse fishing at Farnham, Frensham, **Elstead, Bagshot Lea Pond, Lodge Pond, Stockbridge Pond** at **Tilford,** and **Loddon** at **Arbor-**

field. Tickets for some; apply hon sec for details. Note: All waters heavily fished early in season.

Alton (Hants). Trout; preserved. Hotels: Swan, Crown.

COLNE: Coarse fish, some trout.

Iver (Bucks). Long stretch of river and two adjacent lakes held by "Leisure" Sport, RMC House, Feltham, Middlesex. St £6.

Wraysbury (Bucks). Blenheim AS has 1¾m on **Colne Brook;** coarse fish and occasional trout. Also gravel pits; good carp and crucian carp. Members only. Civil Service AS has Poyle Park Fishery. Hounslow Piscatorials have water on **Wraysbury River** (trib of Colne); much improved; roach, dace, chub, Twickenham PS and Staines AC have gravel pits; no tickets. Wraysbury 1m "Leisure Sport" fishery. St. Apply RMC House, Feltham, Middlesex. **Colnbrook** *(see Thames, Wraysbury).*

West Drayton (G London). Trout, pike, perch, bream, dace, roach, tench, chub. West Drayton Fishery now open following diversion of Colne for new 40-acre reservoir. Entrance in Trout Road. Dt on site (Iver Heath 4607). Grand Union Canal is near.

Uxbridge (G London). Pike, perch, roach, dace and bream. Fishing free on Uxbridge Moor. London AA holds long stretches of **Grand Union Canal,** on which dt are issued (60p). **Osterley Park Lake** holds bream, tench, etc; for details and permits apply the Superintendent of Parks, The Store Yard, Hyde Park, London W2. St £2, reductions for OAP and Young people 10–17. **Farlow's Pit, Iver,** holds roach, tench, carp, bream, pike; limited number of st.

Denham (Bucks). Colne; coarse fish; see also Harefield. Blenheim AS has 3m of **Grand Union Canal;** roach, dace, bream, tench, perch, gudgeon; dt and st at small charge.

Harefield (G London). Blenheim AS has 2m (canalised); roach, dace, bream, perch; dt from bailiff.

Rickmansworth (Herts). Trout, chub, dace, roach, pike, perch. "Leisure Sport" stretch for st holders. Inquiries to RMC House, Feltham, Middlesex. Blenheim AS has 1¾m of **Grand Union Canal;** good roach and bream; fishing now much improved after pollution; dt from bailiff on water. Watford Piscators have 1½m canal (restocked); dt from bailiff: **Batchworth Lake** and **Bury Lake;**

dt on site. Other clubs have private waters. Tackleist: E Sears, 28 High Street. **Gade;** trout; preserved. **Chess;** trout, strictly preserved. North Harrow Waltonians have water in river and lake; members only.

Watford (Herts). Good coarse fishing in **Gade,** canal and lakes. Ticket waters: Batchworth and Stocker's lakes; Elstree and Tring reservoirs *(see Aldenham and Tring under Herts and Middlesex (reservoirs and lakes))* and Grand Union Canal *(see under Grand Union Canal and Gade).* London AA issues dt for canal from Hunton Bridge to Tring. Free fishing in Gade in Cassiobury Park. Further information from tackleists: Angling Centre (Watford), 403–5 Whippendell Road; Pet's Pantry, High Street and St Alban's Road; and from Watford Piscators. Hotels: Maldon, Clarendon, Rose and Crown.

CHESS: Brown and rainbow trout—one of few British streams where rainbows spawn naturally.

Chorleywood (Bucks). Chess; trout. Chorleywood Trout Farm, where fly-casting instruction can be had. *(See also list of fish farms.)*

Chesham (Bucks). Brown and rainbow trout. Private. Tackleist: W Cox & Son, High Street. Hotel: George and Dragon.

Latimer (Bucks). Upper river and two lakes (13 acres in all) now available for trout fishing; brown and rainbow; boat available. Fly only. Season: April 2 to Sept 30. St £228, ½st £124. Frequent re-stocking. Average size: 2lbs. Details from Latimer Park Lakes Ltd (Little Chalfont 2396) where full details can be obtained.

GADE: Coarse fish.

Boxmoor (Herts). Boxmoor and Dist AS has private water at Westbrook and Pixies meres; members only; no tickets. St £125–£155 for gravel pit trout fishery. Inquiries to Boxmoor Trout Fisheries Ltd, 29 High St, Hemel Hempstead.

Berkhamsted (Herts). Visitors can fish London AA water on Grand Union Canal; coarse fish; dt on water *(see also Grand Union Canal).* No free water. Club: Berkhamsted and Dist AS. Hotels: King's Arms (Trust House), Crown, Swan.

LODDON: Coarse fish.

Twyford (Berks). Stretch of Loddon and a lake available at no further charge to holders of "Leisure Sport" permits for other waters. Inquiries to RMC House, Feltham, Middlesex.

Arborfield Cross (Berks). Farnham AS has three stretches here; coarse fish *(see Wey—Farnham).* Dt from bailiff (see notices on water). Cove AS also has water near here at **Shinfield** and on **Hart** and **Whitewater;** members only *(see also Fleet).* Between Arborfield and **Wokingham,** Red Spinner AS has Bearwood Lake; strictly members only. Farnborough AS has water at **Winnersh** *(see Basingstoke Canal).*

KENNET: One of England's finest mixed coarse fisheries; upper reaches noted for trout and grayling.

Theale (Berks). Water west of point 1m upstream of Bridge House (Wide Mead Lock) strictly preserved; few trout and coarse fish. Englefield Lake, 2m. Pike, and fine tench and carp (private). Reading and Dist AA has water on lower Kennet, Holybrooke and backwaters, about 10m in all; association controls from Wide Mead Lock east through Theale to Fobney. No dt. "Leisure Sport" gravel pits at Theale and **Burghfield.** Roach, bream, tench and pike. St respectively. See "Fishery Agents".

Aldermaston (Berks). Coarse fish and few trout. Old Mill Private Hotel issues permits for about 1m of water; dt £1.50 no parties. CALPAC has fishery; dt from bailiff, Wharf House, Padworth, nr Reading. London AA has 2m on **Fisherman's Brook;** coarse fish; members only.

Thatcham (Berks). Excellent barbel, chub, dace and tench on Kennet and Avon canal. Three reaches on the R Kennet and other waters preserved by Thatcham AA; st £10, dt (members' guests) £1. Apply to hon sec. Piscatorial Society has water; strictly members only. Civil Service AS has Ham Bridge Fishery; 2½m; trout, coarse fish; members only. Hotel: Swan.

Newbury (Berks). On Rivers Kennet and **Lambourn** and **Kennet and Avon Canal;** trout and coarse fishing. Newbury AA, Thatcham AA, Civil Service AA, Piscatorial Society, CALPAC and Reading and Dist. AA all hold water in this area. Tackleists: Cording's, 86 Northbrook Street; Pet Shop, Bartholomew Street.

Hungerford (Berks). Kennet and **Dunn;** trout, grayling; strictly preserved. **Hungerford Canal** fishing in hands of Hungerford Canal AA (3m). Frequently restocked with rainbow trout and coarse

8 miles of excellent Salmon, Sea and Brown Trout fishing on R. Torridge. Banks well cleared and fishing easy to approach. Regular stocking of Upper Beats with 1 lb. Brown Trout. First class food and every comfort. Ashley Courtenay recommended.

BLACK TORRINGTON 232

THE SWAN HOTEL, BIBURY

GLOUCESTERSHIRE
Tel: Bibury (028 574) 204
A.A.***   R.A.C.
Famous Old Coaching Inn, carefully modernised.
All rooms with private bathroom and colour TV.
300 yards of the River Coln facing the Hotel.
Dry Fly Trout fishing only.
Bibury Trout farm only 20 yards away.

Northcote Manor

AA***   RAC

Charming, secluded, Victorian manor house now a luxury hotel. Set in 12 acres of landscaped gardens overlooking Taw valley. Central for fishing, riding, walking and touring North Devon.

Northcote Manor, Burrington, Nr Umberleigh, N Devon
Tel: High Bickington (07696) 501

fish from local rivers. Excellent fishing. Recent captures: tench 7½ lb, roach 3 lb 2 oz, bream 5 lb 6 oz, trout 6 lb 14 oz; st and dt from hon sec or Lamb Inn. Tackleist: Paul Good, 24 High Street. Accommodation at Home Cafe, Red Lion, Three Swans, Bear, Lamb Hotel (Canal AA HQ).

Lockinge (Berks). 10m NE of Hungerford, Lockinge stillwater trout fishery. St £250. Enq. to Lockinge Farms, Tel. 023 588200.

Marlborough (Wilts). Trout. Club: Marlborough and District AA, has fishing rights in **Kennet and Avon Canal** from Milkhouse Water to Burbage Wharf and Bruce Tunnel to Little Bedwyn. Excellent roach; regularly restocked. Club also fishes Brimslade Farm Water. St £6, dt £1. Piscatorial Society has water at Axford; strictly members only. **Wroughton Reservoir,** near **Swindon,** stocked with brown and rainbow trout. Eight dt per day. Weekdays £4.80; Sundays and BH, £5.50. 55p extra for punt. Booking with Thames Water, 17 Bath Rd, Swindon. Tel: 24331. No Saturday fishing. Tackleists: H Duck and Leathercraft, both High Street; Tackle Box, Gorse Hill, Victoria Road, Swindon. Hotels: Aylesbury Arms, Savernake, Castle and Ball, Crown (Marlborough AA HQ).

THAME: Coarse fish.

Dorchester (Oxon). Thames and Thame. Coarse fish; good chub and dace, and carp quite numerous. Dorchester AA has water; dt from hon sec or Fleur-de-Lys.

Thame (Oxon). Roach, bream, perch, chub. Leighton Buzzard AC has stretches at **Shabbington, Worminghall** and **Waterperry.** Tackleist: Seal Seam (Thame) Ltd, Chestnuts Yard. Dt for Shabbington Island from Old Fisherman Inn.

Eythrope (Bucks). Roach, bream, perch, chub, good dace. Aylesbury Dist and Izaak Walton AA has water (4m from Aylesbury); members and friends only. Blenheim AS ¾m at **Stone.** Tackleists: S G Waters, Cambridge Street, and H Cobbold, Britannia Street (both Aylesbury).

CHERWELL: Coarse fish.

Islip (Oxon). Cherwell and Ray; good chub, roach, perch and pike fishing may be had in the Cherwell. Preserved by Oxford Angling and Preservation Socie-ty. Good accommodation at either of the inns or in the village. Inns: Red Lion, Swan. *(See also Oxford.)*

Hampton Poyle (Oxon). Leighton Buzzard AC has 1½m. Members only.

Heyford (Oxon). Preserved by Banbury and Dist AA; tickets from hon sec.

Banbury (Oxon). Banbury AA (HQ Reindeer Inn, Parsons Street) has fishing at Cropredy, Nell Bridge, Clifton, Somerton, Heyford and Bletchington. Canal also. St, wt and dt for river, canal and **Clattercote Reservoir.** Tickets from The Suitcase, 3a Church Lane. Coventry AA hold stretch in Aynho area; members only.

EVENLODE: Trout, coarse fish (roach and dace especially).

Hanborough (Oxon). Red Spinner AS rents 10 to 12m of the Evenlode; trout (restocked annually), dace, roach, chub, pike; strictly members only. **Glyme** strictly preserved. Good fishing on **Blenheim Park Lakes,** property of Duke of Marlborough. Excellent tench, perch and roach, with pike in winter. Boat fishing only. *(See Midlands lakes, reservoirs, etc.)*

WINDRUSH: Trout, grayling coarse fish (dace up to 1 lb and 2 lb roach not rare).

Witney (Oxon). Large trout; preserved below; leave must be obtained from the proprietors; good hatch of mayfly. Witney AS (HQ Eagle Vaults) has water *(see Minster Lovell and Newbridge).* No dt and membership restricted to county as a rule, but outside applications considered; apply hon sec. Club now has water on gravel pits at Hardwick and Stanton Harcourt (carp, tench, etc). Tackleist: R Bridgeman, 76 High Street.

Minster Lovell (Oxon); ns Witney. Cotswold Flyfishers have 10m at **Swinbrook** and **Stanton Harcourt;** trout (restocked yearly); fly only; membership limited; no dt. Witney AA has water on Windrush at **Worsham** (1m above village; trout) and Thames at **Newbridge** and **Standlake;** trout, grayling, coarse fish; fishing much improved *(see Witney).* Hotel: Old Swan Inn (no fishing).

Burford (Oxon). Burford AC holds water in vicinity; trout and coarse fish. Dt £1 from club HQ at Royal Oak, Witney Street. TWA licence now required. Hotels: Cotswold Gateway, Lamb, Bay Tree, Bull, Winters Tale.

COLN: notable dry fly fishing for trout of good average size; grayling.

Fairford (Glos). Trout; excellent; April 1 to Sept 30. Dry fly only upstream. Well stocked. Tickets can be had for 1½m from Bull Hotel, Market Place. Size limit 12 in; bag 1½ brace per rod; trout of 1–1½ lb plentiful. Other hotel: Hyperion House, London Street. Nearest tackleist at Lechdale, 4m.

Bibury (Glos). Coln: trout. Swan Hotel *(advt p 156)* has 300yds facing hotel free to residents: dry fly only.

TORRIDGE

(For close seasons, licences, etc, see South West Water Authority, p 38)

Rises near Cornish border of Devonshire and joins Taw estuary at Appledore, to flow into Bideford (also termed Barnstaple) Bay. Salmon, sea trout (peal) and brown trout (small).

Bideford (Devon). For details of sea fishing available, see p 204. Four reservoirs, at **Gammaton** and **Jennetts**, 2m on east and west sides of river, stocked with brown and rainbow trout; leased by Torridge Fly Fishing Club; Tickets from March 15 from hon sec. Tackleist: Pethericks, High Street; Gales of Barnstaple have a branch here. Hotels: Royal, New Inn, Tanton's, Ring o'Bells, Market.

Torrington (Devon). Salmon, sea trout, brown trout, W. of England School of Game Angling has 3½m divided into beats. Dt. £5 and £3, according to date. Phone 080 523256 for bookings. Lower Torridge Fishery has 7 beats on 5m of water from Torrington to Blinsham. 5 beats fly only after April 14. Apply C R Rowe, The Holt, Appledore, Bideford (Tel: 3126). Best months for salmon, March, April, May; (wt £45, dt 7) for sea trout, July, Aug, Sept; (wt £40, dt £6) dt (brown trout) £3.50 whole season.

Woodford Bridge (Devon). Brown trout (av 8–9 in). Woodford Bridge Hotel *(advt facing p 105),* Milton Damerel has 4m of brown trout fishing and 2m of salmon and sea trout water free to residents at hotel. Dt for non-residents as available: S & MT, £7, brown trout £4.

Tel 040 926252.

Shebbear (Devon). Devil's Stone Inn has 2½m of salmon, sea trout and brown trout fishing on Torridge; fly and spinning; excellent dry-fly trout water. Nearest beat 2m. RD licences and tackle, and angling instruction available. Dt sometimes issued to non-residents.

Sheepwash (Devon). Half Moon Inn has 10m of salmon, sea trout and brown trout fishing on Torridge. Banks cleared to facilitate fly fishing on all beats. Spinning allowed. Five upper beats stocked regularly with 1 lb brown trout; fly only. Season opens March 1. Dt (S) £5.50, (T) £4.50. Brochure on request from Charles Inniss *(advt p 156)*

Hatherleigh (Devon). Torridge, Lew, Okement; salmon, sea trout, brown trout. West of England School of Game Angling has 2m on Lew, 2m on Okement, divided into beats. Dt (sea trout) £5 (brown trout) £3. W H B Coham-Fleming, Coham, **Black Torrington,** has furnished cottage/flat available with salmon and trout fishing. Wt £12.50, dt £2.50. Tackleists: Pengelly D.I.Y., The Square, Holsworthy. Hotel: New Inn, Meeth (½m on Torridge; dts for salmon and trout).

Tributaries of the Torridge

LEW: Sea trout, trout.

Hatherleigh (Devon). W. of England School of Game Angling *(See Torrington, above)* have 2m here. Dt (sea trout) £5, (brown trout) £3.

OKEMENT:

Okehampton (Devon). See entry above for details of West of England School of Game Angling fishery. See also under *Torrington,* Torridge and Dartmoor streams accessible. Hotel: White Hart.

TRENT

(For close seasons, licences, etc, see Severn-Trent Water Authority, p 41)

Largest river system in England. Rising in Staffordshire, Trent drains much of Derbyshire, Nottinghamshire and Lincolnshire, and empties into Humber. A hundred years ago, one of England's principal fisheries; now recovering its status following massive effort at water-quality improvement by RWA. The tide-water, in particular, now fishing excellently. Some famous trout-holding tributaries, notably Dove, Wye and Derwent.

Gainsborough (Lincoln). Pike, perch, roach, chub. There are a few fish to 3m below Gainsborough. Tidal. Lincoln & Dist AA has stretches to accommodate 60 and 70 match pegs respectively at N Clifton and Laughterton Marsh. St £5, dt 70p. Goole AA has fishing at **Coates** and **Church Laneham.** No dt.

Torksey (Lincoln). Pike, roach, chub. Fossdyke Navigation; good coarse fishing; largely leased by Witham Joint Anglers' Federation, through whom matches should be booked; runs from Torksey through Saxilby to Lincoln *(see also Lincoln—Witham).* Sheffield and Dist AA has about 5¾m of water on Trent. Tidal.

High Marnham (Notts). Nottingham Fedn has stretch above power station; dt and matches; tidal.

Sutton-on-Trent (Notts). Tidal water. Pike, roach, dace, chub. Sheffield and Doncaster associations have joint rights on 3½m of Ossington Estate. Sheffield Amalgamated AS has sole right of Newcastle Fishery (about 6m, st £2.50, dt 60p. Heavily match-fished; check with hon sec before visiting.

Collingham (Notts). Club water. Trent, 2m W; pike, carp, barbel, roach, dace, chub, perch, bream; dt from King's Head, Royal Oak (see below), or hon sec, Collingham AA, which has 4m from Cromwell Weir to Besthorpe gravel pit. The Fleet of Besthorpe can be reached by bus from here; all round coarse fishing; a noted resort for eels. At Besthorpe Wharf is Newcastle Fishery; dt 50p. Sheffield AAA. Hotels: Royal Oak, King's Head, Grey Horse.

Muskham (Notts). Nottingham PS preserves from Fir Tree Corner (Kelham boundary) to Crankley Point, both sides, including gravel pits; members only.

Averham, Kelham (Notts); ns Newark, 2m. Very good coarse fishing; preserved by Nottingham PS for members only— roach, dace, chub (excellent fly water)— from railway bridge at Averham to South Muskham boundary on both sides of the river.

Newark-on-Trent (Notts). Roach, dace, pike, chub, bream. Newark and Dist Piscatorial Federation has water on Trent Dyke; st and dt from bailiffs. Trent preserved below by Nottingham PS; no tickets. **Newark Dyke;** Notting-

ham Piscatorial Society has a good deal of water on north bank; no tickets. **Cromwell Lake,** just off Newark By-Pass; 29 acres, trout, tench, bream, roach, carp, pike. Doncaster AA; members only. **Farndon Gravel Pit:** Newark and Dist PF; dt from bailiff. Tackleists: C Smith & Sons Ltd, Clinton Arms Yard, Newark-on-Trent, and G M Purvis, 41 Castle Gate, who will be pleased to give local information. Hotels: Britannia Inn, Farndon Ferry.

Farndon (Notts); ns Rolleston or Newark. Trent RD's Newcastle fishery. Nottingham Piscatorial Society has north bank (tickets as Rolleston), south bank let to Nottingham AA; dt issued.

Rolleston (Notts). Nottingham Piscatorial Society water from Greet mouth to Staythorpe power station; good roach and chub; dt from some tackleists and Rolleston Post Office. No permits on bank. Greet, trout; strictly preserved. Nottingham AA has water at Farndon Ferry (opp Rolleston); dt from bailiff or Britannia Inn; matches can be arranged in advance.

Fiskerton (Notts). Good roach and chub fishing. Bromley Arms has water here and beyond Hazleford; dt. The Greet enters Trent at Fiskerton; trout; strictly preserved.

Hazleford (Notts); ns Bleasby. Hazleford Ferry water, Fiskerton, now rented by Star and Garter Hotel; dt for about 1m water from Hotel.

Hoveringham (Notts). Coarse fish. Nottingham PS has stretch to Willow Holt; members only.

Gunthorpe (Notts); ns Lowdham. Good coarse fishing; roach, dace, chub.

Burton Joyce (Notts). Chub, roach (mainly), dace. Nottingham and Dist Fedn has good stretch for which dt issued (matches arranged, booked in advance after Nov 1 for following season); tickets from bailiff, hon sec, Stoke Ferry Boat Inn, Lord Nelson. Nottingham AA has from Colwick Viaduct downstream for one field.

Shelford (Notts). Shelford Fishery (dt from bailiff) on south bank (Lord Carnarvon's waters) is in hands of Nottingham AA. Matches arranged in advance.

Radcliffe-on-Trent (Notts). Roach, chub, dace and gudgeon, with perch, pike and tench in Lily Ponds. From Stoke Weir down to Gunthorpe, Nottingham AA; dt. From Stoke Weir up to Radcliffe Ferry, including Lily Ponds, Nottingham Fedn; dt. Fedn also holds from Radcliffe Ferry upstream (members only) and water below Radcliffe railway bridge *(see Burton Joyce)*. Accommodation at Chestnuts Club.

Nottingham (Notts). Good mixed fishing. Several miles in city free. Clubs with water include: Nottingham AA, for both (Beeston Station) **Shelford Chilwell fishery** on Trent (Beeston station). **Shelford Fishery** (dt issued for both). Nottingham Piscatorial Society has fishing at Rolleston, Fiskerton and Farndon; dt from tacklists only. Long Eaton Victoria AS; Thrumpton Fishery. From Erewash mouth to Attenborough; dt from hon sec, Regal Club. Nottingham and District Federation of Angling Societies comprises upwards of 68 clubs; water at **Burton Joyce** and **Stoke Bardolph.** West Bridgford British Legion AC has some water on Trent; st and dt from hon sec. Lake in **Wollaton Park** may be fished by dt from Parks Superintendent, Wollaton Park; bream, tench, roach, pike, perch. Tacklists: Walkers of Trowell, 9–15 Nottingham Road, Trowell; Redmayne & Todd, Carrington Street; T Watson, 1 Oak Street, Carrington, A Tizley, 55 Kirkewhite Street East; C Smith & Sons Ltd (Newark); Anglers' Shop, 198 Ilkeston Road.

Wilford (Notts). Clifton Fishery from Beeston Weir to Man of Trent; Nottingham AA; dt issued. From railway bridge down is Nottingham AA water; members only.

Beeston (Notts). Chub, roach, dace, bleak, gudgeon; preserved by Nottingham AA. Dt for stretch to Beeston Weir from hon sec. Assn also has water on **Beeston Canal.** Tacklist: T C Saville Ltd, 9 Station Road *(advt p 6).*

Thrumpton and Long Eaton (Notts). Roach, bream, dace, chub. Long Eaton Victoria AS has Thrumpton Ferry field. St £5, dt 50p. No matches. Coventry & Dist AA also has water here now, dt from local tacklists. Canals: society has lengths in **Erewash Canal** and **Cranfleet Canal;** coarse fish. Long Eaton and Dist AF has water on Trent at Trent Lock, on **Soar** at **Kegworth** and on Erewash Canal. Tacklists: Horseshoe Sports Depot, Station Road; and Bridge Tackle Shop, Derby Rd; all in Long Eaton.

Chellaston (Derby). Trent, 1m SW, at Swarkestone. Derby AA has water below, and upstream, through **Ingleby** and **Twyford,** to above **Willington.** Stretches are held on both banks, with few breaks. Most species of coarse fish present. Dt 75p. Club also has 14m on **Trent and Mersey Canal,** but no dt.

Stoke-on-Trent (Staffs). Stoke City & Dist AA has fishing on **R. Sow, R. Roden, Trent and Mersey Canal,** between Aston and Weston Lock; **Shropshire Union Canal** (200-peg match-venue, enq. invited) and **Knighton Reservoir.** Coarse fish. St £8 (reductions for ladies, juvs, OAP). Details and permits for **River Rhiew** (fly only) from J J McDade, 19 Leaside Rd, Trent Vale, or Anglers' Club. Tacklists: J Pitchford, 258 London Rd, Stoke: G T Whitehurst, Scotia Road, Burselm; F Walters, 293 Uttoxeter Rd, Normacott; Webbs, 35 Paradise St, Tunstall; Burtons, 58 Trinity St and Coopers, 30 Pall Mall, Hanley; and others.

Burton-upon-Trent (Staffs). Good free fishing for roach and chub at Newton and Willington. Burton Mutual AA fishes **Dove** at **Tutbury** to confluence with Trent, and Branstone gravel pit; members only. Birmingham AA has six pools (two fly, four coarse) at Bretby. Good pools at Barton and Walton. Tickets for canals, various stretches on the R Trent and a variety of other waters from tacklists Mullarkey, 184 Waterloo Street. Hotels: Queen's, Station and Midland.

Alrewas (Staffs). Perch, dace, roach. Birmingham AA has water here and at **Yoxall.** Trent and Mersey Canal, dt from keeper. Tame, 2m SE; chub, dace. Mease, 3m SE.

Rugeley (Staffs). River polluted. Rugeley and Brereton AS has about 1m on Trent and water on **Trent and Mersey Canal** from Armitage to Wolseley Bridge. From here to Colwich held by British Waterways (dt from them); roach, pike, perch. Tickets available from Manton, Bow Street (tacklists). **Blithfield Reservoir,** 4m NE; trout; South Staffs. Water Co allows fishing on season permit only. Inquiries to: Recreations Office, Blithfield Reservoir, Abbots Bromley, Staffs.

Colwich (Staffs). Coarse fish; fishing very poor through pollution. Sow, 4m W; controlled by Stafford Anglers. Blyth 5m E; preserved. Sherbrook and Oakedge

Pools preserved by Lord Lichfield. Rugeley and Brereton AS has water on canal; roach, pike, chub, perch; dt and st at small fee *(see also Rugeley).* Hotel: Lamb and Flag.

Great Haywood (Staffs; ns Colwich, 1m. Trent polluted. **Trent and Mersey Canal;** roach, pike, chub, perch; length held by Shugborough Park FC (no tickets). Hotel: Clifford Arms.

Trentham (Staffs). Lake in Trentham Gardens; area about 70 acres; pike, perch, roach and tench; st £15, dt £2 Village about 3m from Stoke-on-Trent on main road London to Manchester. Fishing tickets at Lodge Gate. Trentham Hotel 1m. Catering available in Trentham Gardens, caravans site.

Weston-on-Trent (Staffs). Coarse fishing in **Trent and Mersey Canal;** chub, roach, bream, perch; Stoke City DAA water.

Tributaries of the Trent

IDLE: Excellent coarse fishing in parts.

Misterton (Lincs). Trent and Idle. Coarse fish: Sheffield and Dist AA has 4m of water on Idle for members only.

Misson (Notts). Doncaster and Dist AA has from Newington to Idlestop, about 10m. Good roach, bream, perch, pike; st £3.50 and dt from tackle dealers. Assn also has Black Drain and Bandspinner Drain; dt from J Parkin, 19 Asquith Avenue, Ealand Crowle. *(See also Crowle.)* Sheffield and Dist AA also has stretch of Idle; members only. *(See also Misterton.)*

Retford (Notts). Poulter, 4m S. Meden, 4m S. Maun, 4m S. Idle above Retford private. Retford AA rents long stretch of **Chesterfield and Stockwith Canal;** now widely thought to be best canal fishing in England. Carp, tench, bream, roach and chub. No dt. St from hon sec. Club also has stretch at Bolham. From Woodcocks Bridge to Church Lane bridge, Clayworth, belongs to Worksop and Dist Anglers' Association. Tackle Shop at Carolgate.

TORNE and NEW IDLE. Doncaster and Dist AA has 18m from Rossington to Pilfrey Bridges, also **Ring Drain** alongside and water on **Stainforth and Keadby Canal;** dt from E Drury, Candy Corner Pumping Station, Finningly, nr Doncaster.

Althorpe (S Humberside). **Sheffield and South Yorkshire canal;** coarse fish; about 14m of water above and down to Trent; good fishing; rights held by Sheffield, Rotherham and Doncaster associations. Other fishing stations for canal are **Thorne** and **Crowle.**

Crowle (S Humberside). Excellent centre for coarse fishing. **Stainforth and Keadby Canal, Torne** and **Ring Drain,** are ½m from Crowle Central Station; Doncaster AA; roach, tench, bream, perch, carp,

pike. Three Drains on A18; Sheffield and Dist AA; roach, perch, tench, carp. Licences, association books and dt from hotels or hon sec (enclose s/a envelope). Hotels: South Yorkshire, Crowle; Friendship Inn, Keadby. Tackle shops in Doncaster (17m) or Scunthorpe (10m).

RYTON (tributary of Idle); Coarse fish.

Scrooby (Notts). Ryton, From Bramshall's farm to junction with Idle, 2m; dt 12p from Pilgrim Fathers and the garage, Scrooby.

Worksop (Notts). On Ryton and **Chesterfield Canal;** coarse fish. Worksop and Dist AA has 11m of canal from W Retford Bridge to Drakeholes Basin. St only (£1.50) from G March, 262 Kilton Road. Lakes: Dukeries Lakes *(see Nottinghamshire lakes and canals)* especially **Clumber Park Lake** (National Trust), where dt and, st can be had; and **Sandhill Lake;** trout, coarse fish; dt from bailiffs and at gate.

MAUN (tributary of Idle): Polluted.

Tuxford (Notts). Maun, 3m NW polluted. Bevercotes Beck, 3m NW. Idle, 4m NW. Poulter, 4m NW. Meden, 4m NW. Lakes: Haughton Decoy and lower ponds, 3m NW.

Mansfield (Notts). Sand Hills Quarry, Worksop; trout, coarse fish; dt. Other dt waters (coarse fishing): Vicars Pond, Clipstone; Wellow Pond near Ollerton. Mansfield AA has water on **Witham, Trent** and gravel pits and lake; members only. Tackleists: R and M C Dibble, 40 Belvedere Street.

Sutton-in-Ashfield (Notts). Lakes: Lawn Dam. King's Mill Reservoir, 1m NE; tickets on bank. Hardwick Lakes, Hardwick Hall, are 6m W. Hotels: Nag's Head, Denman's Head. Tackleist: H Burrows, 91 Outram Street.

DEVON: Coarse fish.

Bottesford (Notts). Smite, 3m NW at Orston. Car Dyke, 5m NW. Bottesford AA preserves 5m of **Grantham Canal** at Bottesford, Muston and Woolsthorpe-by-Belvoir; st £2 and dt 40p from Bull Inn and Rutland Arms, Woolsthorpe-by-Belvoir (on canal bank); and from hon sec and from bailiffs on bank. Good coarse fishing, with pike over 20 lb.

Belvoir Castle (Leics). Between Melton Mowbray and Grantham. Belvoir Lakes, 3m SE, and Knipton Reservoir, 4m SE (coarse fish); dt from Estate Office, Belvoir Castle, Grantham. Also **Nottingham and Grantham Canal** on which Bottesford and District AA has water. Other stations on canal are **Long Clawson, Harby, Hose** and **Stathern.**

GREET: Trout; coarse fish; preserved.

Southwell (Notts). River private. Trent, 3m SE at Fiskerton. At Oxton, 5m SW, Nottingham Fly Fishers' Club has a trout lake at Gibsmere and about 2m on River Meden in Thoresby Park; strictly members only. Annual membership: £70 Greet FC, too, has trout fishing. Cromwell Fly Fishers, 20 Norwood Gardens, Southwell, has a lake north of Cromwell *(advt p 162).*

NUT BROOK (tributary of Erewash):

West Hallam (Derby). Lakes: **Mapperley Reservoir,** 2m N, is held by the NCB. Shipley Hall Reservoir, 3m N. Locko Park Lake, 3m SW. Smalley Mill Pond, 3m NW.

SOAR: Very popular coarse fishery with anglers in the Leicester area.

Ratcliffe (Notts); ns Kegworth. Good coarse fishing. Long Eaton & Dist AF administrate Lockington Estate and Ferry fisheries. Members only *(see immediately below for other details).*

Kegworth (Derby). Roach, dace, bream, tench, chub, perch. From Kegworth Bridge up to Kegworth Lock held by Long Eaton Victoria AS. Dt 50p, st £4.

Nottingham AA has from noticeboard below Kegworth Bridge to Kingston Dyke (members only). Long Eaton AF has good stretch down to Ratcliffe; st and dt from Anchor Inn. Soar AS has water here *(see Loughborough).*

Normanton-on-Soar (Leics). Good coarse fishing. Recently restocked by Loughborough Soar AS *(see Loughborough).*

Loughborough (Leics). Coarse fish; sport much improved through efforts of Trent RD; preserved by Loughborough Soar AS from Kegworth up to Barrow-on-Soar Weir and Shallow Lock (also canal same length); dt 40p (certain stretches only); Sunday fishing permitted. Tackleist: Wortley & Sons, 45 Baxtergate (licences and permits). Tickets also from Mrs. E Gee, 9 Pasture Lane, Sutton, Bonnington; Rose & Crown, Zouch, hon sec. and tackleists. **Proctor's Lake and River Fishing,** The Park, Barrow-on-Soar (5m SE). Dt issued *(see Barrow).* Hotels: King's Head and Central.

Quorn (Leics). Roach, bream. Quorn AS has rights on stretches of river and 1m of canal; inquire hon sec. River fishes best in autumn and winter.

Barrow-upon-Soar (Leics). About 3m river and canal fishing; good roach and bream; recently restocked. Fishes best autumn and winter. Leicester and Dist ASA Water Navigation AC, previous tenant, now disbanded. Quorn AC has water in area. **Proctor's Lake and River Fishing,** The Park (Quorn 2323). Caravanning and camping and fishing facilities. Dt 50p from machine at entrance. Tackleist: Webster and Barnes, 37 High Street.

Leicester (Leics). Coarse fish; recently restocked by Trent RD. Much water in Leicester district held by Leicester and Dist Amal Soc of Anglers; includes fishing on Soar, **Wreake, Eye, Nene,** and canals. All on dt or st from local tack-leists or bailiffs. Leicester AS (Soar and canal; dt and st). Leicester AC (water on **Grand Union Canal**) and Wigston AS (canal; tickets from C Burnham, Blaby Road, S Wigston). Kibworth and Dist AS fishes **Leicester Canal;** some good coarse fish but boat traffic ruins summer sport. Thornton (7m W), Cripston (5m NW), Saddington (10m SE) and Swithland (6m). Reservoirs all preserved. Quenby Hall Lake, 7m E; preserved. The Pool, Groby, 5m NW; bream, tench, roach, pike; dt from house at pool. Quorndon Brook, 6m NW, at Bradgate Park; trout; preserved. Hotels: Grand, Royal, Hermitage (Oadby). Tackleists: John Adams, Humberstone Gate; N Woodward, Braunstone Gate; Marks & Marlow, King Richards Road; "The Aquaria", Melton Road; J C Townsend, Downton & Son, both Humberstone Road.

Narborough (Leics). Hinckley and Dist AA has water here containing trout and grayling; permits from permits sec.

WREAKE (tributary of Soar): An attractive coarse fishery on which Leicester and Dist ASA has extensive coarse fishing rights.

Syston (Leics). Roach, bream, pike, perch, chub, dace; greater part preserved by Leicester and Dist ASA, between Syston and Melton Mowbray; dt. *(See Leicester above.)*

Ashfordby (Leics). Roach, perch, dace, pike, chub. Mostly Leicester ASA water; dt 30p from bailiff, Riverside Cottage. Ashfordby SOA has water on Wreake and pits at **Frisby** (1m). Members only; no dt. Dt for **Holwell Works Reservoir** from E Madden, "The Limes", Ashford-by-Valley.

Melton Mowbray (Leics). **Knipton Reservoir,** 8m N, at Branston. Melton Mowbray Society of Anglers (dt from club HQ at Rutland Arms, King St; affiliated to Leicester and Dist ASA) has water; also preserve tributary Eye. Tackleist: John F Green, 27 Nottingham Street.

DERWENT: Noted trout and grayling water in upper reaches; downstream coarse fish come into their own.

Sawley (Derby). Coarse fish. Pride of Derby AC has from Wilne Weir to mouth of Derwent (south bank), 750 yd stretch on north bank, and both banks of Trent above Sawley Weir to Red House on one bank and Sutton's Eaves on other. Also

canal from Derwent Lock to Trent and **Trent** to Sawley Lock. Further water on Trent below Sawley Weir to lock house (single bank only) and several ponds. Members only (st are issued to anglers living in 16m radius of Derby only; long waiting list, applications to hon sec or Derby tackleists). Tackleists issue dt for other clubs' waters. Inn: Harrington Arms, Old Sawley, Long Eaton (permits for local waters).

Draycott (Derby). Coarse fish. Trent, 8m SW at Wilne. Now belongs to Hoveringham Gravel Co.

Borrowash (Derby). Coarse fish. Earl of Harrington AC waters *(see Derby)*.

Spondon (Derby). Coarse fish; preserved by Earl of Harrington AC *(see Derby)*. Chaddesden Brook, 1m NW, and Locko Park, 2m N. Private.

Derby (Derby). Coarse fish, Earl of Harrington AC has Derwent from Borrowash Bridge through to Darley Weir, one large meadow on R Trent at Barrow-on-Trent and fly only trout water on **R Ecclesbourne** at Turnditch. St £4.50, dt 75p. Tickets from hon sec. Derby Corporation issues st and dt for Derwent from Darley Abbey to Derby railway station. Corporation also issues tickets for **Alvaston Lake, Markeaton Park Lake, Allestree Park Lake** and Derwent in Darley Abbey Park (dts from keeper). Locko Park Lake and Chaddesden Brook private. "Leisure Sport" gravel pits in **Attenborough Nature Reserve.** Bream, tench, roach. St from RMC House, Feltham, Middlesex. Other clubs: Pride of Derby AA *(see Sawley)*; Derby RIFC (water on Derwent, **Trent, Dove, Ecclesbourne;** canals; dt 50p); Derby AA (water on Trent and canal; some dt). Derby Federation has water at **Duffield,** from Milford Bridge to Little Eaton. Trout and coarse fish. Tackleists: Anglers Corner, 344 Osmaston Road; Artisan Angling, 141 London Rd; Blount, 80 Shaftesbury Cres.

Duffield (Derby). Coarse fish, trout and grayling. Derbyshire AF water. Dt for trout and grayling from Bridge Inn, Duffield.

Belper (Derby). Grayling, pike, trout, coarse fish; 8m held by Belper AC. Dt. Earl of Harrington AC has ¾m of trout fishing on **Ecclesbourne** at Turnditch (3m W); fly only; members only (see Derby). Black Brook. Holbrook Brook, 2m SE.

'There never was so innocent a recreation'. Roach fishing on a midland lake. The ultimate in relaxation. *Photograph: John Tarlton.*

Ambergate (Derby). Few trout, pike, coarse fish. Belper AC has water downstream streams; *see above.* Alderwasley Ponds, 2m NW. **Butterley Reservoir** and **Codnor Park Reservoir;** roach, bream, tench, carp, pike; Ripley's AA; st £5, dt 60p from hon sec or keepers. Loscoe Dam; dt from keeper. Hotel: Hurt Arms.

Whatstandwell (Derby). Mostly grayling and trout, with former predominant. Dt £1 from Derwent Hotel, which has ¼m fishing; rather overhung with trees, but plenty of fish and good wading in low water. Homesford Cottage Inn stretch now let to Cromford Fly Fishers; no tickets. Dt for stretch at Mere Brook caravan site to campers only. Lakes: Alderwasley Ponds, 2m SW; preserved.

Cromford (Derby). Trout; fly only; preserved below road bridge (both banks), as far as and including Homesford Meadows, by Cromford Fly Fishers; members only. Above bridge, Derbyshire CC AC water. No tickets. Cromford Canal too overgrown for fishing. Hotel: Greyhound.

Matlock (Derby). Trout (some rainbows), grayling and coarse fish. Matlock AC issue wt and dt; dt from Midland Hotel (Matlcok Bath); water at Matlock and Matlock Bath; trout and coarse; about 1m.

Rowsley (Derby). Trout, brown and rainbow; grayling. Darley Dale Flyfishing Club has rights on Derwent from ½m north of Rowsley Bridge to ½m north of Darley Bridge; fly-fishing only; no dt; stocked with brown trout. Two dt (£6.40 each) occasionally allowed to guests at Peacock Hotel, **Rowsley** (see below). Two dt at £6.40 each for guests at

Grouse and Claret Hotel for ½m north of Rowsley Bridge. Peacock Hotel, Rowsley also have rights on Duke of Rutland's fishery on **Wye** for guests; rainbow trout; dry fly only. Water not stocked but fish plentiful; limit three brace. Sunday fishing. Fishing available on **River Bradford,** from above Lathkill junction pool, Alport, to Bradford Village, Youlgreave; brown trout; dry fly only. Dt £5 from Estate Office, Haddon Hall, Bakewell (Mon–Sat only).

Baslow (Derby); ns Bakewell, 4m. The **Cavendish Hotel** (famous for many years as **The Peacock**) has 6 rods on the Chatsworth and Monsal Dale fisheries. 6½m of the Derwent, brown trout and grayling; 4½m of the **Wye,** brown and rainbow trout. Dt are £12. Priority booking for residents. For full details, phone Baslow 2311.

Hathersage (Derby). Trout, grayling; preserved by the Derwent FFC; also at Bamford and Grindleford (members only).

Bamford (Derby). Trout, grayling. Derwent FFC has water below Bamford Mill; also from Bamford Mill to Yorkshire Bridge; members only.

Ladybower. Centre for **Ladybower and Derwent Reservoirs;** trout; fly only *(see Midlands reservoirs and lakes).* Hotels: Ladybower Inn, Yorkshire Bridge Inn, Ye Derwent Hotel, Bamford (1m), Anglers' Rest (1m), Marquis of Granby, Bamford (2m), Rising Sun, Bamford (2m).

AMBER (tributary of Derwent): Trout, coarse fish.

Alfreton (Derby). Ripley AA has water for members only. Club issues dt 60p for reservoirs at **Butterley** and **Codnor Park** for pike, perch, roach, tench, bream, and carp; tickets from hon sec or keepers. Sheffield Trout Anglers have water on Amber at Wingfield. Hotels: George, Castle. Also fair fishing in Derwent at Ambergate, 5m SW.

WYE (tributary of Derwent): One of few rivers in which rainbow trout breed. Also holds good brown trout.

Bakewell (Derby). Trout fishing (rainbow and brown) on Duke of Rutland's water for guests at Rutland Arms Hotel; trout average, 12 oz; both banks; dt from hotel (four rods only); limited, three brace; Sunday fishing permitted. Mayfly hatch usually in early June. Peacock Hotel, **Rowsley,** has 6m; rainbow trout and grayling *(see Derwent).*

Monsal Dale (Derby). Trout; preserved by Monsal Dale Fishery from Cressbrook Mill to bridge at Marble Works, Ashford; brown and rainbow trout; good fishing; no tickets; strictly members only.

Buxton (Derby). River private. Brown and rainbow trout fishing in **Lightwood** and **Stanley Moor** reservoirs; Buxton Flyfishers' Club; limited dt from hon sec. Dove *(see Dove),* Manifold *(see Manifold),* Derwent *(see Rowsley up to Ladybower),* Lathkill; trout; private. Hotels: Palace, St Ann's, Old Hall, Leewood, Buckingham, Hartington, Grove, Portland.

DOVE. Dovedale waters, where Izaak Walton and Chas Cotton fished, are now more of historic than sporting interest. Heavily overfished. Good sport with trout and grayling elsewhere. In lower reaches, where polluted Churnet enters Dove, angling is improving. Stretches below Uttoxeter, Doveridge, Marchington, Sudbury, etc, also improving.

Uttoxeter (Staffs). Trout, grayling. Uttoxeter AA preserves good deal of water between Rocester and Uttoxeter; no permits.

Rocester (Staffs). Trout, grayling above town; grayling, few trout below. Churnet; fishing spoilt by pollution, but improving; private.

Ashbourne (Derby). **Henmore Stream** preserved by Ashbourne Flyfishers' Club; trout, grayling. Also rights on Okeover Estates **Yeldersley** and **Shirley Lakes.** Also 3m on **Bentley Stream.** St strictly limited; no dt. £1,000 spent on re-stocking in 1981. In Dovedale 3m of trout and grayling fishing can be had by guests at Izaak Walton Hotel. Dovedale (dt £2.25) fishing best before tourism build-up in May. Charles Cotton Hotel *(see Hartington)* and Crewe and Harpur Arms *(see Longnor).* Hotel in Ashbourne; Green Man; hotel at Mayfield, 2m SW (Staffs); Royal Oak. Tackleist: Foster Bros *(advt p 11)*

Hartington (Derby). Trout. Charles Cotton Hotel has about 250 yards of the River Dove; residents only. Proprietor will give data about stretches available from farmers.

CHURNET (tributary of Dove): Mixed fishery spoilt by pollution, but improving.

Cheddleton (Staffs). Endon Brook, 1m

NW. West Brook, 1m SE. Pond by Wetley, 3m S. Club has canal *(see Leek)*.

Leek (Staffs). Trout, coarse fish; preserved above Leek town by landowners. Fishing improving as pollution decreases. Leek and Morland's FC has water on canal at Leek and Cheddleton, **Crakemarsh** (coarse fish) and stretches on the **Dove**, **Manifold** and parts of Churnet between Rudyard and Leekbrook. Mt, wt and dt from Club for visitors to area. Contact hon sec for details. **Rudyard Lake** is 3m NW; very good bream, with roach, perch and pike; dt. Punts on half and full day basis from I L Nixon (water bailiff), Lake House, Rudyard, near Leek. Match lengths pegged. **Tittesworth Reservoir:** 189-acre Severn-Trent WA trout fishery. *(See Midlands reservoirs and lakes p 102).*

MANIFOLD (tributary of Dove): Offers visitors one or two opportunities for sport with trout and grayling.

Longnor (Staffs). Buxton, 7m; trout. Dove, 1m E; trout, grayling. Fishing (fly only) can be had from the Crewe and Harpur Arms; 8m on Manifold; dt £1.50; waders necessary; limited to guests; non-residents may fish if all rods not taken. Part of Hoo Brook and Manifold is National Trust property; trout restocked.

MEASE. Coarse fish. Fishing stations are: **Measham** (Leics); **Snarestone** (Leics); and **Ashby-de-la-Zouch** (Leics); **Netherseal** (Derby) and **Harlaston** (Staffs); Birmingham AA has water at last two. Willesley Park Lake, 1m SW. Ashby Wolds Reservoir, 4m W. Barrat Pool, 4m SW. Coleorton Ponds, 3m E. Staunton Lake, 4m. Hotels: Queen's Head, Royal.

SEAL BROOK (tributary of Mease):

Over Seal (Leics). Lakes: Ashby Wolds Reservoir, 1m N.

TAME: After a long history of pollution, recovering under the care of the Severn-Trent WA. Fish now present in a number of stretches. Further improvement scheduled.

Tamworth (Staffs). Tributary Anker holds roach, pike and perch. Dt issued for Castle Pleasure Grounds, Tamworth Corporation water; other dt from Warren Farm, Amington. Mease; roach, chub, dace; Haunton, Harleston; dt from W T Ward and Harleston Mill. Lakes: Drayton Park, 2m S; Middleton Park, 4m S; Canwell Hall, 4m SW *(see*

Sutton Coldfield); Cuttle Mill, 5m SW; good carp water. Local clubs: Lamb AC; Fazeley Victory AC; Birch Coppice AC; Tamworth WMC; which fish Coventry and Birmingham Canals; some tickets available. Tackleists: L Bates, Amington Road; H Greenway, Lichfield Street; S Mulvey, Watling Street, Wilnecote. Hotels: Albert (near fishing in Anker); Castle; Peel.

Kingsbury (Warwicks). County council water park, including specialist pike and carp fisheries, also lakes stocked with a variety of coarse fish. St from CC offices, Warwick; dt for some of the fisheries on site.

Sutton Coldfield (W Midlands). Lakes: Bracebridge Pool, 2m NW; Blackroot Pool, 1m NW; Powell's Pool; Longmoor Pool (roach, bream, pike); all in Sutton Park; dt from keepers. Canwell Hall Pool private. Local club: Sutton Coldfield AS, which has lakes; permits for members' guests only.

ANKER (tributary of Tame): coarse fish; best sport in winter. Heavy losses of stock have affected sport.

Polesworth (Warwick). Coventry AA has 3m; good pike fishing. St from hon sec. £5.75. Assn also has 7m on canal; dt 60p from Association, bailiffs and tackleists.

SENCE (tributary of Anker): small stream, but good trout and grayling in places, as well as chub, roach and dace. Members only, but some permits in close coarse season for trout fishing *(see Coventry p 133)*. Coventry and Dist AA has 1½m at **Sheepy** and on the Crown Estate at **Gopsall** between Shackerstone and Heather *(see Narborough)*.

BOSWORTH BROOK (tributary of Sence): Trout; preserved.

Market Bosworth (Leics). Bosworth Brook, 1m N; trout; preserved by owner of Bosworth Hall. Sence, 3m W. Tweed, 3m SW. Coventry AA has 4m of canal here; good tench *(see also Shenton, below)*. Lakes: The Duckery, Bosworth Park, 1m S; pike, etc. Gabriel Pool, 3m NE.

TWEED (tributary of Sence):

Shenton (Warwick). Coventry AA has water on canal; association membership books required; obtainable from Riley's Sports, 37 Queens Road, Nuneaton.

ARLEY BROOK (tributary of Tame). Fishing station: **Shustoke** (Warwick). Brook polluted. Trout fishing in Tame

Division's, S-TWA Shustoke Reservoir *(see Midlands reservoirs and lakes).*

BLYTH (tributary of Tame): Coarse fish. Centres: **Coleshill** (Warwick) (chub, perch, pike, roach); **Hampton-in-Arden** (Warwick) (chub, pike, roach); **Solihull** (Warwick). **Earlswood Lakes,** 6m SW; tickets for three lakes (coarse fish); from boathouse.

REA (tributary of Tame): Polluted and fishless.

Birmingham (W Midlands). Birmingham AA, formed from a number of local clubs, controls water on river, canal and lake from mid-Wales to the Fens; from Staffordshire to the Thames Valley. Charges to members of constituent clubs—salmon: £20. Trout and coarse fishing: £12: coarse fishing: £10. Associate memberships freely available at £15 (trout and coarse) £12 (coarse). OAP: £1, junior: (up to 18 yrs of age) £3. The club-card gives details of all fishing rights, which include water on **Severn and tributaries, Thames and tributaries, Wye and tributaries, Gt Ouse, Arrow, Clun, Ithon** and **Wye, Monnow, Onny** and **Ledwyche** canals and lakes. Some waters reserved for fly-fishing. White Swan Piscatorial Society rents several waters near **Bredon, Bewdley, Holt Fleet, Upton** and **Leominster;** include some miles of **Severn** and **Teme.** Gamefishers Club has trout and grayling fishing on **Leigh Brook** and **R Lugg,** guests permits only. Reservoirs at **Edgbaston** and **Shustoke** fishable on permit from Tame Div, Severn-Trent WA, 156/170 Newhall Street, Birmingham. Coarse fishing on 14 park lakes and pools in the city. Dt 50p from park-keepers. Special st for pensioners available. Tackleists: W Powell, 35 Carrs Lane *(advt p 6)*; H Greenway, 5 Warren Farm Rd, Kingstanding and at Pipe Hayes, Tyseley, Shard End and Tamworth; Bate, 16 Colmore Circus; Simmons & Priddy, 9 Stratford Rd, Shirley; Brooks, 958 Bristol Rd S, A Clissett, Cotterbridge; Keeling, New Market Hall, Bull Ring Centre; J Hickman, 211 Station Rd, Stetchford; Allmarks, 43 Waterloo Rd, Smethwick and Hagley Rd W, Quinton. Many hotels.

Lifford (Birmingham). Bourne Brook, 2m N. Cole, 2m E. British Waterways reservoir. Good coarse fishing. Dt 50p from park-keeper.

FORD BROOK (tributary of Tame). Fishing stations: **Pelsall** and **Walsall** (W Midlands). Brook polluted. Lake: Hatherton Lake; pike. **Sneyd Reservoir** (British Waterways); rented by Walsall and Dist AS, which has also **Hatherton Canal. Park Lime Pits;** carp, bream, roach, perch, pike; dt and st for small charge. **Arboretum Lake;** bream, tench, roach, perch, pike; dt. Tackleists: R Wallace, 35 High Street; Walsall.

SOWE: Coarse fish, some trout.

Stafford (Staffs). Upstream of town; perch, pike, dace, roach, chub. Downstream; perch, roach, bream, chub, occasional trout. Free for about ½m upstream of town on left bank only; remainder preserved by Izaak Walton (Stafford) AA. This association has fisheries on the Sowe, the **Penk, Trent & Mersey Canal, Shropshire Union Canal** and **Hopton Pools,** the latter containing carp and tench as well as the more widely distributed coarse fish. Apply hon sec for annual membership £4.50, wt £1, dt 50p. Juvs £2 OAP 50p. Hotels: Swan, Station, Vine, Royal Oak, Garth, Tillington Hall.

Great Bridgford (Staffs). Sowe; Whitmore Reans AA has water; st only, apply hon sec. Izaak Walton (Stafford) AA has about 1½m *(see Stafford).*

Eccleshall (Staffs); ns Norton Bridge, 3m. Trout; preserved. Offley Brook. Lakes: Oatland Pond, 4m W. Cop Mere, 2m W. All private.

PENK (tributary of Sowe):

Acton Trussell (Staffs); ns Stafford. Coarse fish. **Staffordshire and Worcestershire Canal.** Stafford AA has water *(see Stafford).* Whitmore Reans AA has water here on canal and river. Dt 50p from hon sec annual membership £4.

Radford Bridge (Staffs). Izaak Walton (Stafford) AA has water here *(see Stafford under Sowe).* Tickets from ATC Stores (tackleist) *(see Stafford).*

Penkridge (Staffs). Whitmore Reans AA has water here; also on Whiston Brook and Staffordshire and Worcestershire Canal. Hotels: Littleton Arms, Fox and George, White Hart.

TYNE

(For close seasons, licences, etc, see Northumbrian Water Authority, p 40)

Formed by junction of North and South Tyne at Hexham, and empties into North Sea at Tynemouth (Northumberland). Once famous salmon river, became badly polluted but now reported to be improving for salmon and sea trout; trout fishing fair. Pike are increasing in lower reaches (below Hexham) and dace in the North and South Tyne.

Newcastle-upon-Tyne (North'land). Pollution abating. **Whittle Dene Reservoirs**, 11m W of Newcastle (trout), dt 85p from reservoir keeper. Boats 15p per hour, or £1 per day. At **Hexham** (7m) the DC have fishing. George Hotel has fishing at **Chollerford**. Tackleists: J Robertson, 101 Percy Street; Bagnall & Kirkwood, Grey Street. *(For Northumbrian Anglers' Federation water see Prudhoe.)*

Ryton (Durham). Occasional salmon; trout, coarse fish. Federation water *(see Prudhoe)*.

Wylam (North'land). Federation water, Local association: AA, which has about 2m below Federation water; no tickets. Few salmon; trout, coarse fish.

Prudhoe (North'land). Trout, coarse fish; occasional salmon; preserved by the Northumbrian Anglers' Federation; season tickets only, for salmon, trout and coarse fish, from all Newcastle tackleists. Lakes: **Whittle Dene Reservoirs**, 6m N; trout and perch; from bailiff *(see Hexham)*.

Mickley (North'land). Trout, coarse fish; occasional salmon; Federation water *(see Prudhoe)*. Lakes: Whittle Dene Reservoirs, 5m N *(see Hexham)*.

Stocksfield (North'land). Trout, coarse fish, few salmon.

Corbridge (North'land). Trout and dace; trout plentiful but small; but more sea trout and salmon reported. Corbridge Riverside Sports Club has 1¾m on south bank; membership restricted to persons living locally; dt to members' guests only. ½m free on north bank. Newcastle's Hallington reservoirs (8m N) now private. Whittle Dene Reservoirs (8m E) provide brown and rainbow trout fishing *(see Hexham)*. New Derwent Reservoirs (trout) 10m S *(see Derwent)*. At Allendale (12m SW) visitors staying locally may have dt for **East Allen** (trout). Information and licences from D Lowes, Middle Street. Hotels: Dyvels, Station Rd; Angel, Main Street; Wheatsheaf, St Helen's Street; and those in Hexham.

Hexham (North'land). Trout (av ¾ lb), coarse fish; salmon improving. Salmon fishing at Tyne Green, near town. Spring and October. Permits from Hexham DC, Hexham House, Hexham. Visitors: £1 per year, salmon and trout. All other salmon water preserved. Hallington Reservoirs, 7m N; private. Club: Hexham AA has water; no tickets. Hotels: Beaumont, Beaumont Street, County, Priestpopple; Royal, Priestpopple.

Tributaries of the Tyne

DERWENT: Few Trout. Trout average about ¼ lb, but are hard to catch owing to plentiful feed; early months best.

Swalwell (Durham). Some pollution. Winlaton Mill to Lintzford, 5m, held by Axwell Park and Derwent Valley AA; few trout; membership restricted to 30, but dt available (12½p).

Shotley Bridge (Durham). Derwent, 1m W; trout and grayling. Derwent AA preserves about 14m of river from Lintzford to **Derwent Reservoir** *(trout, see Durham Reservoirs)* and one bank above reservoir to Baybridge; membership restricted: long waiting-list. Hotel: The Lord Crewe Arms, Blanchland.

NORTH TYNE: Useful trout water, with one or two salmon.

Chollerford (North'land). Trout, coarse fish. Dt for ¾m upstream of bridge from The George Hotel, Chollerford and Percy Arms, Otterburn: 50p day, boat 50p day extra; ¾m bank fishing. Trout average ½ lb.

Bellingham (North'land). Trout, salmon and sea trout; runs have improved since 1965; best July–Oct. Bellingham AC has 5m water above and below town. Membership limited to 60; st £25, wt (for holiday-makers staying in Bellingham only) £10, Mon–Sat incl. No dt. Hotels: Rose and Crown, Cheviot. Black Bull, Riverdale Hall.

Tarset (North'land). Trout.

Keilder (North'land). Major NWA reservoir project under construction. Trout fishing already offered on **Bakethin** reservoir (dt £4) and **Fontburn** (ns. Otterburn) (unstocked) £2.20.

REDE: Trout and pike, with few autumn salmon.

Otterburn (North'land). Percy Arms, has 1m near hotel and 1m from Meadowhaugh to Coldtown (west bank); Residents only. Excellent trout fishing on **Sweethope Lake, Kirkwhelpington** April 1 to Sept 30; brown trout, some rainbows; average 8–9 oz; fly only; limit five brace; rods limited to five a day; gillie available. Beats on **Tweed** also available to guests. **Sweethope Lower Lough;** pike, small perch. Dt (bank only) from Swallow Hotels (as above). Good burn fishing. Otterburn Tower Hotel has 3½m on Rede. Northumbrian AF has water on Rede and Durtrees Burn; also 2m (both banks) **River Font** and part of **Font Reservoir** (limited permits) (*see Prudhoe on main Tyne*).

SOUTH TYNE: One or two clubs issue tickets for trout and salmon fishing on this river.

Fourstones (North'land). Trout and occasional salmon. Newbrough and Fourstones AA has 2½m of north bank only; no visitors' tickets.

Haydon Bridge (North'land). Trout and occasional late salmon. South Tyne AA preserves 3½m of water. No spinning before June 1. Wt for visitors staying in parish £5, from hon sec. 10 pools. Hotel: Anchor, adjoins river.

Haltwhistle (North'land). Brown trout, sea trout, salmon. Haltwhistle and Dist AA has 7m on main river and 7m on Haltwhistle Burn; wt £5–£15 from Mrs Burns, Castle Hill, and Greggs Sports Shop, Market Place. Tackleist: K Stott, Lees Hall Gate. Hotels: Grey Bull, Railway, Featherstone, Manor House, Wallace Arms.

Alston (Cumbria). Enjoyable sport with trout at 4 or 5 to lb. Alston AA has water; dt and wt from hon sec, or D & S Middleton, Front Street.

WANSBECK

(For close seasons, licences, etc, see Northumbrian Water Authority, p 40)

Northumberland trout stream which fishes well under favourable conditions of water, but opportunities for visitors are few.

Morpeth (North'land). Brown trout; preserved by Wansbeck AA for 5m; members only; limited to residents and long waiting list. Dt for tidal stretch on Ashington side of Wansbeck and water in town from Wansbeck D.C. Tackleists:

D J Bell, 9 Biltons Court, off Newgate Street, Morpeth; McDermotts, 112 Station Road, Ashington. Hotels: Newcastle House, Queen's Head, Angler's Arms, Weldon Bridge.

Tributary of the Wansbeck

BROOKER BURN;
Longhirst (North'land). Wansbeck, 2m S; trout, free. Lyne, 2m N.

WAVENEY

(See "Norfolk and Suffolk Broads", p 104)

WEAR

(For close seasons, licences, etc, see Northumbrian Water Authority, p 40)

Rises on Kilhope Moors in extreme west of Co Durham and enters North Sea at Wearmouth. In former years river was noted for salmon, but fishing ruined by pollution in lower reaches. With closure of many collieries and energetic restocking by water authority the position is much improved, and sea trout stocks in particular have risen in recent years. Brown trout fishing upstream from Chester-le-Street, although difficult, is well worthwhile. Tributaries Browney and Rookhope are improving. Bedburn preserved (*see Durham*).

Chester-le-Street (Durham). Sea trout, brown trout (stocked by club) coarse fish. AC (annual membership £8) has good water. Dt £1.50. New members welcomed, ladies included.

Durham (Durham). Trout, sea trout. Durham City AC has water; dt for members' guests only. Ferryhill AC has fishery at **Croxdale and Willington** AC has water; dt from Bond's Stores, High Street, Langley Park. Bear Park, Cornsay and New Branspeth Assns all have water on **Browney,** 4m W of Durham; limited dt; restocking. North-West Durham AA has trout water on five reservoirs: Tunstall, Waskerley, Smiddy Shaw, Burnhope and Hisehope (see Burn Hill). Tackleist: N Telfer, 43 North Road.

Bishop Auckland (Durham). Sea trout and brown trout. Bishop Auckland and Dist AC has various stretches between Escomb and Croxdale Bridge (about 14m); membership open; limited wt and dt from Pet Stores, 121 Newgate Street. No maggot fishing or ground-baiting; season March 22 until Sept 30 (sea trout, end of October). Tackle and information from Herdman's and Windrow Sports,

Fore Bondgate. Hotels: Castle, Queen's Head, Wear Valley.

Wolsingham (Durham). Trout, sea trout (good). Wolsingham AA has water; members only (st £25, limited for visitors). Long waiting list. No dt. At Hag Bridge, **Eastgate** (about 8m W). Northumbrian WA has stretch; dt 25p (*see Stanhope*). North-West Durham AA has Tunstall, Waskerley, Smiddy Shaw, Burnhope and Hisehope reservoirs 2½m N (*see Durham Reservoirs; also Burn Hill below*).

Frosterley (Durham). Trout, sea trout. About 3m water belongs to Frosterley AC; no dt.

Stanhope (Durham). Trout, sea trout. About 2m water (both banks) belongs to Stanhope AA; limited st and dt for visitors, £8 and £1.25, from hon sec. Sea trout June onwards. Northumbrian Water Authority has 2m. Dt (limited) from Phoenix Hotel. Hotels: King's Arms, Phoenix.

Upper Weardale (Durham). Trout, sea trout (Sept and Oct). Upper Weardale AA has about 6m of water; st £5, wt £2, dt £1 (limited). Fish run about 4 to lb; no Sunday fishing.

Tributary of the Wear

BROWNEY: Trout, but good deal of pollution.

Lanchester (Durham). Polluted below Langley Park; trout above. Langley Park AA restocking (*see Durham*).

Burn Hill (Durham). Waskerley, Tunstall, Hisehope and Smiddy Shaw Reservoirs; close together on moors between Stanhope and Consett; preserved by NW Durham AA; st issued. Fishing from bank only.

WEAVER

(For close seasons, licences, etc, see North West Water Authority, p 39)

Rises south-west of Cheshire and flows into Mersey estuary. Sport has benefited from recent restocking. Most species of coarse fish, trout in the upper reaches.

Northwich (Cheshire). Good coarse fishing held by Northwich and District AA. Water on Weaver (restocked annually); **Trent and Mersey Canal** (about 17m, being restocked); **Billinge Green Pools; Petty Pool Mere; Great Budworth Mere; Pickmere Lake.** Comprehensive st (all waters) £4.50, dt £1, river, meres and pools. Tackleists: Hyland's Pet Stores; Firthfields Pet Stores. Hotels: Railway, Salter, Woodpecker and Railway (Hartford).

Minshull Vernon (Cheshire). Weaver 1m W. Wheelock, 1m E. Ash Brook, 3m.

Weaver rented by Winsford & Dist JA. Dt 50p and 30p for other fishings in the area from Greenall Whitley AA, available from hon sec. 5m on **Rochdale Canal** (trout, coarse fish), **Drinkwater Park Lake,** coarse fish (all on dt) and **River Dane** (no tickets). Crewe LMR Sports AS has Sandhole Pool (coarse fish) and good tench water at Warmingham (½m); some permits (*see Crewe*).

Worleston (Cheshire). Coarse fish. Weaver. Pool Brook (of little account) and Wistaston Brook.

Crewe (Cheshire). Weaver 2½m W. No

fishing in Crewe, but Crewe LMR Sports AS has 3m of Weaver near Nantwich (4m away) on Batherton Estate, **Sandhole Pool** (1m), and **Doddington Hall Pool** (5m), rights on Shropshire Union Canal and stretches of **Severn, Weaver** and **Dane,** as well as good bream, tench and pike fishing on **Hortons Flash.** Guest tickets are **not** issued for any of these waters. Dt 30p available for Macclesfield Canal; coarse fish; *(see also Congleton).* Tackleists: Wooldridge's, High Street; Jenk's, 109 West Street; F J Jones, Victoria Street.

Nantwich (Cheshire). Trout, grayling, dace, roach, chub. Nantwich AS controls nearly all Weaver near Nantwich; st only; water starts on Reaseheath Estate and stretches SE of town for 7m mainly on both banks, broken at Batherton Mill. Society also has stretch on **Dove** at **Doveridge** and **Severn** at Trewern. Other clubs with water near Nantwich are Pioneer AA, Amalgamated Anglers and LMR Sports (all Crewe), Wyche Anglers and Winsford and District AA (6m Weaver; flashes; pools; st, dt from hon sec). Winsford Club's pools contain fine tench, carp, bream and pike. Weaver is chalk stream here; well stocked with roach, dace and chub; Winsford AA and Middlewich AS have recently stocked a length of **R Dane** with trout at Bostock. Dt issued. Permits on **Doddington Hall Lake** (7m) issued on yearly basis to clubs by Crewe LMR Sports AS *(see Crewe)* and Wybunbury AA; also water on Howbeck Brook; members only. Boats on all waters. **Shropshire Union Canal** controlled by Shropshire Union Canal Association (six clubs); dt from bank ranger; st from hon sec. Other waters within 10m of Nantwich are: Big Mere, Quoisley Mere (boats), Osmere, Blakemere (boat), Combermere (boats). Tackleists: W Jones, Beam Street. Hotels: Lamb, Crown, Three Pigeons.

Audlem (Cheshire). Adderley Brook. Birchall Brook, 2m NE. Lake: Woolfall Pool, 2m NE. Hotels; Lamb, Crown. *For club water see Nantwich.*

Wrenbury (Cheshire). Nantwich AS has water in area; no tickets. Marbury Brook. Sale Brook, 2m S. Baddiley Brook, 2m N. Hotel; Combermere Arms, Burleydam, Whitchurch.

Tributaries of the Weaver

DANE: Good trouting in upper reaches, but difficult to come by. Coarse fishing, with odd trout and grayling lower down.

Congleton (Cheshire). Trout, dace, roach, chub, gudgeon and occasional grayling and perch. From Radnor Bridge towards Holmes Chapel partly controlled by Prince Albert AS, Cheshire AA, Grove and Whitnall AA and Warrington AA. St £3.50 for Cheshire AA stretch at **Somerfordbooths** from secretary or Crewe tackleists. Assn also has water on Severn. Above Congleton controlled by Congleton United AS and syndicates. Moreton Hall Lake, 2m SW, private. **Macclesfield Canal** controlled by Corbridge AS; roach, perch, tench, bream, pike; recently dredged; st and dt at small charge from bailiff.

Bosley nr **Macclesfield** (Cheshire). Trout, dace, roach, chub; private. Lake: **Bosley Reservoir;** dt 40p from Harrington Arms; roach, pike, carp, perch, few trout; Moss Side AA water.

Macclesfield (Cheshire). **Langley Bottoms and Lamaload Reservoirs** (trout; fly only) controlled by Prince Albert AS, a nationally famous club with many fisheries in the NW of England and in Wales. These include stretches on the R Dane, the **Severn,** the **Ribble, Banwy, Twymyn, Trent, Dove-Winster, Vyrnwy, Lledr, Dulas, Dysinni, Dee, Dovey** and **Lune; Marbury Mere,** Whitchurch, **Isle Lake** Shrewsbury, **Langley Bottoms** and **Lamaload** Reservoirs, Macclesfield and others. St £25 + £6 entrance; long waiting list. Dt issued for a few of their waters.

Teggsnose Reservoir (trout, coarse fish) is Macclesfield Waltonian AS water; no tickets. Other clubs: Macclesfield Flyfishers' Club (12m on Dane and **Clough,** strictly preserved; no tickets), and Macclesfield and District Amalgamated Society of Anglers. **Macclesfield Canal;** good carp, pike, roach, etc; st £2.50 and dt 40p from tackleists. County Palatine AA has water. **Bosley Reservoir;** dt 25p from Harrington Arms, Bosley and bailiff, 1 Lakeside Estate. **Redesmere** and **Capesthorne;** roach, bream, tench, perch, pike, mirror and crucian carp; dt from bailiff, East Lodge, Capesthorne *(see Cheshire lakes, meres, etc).* Other waters in area: **South Park Pool;** carp, roach, perch, pike; dt **Knypersley Pool** controlled by Cheshire AA; st and dt issued. Tackleists: Ray Newton, 5–7 Park Green; Albert Brough, Waters Green; Fred Bulger, Bridge Street; licences and canal tickets.

WHEELOCK (tributary of Dane):

Sandbach (Cheshire). Wheelock and brooks polluted. Pool at Hassall is Holly Bush AA water. Taxmere (2m); carp, bream, roach, tench, pike, perch; dt from I F McDonald, 49 Welles Street, Sandbach, or Johnson's (see below). Elworth Anglers have much subsidence

water; residents only. Tackleist: B Johnson, Bold Street. Hotels: Wheatsheaf, Old Hall.

ARTLE BROOK:

Keele (Cheshire). Artle, 1m W. Lake: Madeley Manor, 1m W. Doddington Pool (permits only); coarse fish.

MARBURY BROOK:

Malpas (Cheshire). Holywell Brook, 2m NE. Weaver, 3m NE. Marbury Brook, 3m SE. Moss Meres, Capel Mere (Cholmondeley Park), 3m NE and Barmere, 3m SE.

WELLAND

(For close seasons, licences, etc, see Anglian Water Authority, p 40)

Rises near Market Harborough and flows through Lincolnshire Fens to the Wash. Coarse fishing very good, much of it controlled by clubs. Bream and roach plentiful and run to good size in most areas and pike, perch, dace, chub, with some carp and tench, also taken. River stocked with trout in upper reaches. Fen Drains hold roach, bream, tench and pike, but few fish in North and South Drove Drains.

Spalding (Lincs). Welland, **Lincolnshire Drains;** good coarse fishing. Spalding FC preserves Counter, North, South and Vernatts Drains; pike, perch, roach, carp, rudd, bream, tench; also **River Glen** from Guthram Gowt to Surfleet village bridge and **New River** from Spalding to Crowland *(tickets, see Crowland);* dt on recommendation of member only. Welland, from Spalding to The Deepings, provides 12m of good fishing for pike, perch, chub, roach, dace, bream and tench; st and wt at small charge from RD Treasurer or licence distributors. **Coronation Channel** also fishable (east bank reserved for matches). RD arranges matches on 12m of accessible water between Spalding and Crowland. Golden Ball Inn, River Bank, issues tickets and RD licences.

Cowbit (Lincs). Pike, perch, dace. Spalding FC water *(see Spalding).*

Crowland (Lincs); ns Postland, 3m. Pike, perch, dace. Nene, 2m SE at Black Horse Mills. New River from Spalding to Crowland preserved by Spalding FC; pike, roach, perch, dace, rudd, bream, tench; tickets from Golden Ball, Gradge Bank *(see also Spalding).*

Deeping St James (Lincs). Chub, dace, roach, pike, perch; preserved. Deeping St James AC controls Several Fishery at Market Deeping *(see entry below).* Hotels: Bell, Goat, Waterton Arms. *(See also Spalding.)*

Market Deeping (Lincs). Several Fishery controlled by Deeping St James AC. Extends 6½m from Market Deeping to Kennulph's stone, on Deeping high bank. Notice boards erected. Dt 60p. For matches, inclusive of pegging. Apply D W Adams, 22 Whetstone Court, Welland Estate, Peterborough. Tickets from bailiff (A Moyse, 15 Bridge Street, Deeping St James). Fishing opens June 16 to Mar 14. Glen, 4m N, at Kates Bridge. Hotels: Bull, New Inn, White Horse, Vine, Three Tuns.

Stamford (Lincs). Chub, dace, roach, pike, perch; fishing free to RD licence holders on N bank between Town and Broadeng Bridges; approx 1¼m. Elsewhere preserved by Stamford Welland AA. Association open to members outside 12m radius of Stamford. Approx 18m of water, stretching from Barrowden to Tallington. Dt from hon sec. Lakes: Burghley Park, 1m SE (bream and tench, some rudd) Tuesdays, Thursdays and Saturdays only; permission to fish island side of **Burghley Lake** from Estate Office, St Martin's, Stamford. Tackleists: L Godsland, St Mary's Street; Hardingham Sports, Ironmonger Street; Sports & Hobbies, All Saints Street. Hotel: Stag and Pheasant, Broad Street (club HQ).

Ketton (Leics). Oakham AS has water here and on **River Chater;** members only;

coarse fish *(see also Midlands Reservoirs)*.

Rockingham (Northants). Eye Brook Reservoir; good trout fishing *(see Midlands reservoirs and lakes)*. Hotels: Falcon; Central (both Uppingham, 5m N); Castle Inn, Caldecott.

Market Harborough (Leics). Market Harborough and District Society of Anglers has about 6m of **Grand Union Canal** (good for tench, bream, carp early in season; roach Nov–March); membership cards £2.50, dt 75p from Sports & Toys, 7 St Mary's Road; or bailiffs on bank. Other tackleist, Wilkinsons, 26 Coward St. Hotels: Angel, Peacock, Grove.

Tributaries of the Welland

GLEN: River free from Surfleet village to reservoir, coarse fish; trout above Bourne.

Surfleet (Lincs). Glen free below village. Preserved above by Spalding FC *(see Spalding)*.

Pinchbeck (Lincs). Permits issued by Welland and Nene RD. River Welland, 2m SE at Spalding; also Coronation Channel.

Counter Drain (Lincs). Counter Drain; coarse fish; Spalding FC.

Bourne (Lincs). Glen holds trout upstream; landowners sometimes give permission.

GWASH: Fair trout and grayling stream. Private fishing.

CHATER:

Luffenham (Leics). Roach and dace. Stamford AA has stretch near junction with Welland. Oakham AS has water on river; members only *(see also Stamford)*.

EYE BROOK: Good head of roach, dace and chub; trout upsteam.

Uppingham (Leics). Welland, 3m SE, at Seaton. Chater, 3m N. Gwash, 4m N at Manton. Eye Brook Reservoir *(see Rockingham)*.

WITHAM

(For close seasons, licences, etc, see Anglian Water Authority, p 40)

Rises in E Leicestershire and flows through Grantham and Lincoln to Boston, where it enters the Wash. A noted coarse fishing stream and abundantly stocked. In its upper reaches, particularly above Grantham, it holds good stock of trout and dace. Mostly coarse fish from Grantham to Lincoln—chub, roach and dace. From Lincoln to Boston river canalised, providing excellent bream and roach fishing.

Boston (Lincs). Angling facilities exceptionally good; at least 100 miles of good coarse fishing (pike, perch, dace, tench, roach, rudd and bream) in Witham, **South and North Forty Foot Drains,** and **Hobhole, Maud Foster, Sibsey Trader** and **West Fen Drains.** Witham noted for bream and roach. June–Sept best for bream and winter usually produces good-quality roach fishing, though plenty of fish can be taken on creed wheat in the summer. With few exceptions these waters may be fished by holding RD rod licence, but match permits (drains only) from J D McGuire, 6 Churchill Drive. Witham Joint Angling Committee (HQ Lincoln) leases major portion of Lower Witham. To fish these waters, anglers should be members of associations comprising committee. Applications for match lengths to hon sec, Lincoln & Dist AA. Tackleists: J Morley & Son, 5–7 Wide Bargate; J Clayton, 71 Main Ridge *(see Lincoln)*.

Lincoln (Lincs). Good coarse fishing. Witham fishes best from Aug–Oct, with bream predominant. Lincoln is HQ (Millers Arms) for Lincolnshire Anglers Fedn and Lincolnshire Rivers Anglers Consultative Assn. Lincoln AA has excellent coarse fishing on **Trent, Till, Old River Witham,** drains, dykes and **Hartsholme Lake** (good bream and carp). Assn controls match fishing upstream to Hykeham. Membership £5 year. Books from tackleists. **Foss Dyke** leased by Witham Joint AC *(see Boston and Torksey—Trent)*. **Lincoln Fisheries,** Doddington Road, Hartsholme: Two eight-acre trout lakes; fly only; boat fishing only; limited to five boats per lake. Bookings in advance by phone (Lincoln 20618 and 63175). Off A15 north of Lincoln, **Toft Newton Reservoir;** AWA fly-only trout fishery stocked with brown, brook and rainbow trout. Dt (4 brace limit) £4.50: (1 brace limit) £3. No boats. Self-service permits at reservoir. Tackleists: George

Harrison & Son (Lincoln) Ltd, Brayford Wharf; South End Pet Stores, 447 High Street; Abbey Sports, 263 Monks Road; Chambers Tackle Shop, 14 Cornhill; R H Beales, 108 Ripon Street; Nobbs Fishing Tackle, Norman Street; Newport Tackle Shop, 85 Newport, Lincoln.

Grantham (Lincs). Grantham AA has good coarse fishing on Witham, **Grantham Canal** and **Denton Reservoir;** dt for reservoir and canal from hon sec and local tackleists. (Note: Grantham AA is a member of the federation of Midlands clubs. This federation, which includes Peterborough, Stamford, Oakham, Newark, Asfordby, Leicester and Deeping St James Clubs, has been established to protect fisheries in area and leases waters on **Bourne Eau** and the **Glen.**)

Long Bennington (Lincs). Chub, roach, perch, grayling, etc. No dt. River recently dredged, but recovering.

Tributaries of the Witham

SOUTH FORTY FOOT:
Good coarse fishing. Much private water owned by Lincolnshire RD; rod licences only required. Matches booked through Lincs RD; applications after Jan 1. Centres are **Boston, Swineshead** and **Donington.**

RIVER BAIN. Trout and coarse fish; well stocked. Preserved for most of length. Free at Coningsby.

Horncastle (Lincs). Rivers Bain and Waring; trout, roach; preserved. Tupholme Brook, 7m NW. Horncastle AA has an old brick pit in Hemingby Lane (wt and dt) and about 1½m on canal from Bath House to lock pit; no dt for canal but st covers canal and brick pit (from hon sec). **Revesby Reservoir;** coarse fish; contains big pike; apply at estate; dt limited and not granted Sundays. Tackleist: F Bryan, 15 North Street. Hotels: Bull, Red Lion, Rodney.

FOSS DYKE NAVIGATION: Foss dyke held by Witham Joint AC *(see Boston).* Centres: **Lincoln, Saxilby** and **Torksey.** Good coarse fishing.

HOBHOLE DRAIN, EAST AND WEST FEN DRAINS: All canalised lengths of river forming part of fen drainage system. Hold good stock of coarse fish (bream, roach, perch, pike, tench), and include following waters: Maud Foster, Sibsey Trader, East Fen Catchwater drains, West Fen, Kelsey and Bellwater drains. St £2.50 and dt 45p from Boston tackleists and J D McGuire, 6 Church Drive, Boston, Hobhole and West Fen drains may be fished on AWA licence only. St covers also fishing on **Witham, Steeping, Steeping Relief channel, Glen, Bourne Eau, South Forty Foot, Louth canal** and **Swanholme Lakes.**

SLEA: Rises west of Sleaford and enters Witham at Chapel Hill. Trout in upper reaches. Coarse fish, particularly roach, elsewhere. Suffering from abstraction, RD trying to augment flow. Private fishing throughout length except for about half a mile above Chapel Hill and village centre South Kyme. Centre: **Sleaford,** where trout fisheries being created in town ballast pits and River Slea by Bristol Estates. Inquiries to Estate Office, Bristol Arcade, Sleaford. Tackleist: Slingsby. Hotel: Carr Arms.

WYE

(For close seasons, licences, etc, see Welsh Water Authority, p 43)

Most famous of English salmon rivers. Rises on south side of Plynlimmon near source of Severn and enters estuary of Severn 2m south of Chepstow. About 55 years ago this river, owing to over-netting and other misuse, had deteriorated so much that it hardly paid netting interests to operate. Through careful conservation and control of nets, river today produces larger rod catch of salmon than any other English or Welsh river and is outstanding example of benefit of proper control of commercial fishing. Most of rod fishing in private hands, but there are several hotels and one or two associations with rights on river. Richard Harris & Co, *(advt p 176)* have more than 20m under management. Salmon run large. Sea trout fishing of no account, but coarse fishing in lower reaches exceptionally good. No free fishing. Licences may be obtained from distributors in most villages and have usually to be produced when obtaining tickets or other permits to fish. Good brown trout fishing in Upper Wye and tributaries.

Tintern (Gwent). Tidal; mostly eels and flatfish, though salmon sometimes taken. Tintern AC has **Angidy;** members only. Rose and Crown Inn.

Redbrook (Gwent). Chub, dace, pike, perch, salmon. *(See Monmouth.)*

Monmouth (Gwent). Wye holds salmon, pike, trout, grayling, chub, dace; preserved. Birmingham AA has water on Wyastone Leys Estate; salmon rights excluded. **Monnow;** trout, grayling, chub, dace; Monmouth Dist AS has water. Trothy; trout; preserved. Brockweir to Livox Quarries, trout and coarse fish; dt from Messrs Keelings *(see below);* water affected by tide. RD licences from tackleists, Monnow Street.

Symonds Yat (Hereford). Salmon, trout and coarse fishing all preserved. Birmingham AA has about 1m, both banks, above Saracen's Head Inn.

Kerne Bridge (Hereford). Chub, dace, pike, perch, salmon, trout; preserved. Castle Brook, Garron, 2m; trout. Luke Brook, 2m. Lammerch Brook, 5m.

Ross (Hereford). Salmon, trout, grayling, roach, large pike and chub and good dace. Ross AC has coarse fishing; wt £4, dt £1. Permits may be obtained at Deans, 31 Broad Street and G & B Sports, High Street. Town water available to visitors at small charge. Birmingham AA has ½m (single bank) below Wilton Bridge; Garron Gamber, 6m, and Monnow, 9m, are very good trout streams; landowners sometimes give permission. Salmon fishing available through Ross AC. Contact John Martin, Tel Ross (0989) 3574. Hotels: Pengethley, *(advt p 18)* Royal (Trust House), Chase, Ross AC will be pleased to help visitors; send sae if writing.

Hereford (Hereford). Salmon, trout, grayling, other coarse fish. Hereford and Dist AA holds water on Wye and **Lugg.** Tickets (Wye only): dt and wt for trout and coarse fish only. When vacancy occurs, special membership may be granted to visitors for salmon, trout and coarse fish, or for trout and coarse fish only. Membership applications to hon sec. Tickets from tackleists *(see below).* Birmingham AA also has water on Wye and Lugg. Longworth Hall Hotel, **Lugwardine,** has four-rod salmon stretch on Wye, and trout and coarse fishing on Wye and **Lugg** for guests only wt £5, £1.25, (Tel. Hereford 850223). For other fishing inquire Garnons Estate Office, Bridge Sollars; W Jones, Carrier Cottage, Whitney-on-Wye; and Red Lion, Bredwardine. Local tackleists: Herbert Hatton (also fishery agent, pleased to give information), 73 St Owen Street (2317); H Webb, East Street; Mrs Perkins, Commercial Road. Hotels: City Arms, Green Dragon, Kerry Arms, Booth Hall. Red House Farm, Eaton Bishop, caters for anglers.

Bredwardine (Hereford). 7–8m salmon, trout and coarse fishing available (Moccas Water) subject to bookings, at Red Lion Hotel (500 yds from river. Tel: Moccas 303) Dt (S) £20 (T) £5 (coarse) £2.

Whitney-on-Wye (Hereford). Salmon, trout and coarse fish. A stretch of 100 yards, owned by Boat Inn, dt £2; campsite £1 p.d. per rod. The remainder of the Whitney Court fishery now privately let. The Rhydspence Inn has private fishing available to guests.

Hay-on-Wye (Hereford). Salmon, trout, pike, perch, chub. Tackle, RD licences and information from H R Grant & Son, 6 Castle Street. Hotels: Crown, has fishing on **Llynfi,** Swan. Llangorse Lake can be fished from here. Other fishing in

Air-Commodore Douglas Iron fishes a plug-bait for salmon, near Hay-on-Wye.
Photograph: John Tarlton.

area from Mrs Lewis, Bronydd Farm, Clyro.

Glasbury-on-Wye (Hereford). Salmon, trout, chub, dace, grayling, pike. Fishing can be arranged for guests by the Maesllwch Arms House. Other fishing in Wye and Llynfi preserved. Llangorse lake is accessible.

Builth Wells (Powys). Salmon (best March, April and May); trout (av ½ lb), grayling, chub, dace, pike. Groe Park & Irfon AC have 2½m on **Irfon,** including some double bank, with seven salmon catches. Club stocks with takeable trout. Wt (S)

£10, (T) £5, 3-dt (S) £7.50, (T) £3. Mr G Phillips, Laundry Cottage, Doldowlod, manages four holiday cottages with salmon and trout fishing. Occasional beats on wt and dt; S £35 and £7. T (dt only) £3. Tackle and permits: Mrs N Asbrey, High Street. Elan Estate Reservoirs accessible *(see Rhayader).* Cueiddon, Duhonw, Baili and Edw preserved. Pencerrig Country House Hotel has 3m; wt £2.10.

Newbridge-on-Wye (Powys). Salmon, trout, grayling, chub, dace, pike, roach; preserved, Ithon; trout; preserved.

Accommodation and further information at New Inn.

Rhayader (Powys). Wye; trout (av ½ lb; Wye record, 10½ lb, caught at Rhayader Bridge), salmon. Marteg; trout (3m). For information apply hon sec, Rhayader AA, which has 4m on Wye and 16-acre lake (Llyngyn) (trout; fly only); mt, wt and dt. Birmingham AA has Penlanole Estate fishery at **Doldowlod** (3m). Near here too are Craiglyn Fishings; good fly water with several holding pools; well stocked with trout, some salmon. Apply D Faulkner, Vulcan Inn, Doldowlod (accommodation also). **Elan and Claerwen Reservoirs.** Claerwen 650 acres, Caban Coch and Garreg Ddu, 500 acres, Penygarreg, 124 acres, Craig Goch, 217 acres. Fly only except Craig Goch, where spinning is allowed. All WWA waters. St £50, wt £9, dt £2.50 cover all waters. Tickets from Elan Office, Elan Village, Rhayader. Boats (Claerwen and Caban Coch) extra. Hotels: Royal Oak; Lion; Castle; Elan Valley (fishing arranged on Wye, **Elan**, **Marteg** and lakes); *(advt p 178)* Lion Royal (1m on Elan; 30p day); Penrally Guest house has 4m; Vulcan Arms has ½m. Tacklists: E R Davies, West Street, Rhayader; M Power, Garth House, Rhayader.

Llangurig (Powys). Trout, March 1 to Sept 30; fly only. Salmon, March 1 to Oct 25; fly and spinning. Black Lion Hotel has 8m of water on Wye for its guests. Dt and wt for residents, and for non-residents. Best months May/June and Sept. Blue Bell Inn has 8m also. Dt and wt.

Tributaries of the Wye

TROTHY: Trout, some assn water.

Dingestow (Gwent). Trout; preserved. Glamorgan AC, Cardiff, has 6m fishing. Inquiries to the hon sec. Monmouth and Dist AS has water.

MONNOW: Good trout and grayling stream.

Skenfrith (Hereford). Trout, chub, dace. Birmingham AA has fly fishing here. The Priory Hotel has 300 yards; free to guests.

Pontrilas (Hereford). Trout, grayling; preserved by owner of Kentchurch to 3m below here, thence by private owners to within 1m of Monmouth.

Pandy (Gwent). Trout, grayling; private throughout and strictly preserved. Honddu: trout; strictly preserved. Hotel: Pandy Inn.

HONDDU (tributary of Monnow): Trout; some hotel water.

Llanfihangel Crucorny (Gwent). Trout only, preserved. No tickets issued.

LUGG: Trout and grayling, with coarse fish in some stretches.

Mordiford (Hereford). Trout, grayling etc; Birmingham AA has good stretch here, also water at Tidnor, Lugg Mill, Sutton and Moreton. Inn: The Moon.

Longworth (Hereford). Salmon, trout, grayling, coarse fish. Longworth Hall Hotel, Lugwardine, has salmon beat on Wye for 4 rods and good trout and coarse fishing on **Lugg**. Fishing available only to residents and patrons *(see Hereford)*.

Lugwardine (Hereford). Preserved by Hereford and District AA *(see Hereford)*.

Leominster (Hereford). Trout, grayling, pike, perch, dace. Above town Lugg preserved by landowners. Birmingham

AA has water on Lugg at Ox Pastures, Dinmore and Bodenham; grayling, dace. White Swan Piscatorials also have water; otherwise preserved by landowners. **Pinsley Brook;** trout, grayling; landowners sometimes give permission. Ridgemore Brook. Stretford Brook, 1½m. Humber Brook, 3m. Puddleston Brook, 4m. Hotels: Royal Oak (where fishing can be arranged for guests); Talbot.

Kingsland (Hereford). Lugg, Arrow, and Pinsley Brook; trout, grayling. Fishing generally preserved by landowners. 2m from Kingsland is River Arrow at Eardisland. Tackleist: S Preece. Accommodation: Angel and Mortimer Cross.

Presteigne (Powys). Lugg, Arrow and Teme afford excellent trout and grayling fishing, generally dry fly; preserved but landowners may give permission.

FROME (tributary of Lugg): Trout, preserved.

Ashperton (Hereford). Frome, 2½m Leddon, 2½m. Lakes: Devereux Park lakes, 4m.

ARROW (tributary of Lugg): Trout, grayling, dace; but few opportunities for visitors.

Pembridge (Hereford). Trout, grayling, dace; preserved by landowners. Birmingham AA has a stretch at Ivington. Inn: New Inn.

Kington (Hereford). Trout; preserved. Trout lake at Hindwell Farm, Walton (4m); brown, rainbow; fly only. Reserved to occupants of holiday cottage. Enquiries to H Price, Hindwell Farm, Walton. Inns: Swan, Royal Oak.

LLYNFI: Trout, grayling, etc; preserved.

Glasbury-on-Wye (Hereford). Lynfi falls into Wye here. Trout, grayling, chub. Fishing good, but mostly preserved. Hotel: Maesllwch Arms.

Talgarth (Powys). Llynfi. Dulais brook. Rhiangoll; trout. Treffrwd, 2m. **Llangorse Lake** (pike, perch) can be fished from here (4m); boats available. Hotel: Castle. Visitors' tickets from local association.

IRFON: Salmon, trout, grayling, chub.

Llangammarch Wells (Powys). Excellent trout fishing April, May, June, and September, and good spring and autumn salmon fishing. Lake Hotel has about 8m of Irfon and nearby streams (**Garth Dulas, Chwefri,** etc), and some rods for salmon fishing on Wye negotiated each year and charged accordingly. Also small trout lake (brown and rainbow; fish average 1½ lb) in grounds. Waders advised. Lake and rivers restocked annually. Fly only on some beats. Wt and dt for **residents only** *(advt p 229)* Cammarch Hotel has about 7m of **Cammarch** and two permits for **Wye** at Builth. Wt and dt on hotel water for residents. Licences and tackle at both hotels.

Llanwrtyd Wells (Powys). Trout. Dol-y-Coed House Hotel *(advt p 253)* has trouting for guests on 7m of Irfon. Lakes; 3m of Association water. Hotels: Neuadd Arms (1½m of fishing) Llwynderw.

ITHON: Trout, chub, few salmon. Good hotel and assn water.

Llandrindod Wells (Powys). Llandrindod Wells AA controls 5m of trout fishing close to town. Available to visitors on wt and dt basis, limit five brace per day. Sunday fishing; spinning allowed after August 1; waders essential. Tackleists: C Selwyn & Sons, Park Crescent (Tel. 2397), Wye Authority licences and association tickets. Hotels: Metropole, Commodore, Glen Usk, Mostyn.

Penybont (Powys). Trout, chub, some salmon. Birmingham AA has stretches here and at **Llanbadarn** and **Llandrindod Wells.** Arran, 10m; trout. Clywedog, 1m; trout. Camloo, 1m. Dulas, 2m. Llandegeley Brook, 2m. Edw, 3m; good trouting. Crych Brook, 5m. Hotel: Severn Arms, which has about 7m of trout fishing (mainly on Ithon) for visitors (3 to lb average); mt £28, wt £8 and dt £1.50. Licences at hotel; tackleists in Llandrindod.

Llanbadarn Fynydd (Powys). Upper Ithon. New Inn has 3½m trout fishing; free to guests (fly only); also rough shooting.

WYRE

(For close seasons, licences, etc, see North West Water Authority, p 39)

From Churchtown downstream coarse fish and brown trout. Above Churchtown limited amount of salmon fishing and good sea trout and brown trout fishing.

Fleetwood (Lancs). Sport in estuary improving as pollution lessens; flatfish mostly.

St Michael's (Lancs). Mainly brown trout and coarse fish. Local club: St Michael's AA; dt from Miss G Martin, Bridge Cottage and C Calderbank (Preston). Dt for Northern AA waters from Miss Martin, as above. Hotel: Grapes.

Churchtown (Lancs). Salmon, sea trout, trout and coarse fish. Ribble and Wyre FA controls good deal of water between Churchtown and Garstang at St Michael's and at Great and Lower Eccleston; st and dt from hon sec.

Garstang (Lancs). Salmon, sea trout, trout and coarse fish. Garstang AA preserves 3m both banks, No dt. Wt £4.20 for temporary residents in area from hon sec; fly only. Hotels: Royal Oak, Eagle and Child, Crown.

Scorton (Lancs). Salmon, sea trout, trout, coarse fish. Wyresdale Anglers have 7m water; no tickets.

YARE

(See Norfolk and Suffolk Broads, p 107)

YORKSHIRE (lakes, reservoirs, canals and streams)

(For close seasons, licences, etc, see Yorkshire Water Authority, p 40, unless otherwise stated)

BRANDESBURTON PONDS. Twenty coarse fish ponds. Hull and District AAA members only.

BURTON CONSTABLE LAKES. In grounds of Burton Constable Hall; excellent coarse fishing for roach, bream, perch, tench, carp and pike. St from J R Chichester-Constable, Burton Constable, nr Hull (Tel 040 162508). 25 acres of fishing.

CASTLE HOWARD GREAT LAKE. Fishing station: **Malton.** Specimen pike, perch, tench, bream, roach and dace. Dt £1.60, OAP and children 60p, from C Barr, water bailiff. Close season Feb 28 to June 1. Sunday fishing.

CHELKER RESERVOIR. Trout; let to Bradford Waltonians; no tickets *(see also Bradford).* Near **Silsden** and **Ilkley.**

COD BECK RESERVOIR. Osmotherley. YWA (North Central Div). Trout. Dt £2 from Sub-P.O. Osmotherley.

DAMFLASK and UNDERBANK RESERVOIRS. YWA, Southern Division. Damflask 5m from Sheffield, Underbank 10m. Both stocked with trout and coarse fish. Season: March 25 to following Jan 31. Dt £1.25 sold at reservoirs.

DOE PARK RESERVOIR. Trout, coarse fish; let to Bradford City AA; members only.

WHINNYGILL and JENNYGILL RESERVOIRS. Let by YWA to Skipton AA. Trout and roach. St £15 + £15 entrance fee. Wt £8 and dt £2.50.

EMBSAY RESERVOIR. Let by YWA to Skipton AA. Trout. Limited st £10, wt £8 and dt £2.50 to people living in WA area.

FEWSTON and SWINSTY RESERVOIRS. YWA. Trout; dt £2 from machine at Fewston Reservoir Lodge; *(see also Leeds).* Near **Harrogate** and **Otley.**

THRUSCROSS RESERVOIR. YWA. Trout. Dt £2 from self service machine at lodge.

HEWENDEN RESERVOIR. Between **Keighley** and **Bradford.** Trout, pike, roach, bream. Central Division AC. St from hon sec, H L Byron, 25 Ripley Street, Lightcliffe, nr Halifax. Waiting list.

HORNSEA MERE. Fishing station: **Hornsea.** Yorkshire's largest inland water (472 acres). Very good pike, carp, bream, rudd perch, roach, tench. Hornsea Mere Marine Co (Tel 3277). Dt 40p, evening (and junior) 15p, punts £2.50 day (limited boat and bank fishing).

LEEMING RESERVOIR. Fishing station: **Oxenhope.** Good trout fishing, brown and rainbow. Bradford City AA; members only. St £10 + £5 joining fee.

LEVEN CANAL. Beverley 6m. 3m of good coarse fishing. Hull and Dist AA. Dt from tackleists.

LINDHOLME LAKE. 12m E of **Doncaster.** 18 acre fly only trout fishery. St (35 visits) £75. Extra visits by arrangement. Bag limit. Severn-Trent licence required. Inquiries to Epworth 872015.

MALHAM TARN. 6m from **Settle.** A Nature Reserve leased from National Trust by the Malham Tarn Field Centre. Boat fishing only, for trout with fly, and for perch with worm. Fish may run large. Weekdays £4 per boat plus £3 per rod (£2 per rod in October—perch only). Weekdays and Bank holidays £5 per boat. Bookings and detailed information from Warden or Secretary (Tel Airton 331). Phone bookings recommended. Seasons May 1 to Sept 30 for trout; July to October 31 for perch. Accommodation available at Centre.

MARKET WEIGHTON CANAL. Fishing stations: **Newport** and **Broomfleet.** 6m long; bream, perch, roach, pike. Tributary **Foulness,** has good head of roach and bream. Yorkshire WA. Inquiries to Fisheries Officer.

MOREHALL RESERVOIR. Sheffield 7m. YWA. Southern Division. Trout, fly only; dt £1.25, on sale at reservoir.

NOSTELL PRIORY LAKES. Foulby, Nr Wakefield. Well-stocked with pike, carp, bream, tench and roach. St £60, dt from 75p. Various concessions. Details from J Austerfield, Head Bailiff, Foulby Lodge. Tel 0924 863562.

SCOUT DIKE, Penistone. 16m from Sheffield. YWA (Southern Division). Trout. Dt £1.25, sold at reservoir and at Castle Market Building, Exchange Street, Sheffield S1 1GB.

SEMERWATER LAKE. Fishing station: **Bainbridge.** Trout, perch, bream and rudd. Water ski-ing at weekends. Dt £2 for Wensleydale AA waters (west side and 2m of River Bain near lake) from Rose & Crown, Bainbridge *(see Yore—*

Bainbridge).

SHIPTON LAKE. Shipton-by-Beningbrough. Tench, perch, roach, trout, pike. Bradford City AA.

STAINFORTH AND KEADBY CANAL. Controlled by joint committee including following clubs: Rotherham, Doncaster, Sheffield Amal, Sheffield and District and British Railways. Polluted by seepage from Don, but reported improving. Coarse fish.

TEES VALLEY AND CLEVELAND RESERVOIRS. This group of reservoirs, managed by the Northumbrian WA, includes both stocked and wild waters. **Grassholme, Selset, Scaling Dam, Hury** and **Lockwood Beck** are stocked (st £120, wt £14 and dt £3.50). **Cow Green, Blackton** and **Balderhead** unstocked (st £120, wt £9, dt £2.20. Concessions for OAP, juniors and regd. dis.

THORNTON STEWARD RESERVOIR, Masham. Season: March 25 to Sept 30. Trout, fly only. Limited dt £2 from Thornton Steward Sub-P.O.

WORSBOROUGH RESERVOIR, Barnsley. Coarse fish. Barnsley AS has rights (st £3) fishing June 1 to Feb 28. Dt 40p from bailiffs walking the bank. Sunday fishing to assn members only; hempseed barred.

ULLEY. Sheffield; 9m. YWA (Southern Division). Trout and coarse fish. Seasons: March 25 to Sept 30 and June 1 to Jan 31. Dt (March 25 to Sept 30) £1.25 (Oct 1 to Jan 31) 75p. Tickets on sale at reservoir.

PRINCIPAL ENGLISH CANALS

(Angling inquiries to T G Leatherland, Fisheries Officer (Watford 26422))

ASHBY CANAL

British Waterways Board (Southern Region), Willow Grange, Watford, Herts. WB1 3QA.

Canal holds coarse fish and is let to various clubs, the principal ones being Coventry and Dist AS **(Burton Hastings, Dadlington** and **Market Bosworth),** Hinckley and Dist AA **(Hinckley),** Leicester and Dist Amal SA **(Wykin** to **Dadlington),** and Measham FC (near **Snarestone**). *(See also Coventry Canal, Grand Union Canal and Oxford Canal).*

BIRMINGHAM CANAL

British Waterways Board (Southern Region), Dock Office, Gloucester

Bream, roach, perch and pike. Apart from short lengths let to clubs, including Birmingham AA, most parts of the network available to anglers by tickets. St and day tickets available from Rushall Junction to Huddlesford Junction and from Sneyd Junction to Cannock Extension. **Wyreley and Essington Canal, Rushall Canal** and **Tame Valley Canal.** Sections can be booked for matches; inquire W J Bust, Lock Cottage, Parkhead Locks, Park Hall Road, Walsall.

Sneyd Reservoir (Walsall). Rented by Walsall AA. *(See also Walsall.)*

Lodge Farm Reservoir, Dudley. Coarse fish; inquiries to Dudley Corporation.

Himley Hall Lake, Himley. Trout, coarse fish. Inquiries to Dudley Corporation.

COVENTRY CANAL

British Waterways Board (Southern Region), Willow Grange, Watford, Herts. WB1 3QA

Canal holds coarse fish. Rights to various angling associations, principal ones being Coventry and Dist AS (from **Coventry** to **Polesworth**) and Birmingham AA & **Whittington Brook** to **Huddlesford**). Dt for stretch near Lichfield from British Waterways Board (Northern Region). *(See also Ashby Canal, Grand Union Canal and Oxford Canal).* **Fradley Junction** to **Huddlesford Junction**—day or season tickets available. Also match fishing. Inquiries to J G Taylor, Amenity Supervisor, BWB Office, Chester Road, Nantwich, Cheshire (Tel 65122).

GLOUCESTER AND SHARPNESS CANAL

British Waterways Board (Southern Region), Dock Office, Gloucester, GL1 2EJ.

Coarse fish; Severn-Trent licence and permit required, latter from tackleists, BWB regional office and bridge-keepers. St and dt. For match fishing apply Amenity Services Supervisor (South West), Dock Office, Gloucester (Tel 25524). The canal is 15½m long, with good tow-path and many access points. An excellent match venue.

GRAND UNION CANAL

British Waterways Board (Southern Region), Willow Grange, Church Road, Watford, WD1 3QA.

Holds coarse fish, and for whole length from London to Birmingham is let to various angling clubs. Details given below should be read in conjunction with those given for Thames tributaries, Colne and Gade. Lengths in Bletchley area restocked by BWB in 1972. Berkhamstead to Tring sections restocked by BWB in 1973.

PADDINGTON (London). London AA has water from here to **Tring** (42m in all). All of it is available to associates *(see p 82)* and dt issued. Popular centres are **West Drayton, Uxbridge, Kings Langley** and **Tring.** Tring Anglers have several stretches in their locality. Rest of canal let to clubs as follows: **Chedding-** ton, **Stoke Hammond (Bucks), Luton AC; Fenny Stratford** (Bucks), **Long Buckby** and **Braunston** (Northants), Coventry and Dist AA; **Weedon** (Northants), Nene AC; **Market Harborough** (Leics), Market Harborough AC; **Mowsley** (Leics), Leicester AC; **Hatton** (Warws), Birmingham AA. Most issue dt; inquiries to hon sec.

KENNET AND AVON CANAL

Controlled by the British Waterways Board (Southern Region), Dock Office, Gloucester.

Several clubs have rights on this water, noted for large carp. Canal was built to join navigable Kennet (Thames) and Somerset Avon. Reaches of both Kennet and Avon canalised in places. Rights in County Weir Lock, Reading, and at Sulhamstead owned by Southern Region of British Waterways. Parties of up to 30 can be catered for. Inquiries to Mrs Bartlett, Bailiff, Tel Reading 302370.

Bath (Avon). Coarse fish, including carp and tench. Bathampton AA has 5m up to Warleigh *(see Limpley Stoke)*.

Limpley Stoke (Wilts). Bristol and West of England Federation has 2m to Avoncliffe Halt; well stocked with roach, rudd, perch, bream, tench and pike, members only. Bathampton AA has 5m from Limpley Stoke aqueduct to Avon at Bath; roach, rudd, few chub, carp, good bream and tench, perch and large pike; water weedy; dt from hon sec, bailiffs and tackleists. Bristol Amal has water here *(see Bristol Avon).*

Bradford-on-Avon (Wilts). Perch, roach, pike, bream; preserved by Bradford-on-Avon AA *(for tickets see Bristol Avon).*

Trowbridge (Wilts). Perch, roach, bream, pike, tench. Bradford-on-Avon AA has water on river and Kennet and Avon Canal. Tickets for both (50p day, £1 month) from West's (tackleist), 32 Roundstone Street (RA licences; assn permits). Other tackleist: Rose's, Fore Street.

Devizes (Wilts). Pike, bream, roach and tench; fishing good; preserved by Devizes AA for 7½m each side of town (Lady Bridge, Wilton, to Semington Road Bridge, Semington); dt £1 from hon sec (assn membership available to persons living outside 6m radius; sub

£5). Avon 8m; trout and grayling; preserved by landowners. Also several brooks holding trout. Hotels: White Bear, Bear, Elm Tree, Castle, Old Crown. RD licences from Sports House, Market Place.

Seend (Wilts). Pike, perch, tench, chub, etc. Some good water held by Devizes AA.

Marlborough (Wilts). Marlborough and Dist AA has rights. Coarse fish. Tackleists: H Duck; Leathercraft; both High Street. Hotel: Savernake *(see Marlborough—Kennet).*

Hungerford (Berks). Hungerford Canal AA holds 3m (mostly both banks); coarse fish, few trout; excellent. *(See Hungerford—Kennet).*

Newbury (Berks). Newbury AA has fishing rights in canal; coarse fish *(see Newbury—Kennet).*

Aldermaston (Berks). Central Association of London and Provincial ACs has a stretch here; dt.

LANCASTER CANAL

Controlled by British Waterways Board (Northern Region) PO Box 9, 1 Dock Street, Leeds.

Fishing station: **Wigan.** HQ of the Northern Anglers' Association, about 25,000 members. Association has centres each consisting of clubs in towns in Lancashire, Yorkshire and Cheshire, and senior and junior individual members. Fishing water: **Leeds and Liverpool** and **Shropshire Union Canals,** parts of **Ribble** and **Worthenbury Brook,** stretch on **Dee** at Shocklach, Flintshire, and other stretches on Rivers **Alyn, Calder, Banwy** and **Vyrnwy;** all on membership cards. Association has rights in **Lancaster Canal** from Preston to Natland, and Glasson lockage from Galgate up to and including Glasson Dock; dt issued. Cards from bailiffs or approved agents. Wigan & Dist AA has 9m on **Ribble** and 8m on **Wyre** (by agreement with Preston and Bolton), water on **River Winster, Lake Windermere, Leeds and Liverpool Canal,** reservoirs, ponds and flashes; full details from hon sec. Dt for most waters. Bolton and Dist AA leases the **Manchester, Bury and Bolton Canal.** Assn also has trout water on **Yore.** Tickets (two per day after June 1). Tackleists: **Wigan:** H Glover, 217 Ormskirk Rd, Newtown; J A Blackledge, 4a The Wiend, Market Place; Bartons, Wigan Road, Hindley; Bill Gratton, 132 Manchester Road, High Ince (Ince Bar); H Porter, 2a Loch Street, Lamberhead Green, Orrell. Tackleists in **Bolton:** Harold Windett, 84 Bradshawgate; W Ince, 103 Great Moor Street. **Preston:** E Carter, 87 Church Street.

SHROPSHIRE UNION CANAL

Controlled by British Waterways Board (Northern Region), PO Box 9, 1 Dock Street, Leeds

Holds roach, bream, dace, perch, pike, gudgeon and eels. 4,000 mirror carp included in a recent stocking programme. Controlled by assn of six clubs—Shropshire Union Canal Anglers Assn; dt from bank ranger. Most popular fishing venues: **Autherley, Wheaton Aston, Church Eaton, Norbury, Knighton, Cheswardine, Market Drayton, Audlem, Adderley, Hack Green, Barbridge, Nantwich, Bunbury, Christleton** and **Chester** (on the main line) and at **Middlewich, Church Minshull, Acton** and **Barbridge** on Middlewich branch.

At Nantwich BWB has an office which deals with angling facilities on over 100 miles of canals in the area. Bridge lists, match bookings and other data from Amenity Supervisor, BWB, Chester Road, Nantwich, Cheshire, or phone Mr Taylor at Nantwich 65122.

STAFFORDSHIRE AND WORCESTERSHIRE CANAL

Controlled by British Waterways Board (Southern Region), Dock Office, Gloucester

Holds bream, roach, perch and pike. Stretches from Wombourne Lock, through **Swindon, Cookley** and **Kidderminster** to **Stourport** held by Birmingham AA and Whitmore Reans Constitutional AA *(see also Kennet and Avon Canal, Birmingham Canal, and Worcester and Birmingham Canal)*. For Contest-bookings, contact Amenity Services Supervisor, BWB, Chester Road, Nantwich, Cheshire (Nantwich 65122).

TRENT AND MERSEY CANAL

Controlled by the British Waterways Board (Northern Region), PO Box 9, 1 Dock Street, Leeds LS1 1HH.

Holds pike, bream, roach, dace, gudgeon, tench, carp, chub, eels. 6,000 fish (bream, carp and roach) introduced by BWB in 1972 under restocking programme at **Aston** and **Colwich.** Other fishing stations: **Stone, Barlaston, Armitage, Great Heywood, Fradley Junction, Burton upon Trent, Lichfield** (G Larkin, tackleist, St John Street, will give information). From Preston Brook to King's Bromley, except Colwich, and from Alrewas to Burton-on-Trent fishing mostly let to clubs, but stretch near Lichfield and at Colwich available for casual anglers and small club matches; dt from bailiff, T McNally, Lock House, Colwich, Staffs. Section between Handsacre Bridge No 58 and Wynchnor Lock available for matches. Applications to Amenity Supervisor (J W Taylor), BWB, Nantwich Office, Cheshire (Nantwich 65122).

WORCESTER AND BIRMINGHAM CANAL

Controlled by the British Waterways Board (Southern Region), Dock Office, Gloucester.

Between **King's Norton** and **Blackpole,** near Worcester, fishing rights held by Birmingham AA. Canal holds bream, roach, perch and pike. *(See also Birmingham Canal, Kennet and Avon Canal, and Staffordshire and Worcester Canal).*

Tardebigge Reservoir (Bromsgrove). Rights rented by Bournville Athletic Club.

Upper and Lower Bittell Reservoirs (near Bromsgrove). Rights owned by Barnt Green FC, who stock Lower Bittell and adjacent Arrow Pools with trout; other pools hold coarse fish, including pike and bream. Guest tickets for coarse fishing to members' personal friends only *(see also Arrow, tributary of War-*

wickshire Avon).

Lifford Reservoir. Birmingham Parks. Dt from park keeper.

Earlswood Lakes. Three lakes totalling 85 acres stocked with roach, perch, bream, pike; carp and tench in two. Large eels caught in 1980. Dt 70p & £1.40 on bank from bailiff. Match booking enquiries to Mrs Palmer, The Bungalow, Valley Road, Earlswood, Birmingham. Tel Earls. 2379.

ENGLISH SEA FISHING STATIONS

IN the following list the principal stations are arranged in order from north-east to south-west and then to north-west. Sea fishing can, of course, be had at many other places, but most of those mentioned cater especially for the sea angler. Names and addresses of club secretaries will be found in the list of angling clubs; secretaries and tackleists are usually willing to help visiting anglers either personally or by post on receipt of a stamped and addressed envelope. Details of accommodation, etc, can generally be had from the local authority amenities officer or information bureau of the town concerned.

Seaham (Co Durham). Cod (Sept–June; all beaches especially Blast), codling, whiting (all in winter), mackerel (July–Aug), coalfish, flounders, plaice (mainly from boats), skate (Seaham Hall beach, June–Sept, night fishing, early flood), pouting, gurnard, etc. Excellent fishing from two piers to members of Seaham SAC; details and boat information from J Franklin, 14 Conningham Terrace, Houghton-le-Spring (Tel 842271). Tackleists: R Wright, 20 Green Street; K B Fox, North Terrace. Further information from R M Shenton, 54 Fern Crescent, Parkside.

Sunderland (Co Durham). Cod and codling (best Jan–Feb), whiting (best Dec), mackerel (July–Aug), coalfish, gurnard, flounders, dabs, plaice, pouting, skate. Fishing throughout year. Roker Pier provides good sport with cod and flatfish. Several small-boat owners at North Dock will arrange fishing parties, but there are also good beaches. Bait can be dug in Whitburn Bay and bought from tackleists. Clubs: Sunderland Sea AA. Ryhope Sea AA (both affiliated to Assn of Wearside Angling Clubs). Tackleists: J Robson, 22 Vine Place; J H Tennick, 51 Dundas Street (bait supplier); Palmers, Market Square Arcade.

Saltburn (Cleveland). Flatfish, coalfish, codling, whiting, mackerel, gurnard, some bass in summer and haddock late autumn. Float-fishing from pier in summer gives good sport; good codling fishing Oct to March. Tackleists: Gresty's, 43 Milton Street. Club: Saltburn and Dist SAA.

Redcar (Cleveland). Five miles of fishing off rock and sand. Principal fish caught: Jan–April, codling; April–June, flatfish; summer months, coalfish (billet), whiting, mackerel, gurnard. Larger codling arrive latter part of August and remain all winter. South Gare breakwater (4m away); good fishing, but hard on tackle, spinning for mackerel successful. Good fishing from beach two hours before and after low tide. Competitions every month. Tackleists: Harry Brough, 20 West Terrace.

Whitby (N Yorks). Increasingly popular centre for boat, pier and beach fishing. Cod up to 42 lb taken from boats, as well as large catches of haddock, whiting, flatfish, black bream, wolf fish, ling, etc. From East and West Piers billet (coalfish), flounders, mackerel, whiting and eels can be caught during the holiday season. Good beach angling may be obtained between Whitby and Sandsend, at Upgang, and Newholme Beck; flounder, mackerel, billet, and (after October) codling. Basic bait here is mussel and in summer herring and mackerel pieces are ideal for flounders and mackerel from piers, or for larger fish from boats, but most successful large-fish bait for past few years has been heavy breaking-strain feathered cod jig. Boats: J Grayson, 42 Brook Park, Sleights (Tel 0947 81606) and from tackleists: Roy (R Blackburn), 6 South Terrace (Tel 0947 2478) and E Wilson, 65 Haggersgate (Tel 0947 3885) who also hires rods.

Scarborough (N Yorks). Sea fishing good from boat or harbour piers most of year. Autumn whiting very good in bay. Codling most plentiful Aug onwards. Winter codling fishing from First or Second Points to south of Scarborough and Cowlam Hole or Beast Cliff to north. Mackerel, June–Sept, float or spinning. Boats: W Wood and Westwood, both Longwestgate. Festival in Sept. Clubs: Scarborough Rock AC; South Cliff AC; Scarborough Boat AC. Tackleists: Pritchards, 56 Eastborough (who issue dt for the Mere; coarse fish); H Buckley, Anglers' Supplies, Leading Post Street. Sixteen charter boats available, taking

8–12 anglers. Charge: approx £2.50 per person for 4 hrs. Phone (STD 0723) 890134, 72791 or 71775. Casting instruction from Northern School of Casting (principal Jack Martin), 26 Linghill, Newby, Scarborough (Tel 5590).

Filey (N Humberside). Famous Filey Brig, ridge of rocks from which baits can be cast into deep water, is best mark. From June to Sept very good float fishing with sliding float for mackerel, coalfish (billet) and pollack. Good flatfish from shore and boats in summer. Best for mackerel mid-July to end of Sept; for cod Sept to March (fish of around 30 lb taken on Brig recently). Tackle and bait from R Lewis, 12 Hope St Tel 513732. Lugworms and razorfish may be dug locally. Boats may be hired from beach from May to Sept. Advanced booking advisable in winter. Filey Brig AS (st £1.50) organises fishing festival every year (first week of Sept). Good fly-fishing for coalfish (billet) from the Brig. Hotels: White Lodge, Hylands.

Bridlington (N Humberside). South Pier may be fished free all year and North Pier from Oct 1 to March 31. Sport in summer only fair—small whiting, billet, flatfish mainly—but good codling from Dec–March. Good flatfish, thornback ray and codling (winter) from small boats in bay. Yorkshire "cobbles" fishing **Flamborough** marks take variety of fish, including cod, haddock, mackerel and plaice, with pollack and coalfish in rocky areas. Rock fishing from shore at Thornwick Bay. Bait: lugworm may be dug in South Bay and small sand-eels caught by raking and digging on edge of tide. Tackleists: Linford's, Hilderthorpe Road; and Buckley's, Harbour Road (also supply bait). Many boatmen.

Hornsea (N Humberside). Tope, skate, flounders, occasional bass from shore; cod, haddock, plaice, dabs, tope, skate from boats, May to Oct. Whiting, dabs, codling, Oct to May. *(For tackleists see Bridlington.)*

Grimsby (S Humberside). Sea fishing along Humber bank free, and along foreshore to Tetney Lock; plaice, codling, dabs, flounders, eels. West Pier: st £4.95 from Dock Office. Good centre for fens and broads. Clubs: Humber SAC, Cromwell Social Club (SA section) st £3.50. Tackleists: T C Dawes, Oxford Street; Cromwell Pet Stores, Cromwell Road; F W Lightwood, 172 Cleethorpes

Road; Weelsby Angling Stores, 413 Weelsby Street; Pets Pantry, 245 Grimsby Road, Cleethorpes.

Skegness (Lincs). Beach fishing for cod, whiting, dabs and flounders in winter; for silver eels, flounders and dabs in summer. Boat fishing for same winter fish, for thornback skate, tope, dogfish, flounders and dabs in summer. Chapel St Leonards, and Ingoldmills the best beaches in winter. Tackleists: Palmer Sports, High Street and P Gibson, Roman Bank. Clubs: Skegness SAC, with beach and boat sections. Annual sub. £2 and £8 respectively. HQ. now Working Mens' Club, Briar Way.

Mablethorpe (Lincs). Good sea fishing from Mablethorpe to Sutton-on-Sea. Beach all sand; mainly flatfish, but some bass, skate, mackerel, tope from boats. Cod in winter. Sept–Dec best. Boat fishing limited by surf and open beach. Good flounders in Saltfleet Haven; also sea trout in Sept. Local club: Mablethorpe, Sutton-on-Sea and Dist AC (water on Great Eau for members only). Tackleists: T Clarke & Co, 25 High Street; Bela's, Victoria Road. Hotels at Mablethorpe, Trusthorpe, Sutton-on-Sea.

Salthouse, near Sheringham (Norfolk). Sea here is deep quite close in shore, and fishing considered good. Good flatfish, Oct–Jan. Occasional bass and mackerel in summer. Guest house: Salthouse Hall.

Sheringham (Norfolk). Flatfish all year; cod autumn and winter, mackerel June–Sept. Beaches good all year, except April and May. Best sport west of lifeboat shed towards Weybourne or extreme east towards Cromer. Centre beaches too crowded in season. Bait can be ordered from tackleists. Boat fishing best well offshore. Tope to 40 lb and thornbacks to 20 lb; plenty of mackerel. Tackleists: Coastal Supplies, 28 Beeston Road. Club: Sheringham Sea AC.

Cromer (Norfolk). Good all-year fishing; mainly cod (Sept–April), whiting and dabs, with odd tope (summer); skate and bass (summer) from pier and beaches. Boat fishing in calm weather (beach-launching). Parking at owner's risk on W. Prom. Clubs: Cromer Inshore Sea AC, Cromer Sea AC. Fresh lugworm available from Randall's (tackleists), 9 Church St; and Marine Sports (open Sundays), High St. Hotels: Cliftonville,

Red Lion, Hotel de Paris, Grange Court, Colne House, Cliff House.

Yarmouth, Great (Norfolk). All styles of sea fishing catered for, including two piers, several miles of perfect shore line for beach angler, two miles of well-wharved river from harbour's mouth to Haven Bridge, and boat angling. To north are Caister, Hemsby, Winterton, Horsey, Palling, Weybourne etc, and to south, Gorleston-on-Sea and Corton. Sport very similar in all these places; ie Oct, Nov, Dec: cod, codling, whiting, dabs, flounders, dogfish. Jan, Feb, March: codling, dabs, flounders. April, May, June, July, Aug and Sept: dabs, flounders, eels, skate and tope; from boats and shore from the north end of Yarmouth and particularly from offshore boat angling at those places previously noted to the north. Most successful baits are lugworm, herring or mackerel, soft-back crab and ragworm. Sea-angling festival held annually. Further information from tackleists Pownall & Sons Ltd, Anglers' Depot, 74 Regent Road, who issue RD licences. Other tackleist: J Markham, 43 South Market Road. For charter-boats, contact F Moore, Nelson Rd South.

Gorleston-on-Sea (Norfolk). Whiting, cod, dabs and flounders from beaches and in estuary (best Oct to March); good skate Aug and Sept. Sport good in these periods from boats, pier or at Harbour Bend in river and on beaches. Baits: lugworm, crab and ragworm. Freshwater fishing (coarse fish) within easy reach on rivers and broads. Further information from Baker & O'Keefe Ltd, Anglers' Depot, 7 Pier Walk. Other tackleist: K & E Edwards, Harbour Bend.

Lowestoft (Suffolk). Noted centre for cod, autumn-May. Also whiting, flatfish, pollack and coalfish, with bass, tope, ray and mullet in warmer months. Good sloping beaches to north and south. North best on flood, south on ebb. Claremont Pier good for cod (day fishing only); mullet up to 7 lb, sole and eels from South Pier. Boats from Williams, 95 Waveney Crescent; Fuller, Avondale Road; Colby, Cliftonville Caravans, Parkfield. Terry Ling, 149 St Peters Street. Open festivals in October. East Anglian beach championships; inquire hon sec, Assn of E Anglian Sea Anglers. Tackleists: Ted Bean, 175 London Road N; Sam Hook, 132 Bevan Street;

Laurie Phillips, 189 London Road South; Arthur Collen, 17 Commodore Road, Oulton Broad. Other clubs: South Pier, Lowestoft SA. Further information from Publicity Officer, 7 The Esplanade.

Southwold (Suffolk); ns Halesworth. Good codling, whiting and sole fishing from beach, October to March. Bass main species in summer from harbour or shore; soles and silver eels also provide sport May to Sept. Tackleist: Southwold Angling Centre, 64 High Street (Tel 2085) who will supply information on freshwater and sea fishing in locality. Hotels: Swan, Crown, King's Head, Pier Avenue, Craighurst, Lord Nelson.

Felixstowe (Suffolk). Best in autumn and winter, when cod are about. Good sport with bass in summer and skate fishing good in May, June and July, especially in harbour. Best sport from boats and pier. Boatman: M Brien, 2a Bent Hill. Tackle and bait from Anglers' Depot and L T Bobby, both Undercliff Road, Ipswich SAS fishes here.

Harwich and Dovercourt (Essex). Bass, mullet, eels, garfish, flatfish, sting-ray, thornback skate, soles (all May to Sept), whiting, pouting, codling (Sept to March). Best fishing from boats, but Stone Breakwater, Dovercourt is good. Several good boat marks in estuary of Stour and Orwell and in harbour approaches. Best baits: lug, king rag, soft and peeler crab. Boats: H Garnett. Club: Harwich and Dovercourt AC. Tackleists: Messrs Howlett's, Kingsway, Dovercourt; G K Cann, 4 Market Street, Harwich. Copy of Borough Guide supplied by Town Clerk on request.

Walton (Essex). Bass, whiting, pouting, flatfish, codling, skate, tope, from boats, shore and pier. Cod fishing begins about second week in Sept and runs to end of March. Dt for pier 35p, st £5.50. Walton-on-Naze Sea Angling Club has a hut on the pier. HQ at Royal British Legion Club. Tackle (and bait): J Metcalfe, 15 Newgate Street. Boats: J Moore, 159 Hall Lane (Tel Frinton 5955) and S Murphy, 67 Woodberry Way (Tel Frinton 4274) and D Finch (Tel Frinton 3217). Hotels: Marine, Tudor Inn; Frinton Lodge, Frinton.

Clacton (Essex). Mainly autumn and winter fishing for whiting and cod. Summer fishing confined to pier and boats—bass, thornback, dogfish, tope, flatfish. Annual festivals arranged by Clacton

188   *Where to Fish*

Sea AC which has 104 boats at Holland Haven; anglers welcome at pier clubroom. Tackleists: Porters, 43 Pallister Road; J Metcalfe, Pier Entrace. Both supply bait; boats from Porters.

Southend-on-Sea (Essex). Mullet, bass, mackerel, scad, garfish, plaice and flounders are the main catches from the pier during the summer, with cod, codling and large flounders in the winter. A fleet of registered charter boats operate daily from the Pierhead, but prior booking is recommended. Thornback, stingray, smoothound, bass, tope, plaice and cod can be expected. Pier: st £12, dt 15p. Application form for st from Goings. Off season shore fishing available, with all year round facilities at the Thorpe Bay and Westcliff bastions and Westcliff jetty, also the river Crouch. Numerous open, pier, shore and boat events organised, including the Borough three-day festival. Tackleists: (Southend) Goings, (AT Report Station), Jetty Anglers. Essex Angling Centre. (Westcliff)

Whitstable and Tankerton (Kent). Good sea fishing. Dabs, plaice, bass, skate, flounders, eels, etc. Cod in winter from Tankerton beach. Boats available. Freshwater fishing on Seasalter Marshes, near Whitstable; roach, rudd, tench, pike, eels. Rod licences and information on sea and coarse fishing from tackleist: Boulting's, 33 Harbour Street. Hotels: Duke of Cumberland, Marine. Illustrated guide from Clerk of the Council, The Castle, Whitstable.

Herne Bay (Kent). Tope centre: mid-May to Sept. Also skate, plaice, flounders, dabs, silver eels, mullet, dogfish, codling, stingray and garfish. Bass can be taken in numbers either spinning or bottom fishing from June to Sept. Short length of pier opened for fishing following fire. Reculver Beach good for thornbacks in spring, Cod autumn and winter, and bass in summer. Boats: Turner Bros, Lane End; J Heathcote, Market Street; and T Burford, 9 Alvis Avenue, Stud Hill. Clubs: Herne Bay AA (HQ 59 Central Parade), Heron AS (HQ West Beach). Tackle, bait and RA licences: F J Whitehead, 29 William Street; R Edwards, 46 High Street. Hotels: Prince of Wales (Herne Bay AA HQ); Railway (Licensed Victuallers, South Eastern, HQ).

Sandwich (Kent). Bass at the mouth of the haven; sea trout and mullet run up the river; flounders, grey mullet, plaice, dabs, codling and pouting more seaward. Freshwater fishing at Reed Pond; dt. Local club: Sandwich and Dist AS. Tackleists: Mr Francis, The Butchery. Hotels: Bell, Haven Guest House. *For freshwater fishing, see Stour (Kent).*

Margate (Kent). Noted for mixed catches. Fine bass often taken from shore on paternoster, and boat by spinning. Mullet fishing from wooden pier; stone pier good for cod in winter. Bass and cod from rocks at low water. Spring and autumn cod plentiful; fish up to 20 lb. Big catches of flatfish on sand outside Newfoundland Rocks. Skate at Minnis Bay, Birchinton. Tope fishing from boat from June on through summer. Also dogfish and conger. Clubs: Margate Fishing Club (HQ Saracen's Head, High Street); Dolphin FC (Queen's Head); Old Centrals AC (130 Grosvenor Place); Wayland Boating Club. Tackleists: Kingfishers, 34 King Street. Boats can be hired in harbour.

Broadstairs (Kent). Bass, plaice, pouting, whiting, codling, tope, etc; shore and boats. Club: Broadstairs and St Peter's SAS (hon sec will provide further information). Annual sea angling festival usually in October.

Ramsgate (Kent). Good sport along 2m of shore, harbour piers, and Eastern and Western Chines. Beaches crowded in summer, so night fishing best. In spring and summer good bass fishing (from shore), also soles, flounders, dabs and thornbacks. In autumn and winter; cod (in large quantities), conger, dabs, flounders, soles, whiting, pouting, dogfish. Pegwell Bay (thornbacks, dogfish, dabs), The Rough (conger) and Dumpton Gap (flatfish) are good boat marks. Good boats always available and experienced boatmen, with excellent prospects of big catches of skate, cod, dabs, dogfish, whiting, pouting, conger eels and a few tope. Bait may be dug in Pegwell Bay or gathered from rocks. Boat and pier festivals held in October and November respectively. Tackleists: Ramsgate Bait and Tackle Shop, 7 Westcliff Arcade; Decca Sports, 4 Kent Place; Anglers Retreat, 32 Addington Street. Club: Royal Ramsgate Invicta AA. Hotels, etc, from Information Bureau, 24 Kings Street (Thanet 51086).

Deal and Walmer (Kent). Excellent sea fishing throughout the year. Spring;

skate, dogfish and codling. Summer; bass, mackerel, garfish, black bream, flatfish, occasional tope, and john dory. Autumn and winter; cod and whiting. Pouting all year. Boats out of Deal and Walmer enjoy good wrecking sport in the summer with modern cabin boats now in use as well as traditional open boats. Boat and Pier Festivals run by local clubs and area council. Excellent facilities for visiting anglers. Boat, pier and beach fishing all available. Clubs; Deal and Walmer Angling Association. Deal Angling Club (1919). Tackleists; Channel Angling, Deal Pier; The Foc'sle opposite the pier; The Downs Tackle Centre, The Strand, Walmer. All supply bait and tackle. Hotels: Beachbrow, Clarendon, Royal, Pegasus Restaurant, Lobster Pot Cafe.

Dover (Kent). The future of sea angling at Dover is obscured by hoverport plans. The Prince of Wales pier is now closed and the future of the Admiralty pier is in doubt because of vandalism. Fishing and competitions continue for the time being from the Southern breakwater and there is beach fishing in the vicinity. Species roughly as for Deal. Tackle and bait from D J Brazil, Snargate Street.

Folkestone (Kent). Good boat, beach and pier fishing. Conger (one of 42 lb landed recently), cod, bass, bream, flatfish, whiting, pouting and pollack, with mackerel in midsummer. Best for cod, Oct–Feb. Beach fishing best dusk onwards for bass and conger. Good sport from Harbour Mole (7p). Some good offshore marks. For boats and bait apply: Garry's (tackleists), Tontine Street. Boats also from Folkestone Sea AA (annual pier and boat festivals). Hotels: Cavendish Court (club HQ), Barrelle, and others; details from Information Bureau, Civic Centre, Castle Hill Avenue.

Sandgate (Kent). Very good fishing from beach and boats. There is a ridge of rock extending for over a mile 20 yds out from low-water mark. Bass good July–October; codling, whiting, pouting, conger March–May, August–Nov; good plaice taken May–June, especially from boats. Best months for boat fishing, Sept–Nov. The hon sec, Sandgate AS, will be glad to give information. Hotels: Wellington, Esplanade.

Hythe (Kent). Fishing from boat and shore for bass, codling, pouting, whiting, conger and flats. Princes Parade, **Seabrook,** is popular. Open storm beach, giving pouting, whiting, mackerel, sole, dab and flounder in summer and cod (up to 20 lb), whiting and pouting in winter. Few bass. Tackleists: J B Walker Ltd, 5–7 Marine Walk Street. Hotels: Imperial, Stade Court, White Hart, Swan. Clubs: Seabrook Sea AS; Sandgate Sea AS.

Dungeness (Kent). Boat and shore fishing, latter all year round. Whiting, pouting, codling, conger, dabs, plaice, mackerel. Good bass fishing in summer from shore and boat. Best months: May to Oct for boat fishing; Oct to Feb for shore fishing. Bait (lugs) obtainable locally. Tackleists: J G Woolley Ltd, Coronation Square, Lydd. Hotels: George, Railway, Dophin; Jolly Fisherman at Greatstone. Club: Brett Marine AC.

Hastings (Sussex). Sea fishing from pier and boats. Tope, bass, conger, plaice, codling, whiting, etc. Boats available from local fishermen. Hastings and St Leonards SAA has its own boats on beach opposite headquarters. Association also has clubroom on Hastings Pier. Annual membership £5. £1 charged p.d. for guest in club boat. East Hastings Sea AA has clubhouse and own boats on foreshore. Annual International Sea Angling Festival in October. Bait, tackle: Redfearn's, Castle Street; George's, opposite pier; Cavendish Tackle, 36a White Rock. International boat and pier festivals held in the autumn.

St Leonards (Sussex). Good sea fishing all the year round from boats and beach for flatfish, bass, mackerel, conger, tope, whiting, cod, bull huss, turbot. Boats, bait and boatmen from Warrior Square slipway. Clubhouse at 16 Grand Parade. Competitions run throughout the year boats and beach. Annual subscription £4.50 (subject to alteration annually).

Bexhill (Sussex). Boat and shore fishing. Cod, conger, whiting (Sept to end Dec). Dabs, plaice, mackerel, tope (July–Sept). Bass, best months May, June and July. Tackleist: Renne's, 10 Buckhurst Place. Club: Bexhill Sea AC (hon sec will help visitors; enclose sae). Freshwater fishing in Pevensey Sluice, Pevensey Haven and dykes; coarse fish. Hotel: Granville.

Eastbourne (Sussex). Boat, pier and shore fishing. Dabs, huss, pouting and conger (all year), cod in winter and skate (May to Dec). Best for place and bream from

June to Nov. Also soles, whiting, flounders, mullet. Good bass and mullet in warmer months. Notable tope centre, many around 40 lb; June and July best. Some of best beach fishing for bass around Beachy Head (up to 17 lb). Pollack from rocks. Flatfish off Langney Point and from pier. Few boats; inquire Eastbourne AA; new clubhouse and 18 boats for members' use. Other clubs: Nomads SAC. Bait mainly from Langney Point area and tacklists: Eastbourne Tackle Shop, 183 Langney Road; Anglers kiosk on pier; Compleat Angler, Pevensey Road; Tony Kirrage, Seaside.

Seaford (Sussex). Beach and boat fishing. Bass, cod, codling, conger, flats, huss, mackerel and few ling and pollack. Good catches of tope few miles offshore. Club: Seaford AC (open to new members; inquiries hon sec). Tacklists: R Hutchinson, 18 South Street, where information about local coarse fishing can be had.

Newhaven (Sussex). Variety of sport from beach and boat. Beach fishing for bass excellent May–Oct. Flounders from Tide Mills Beach. Good cod fishing from beaches between Seaford Head and Newhaven's East Pier, late Oct to early March. Breakwater gives good all-round sport, with bass, conger and cod all running large. Boat fishing excellent for cod in winter, large Channel whiting also give good sport. Monkfish off Beachy Head late August and Sept. Boats from Harbour Tackle Shop, Fort Road. Bait should be ordered (Tel 4441). Other tacklists: Dennis's, 107 Fort Road; Book & Bacca, 8 Bridge Street. Hotel: Hope Inn and Sheffield.

Brighton and Hove (Sussex). Noted for black bream (June–Sept) from pier and boats. Bass from pier (12 lb biggest) and beaches. Mullet and mackerel from pier. Good tope from boats. Beach anglers take flatfish as well as bass. Good cod from pier and boats in winter. Shark sport growing. Boats mainly from Shoreham and Newhaven; a few at Brighton. Details from tacklists. Several beach, pier and boat festivals. Tacklists: Brighton Angler, 15/16 Church Street; Preston Aquarium, 44 Beaconsfield Road; Lagoon Bait and Tackle, 327 Kingsway, Hove. Most dealers supply bait. Clubs: at Kings Road Arches are three clubs—Brighton Deep Sea Anglers, Brighton Cruising Club and Sir

Robert Peel AC (first two deep-sea fishing only). Queens Head AC specialises in beach fishing but membership limited (HQ Madeira Drive). Hove Deep Sea AC has boats for tope, conger, skate, turbot, place, dabs, etc. Friends of members can fish with members. Good trolling for bass, July–August, around Marina arms.

Shoreham and Southwick (Sussex). Boat and harbour fishing. Bass (July and August); grey mullet, skate and huss (June to Sept); cod and whiting (Sept to Dec); dabs, plaice, pouting, black bream, conger, mackerel and flounders (May onwards). Mullet fishing in River Adur near Lancing College very good July–August; light paternoster tackle and red ragworm recommended. Baits: white rag, red rag and lugworms may be dug from beach and mudbanks of river. Mussels and other baits can also be obtained. Tacklists: Paules, 13 Ferry Road.

Worthing (Sussex). Boat, beach and pier fishing. Bass, codling, flounders, pollack, whiting, plaice, eels, bream, mullet (good). Excellent bass and flounder fishing from beaches, spring and autumn. Mixed catches from boats. River Adur, east of Worthing, noted for flounders, mullet and eels. Local association: Worthing Sea AA (HQ, Worthing Pier). Tacklists: Ken Dunman Ltd, 2 Marine Place (opp Pier entrance). Boats from harbours at Shoreham and Littlehampton. Popular 2-day pier festival held in early September.

Littlehampton (Sussex). Noted for black bream, but wide variety taken, including skate (all year), bass (June–Oct), cod (winter best) and plaice. Bait can be dug from beaches or ordered from tacklists: Fishermen's Quay Angling Centre, Pier Road; David Jones, High Street. Boats through Littlehampton Skippers Assn, c/o Harbour View Cafe, Pier Road. Club: Licensed Victuallers Deep Sea AC (HQ Arun View Inn, The Bridge; membership open to publicans; £5.50 annually); Littlehampton and Dist AC. Best sport from boats.

Bognor Regis (Sussex). Good sea fishing at several marks off Bognor. Tope, bass, pollack, mackerel, whiting, wrasse. From May to July bream are plentiful. The conger, skate and sole fishing is very good. Grey mullet abound in the Shallow water between Felpham and Littlehampton Harbour. Good cod fishing between September and November. Bass weighing 5–10 lb and more caught from pier and shore. Also good pouting and pollack caught from coarse fishing in the Arun. The hon sec of Bognor Regis Amateur AS will supply information *(see also Sussex—lakes)*. Tackleist: Sports & Radio, 25–39 Aldwick Road. Boats can be had from local fishermen.

Hayling Island (Hants). From the South Beach of Hayling Island good fishing can be had with a rod and line for bass, plaice, flounders, dabs, whiting, etc, according to season. Fishing from boats in Hayling Bay for tope, skate, bass, mackerel, etc, is popular and a much favoured area is in the vicinity of the Church Rocks and in Chichester Harbour.

Southsea (Hants). Over 4m of beach from Eastney to Portsmouth Harbour provide good sport all year. Bass fishing especially good from spring to September. Flatfish and rays numerous, large mackerel shoals in mid-summer. Best sport from boats. Boom defence line from Southsea to IoW, although navigational hazard, is probably one of the best bass fishing marks on the South Coast. Vicinity of forts yields good bags of pollack, bass, black bream, skate, etc. Tope fishing excellent during summer. Portsmouth, Langstone and Chichester within easy reach and provide good sheltered water in rough weather. Boats can be hired from Portsmouth and Langstone Harbour boatmen. Bait from harbours but not plentiful can be ordered from tackleists: R W Wakely, 65 Highland Road; L T Bloxham & Son, 14 Highland Road (trout permits for Meon and Chichester gravel pit); B Osborne, Bridgemary, Gosport; G Taylor, 88 Copnor Road; Paige & Goodall, 165 New Road, Portsmouth. Club: Southsea Sea AC, who have club boats. Tel 25508.

Southampton (Hants). Fishing in Southampton Water really estuary fishing; thus not so varied as at some coastal stations. However, flounders abound (float and/or baited spoon fishing recommended), and whiting, pouting, silver eels, conger, bass, grey mullet, soles, dogfish, thornback, skate, stingray, plaice, dabs, scad, shad, mackerel have all been caught. At the entrance to Southampton Water, in Stokes Bay and the Solent generally, excellent tope fishing may be had. Angling from Hythe Pier, and from Netley and Hamble shores, but best fishing from boats. Southampton Water is rarely unfishable. Good sport in power station outflow. Southampton Sea AC (annual sub £2.50) holds competitions throughout the season and an annual shore festival; information from hon sec. Boats, bait, tackle from Sea Anglers Supplies, Regents Park Road. Tackle also from Patstone & Cox, 25 High Street; Waterhouse & Connings, Woolston; Holt & Haskell, High Street, Shirley; Connor & Mitchell, St Marys; St Denys Sea Bait and Tackle, St Denys.

ISLE OF WIGHT

The Island provides wealth of shore and boat fishing, and sheltered conditions can always be found. Bass are main quarry for beach anglers, but pollack, conger, mackerel, pouting, thornback rays, flatfish and wrasse, with occasional tope, are also taken. Black bream, skate and shark are caught by boat anglers as well as the species already mentioned.

Alum Bay. Bass from shore in rough weather; at times large shoals at the Needles. Scratchels Bay good for pollack on feather. Tope numerous in Pot Bank area. For boat, phone Harry Simmonds (Tel Yarmouth 392).

Atherfield. Fine pouting, few conger, but difficult to arrange boats. Quite good pouting and few bass and congers taken off shore after dark. Tope also caught.

Bembridge. Mackerel (June onwards), conger, pouting, black bream and skate off ledge, especially in May to Oct; plaice, turbot and brill. Tope and nursehound between ledge and Nab Tower. Bass from by Lifeboat Station, June–Sept. Tackleist: Davids, Foodmarket, Lane End. Club: Bembridge AC.

Bonchurch. Bass, conger, plaice, flounders, pout from beach.

Brooke. Bass off ledge and pouting on marks. Few good bass taken off shore at point in rough weather.

Chale. Bass from shore, pouting, mackerel and few conger, but difficult to arrange boat. Shore fishing after dark. Some tope. Hotel: Clarendon.

Colwell Bay. Mackerel, bass, pollack, and wrasse off ledge. Boat obtainable. Hotel: Holmes Court.

Compton Bay. 1m west of Brooke. Good bass fishing from shore and near wreck.

Cowes. Medina River. Flounders from April and small bass from July. In harbour, whiting, pout in 'Roads' and Solent. Bass, mullet and pollack off Parade, larger bass off shore at Egypt Point. Mackerel off Old Castle Point, late summer. Boats from: W Souter and E Williams, both Arctic Road. Hotels: Gloster; Fountain; Woodvale; Gantham; Holmwood; Waverley.

Freshwater Bay. Pouting, small pollack and few conger on marks. Few bass and occasional conger off shore in rough weather. Boats available. Hotels: Albion, Farringford, Osborne Private. Tackleist: Evalyn's, Avenue Road, Freshwater.

Newport. Nearest sea fishing in River Medina; flounders, school bass, mullet. Shark and general boat fishing arranged. Bait and tackle from Sports and Pastimes, 140 High Street.

Newtown. Bass and flounders in Newtown River. Clamerkin reach is best.

Niton. Pouting and conger. A few bass taken, fishing from the wall at Binnell Bay.

Osborne Bay. Small whiting and pouting in autumn. Boat from Cowes.

Ryde. Bass, small pollack, plaice, flounders, eels, bream and grey mullet from pier. Conger, dogfish, dabs, skate, mackerel from deep water marks, and plaice, flounder, bass and sole fishing inshore. Cod up to 24 lb taken in autumn. Sheltered resort giving ideal fishing conditions all year. King rag and lugworm plentiful. Vectis Boating and Fishing Club offers temporary membership (not including use of club boats). Details from hon sec (enclose sae). Boats can be hired along shore. Bait and

tackle: Don's Sports, 14 Cross Street; The Tackle Box, 73 High St. Inquiry office at Ryde Esplanade.

Sandown. Good beach and pier fishing. Bass all year, with largest in early autumn. Plaice, sole, dabs, pollack and grey mullet (doing very well of late), turbot, mackerel, garfish. Large skate, ray and conger from pierhead late summer and autumn, cod in winter. Best baits: ragworm, lugworm, herring, sandeels, slipper limpet. Local club: Sandown and Lake AS, organising frequent open competitions. Visitors welcome. Tackleist (and boats): Sea-Tac, 6–8 Wilkes Rd.

Seaview. Plaice and bream (Seagrove and Priory Bay); Straight off Seaview for bass, skate, conger, etc. Boats from Mr Newell, High Street, and Seagrove Bay. Tackleists: Mr Dobson, Pier Road; Alvera's, High Street. Hotels: Seaview, North Bank.

Shanklin. Bass, conger and pollack from Luccombe and Horseshoe Ledges in boat. Pouting and flatfish from pier; bass and flatfish from beaches. Club: Shanklin AS. Tackleist: The Sports Shop, 74 Regent Street.

Totland. Bass off shingle bank from boat. Bass, conger from shore. Fishing also from pier. Boats from Totland Bay Pier & Beach Co, Granville Road, Heathfield Villas, The Broadway. Hotels: Totland Bay, Chalet, Sentry Mead.

Ventnor. Sea fishing from pier now owned by Fairdeal Amusements for bass, plaice, a few sole, flounders, bream, conger, skate, grey mullet, pollack, mackerel, pouting and wrasse. Season Easter–Sept 30 dt 10p. Boat (from Blakes) for pollack and mackerel. Club: Ventnor AC (associate members welcome). Tackleist and bait: Bates & Son, 5 Spring Hill. Beach fishing *(see also Bonchurch)*.

Wootton. School bass and flounders.

Yarmouth. Bass, small pollack from pier, also from Victoria Pier. Yar Bridge, bass and flounders.

Lymington (Hants). Tope, sting-ray (May–July), conger (May–Nov), cod (Oct–March) from boats and beach. Hurst Castle area good beach spot for cod and large bass. Flounders (Oct–Feb) Hurst and Pennington–Lymington Marshes,

boat and shore. Pouting (March–Nov), whiting (Oct–March), bass, flatfish (April–Nov). All beaches from Hurst Castle westwards to Mudeford. Tackleists: Smiths Sports, 25 Queen Street, Lymington; Handicraft Shop, Gore

Fishing for bass from the beach on an incoming tide near Bournemouth. *Photograph: John Tarlton.*

Road, New Milton. Boats from Lymington and Keyhaven. Hotels: Angel, Londesborough. Club: Lymington & Dist Sea FC (HQ: The Railway Hotel) annual memb £2.

Mudeford (Dorset). At entrance to Christchurch Harbour. Good all-round sea fishing in Christchurch and Poole Bay, the vicinity of the Ledge Rocks and farther afield on the Dolphin Banks. Tope, dogfish, conger, bream, pout, pollack, whiting and good sport spinning for mackerel and bass. Plaice off Southbourne; flounders, dabs, skate and soles off beaches at Highcliffe, Barton and Southbourne; flatfish, bass, whiting, etc, from quay, beach, groyne or shore at Hengistbury Head; large tope, stingray, skate and occasional thresher shark

off The Dolphins. Fairly good cod fishing in winter, Needles–Christchurch Ledge, Pout Hole and Avon Beach (off Hengistbury Head). Whole squid favourite bait, but large baited spoons and jigs also successful. Good sole from Taddiford and Highcliffe Castle (best after dark). Groyne at Hengistbury good for bass in summer; sand eels by day and squid by night. Best months for general sport, mid-June to mid- or late Sept. Further information, bait, etc, from tackle shop at 76 Purewell. Most local fishermen now take parties out mackerel fishing in summer. Flounders, eels, bass and mullet taken inside the harbour. Boats bait and tackle from R A Stride, The Watch House, Coastguards Way, Mudeford, and R Keynes, The Quay,

Christchurch. Hotels: Avonmouth, Waterford Lodge, The Pines Guest House. *For other tackleists and fresh-water fishing see Christchurch under Avon (Hampshire) and Stour (Dorset).*

Bournemouth (Dorset). Fishing good at times from the pier yielding bass, grey mullet, plaice, dabs, etc. Excellent catches of plaice, dabs, codling, silver whiting, mackerel (spinning), tope up to 40 lb, conger, skate, from boats. Shore fishing, when sea is suitable, for bass and other usual sea fish. Bait supplies fairly good. Clubs: Boscombe and South-bourne SFC; Bay AS; Christchurch AA; Christchurch Sea FC. Tackleists: Field Sports, 918 Christchurch Road; Custom Tackle, 17 Columbia Road; The Tri-angle Sports Shop, 111 Commercial Road, who will advise visitors, arrange trips from pier. Good accommodation for anglers at Edelweiss Guest House, 32 Drummond Rd, and Malvern Guest House, 7 Hamilton Rd, Boscombe (angling proprietor). For freshwater fishing, *see Avon (Hampshire) and Stour (Dorset).*

Poole (Dorset). Boat, beach and quay fishing in vast natural harbour. Great variety of fish, but now noted for deep-sea boat angling and bass fishing. Con-ger, tope, bream, etc, are caught within three miles of the shore. Bass, plaice, flounders, etc, caught inside the harbour at Sandbanks and Hamworthy Park in their seasons. Local tackle shops should be consulted for up-to-the-minute in-formation. Boat fishing facilities largely controlled by Derek Case Angling Agen-cy, 5 High St, Poole (tel 6597), who has over thirty boats available. Sea Fishing (Poole) Ltd also cater for bass and deep-sea angling (tel 2426). Baits favoured locally: mackerel, squid, sand eel and ragworm. Tackleist: Derek Case Angling Agency.

Swanage (Dorset). Four tides a day in area. Many species taken from pier, incl bass, mullet, pollack, mackerel, flounder and pouting. Beach here and at **Studland Bay** produces good bass, flounder and dabs at night; too crowded for daytime fishing. Tope, skate, conger black bream and brill taken from boats outside bay. Boats available daily from Swanage.

Around Peveril Ledge and Durlston Head there is good pollack fishing to St Alban's Head; also bass and mackerel. Chapman's Pool: pollack, codling, bass, pout. Old Harry Rocks; bass, prawns. Durlston Bay good for mullet. Local association: Swanage and Dist AC. De-tails of accommodation from informa-tion bureau and Swanage Angling Cen-tre, 6 High St.

Weymouth (Dorset). Centre for the famous Chesil Beach, Shambles Bank, Portland and Lulworth Ledges. The steeply sloping Chesil Beach provides year-round sport for many species, but autumn and winter best for mackerel, codling, whiting, bream and dogfish; beach fishes best at night; fairly heavy tackle required. Good conger fishing at the Chesil Cove end, Ringstead Bay, Redcliffe and round the piers. Piers yield good sport with grey mullet. Good bass from Greenhill beach in heavy surf, with variety of flatfish at most times. Ferry-bridge and the Fleet noted for bass, mullet and flounders. Boat fishing: In the area around Portland Bill some big skate and stingray give good sport, while the notable Shambles Bank continues to yield turbot and skate, etc. Lulworth Ledges have a large variety of fish in-cluding tope, blue shark, conger, skate, dogfish, black bream, pollack, whiting, etc. Best baits are lugworm, ragworm, soft crab, mackerel and squid. No boats from Chesil Bank, but 16 boatmen oper-ate from Weymouth throughout year. Secretary of Assn: Brian Caddy, 4 Franchise Street, Weymouth, who will give information. Society booklet from Weymouth Publicity Office, Weymouth Corporation and hon sec. Tackleists: Anglers' Tackle Store, 56 Park Street; S Hayman, 13 Trinity Road; Gilbert Sports, 4 St Alban Street; J M Hocka-day, Portland Road, Wyke Regis.

Portland (Dorset). Good bass fishing in harbour; live prawns for bait. Mullet, mackerel, whiting and conger are plenti-ful. Boats from fishermen at Castletown (for the harbour), Church Ope, The Bill and on the beach. Near the breakwater is a good spot, where refuse from the warships drifts up.

CHANNEL ISLANDS

Wide variety of sport from beaches, rocky headlands and boats. Many specimen fish landed from deep-sea marks. Shark fishing growing in popularity. Boats often difficult to come by.

Guernsey. No fewer than 52 different species recorded in Bailiwick of Guernsey rod-caught record list. Many headlands offer first-class spinning for pollack, mackerel, garfish and scad; grey mullet everywhere. Other species are red and black bream, red mullet, wrasse, whiting, pouting and conger. A flat, sandy west coast gives good surf-casting for bass and a few flatfish. Several Guernsey fish accepted as new British records. Boat fishing for shark, turbot, etc, but organised fishing trips are few, due to difficulties in obtaining licensed boats. There is, however, one boat which makes to two trips a day for general fishing from St Peter Port; details from Roy Taylor, Le Baugy Estate, Jerbourg, St Martin. Occasional vacancies for visitors interested in shark and tope with Guernsey 30 Fathom Club; inquire at Baker's, 43 The Pollet, St Peter Port. Private arrangements might also be made. Fresh sand-eel is best; available at very nominal price in local fish market. Ragworm widely used but fairly difficult to obtain. Clubs: Guernsey Sea AC; 30 Fathom Club. Tackleists: Baker's, 43 The Pollet; Druee, Victoria Road; Fletcher's, Arcade; Marquand Bros, North Quay; Sarnian Sports Stores, States Arcade (all in **St Peter Port**); T Henry, The Hermitage, Vale; G Domaille, The Bridge, St Sampson.

Brochure and accommodation guide from States Tourist Committee, St Peter Port.

Jersey. The island offers a great variety of first-class sea fishing from beaches and harbours for a wide variety of fish. Several records have been broken here in recent years. Species caught at various stations around the island include pollack, wrasse, conger, plaice, scad, bass, garfish, mackerel, mullet, pouting, flounder, black bream, sole, skates and rays. Fishing is particularly good at the following venues: St Helier's harbour heads; St Aubin's Bay, harbour, and fort; Noirmont Point; St Brelade's Bay; La Corbiere; L'Etacq; Greve au Lancon; Plemont; Greve de Lecq; Bonne Nuit Bay harbour; Bouley Bay harbour; Rozel Bay harbour; St Catherine's breakwater; Gorey harbour; Grouville Bay; La Rocque harbour, St Clement's and St Aubin's bays. Jersey SFC (HQ 16 Broad Street, St Helier) will help visitors. Coarse fishing in St Ouens Canal, wt £1 from The Jewellery Workshop, Burrard St, St Helier. Permits for reservoir trout fishing (dt £3) from G. Pile, Reads & Co, 3 Westaway Chambers, St Helier. Five sea angling clubs hold competitions. Tackleists: Wheways, 16 Broad St, Hunt, 71 King St, The Fishing Centre, 20 Sand St, and Tackle Shop, Vegetable Market; all St Helier.

Bridport (Dorset). Beach fishing yields bass, pouting, flatfish, thornback rays and conger, with whiting and cod in winter. These and other species taken from boats. West Bay (1½m distant) the angling centre. Burton Bradstock, West Bexington and Abbotsbury are popular venues on Chesil Breach. Eype and Seatown favoured to west. Black bream caught from boats. Bait: ragworm, squid mackerel favoured. Tackleists: L A Rathbone, The Tackle Shop, West Bay Road, West Bay, who arranges boatfishing. (Tel 23475.) Lyme Bay Marine, Old Customs House, West Bay. Club:

West Bay Sea AC. Hotel: The George, W Bay.

Lyme Regis (Dorset). Bass may be caught from the shore (bait with fresh mackerel obtained from motorboats in harbour or lugworm dug in harbour at low tide). Mackerel may be caught from May to October. Conger fishing from the high wall of harbour. Pollack plentiful in spring months. Conger and skate can be caught from boats about 2m from shore. Motor and rowing boats can be hired at harbour. Tackleists: R J Stratton Ltd, 15 Broad Street.

Seaton (Devon). Boat fishing. Pollack,

pouting, conger, wrasse (March to Sept), bass (virtually all year, but best Sept–Nov), bream, mackerel, dabs, skate, plaice, dogfish. Axe estuary good for bass, mullet and sea trout. Hotels: Pole Arms, Bay. Tackleists: F Ackerman & Co Ltd, Fore Street.

Sidmouth (Devon). Sea fishing in Sidmouth Bay. Mackerel (May to Oct), pollack (excellent sport spring and summer east and west of town), bass (to 13¼ lb in surf at Jacob's Ladder beach during summer), large winter whiting (July–Oct on rocky bottom), skate to 105½ lb and conger to 44 lb have been taken; bull huss to 19½ lb, and tope. Also plaice, dabs, flounders and occasional turbot. Hon sec, Sidmouth Sea Angling Club, can give information about baits and temporary membership. *For freshwater fishing see Axe, Otter, Sid (trout) and Exe and Exeter Canal (coarse).* Information, bait and tackle from J Bloxham Sports Shop, Market Place. Boats from S French and S Bagwell. Details of accommodation from Publicity Officer, Council Offices.

Exmouth (Devon). Bass are caught here all the year round, from the 3½ miles of sandy beach, or with live sand-eel from a boat at anchor or drifting. Mackerel fishing popular in summer. Flounders, eels, plaice and dabs may be taken with soft crab, lug or ragworm; pollack with sand-eel, ragworm or artificial lure off Straight Point and pier, where pout, bream, mullet, conger and bass are also taken. Bait may be purchased from the Exmouth Sea AA on pier. There is also a deep sea fishing assn; both clubs have pier clubrooms. Tackleist: Fred Statham, Pier Head: Exmouth Tackle Shop, 20 The Strand. Boat-bookings from both.

Dawlish (Devon). Dabs and whiting in bay off Parson and Clerk Rock and between Smugglers' Gap and Spray Point. Mackerel good in summer. Conger eels and dogfish about ¾m from shore between Parson and Clerk Rock and Shell Cove. Good fishing sometimes off breakwater by station and from wall of Boat Cove. Boats from Boat Cove. Good trout fishing at Chagford and Moretonhampstead.

Teignmouth (Devon). Sea fishing ideal (especially for light spool casting with sand-eels for bass). Bass, pollack, flounders in estuary. Mackerel, dabs and whiting in the bay. Good bass and flounder fishing from the shore. Deep sea, wreck and offshore trips available. The town has an annual sea fishing festival. Club: Teignmouth SAS (HQ, River Beach). Tackleists: Doel Sports, 12/13 Bank Street (for RD licences, permits for Newton Abbot waters, coarse fishing; bait for sea angling; information); The Sea Chest, 8 Northumberland Place. Boats and bait from John Perry, Alf Dodd, Sid Back, Harvey and Hussey. Details of accommodation from Town Enquiry Bureau, The Den.

Torcross; nr Kingsbridge (Devon). Hotel: Torcross Hotel. The sea fishing is very good, especially the bass fishing. Hotel can make arrangements. *For coarse fishing see "Slapton Ley".*

Torquay (Devon). Base for famous Skerries Bank and Torbay wrecks: conger, cod, pollack, turbot, flatfish, whiting, etc. Hope's Nose peninsula provides best venue for shore angler, with bass and plaice mainly sought. Babbacombe Pier good for mackerel. Bass and pollack off the rocks. Natural bait hard to come by except for mussels from harbour walls, but tackleists can supply. Tackleists: Fletcher's Sports, 9 Fleet Street. Russ Evans, 67 Newton Road, has boat for bass and Skerries fishing. Local associations: Torquay Sea AA (HQ, Princess Pier); Torbay ASA (HQ, Beacon Quay); English Riviera Shark AC, Babbacombe SA (HQ, Babbacombe Beach Café). Details of accommodation from Local Authority Publicity Dept, 9 Vaughan Parade. *For freshwater fishing, including Torquay Corporation reservoirs, see Teign and Dart.*

Paignton (Devon). Summer and autumn best. Bass, mackerel and garfish can be taken from beaches between Preston and Broadsands and from harbour, promenade and pier respectively. Mullet also present, but very shy. Fishing from rockmarks, too. Small boats to be hired by the hour, mackerel trips, and a charterboat, "Tuonela", takes parties to fish Torbay. Good catches recorded. Tackleists: H Cove Clark, 45–47 Torbay Road; Jacks Sports, 371 Torquay Road; Sangsters Sports, 23 Victoria Street. Club: Paignton Sea AA, who have information service and social centre for anglers at HQ at South Quay, The Harbour (open 7.30 pm onwards). Details of accommodation from Publicity Officer, Old Town Hall, or assn hon sec (advice and information).

Brixham (Devon). Boat fishing in bay for plaice, dabs, mackerel. Good pollack off East and West Cod rocks off Berry Head (neap tides best; worms or prawn). Farther out is Mudstone Ridge, a deep area, strong tide run, but good general fishing with big conger. Local boats take visitors out to deep water marks (wreck fishing) or to Skerries Bank, off Dartmouth, for turbot, plaice, etc; advance bookings (at harbour) advisable. Shore fishing: Bass, pollack, wrasse, conger, mackerel from Fishcombe Point, Shoalstone and the long Breakwater. Grey mullet abound in the harbour area (bait, bread or whiting flesh). Bass from St Mary's Beach (best after dark) and south side of Berry Head (bottom of cliffs) for flat fishing. Sharkham Point good for mackerel and bass (float with mackerel, strip bait or prawn for bass). Mansands Point good for bass and pollack (float). Night fishing from Elbury or Broadsands beach for bass, flatfish or conger (use thigh boots). Tackleists: Angler's Den (R Crank), 13 Bolton Street; Yacht Supplies, 72 Middle Street; George's (next to bus station). Quayside hotel has boats.

Dartmouth (Devon). Boat and rock fishing for pollack, mackerel, dabs, pouting, conger, whiting, bass and wrasse. Skerries Bank excellent; turbot, plaice, etc. Bass, plaice, dabs, flounders and mackerel in Dart estuary. Tackleists: Sportsman's Rendezvous, Fairfax Place (RD licences); Sea Haven, Newcomen Road, Bosun's Locker, Bayard's Cove (also boats). Boatmen include J Atkins, E R Curl, R Leech, B Lineham, J Goddard (c/o Dartmouth & Dist AA HQ at 5 Oxford St). Hotels: Castle, Victoria, Dart Marina. *For freshwater fishing, see Dart.*

Salcombe (Devon). Good bass fishing in estuary, and bass, pollack, etc, from nearby coves. Best April to Oct. Mackerel June to Sept and turbot, dabs, flounders, plaice, skate and rays rest of year. Plenty of natural bait. Beaches crowded in summer, but bass can be taken in winter. Wreck fishing for conger, bream, etc. June–Oct. Turbot numerous. Boats: Taylor Marine, White Strand; H Cook, White Strand (live sand-eels). Club: Salcombe and Dist SAA (HQ: Shipwrights' Arms); annual festival seven days from first Sunday in October special prizes and trophies for visitors throughout season. Bait and tackle from The Tackle Shop. Hotel: Fortescue.

Newton Ferrers (Devon). Noted station on Yealm Estuary. All-year bottom fishing; bass, flounders, pollack (from rocks), with mullet, conger, mackerel and flatfish from boats; shark June–Oct. Good base for trips to Eddystone. Boats from D Hockaday (Tel: 359); L Carter (Tel: 210). Abundant bait in estuary. Hotels: River Yealm, Family, Anglers, Yachtsmen.

Plymouth (Devon). One of finest stations in country for off-shore deep water fishing at such marks as East & West Rutts, Hands Deep and, of course, famous Eddystone Reef. Specimen pollack, conger, ling, whiting, pouting, cod, bream and mackerel plentiful. Fishing vessels available for charter are Decca and Sounder equipped—fast exploring numerous wrecks within easy steaming of port; outstanding specimens taken. Inshore fishing for same species off Stoke Point, The Mewstone, Penlee, Rame and The Ledges. Sheltered boat and shore fishing in deep water harbour and extensive estuary network—at its best in autumn for bass, pollack, flounders, thornback and mullet. Shore fishing from rocks at Hilsea, Stoke, Gara Point, Rame Head, Penlee and Queeners for bass, pollack and wrasse, etc. Beach (surf) fishing at Whitsands and sand bar estuaries of Yealm, Erme and Avon rivers for bass, flounder and ray. All angling associations in city—British Conger Club, Plymouth Federation Sea AC and Plymouth SAC—now under one roof, on waterfront, at Plymouth Sea Angling Centre, Vauxhall Quay. Visiting anglers cordially welcomed. Tackleists: Cloads, The Barbican; Jeffreys, Old Town Street; Sea Angling Centre, Vauxhall Quay. Boats: Bob Armstrong, Homer Rise, Elburton (Plymouth 43239); Robin Gavin, 43 Westbourne Road, Peverell (Plymouth 62976); Bill Broom, Tamar Street, Devonport (Plymouth 60447); Plymouth Sea Angling Centre, Vauxhall Quay (Plymouth 67746).

Looe (Cornwall). Excellent centre for all-round sport. Bass, pollack and mullet from "Banjo Pier" breakwater from mid-September to May 1. Good rock fishing from White Rock, Hannafore, westwards to Talland Bay and Llansallos, where pollack, bass, conger and wrasse can be taken. Eastwards, flatfish and bass from beaches at Millendreath, Downderry and Whitsand Bay. Bass, flounders, eels, pollack and mullet from river at quayside and upriver. Excellent sport from boats on deep-sea marks; porbeagle, mako, blue and some thresher shark taken, and wide variety of other fish. Deep sea boats from C Cotton, the tackle shop, Quay, East Looe (Tel. 2189). Shark tackle for hire. Other tackleist: Jack Bray, The Quay, East Looe. Bait from tackleists or may be dug in river estuary. Clubs: HQ of Shark AC of Gt Britain is at The Quay, East Looe; Looe is official weighing-in station for British Conger Club; Looe Sea AA (information from hon sec, Vic Sneed). Temporary membership gives access to club boat at slightly less than commercial rates. Information also from Looe Information Bureau. Useful booklets from tackleists.

Polperro (Cornwall). Boat, shore and pier fishing. Cod, ling, conger, bass, bream, whiting, skate, pollack, mackerel, gurnard, turbot, brill (best months July to October). Hotels: Claremont, Noughts & Crosses, Ship, Three Pilchards; also farm accommodation.

Fowey (Cornwall). Excellent sport with bass (June to Oct) in estuary and local bays from Udder to Cannis. Pollack numerous and heavy (20 lb and more). Good bream, cod, conger, dogfish, ling, mullet, mackerel, wrasse, whiting and flatfish (big flounders and turbot). Bass, mullet and flounders taken from river. Par Beach to west also good for bass. Rock fishing at Polruan. Sand-eel, rag and lugworm obtainable. Boats: Digby, Battery Lane, Polruan; Raymond, 11 Esplanade; Affleck, c/o Hunstow, 27 Station Road; Tabb, 2 Fore Street, Golant. Self-drive boats from Town Quay. Tackleists: Sports Shop, 10 Esplanade. Local club: Fowey AC (HQ Safe Harbour). Small waterside hotel, "The Square Rig", has boats for hire (Tel 2328).

Mevagissey (Cornwall). Excellent sea fishing, especially in summer. Six shark boats are based here (local club affiliated to the Shark AC of Great Britain). Shark Centre & Quay Tackle Shop will make arrangements for shark and deep-sea trips. Limited scope for shore fishing, but results excellent, especially bass from beach. Good pollack off Dodman

Point and from marks out to sea. Bass in large numbers were at one time taken at the Gwinges, but few have been caught in recent years. Excellent sport with large mackerel at Gwinges and close to Dodman from late Aug. Sport from the pier can be very good at times, especially with mullet. Boatmen can be contacted through Shark Centre or Mevagissey SAC. Other tackleists: The Tackle Box, Fore Street; P Johns, The Quay. Bait usually available. Club: Mevagissey SAC (HQ, The Ship Inn, Pentewan; visitors welcome). Annual sub £3.

Gorran Haven (Cornwall). Same marks fished as at Mevagissey. Rock fishing available. Bass from sand beach. The Gorran Haven fishermen offer some facilities for visitors wishing a day's fishing. Excellent pollack fishing from boat with rubber sand-eel off Dodman Point. Limited accommodation at the Barley Sheaf (1½m); also Llawnroc Country Club and houses.

Falmouth (Cornwall). Excellent estuary, harbour (pier, shore and boat) and offshore fishing, especially over Manacles Rocks. Noted for big bass and pollack, latter taken off wreck and rock marks. Most other species present in numbers. Bait in estuary or from tackleists. Boats from Customs House Quay on Prince of Wales Pier. Club Falmouth and Penryn AA (festival each autumn). Tackleists: J Bray, Market Street, Penryn; Berks & Langdon, 32–34 Arwenack Street; Goodwins, Church Street. Shark fishing and other deep-water fishing from various MVs. Apply: Frank Vinnicombe, West Winds, Mylor Bridge, near Falmouth (Penryn 2775), or Berks & Langdon (as above). Details of hotel accommodation from Town Information Bureau, Prince of Wales Pier. *For freshwater fishing, see River Fal.*

Porthleven (Cornwall). Bass are to be taken from the rocks in Mount's Bay. Best bass fishing from Loe Bar, 1½m E. Good pollack and mackerel fishing outside the rocks. Nearly all fishing is done from the Mount's Bay type of boat in deep water. Small boats for fishing parties; some for private hire. Hotel: Tye Rock.

Penzance (Cornwall). Excellent boat, pier, rock and shore fishing for pollack, mackerel, mullet and bass. Shark fishing also available. Best months: June–Nov. Club: Mount's Bay AS (headquarters:

Dolphin Inn, Newlyn). Annual fishing festival, five weeks, Aug–Sept. Tackleists: The Quay Shop, Quay Street; F Westren, Newlyn Bridge, Newlyn; Lanxon Bros, Causewayhead; Sports Centre, Union Street; Dunns Sports, Market Place. Live and preserved bait supplied during summer months. Coarse fishing available. Phone W Knott, 0736 710249.

Mousehole, via Penzance (Cornwall). Good station for fishing Mount's Bay. Excellent mackerel, bream, pollack, conger, whiting, bass close to harbour according to season. Sheltered from west. Rock fishing available in rough weather. Some boats and boatmen; inquire of harbour master. Best grounds: Longships and Runnel Stone. Good results with sharks. Hotels: The Ship; Old Coastguards; The Lobster Pot.

Isles of Scilly. From shores and small boats around islands, wrasse, pollack, mackerel, conger and plaice; farther off in deep sea, particularly on The Powl, south-west of St Agnes, big catches made of cod, ling, conger, pollack, etc. Mullet pay periodical visits inshore, but usually caught by net; bass rare in these waters. Some shark fishing, but visitors advised to take own tackle. Peninnis Head and Deep Point on St Mary's are good rock marks for pollack, wrasse and mackerel; Pelistry Bay likely beach venue. Boating can be dangerous, so experience essential. Accommodation limited, early booking advisable between May and Sept. Full information from Clerk of Council, Town Hall, St Mary's. For boats inquire of St Mary's Boating Assn, Hugh Street, St Mary's. Several shops stock tackle.

St Ives (Cornwall). Surf fishing for bass principal sport. Mullet, mackerel, pollack, flatfish (plaice, flounders, occasional turbot) can all be caught from shore, especially from island, Man's Head, Clodgy Point and Godrevy Point. Boat fishing gives sport with mackerel (summer months) and large pollack (off reef from Godrevy Island). Bass, tope, mullet, flatfish and occasional sea trout taken in Hayle river estuary. Trout fishing on Drift Reservoir, Penzance and St Erth Stream (4m). Licences for river fishing from Digey Corner Gift Shop, 52 Fore Street.

Newquay (Cornwall). Boat, beach; rock and estuary fishing. Mackerel (April to Oct); school bass (June–Sept); larger fish July onwards, including winter; pollack (May–Nov); flatfish, wrasse (May–Sept); whiting in winter. Mullet good from June–Sept. Shark and deep sea fishing possible (two or more boats). Trout fishing in Porth Reservoir. Sea trout and brown trout in Gannel estuary. Local angling guide from L D Clay, 13 Veor Road, for Newquay AA. Numerous hotels; details from town guide.

Padstow (Cornwall). Mackerel, plaice, whiting (winter only), bass, pollack, rays, turbot, grey mullet, conger. Sport with tope can be good at times. Several boatmen. Tackleist: H Radford Ltd, Duke Street, who will give information about freshwater fishing (salmon, sea trout, brown trout). Hotels: Dinas, Metropole.

Bude (Cornwall). Bass and ray main quarry. Northcott Mouth and Sandymouth good for bass. Rays may be taken from shore in late summer and autumn. Very little boat fishing and bait difficult to obtain, except from tackleists, N Cornwall Pet Supplies, Princes Street. Club: Bude and Dist SAC.

Hartland (Devon); nr Barnstaple, 24m. Good all-round sea fishing, especially for bass at times with india-rubber sand-eel, prawn or limpet from beach or rocks according to tide (bass up to $11\frac{1}{2}$ lb have been caught); whiting, mullet, conger and pouting also taken. Spekes Millstream (trout) is available to guests at Hartland Quay; best fish 1 lb 5 oz; dt for non-residents, 50p. Torridge is 5m. Hotels: Hartland Quay, New Inn, King's Arms.

Lundy Island (Bristol Channel). Good mackerel, conger, pollack and wrasse inshore. Ray, plaice, dabs, tope and bass at East Bank. $1\frac{1}{4}$ to $2\frac{1}{2}$m E. Good anchorage at Lundy, but no harbour. No boats for hire. For accommodation write to The Agent, Lundy, via Ilfracombe, N Devon.

Clovelly (Devon); W of Bideford. Whiting, cod, conger, bull huss, dogfish and the occasional plaice caught all the year round; ray in spring, bass and mackerel in summer. Few inshore boats; fishing from the breakwater forbidden from 9 am to 6 pm in summer. Tackleists: see Bideford. Hotels: New Inn; Red Lion.

Appledore. N of Bideford in Torridge estuary. In summer, good bass fishing from rocks, Greysands and boats. Cod, some over 20 lbs, and whiting in winter. Lugworm beds at Appledore and Instow. Few boats. Tackleists: see Bideford.

Bideford (Devon). Bass (from the bridge, in summer) flounders, mullet higher up the river. 2m away at Westward Ho, extensive beach and rocks from which bass, dogfish, smoothhounds, bull huss, tope and mackerel may be taken in summer; cod in winter. Tackleists: Pethericks, 22 High Street; Gales Sports, Mill Street. Local club: Bideford and District AC. Hotels: Royal; New Inn; Tantons; Ring o' Bells; Market. Yeoldon House nr Bideford. *For freshwater fishing, see Taw and Torridge.*

Ilfracombe (Devon). Good sea fishing from rocks, pier, boats. Bass, pollack, mackerel, tope, skate, conger, mullet, etc. Best July–Oct. Shark fishing Aug and Sept depending on mackerel shoals. Boats from harbour reliable, boatmen being available and essential. Club: Ilfracombe and Dist AA. Reservoir trout fishing available *(see Freshwater Section)*. Hotel: Longwood, Montpelier Terrace *(advt p 144)*, Royal Britannia *(advt p 66)*. Details of other accommodation from Publicity Officer, Tourist Information Centre, The Promenade. Tackle and bait from Labbets, 61–2, High St, who act as secretary to the angling club.

Lynmouth (Devon). Good harbour and boat fishing. Grey mullet and bass from harbour arm. Trolling for pollack and mackerel. Tope, skate and conger in Lynmouth Bay and off Sand Ridge, 1m. Motor boats with skipper available. Best months: June to Oct. Several hotels in Lynton and Lynmouth; details from Information Bureau, Lynton. *For freshwater fishing see Lyn.*

Minehead (Som). Beach, boat and rock fishing, principally for conger, cod, bass and flatfish (Dunster to Porlock good for bass from beaches). Dogfish in bay. Mackerel in summer. Harbour and promenade walls provide sport with mullet, codling and some bass. Boats: E James and T Rawle, both Quay Street. Bait from sands at low water. Club: Minehead and Dist SAC. Tackleist: Minehead Sports (A J Holman) 55, The Avenue. For further information and for boats contact Harbourmaster, 7 Quay Street, or Information Centre, Market House, The Parade.

Watchet (Som). Watchet and Dist Sea Angling Society fishes all the year round, covering coast from St Audries Bay to Porlock Wier. Monthly competitions from piers and shore. Codling, bass, whiting, conger and skate, according to season. Good boat fishing. New members welcomed by AS.

Weston-super-Mare (Avon). Flounders, sole, bass, skate, conger and silver eels taken during summer, and whiting, pout and cod in autumn and winter. Shore fishing from Berrow Sands, Brean Down, Black Rock, Axe estuary, Town beach, Old Pier, Kewstoke Rocks and Sand Point. Best baits: local-dug lugworm, and herring. Best times: low water at Brean Down and two hours before and one hour after high tide on inshore rocks and beaches. Tackleists: Evans, 19 Orchard Street; Maroli, 19 Oxford Street; Jotchams Sports, 10 High St, Burnham.

Southport (Merseyside). Dabs, flounders, plaice, with whiting and codling in winter, are the chief fish caught here; also skate, mullet, dogfish, sole, conger, gurnard and some bass. Shore flat and sandy, and fishing mainly from pier. Local clubs; Southport SAS. Good coarse fishing on River Crossens; dt. Tackleists: James Fay Ltd, 8–10 Hoghton Street; Rimmer & Smethurst. 3–5 Burton Arcade; S Baxter, 71 Sussex Road.

Blackpool (Lancs). Fishing from North Pier for codling, whiting and dabs. Oct to March best; night fishing allowed Nov–May. Tackle and bait obtainable at both piers and S Waterhouse & Son, Cookson Street; Anglers Den, 41 Warley Road (near Derby Baths); B Ogden, 254 Church Street; Sports Shop, 63 Whitegate Drive. No boat fishing. Club: Blackpool and Layton AS. Coarse fishing in Stanley Park Lake. Dt.

Morecambe and Heysham (Lancs). Beach, pier and boat fishing throughout year. Beaches yield plaice, flounders, dabs, bass and eels from June to October, and dabs, whiting and flounders in winter. Estuary catches up to 100 flounders to 2 lb weight at Arnside. Central Pier open for angling: place, bass, flounder, eels. From Stone Jetty angling free; good catches of plaice, flounders, whiting. At Heysham Harbour day permits. Flounders, dabs, pouting, conger and mullet can be taken. Boat sails daily from Stone Jetty and several boats available at week-ends. Tackle and bait from Charlton and Bagnall, 15 Yorkshire St; Club:

Morecambe Bay AC (annual open contest).

Fleetwood (Lancs). Plaice, whiting, skate, codling, tope, etc, from boats and shore. Club: Fleetwood and District AC. Tackleists: G W Clarke, 65 North Albert Street; D Langhorne, 80 Poulton Road. Boats: C B Bird, 25 Upper Lune Street.

Barrow-in-Furness (Cumbria). Tope bass, cod, plaice, whiting, skate. Good marks include Foulney Island, Roa Island, Piel Island, Scarth Hole and Black Tower (Walney Island) and Roanhead. Fulltime charter-boat arranged by Hannays Tackle Shop, Tel 0229 22571. Plenty of rag, lug and mussel bait. Tackleists: Hannay's, 50 Crellin Street, J V Quigley, Forshaw Street.

ISLE OF MAN

Popular sea anglers' venue. Pollack, mackerel, cod, mullet, conger, bass and flatfish taken in large numbers. Bait freely available and boats, too, at some resorts.

Castletown. Conger, pollack, cod, wrasse, tope, flatfish from beach and boat; best months, June to Oct. Big skate from boats 600 yds off Langness; best Aug–Sept. Boats available locally.

Douglas. Cod, plaice, sole, dogfish, coalfish, congers, from Victoria and Battery Piers; best months, May to Oct, coalfish, wrasse, cod, plaice, dabs, sole from boats in Douglas Bay. Rock fishing off Douglas Head; float or spinner (good for pollack). Cod, wrasse, red gurnet, plaice, Little Ness Head to Douglas Head; skate from boats 2m out, and large tope, conger, cod, etc. Club: Douglas (IOM) and District AC. (HQ Ridgway Hotel).

Kirk Michael. Beach fishing from here to Point of Ayre is excellent for bass, flatfish, dogfish.

Laxey. Plaice, dabs and bass from Oct to March from beach. Cod, mackerel, flatfish, offshore from boats at Garwick Bay. Club: Garwick Sailing and Fishing Club.

Peel. Cod, haddock and flatfish (Dec to May), and mackerel (big), coalfish and bass (May to Oct) from breakwater. Bass, plaice, sole (best July to Dec), from beach. Plaice, sole, skate (best June to Sept) from boats 400 yds off. White Strand, Peel Bay. Rock fishing off St Patrick's Isle for mackerel, wrasse, coalfish; float and spinner. Information from M W Clogue, West View, Peel. Club HQ, White House Hotel.

Port Erin. Good sport from pier and breakwater for pollack, mackerel, wrasse, grey mullet, coalfish, angler fish and conger. The bay yields flatfish and mackerel, with cod in the colder months. The Sea Fish Hatchery & Aquarium here is worth a visit. Tackleist: Henry Crellin, Strand Road.

Port St Mary. Probably best centre on island. Pollack, coalfish, wrasse from rocks, pier, boats (most of year). Flatfish and mackerel offshore and pier during herring season. Tope, skate, cod, conger, ling from boats. Boats from J Williams, c/o Albert Hotel and W Halsall, Lime Street PSM. Several competitions. Inquiries to hon sec, Southern AC. Visitors welcome. Hotels: Station, Albert and Bay.

Ramsey. Plaice and cod from pier. Dogfish, flatfish, conger and (in Sept) bass from Ramsey beach to Point of Ayre. Coalfish, pollack and wrasse may be caught float fishing from rocks, using lugworm for bait. Pollack also taken by spinning with artificial sand-eel. Tackleists will help with bait and boats (see below). Tackleists: J Mead, Parliament Street; W S Skinner, North Shore Road, Club HQ at Stanley Hotel, The Quay.

Check before you go

While every effort has been made to ensure that the information given in "Where to Fish" is correct, the position is continually changing and anglers are urged, in their own interests, to make preliminary inquiries before travelling to selected venues. This is especially important with reference to prices quoted.

Inevitably, the rate of inflation is affecting stability in this quarter. Anglers' attention is also drawn to the fact that the hotels mentioned under the various fishing stations do not necessarily have fishing of their own. Any amendments or further data for inclusion in subsequent editions, and any criticism, will be welcome.

FISHING CLUBS & ASSOCIATIONS IN ENGLAND

THESE lists have once again been expanded and now total well over 1,000, covering freshwater and sea angling. Further information can be had from the secretaries. A stamped addressed envelope should be enclosed with postal enquiries. Some clubs have had to be omitted because of lack of space. **Note:** *Where information has been supplied, waters held by club are noted, and availability of tickets, at end of each entry. Further details under individual centres.*

NATIONAL BODIES

Anglers' Co-operative Association. Ken Sutton, Director, Midland Bank Chambers, Westgate, Grantham, Lincs NG3 1LE. Tel: 0476 61008.

Angling Foundation. 7 Swallow Street, Piccadilly, London W1R 7HD. Tel 01 437 7281.

Angling Trades Association. 7 Swallow Street, Piccadilly, London W1R 7HD. Tel 01 437 7281.

Atlantic Salmon Trust. 14 Downing Street, Farnham, Surrey. Director: G D F Hadoke MA MSC FIFM.

British Casting Association. J A Martin, 26 Ling Hill, Scarborough, N Yorks.

British Conger Club. Reginald Quest, 5 Hill Crest, Mannamead, Plymouth, P3L 4RW. Tel 262068. HQ: Sea Angling Centre, Vauxhall Quay, Plymouth, Devon.

British Field Sports' Society. Robin Brockbank, 59 Kennington Road, London SE1 7PZ. Tel 01 928 4742 *(advt p 4)*

British Record (rod-caught) Fish Committee. Peter H Tombleson, Secretary, National Anglers' Council, 5 Cowgate, Peterborough, PE1 1PJ. Tel: 0733 54084 and Peakirk, Peterborough. Tel: Glinton 428.

British Waterways Board. Melbury House, Melbury Terrace, London NW1. Tel: 01 262 6711. Fisheries Officer: T G Leatherland, Willow Grange, Church Rd, Watford, Herts WD1 3QA. Tel: Watford 26422. All angling inquiries to him.

European Federation of Sea Anglers (English Section). C Richards, 66 Linden Ave, Herne Bay, Kent.

Flyfishers' Club. H A Rickett, 43 Brook St, London W1Y 2JL. Publishers of The Flyfishers Journal—editor Donald Downs. Tel: 01 629 6776.

Freshwater Biological Association. The Director, The Ferry House, Far Sawrey, Ambleside, Cumbria LA22 0LP. Tel: Windermere 2468.

Marine Biological Association of the United Kingdom. The Secretary, The Laboratory, Citadel Hill, Plymouth. Tel: 21761.

National Anglers Council. Peter H Tombleson, 5 Cowgate, Peterborough, PE1 1PJ. Tel: 0733 54084 and Peakirk, Peterborough. Tel: Glinton 428. Representative body for all anglers.

National Association of Specimen Groups. A Otter, 22 Peveril Street, Radford, Nottingham NG7 4AL.

National Federation of Anglers. Chief Administrative Officer, Halliday House, 2 Wilson Street, Derby. Tel: 362000.

National Federation of Sea Anglers. R W Page, 26 Downsview Crescent, Uckfield, Sussex TN22 11UB. Tel: 01 462 4096.

National Water Council. 1 Queen Anne's Gate, London SW18 9BT.

Pure Rivers Society. J R Fleetwood, 74 Dagenham Ave, Dagenham, Essex RM9 6LH.

Salmon and Trout Association. H. de W. Waller, Fishmongers' Hall, London Bridge, London EC4R 9EL (full list of local organisers on pages 456–60). Tel: 01 626 3531. *(advt p 22)*

Shark Angling Club of Great Britain. Brian Tudor, The Quay, East Looe, Cornwall PL13 1DX. Tel: Looe 2642.

Sports Council. 70 Brompton Road, London SW3 1EX. Tel: 01 589 3411.

Tope Club of Great Britain. J D Williams, secretary, 24 Church Walks, Llandudno, Gwynedd. Tel: 75105.

Water Space Amenity Commission. 1 Queen Anne's Gate, London SW18 9BT.

Abbey Cross Angling Society. P G Leigh, 22 Lower Green, Tewin, Hertfordshire. Rib, pits. Private.

Abingdon and District Angling and Restocking Association. R Pitson, 11 Finmore Close, Abingdon, Berkshire. Thames. Guest tickets only.

Accrington and District Fishing Club. A Balderstone, 42 Towneley Avenue, Huncoat, Lancashire. Greta. Tickets.

Addlestone Angling Society. Mrs Sharp, 24 Heathervale Road, New Haw, Addlestone, Weybridge, Surrey. Wey. Members only.

Aire Fishing Club. W Peyton, 87 Gargrave Road, Skipton, Yorkshire. Aire, Restricted tickets.

Aln Angling Association. F J R Moir, Thistledowne, 49 Swansfield Park Road, Alnwick, Northumberland, Aln. Tickets.

Alston and District Angling Association. P Renwick, Swans Head Hotel, Alston, Cumberland. S Tyne. Tickets.

Altrincham Angling Society. A Lea, 37 Crossgates Avenue, Sharston, Manchester.

Ampthill and District Angling and Fishing Preservation Society. B H Stringer, 1 Greenfield Road, Flitwick, Bedfordshire.

Amwell Magna Fishery. Colonel N Blair, 41 Bolton Gardens, London SW5. R Lee. No tickets.

Anchor Angling Association. F James, 54 Hilliat Fields, Drayton, near Abingdon, Berkshire.

Andover Angling Association.

Appleby Angling Association. J A Henderson, c/o Barclays Bank, Appleby, Westmorland. Eden. Tickets.

Appletreewick Barden and Burnsall Angling Club. R C Whittington, Moorside Farm, Moor Lane, E Keswick, Leeds LS17 9HN. Wharfe. Tickets.

Asfordby Society of Anglers. Mr & Mrs H Birch, Riverside Cottage, Mill Lane, Asfordby, Melton Mowbray, Leicestershire.

Ashbourne Fly-Fishers' Club. F W Mellor, 2 Boothby Avenue, Ashbourne, Derbyshire. Dove. Members only.

Ashford and District Angling and Preservation Society. C J Hyder, 37 Northumberland Avenue, Kennington, Ashford, Kent. Royal Military Canal. Tickets.

Ashmere Fly-Fishing Club. Mr and Mrs K Howman, Felix Lane, Shepperton, Middlesex. Trout lake. Season tickets only.

Aspatria Angling Club. R Baxter, 25 Outgang Road, Aspatria, Cumberland. Ellen. Members only.

Association of East Anglian Sea Anglers. F Culshaw, 84 Westwood Avenue, Lowestoft, Suffolk.

Association of Teesside and District Angling Clubs. A Allan, 1 Scalby Grove, Fairfield, Stockton-on-Tees, Teesside. Reservoir. Tickets.

Association of Wearside Angling Clubs (for sea fishing in NE). T Wright, 9 Dene Gardens, Houghton-le-Spring, Co Durham.

Avon Fishing Association (Devon). J E Coombes, 19 Stella Road, Preston, Paignton, South Devon. Devonshire Avon. Tickets.

Avon and Tributaries Angling Association. Rev D D Sceats, The Sett, 24 Little Stoke Road, Stoke Bishop, Bristol BS9 1HQ.

Axminster Sea Angling Club. Miss K Hawkes, 208 Henson Park, Chard, Somerset.

Axwell Park and Derwent Valley Angling Association. *Post vacant at time of going to press. Enquire local tackleists.* Water on Derwent (Tyne). Tickets.

Aylesbury District and Izaak Walton Angling Association. W Cheney, 14 Yardley Green, Elmhurst Estate, Aylesbury, Buckinghamshire.

Aylsham and District Angling Club. K Sutton, 17 Town Lane, Aylsham, Norfolk.

Babbacombe Sea Angling Association. W J Hern, 29 Westhill Road, Torquay.

Banbury and District Angling Association. P M Handley, 8 Deene Close, Adderbury, Banbury OX17 3LD. Cherwell and Oxford Canal. Tickets.

Barking Angling Society. A J Sperden, 27 Cambell Road, East Ham, London, E6. Water for members only.

Barkingside and District Angling Society. D J French, 64 Khartoum Road, Ilford, Essex. Roding and Blackwater. Tickets.

Barnard Castle Angling Society. G Richardson (Chairman), 17 Galgate, Barnard Castle, Co Durham. Tees.

Barnard Castle Fly-Fishing Club. J C Walker, 3 Vane Road, Barnard Castle, Co Durham. Private.

Barnes and Mortlake Angling Society. K Dellard, 23 Cleveland Gardens, Barnes, SW13 0AE.

Barnsley and District Amalgamated Angler's Society. A Noble, 9 Coronation Drive, Birdwell, Barnsley, Yorkshire.

Barnstaple and District Angling Association. A J Tyacke, 5 The Bank, Landkey, Barnstaple, Devon. Taw. Visitors' tickets only from local tackleists.

Barrow Angling Association. D M Adams, The Old Post Office, Woodland, Broughton-in-Furness, Lancashire. Reservoirs. No Tickets.

Basingstoke Angling Club. M J Callow, 198 Winchester Road, Basingstoke, Hampshire.

Bath Anglers' Association. C F Sutton, 147 Sheridan Road, Twerton, Bath BA2 1RA. Avon, brooks. Tickets.

Bathampton Angling Association. D Crookes, 25 Otago Terrace, Larkhall, Bath, Avon. Trout and coarse fishing. Avon, canal, brooks. Tickets.

Beachcasters (Brighton) Angling Club. D H Shead, 53 Scotland Street, Brighton.

Beccles Angling Club. W D Holmes, 21 Glenwood Drive, Worlingham, Beccles, Suffolk.

Bedford Angling Club. Mrs M E Appleton, 155 Marlborough Road, Bedford. Great Ouse. Limited date.

Bedlington and Blagdon Angling Association. S Symons, 8 Moorland Drive, Bedlington, Northumberland, NE22 7HB, Blyth. Tickets.

Bellingham Angling Club. T H Armstrong, Westlands, Bellingham, Hexham, Northumberland. Tyne. Some tickets.

Belper and District Angling Club. H Fitton, 9 Holbrook Road, Belper, Derbyshire.

Bembridge (IOW) Angling Club. R Green, 22 Downsview Road, St Helens, IOW.

Benson and District Angling Club. W Aldridge, Crown Square, Benson, Oxfordshire.

Bentham Angling Association. E Jackman, Whernside, Bentham, via Lancaster. Wenning. Tickets.

Betteshanger Colliery Welfare Angling Society. A Herbert, 22 St James Hall Gardens, Walmer. Kent. Medway. Tickets.

Bexhill Sea Angling Club. C Hunnisett, 48 Towers Croft Road, St Leonards, Sussex.

Bicester Angling Society. B Truby, 91 Bucknell Road, Bicester, Oxfordshire. Lake. No tickets.

Bideford and District Angling Club. V B Eveleigh, 21 Capern Road, Bideford. Sea and coarse fishing.

Bideford and District Sea Angling Club. Harry Bottomley, Glen View, Raleigh Hill, Bideford, Devon.

Biggleswade and District Angling Association. H Taylor, 14 Broadmead, Biggleswade. Bedfordshire. Ivel and Ouse. No tickets.

Billericay and District Angling Society. H E Brown, 107 Kennel Lane, Billericay, Essex.

Bingley Angling Club. P Exley, 5 Highfield Road, Frizinghall, Bradford BD9 4HY, Yorkshire. Aire, lakes. Members only.

Birmingham Anglers' Association. 100, Icknield Port Road, Rotton Park Birmingham B16 0AP. Severn and tributaries, Avon, Thames and tributaries, Wye and tributaries, canals and lakes. Members only.

Birstwith Private Angling Club. R W Gaunt, 'Buttersyke', Malt House Lane, Burn Bridge, Harrogate, Yorkshire, Nidd. Members only.

Bishop Auckland and District Angling Club. R B Wakefield, The Bungalow, Binchester, Bishop Auckland, Co Durham. Wear. Tickets.

Bishop's Stortford and District Angling Society. C Costema, 31 Thornbera Road, Bishop's Stortford, Hertfordshire. Stort. Tickets.

Blackburn and District Anglers' Association. A Smith, 25 Pickering Fold, Blackburn BB1 2LH. Ribble, Lune, Wenning. Members only.

Blackburn and District Sea Anglers' Association. Harold Walton, 55 Redlam, Blackburn, Lancashire.

Black Ox Angling Club. Hon Sec, 5 Lascelles Lane, Northallerton, N Yorks. Bedale Beck and Swale. No tickets.

Blackpool and Layton Angling Society. E Wadeson, 24 Elgin Place, Blackpool, Lancashire.

Blandford and District Angling Club. J Bell, 15 Albert Street, Blandford Forum, Dorset. Dorset Stour. Tickets.

Blenheim Angling Society.

Blunham Angling Club. Hon Sec, c/o Horse Shoes Inn, Blunham, Bedfordshire. Ivel. No tickets.

Bodiam Angling Club. A T Weddle, 4 The Green, Bodiam, Robertsbridge, Sussex. Rother. Tickets.

Bodmin Anglers' Association. Lieut-Col H M Ervine-Andrews VC, Butterswell, Nanstallon, Bodmin, Cornwall. Camel. Tickets.

Bognor Regis and District Freshwater Angling Club. R J Thomas, 4 Crouch Cross Lane, Boxgrove, near Chichester, Sussex. Rother, canal, lakes. Tickets.

Bolton and District Angling Club. J A Shanahan, 4 Sunninghill Street, Bolton.

Bolton Fishing Association. J H Siddall, Fairfields, The Shawl, Leyburn, Yorkshire. Ure. Restricted tickets.

Boroughbridge and District Angling Club. G Whitaker, 9 Manor Drive, Kirby Hill, Boroughbridge, Yorkshire. Ure. Tickets.

Boscombe and Southbourne Sea-Fishing Club. C J Searle, 12 Cedar Avenue, Christchurch, Dorset.

Boston and District Angling Association. J D McGuire, 6 Churchill Drive, Boston, Lincolnshire. Witham. Membership book needed.

Boston Spa Angling Club. A Waddington, The Cottage, Main Street, Thorp Arch, Wetherby, Yorkshire, Wharfe. Tickets.

Bottesford and District Angling Association. B C Cross, 12 The Square, Bottesford, Nottinghamshire. Grantham Canal (dated). River Devon (summer time only).

Bradford City Angling Association. A Scaife, 80 Whetley Hill, Bradford 8, Yorkshire. Ure, Wharfe, Aire, Swale, canals, lakes. Tickets.

Bradford No 1 Angling Association. S Talbot, 15 Southland Grove, Leventhorpe, Thornton, Bradford, Yorkshire. Wharfe, Ure, canal, lake. Tickets.

Bradford-on-Avon and District Angling Association. J B Webster, 6 Lyneham Way, Trowbridge, Wiltshire, Avon, Biss, Frome, canal, brook. Tickets.

Bradford Waltonians' Angling club. E N Williams, East Rombalds, Rombalds Lane, Ben Rhydding, Ilkley, Yorkshire. Wharfe and reservoirs; no tickets.

Braintree and Bocking Angling Society. P Thompson, 80 Kynaston Road, Panfield nr Braintree, Essex.

Brampton Angling Society. T Bonockley, 1 Denton Crescent, Low Row, Brampton, Cumberland. Irthing and tributaries, Gelt, King, Cambeck. Tickets.

Brandon and District Angling Club. P Cooper, 16 High Street, Feltwell, Thetford, Norfolk. Little Ouse. Tickets.

Brett Marine Angling Club. Galloways Road, Lydd, Kent.

Bridgnorth Angling Society. C Booth, Club Headquarters, Golden Lion, High Street, Bridgnorth, Shropshire.

Bridgwater Angling Association. B Valentine-Slack, 6 Toll House Road, Cannington, Nr Bridgewater, Somerset. Bridgewater and Taunton Canal, Dunwear Ponds, King's Sedgemoor Drain, and Huntspill River. Tickets.

Bridlington Angling Association. W Farr, 53 Milner Road, Bridlington, Yorkshire.

Brighouse Angling Association. T A Riley, 16 Coronation Terrace, Greetland, Halifax, Yorkshire. Calder and canal. No tickets.

Brighton Cruising Club Angling Section. J G Pennell, 79 King's Road Arches, Brighton, Sussex.

Brighton Deep Sea Anglers. F Bean, 139 King's Road Arches, Brighton, Sussex.

Brighton Palace Pier Angling Association. L R Lawrence, 1 Hamblin House, Broadway, Southall, Middlesex.

Bristol and District Amalgamated Anglers. J Parker, 16 Lansdown View, Kingswood, Bristol BS15 4AW. Trout and coarse fishing on Avon, Brue, Chew, Yeo, etc. Tickets for coarse fishing only.

Bristol and West of England Federation. Gilbert Towell, 18 Southfield Avenue, Kingswood, Bristol. Avon, Kennet and Avon Canal, Frome, lake. Affiliated clubs share rights.

Bristol Channel Federation of Sea Anglers. R Rogers, 1 Willow Cottage, East Bower, Bridgwater.

Brixham Sea Anglers' Association. G Walton, 85 New Road, Brixham, Devon. Clubhouse at 16a Castor Road, Brixham.

Broadstairs and St Peters Sea Angling Society. H A Moor, 54 Stanley Road, Broadstairs, Kent.

Brockenhurst Manor Fly-Fishing Club. Mrs Chessell, The Laurels, Dibden Purlieu, near Southampton, Hampshire.

Bromsgrove and District Association of Angling Clubs. D Pennells, 5 Burcot Lane, Bromsgrove, Worcestershire.

Brotherhoods Sports Club. Honorary Secretary, c/o Peter Brotherhoods Ltd, Lincoln Road, Peterborough, Nene. Tickets.

Broughton Working Men's Angling Association. T H Large, 23 Knowefield Avenue, Stanwix, Carlisle. Derwent. Restricted permits.

Buchan Park Angling Association. D W Newnham, The Bungalow, Coombe House Lane, Bolney, Sussex. Lakes. Permits.

Buckingham and District Angling Association. S Vernon, 13, Woodland Crescent, Buckingham. Hyde Lane Pits, Great Ouse. Tickets (limited) from local tackleist only.

Bude Angling Association. Lt-Cdr S F W Blackall RN, 5 Ward Close, Stratton, Bude, Cornwall EX23 9BB. Tamar. Tickets.

Bude and District Sea Angling Club. A J Inch, Fair View Tourist Park, Poughill, Bude, Cornwall.

Bude Canal Angling Association. B Putt, 2 Orchard Close, Poughill, Bude, Cornwall.

Burford Angling Club. P Saunders, 43 Sherborne, Nr Cheltenham, Glos. Windrush. Weekly ticket.

Burgess Hill Angling Society. R Shakeshaft, 23 Holmesdale Road, Burgess Hill, Sussex. Arun. Tickets.

Burnham-on-Crouch Angling Club. W Cole, 35 Station Road, Burnham-on-Crouch, Essex.

Burnley Angling Society. J H Walton, 23 St James Row, Burnley, Lancashire. Reservoir. Tickets to local residents only.

Burneside Angling Association. R Tallon, 28 Beck Nook, Staveley, Kendal, Cumbria. Kent. Tickets.

Burnt Mill and Nettlewell Angling Society. S A Sullivan, 162 Felmongers, Harlow, Essex.

Burton-on-Trent Mutual Angling Association. A H Baldock, 48 Bearwood Hill Road, Burton-on-Trent, Staffordshire.

Bury District Angling Society. F Booth, 142 Bury Road, Tottington, Bury, Lancashire. Ponds, reservoirs. Tickets.

Bury St Edmunds Angling Association. C G Harrison, 9 Klondyke Cottages, Bury St Edmunds, Suffolk.

Buxton Fly-Fisher's Club. K J Legg, 74 Corbar Road, Buxton, Derbyshire. Reservoirs. Tickets.

By Brook Fly-Fishers' Club. M V M Clube, Hilton Lodge, 20 Downleaze, Bristol 9. Trout. Members only.

Byfleet Angling Association. F A Nixon, 12 Heathfield Rd, Hersham, Walton-on-Thames KT12 4PN, Surrey. Wey. No dt.

Calder Angling Association. W N Nixon, 10 The Knoll, Thornhill, Egremont, Cumbria CA22 2SN.

Calne Angling Association. S G Fairbrass, 5 Stokes Croft, Calne, Wiltshire. Marden. Tickets.

Camborne Angling Association. J Evans, 1 Enys Road, Camborne, Cornwall.

Cambridge Albion Angling Society. H R Jeffrey, 245 Ditton Fields, Cambridge.

Cambridge Fish Preservation and Angling Society. A C Moden, 2 Birch Avenue, Chatteris, Cambs.

Cambridge Trout Club. J Dillon-Robinson, Sammy's, Widdington, near Saffron Walden, Essex.

Cambridgeshire and Isle of Ely Federation of Anglers. H R Page, 35 Old School Lane, Milton, Cambridgeshire, 24 affiliated clubs.

Canterbury and District Angling Association. N Stringer, Riverdale, Mill Road, Sturry, near Canterbury, Kent CT2 0AF.

Carlisle Angling Association. E Cave, 9 Brunton Crescent, Carlisle, Cumbria. Eden. Tickets.

Carnforth and District Anglers' Association. A McCartney, 114 Kellet Road, Carnforth, Lancashire. Keer. Tickets.

Carshalton and District Angling Society. J Fiddimore, 17 Prestbury Crescent, Woodmansterne, Banstead, Surrey. Mole. Season permits.

Castle and Sible Hedingham Angling Club. G F Ruffle, New England, Sible Hedingham, Essex.

Castleford and District Amalgamated Society of Anglers. C Hardwick, 19 Church Hill, Selby, Yorkshire. Nidd, Ouse, Wharfe, Rye, Derwent. Pickering Beck, etc. Some tickets.

Central Association of London and Provincial Angling Clubs. J C Watts, 9 Kemble Road, West Croydon, Surrey.

Charing and District Angling Club. E R Bennett, Rosary, Warren Street Road, Charing, Kent.

Chatton Angling Association. A Jarvis, New Road, Chatton, Alnwick, Northumberland. Till. Members and associates only.

Cheadle Angling Club. R F Heakin, Police House, Barnfields Lane, Kingsley, near Cheadle, Staffordshire.

Cheddar Angling Association. A T Lane, 1 Orchard Close, Cheddar, Somerset.

Chelmsford Angling Association. J Peachey-Edwards, 15 Helston Road, Chelmsford, Essex. Chelmer. Tickets.

Cheltenham Angling Club. F J Selley, 35 Warden Hill Road, Cheltenham, Gloucestershire. Avon. Tickets.

Chepstow and District Angling Club. A J Black, 51 Severn Avenue, Tutshill, Chepstow, Gwent.

Cherry Tree Angling Club. I Gosling, 37 St Mary's Terrace, Flixton Road, Bungay, Suffolk. Waveney. Members only.

Cheshire Anglers' Association. F R James, 34 Sweet Briar Crescent, Crewe, Cheshire. Severn, Dane, canal. Members only.

Cheshunt Angling Club. R Carpenter, 37 Spencer Avenue, Hammond Street, Cheshunt, Hertfordshire. Lake. Members only.

Chester-le-Street and District Angling Club. T Wright, 156 Sedgeletch Road, Houghton-le-Spring, Tyne and Wear. Wear. Day ticket.

Chew Fly-Fishing Club. Dr R R Fells, 17 Mortimer Road, Clifton, Bristol 8. Chew. Members and guests only.

Chichester and District Angling Society. Mrs M Stimpson, 17 Willowbed Drive, Chichester, Sussex PO19 2HX. Pits. Weekly tickets.

Chichester Canal Angling Association. D S Richardson, 117–121 Rose Green Road, Rose Green, Bognor Regis, Sussex. Tickets.

Chippenham Angling Club. Mrs M Steel, 21 Braemor Road, Calne, Wilts. Bristol Avon. Tickets.

Christchurch Angling Club. E Chislett, 9 Woodfield Road, Kinson, Bournemouth, Dorset. Avon, Fleet Pond. Some tickets.

Christchurch and District Sea Fishing Club. A Palmer, 18 Hengistbury Road, Southbourne, Dorset.

Cinque Ports Angling Society. Mrs A Masters, 1 The Bogs, Hothfield, Ashford, Kent.

Cinque Ports, Sea Angling Society. G Colley, 8 Wingate Road, Folkestone, Kent.

Civil Service Angling Society. N J Day, 74a Honor Oak Road, London SE23 3RR. Thames, Medway, Kennet, lakes, reservoirs. No tickets.

Civil Service Sports Council. E A Sykes, 140 Faversham, Southill Garden Drive, Weymouth, Dorset. Brit, Radipole, lakes. Permits.

Clacton Sea Angling Club. M W Lilley, 59 Tudor Green, Clacton, Essex.

Clifton Hampden Piscatorial Society. David Corke, French's Cottage, Long Wittenham, Berkshire.

Clitheroe Angling Association. E Hodgkinson, 288 Whalley Road, Accrington, Lancashire. Ribble, Hodder and Lune. Limited tickets through members only.

Clive Vale Angling Club. R Glazier, 43 Rye Road, Hastings, Sussex. Reservoirs. Period tickets.

Cockermouth and District Angling Association. Wm Hobson, "Hillside", Egremont Road, Cockermouth, Cumberland. Cocker. Season tickets only.

Colchester Angling Preservation Society. N F J Binks, 7 Churnwood Road, Colchester, Essex. Colne, Stour and gravel pits. No tickets.

Colchester Piscatorial Society. Curtis, 43 All Saints Avenue, Colchester, Essex. Colne. No tickets.

Collier Row Angling Society. A Chopping, 16 Rush Green Road, Romford, Essex. Roding. Members only.

Collingham Angling Association. Mrs J Wilson, 93 Braemar Road, Collingham, Nottinghamshire.

Colne (Lancs) Angling Association. B Dean, 282 Gisburn Road, Blacko, Nelson, Lancashire. Brownhills Reservoir. Members only.

Colnes' Angling Society. K Murrells, 1 Hillie Bunnies, Earls Colne, Colchester, Essex. Suffolk Stour.

Colt Crag Angling Association. F L Brogdon, The Bungalow, Hexham, Northumberland.

Compleat Angler Fishing Club. V W Honeyball, The Cottage, Parkland School, Brassey Avenue, Hampden Park, Eastbourne. Cuckmere and Pevensey Levels. Tickets.

Comrades Angling Club. L J Wickham, 1 Hollands Lane, Henfield, Sussex.

Congleton Angling Society. M Minshull, 3 Vale Terrace, Congleton, Cheshire.

Coniston and Torver Anglers' Association. D E Lancaster, Wetherlaw, Mount Pleasant, Greenodd, Nr Ulverston, Cumbria LA12 7RF.

Cookham and District Angling Club. R H Newton, 11 St Hughes Ave, High Wycombe, Buckinghamshire. Thames. No tickets.

Coquet Angling Club. J Eagles, 5 Fontburn Crescent, Ashington, Northumberland. Fish waters of Northumbrian Federation.

Corbridge Riverside Sports Club. G K Johnson, 2 Leazes Terrace, Corbridge, Northumberland NE45 5HS. Tyne. Tickets for members' guests.

Cotswold Flyfishers. A W Smith, 95 Islip Road, Oxford. Windrush. No tickets.

Cotterstock Angling Association. Mrs Joan E Popplewell, 40 North Street, Oundle, Peterborough PE8 4AL. Nene. Tickets.

Countess Wear Salmon FA. K Carver, "Torcross", 31 Matford Avenue, Exeter. Exe. Tickets.

Cove Angling Society. D Chambers, 24 Bridge Rd, Cove, Farnborough, Hampshire. Loddon, Hart, Whitewater, Fleet Pond. No tickets.

Coventry and District Angling Association. L Massey, 88 Clifford Bridge Road, Coventry. Avon, Anker, Vyrnwy, Nene, Cherwell canals, reservoirs, etc.

Crawley Angling Society. D Wild, 247 Ifield Road, Crawley, Sussex. Lakes, streams. Some tickets.

Crawley and District Sea Anglers. C R Woolger, 70 Wakehurst Drive, Southgate, Crawley, Sussex.

Crayford Kingfishers Angling Preservation Society. E G Costen, 4 Ravensbourne Road, Crayford, Kent. Cray and lake. Season tickets.

Crediton Fly Fishing Club. R B King (Fishing Flies), 24 High Street, Crediton, Devon. 5m of trout fishing on Yeo and Creedy; tickets.

Crewe LMR sports AS.

Crewe Amalgamated Anglers. E H Ravenscroft, 9 Beech Street, Crewe, Cheshire.

Croft Angling Club. L H Dent, 11 High Street, Skegness, Lincolnshire. Steeping. Permits.

Cromer Sea Angling Club. T Riches, Lynewood Road, Cromer, Norfolk.

Cromer Inshore Sea Angling Club. J Kimp, High Street, Overstrand, Cromer, Norfolk.

Cromford Fly-Fishers Club. F W Cooper, Wishing Stone Cottage, Asker Lane, Matlock, Derbyshire DE4 5LA.

Cromwell Sea Angling Club. J Blake, 25 Newsham Drive, Grimsby, S Humberside.

Croydon Angling Society. G Hobbs, 69 Woodmere Avenue, Shirley, Croydon, Surrey. Use of water on Arun, Mole and Medway.

Croydon and District Sea Angling Association. H J Summers, 358 Purley Way, Croydon, Surrey.

Cumberland and Westmorland Angling Alliance. T Cousin, 28 Mayburgh Avenue, Penrith, Cumbria. An advisory body.

Danby Angling Club. F Farrow, 11 Dale End, Danby, Whitby, Yorkshire. Yorkshire Esk. Tickets.

Darent Valley Trout Fishers. R F Cobbett, 15 Birchwood Drive, Wilmington, Kent DA2 7NE. Darent. No tickets.

Darley Dale Fly-Fishing Club. A L Carter, Overdale House, Biggin-by-Hartington, Nr Buxton, Derbyshire.

Darlington Anglers' Club. F C Birkbeck, 11 Clareville Road, Darlington, Co Durham. Tees. Tickets.

Darlington Brown Trout Anglers' Association. B Langstaff, 5 Moffatt Close, Darlington, Co Durham. Tees.

Darlington Fly Fishers' Club. R Healey, 14 Oakdene Avenue, Darlington. Tees. Members only.

Darlington Silver Trout Anglers' Association. K Whittam, Hillcrest, 11 Hurworth Road, Hurworth Place, Hurworth, Darlington, Co Durham. Swale. Tickets; members' guests only.

Dartford and District Angling and Preservation Society. D E Reeve, 29 Berkeley Crescent, Dartford, Kent.

Dart Angling Association. G Fawcett Butler BSc, Southern Cross, 19 Shiphay Avenue, Torquay, Devon. Dart. Some tickets.

Dartmouth and District Angling Association. E R Curl, c/o Club HQ, 5 Oxford Street, Dartmouth, Devon.

Darwen Anglers. Association. J Priestley, 24 Knowlesly Road, Darwen, Lancashire. Reservoirs. Limited day tickets.

Dawlish Sea Angling Club. L Loram, 82 Churchill Avenue, Dawlish, Devon.

Deal Angling Club. Mrs Hilary Green, c/o The Marina, Deal, Kent.

Deal and Walmer Angling Association. R L Emmins, 29 The Strand, Walmer, Kent.

Deanshanger Angling Association. Eric Longhurst, Puxley, Potterspury, Towcester, Northamptonshire. Great Ouse, Members only.

Debden Angling Society. Hon sec, 15 Cleland Road, Loughton, Essex. Roding. Tickets.

Deeping St James Angling Club. J Cran, 53 Castle Drive, Northborough, Peterborough. Market Deeping Several Fishery. Tickets.

Derby Angling Association. T Hickton, 7 Crecy Close, Derby. Trent. Members only.

Derby Joint Anglers' Council. H Amos, 78 Morley Road, Chaddesden, Derbyshire.

Dereham and District Angling Club. A F Youngman, Stranton Avenue, Yaxham, near Dereham, Norfolk. Wensum. Tickets.

Derwent (Durham) Angling Association. H Walton, 13 Woodlands Road, Shotley Bridge, Co Durham. Derwent (Tyne). Members only.

Derwent (Yorks) Angling Association. J V Brett, Estates Office, Town Hall, Scarborough, Yorkshire. Derwent. Tickets.

Derwent Flyfishing Club. R A Bingley, 25 Bushey Wood Road, Totley Rise, Sheffield S17 3QA.

Devizes Angling Association. K Nisbeck, Park View Cottage, Bath Road, Devizes, Wiltshire. Kennet and Avon Canal. Tickets.

Ditherington Angling Society. G Moss, 4 Morville Road, Heath Farm Estate, Shrewsbury.

Doncaster and District Angling Association. A Slater, 52 Harcourt Close, Bessacarr, Doncaster, Yorkshire DN4 7RN. Idle. Tickets.

Dorchester (Oxon) Angling Association. K Barker, 93 Fane Drive, Berinsfield, Oxfordshire. Thame, Thames. Tickets.

Dorchester (Dorset) Angling Association. P T Blacker, 23 Kingsbere Crescent, Dorchester, Dorset. Stour, Frome, ponds; coarse fishing. Members and friends only.

Dorchester (Dorset) Fishing Club. J Fisher, Rew Hollow, Godmanchester. Nr Dorchester, Dorset. Frome (Dorset). No tickets.

Dorking and District Angling Society. F Aldred, 46 Glorymead, Dorking, Surrey. Mole. Tickets.

Douglas (IOM) and District Angling Club. G Hull, ACIS AAAI, 1 Hillcrest Grove, Birch Hill Park, Onchan, IOM.

Dover Sea Angling Association. R G Brittenden, 129 Canterbury Road, Folkestone, Kent.

Dreadnought Sea Angling Society. E F Joslin, 61 Sherrick Green Road, Willesden, London NW10.

Droitwich and District (Talbot) Angling Society. c/o Talbot Hotel, High Street, Droitwich, Worcestershire. Severn, Tickets.

Dudley Angling Society. A G Dallwood, 50 Bunns Lane, Dudley, Worcestershire. Severn.

Duke of Gloucester Angling Society. Barry Neville, 21 Lincoln Close, Woodside Green, London SE25. Medway. Members only.

Dulverton Angling Association. F J Stanton, 15 Pixton Way, Dulverton, Devon.

Dunmow and District Piscatorial Society. E G Gilbey, 11 Market Place, Dunmow, Essex.

Durham City Angling Club. C Johnston, 3 St Monica Grove, Durham. Wear, ponds. Dt for members' guests.

Durweston Angling Society.

Earl of Harrington Angling Club. J Callaghan, 12 Spencer Street, Alvaston, Derby DE2 8RW. Derwent. Tickets.

East Anglian Piscatorial Society. J March, Clarence Harbour, Clarence Road, Norwich.

Eastbourne Angling Association. The Club House, Royal Parade, Eastbourne, Sussex.

East Grinstead Angling Society. W Ford, 20 Greenstede Avenue, East Grinstead, Sussex.

East Hastings Sea Anglers' Association. C F Thomas, 17 Rymill Road, St Leonards-on-Sea, Sussex.

Ecclesbourne Flyfishers' Club. W Smith, "Wayside", Longfield Lane, Ilkeston, Derbyshire. Ecclesbourne. Strictly private.

Edenbridge Angling Society.

Egremont Angling Association. C Fisher, 69 North Road, Egremont, Cumbria. Ehen. wt.

Elan Valley Angling Association. Honorary Secretary, 2 Glangrafon, Elan Valley, Rhayader, Powys.

Ellen Angling Association. G Howard, 36 Main Street, Ellenborough, Maryport, Cumbria. Ellen. Permits.

Elm Park, Hornchurch and District Angling Society. W Holton, 4 Fairford Way, Harold Hill, Romford, Essex. Roding and lakes. Tickets.

Ellesmere Angling Club. J Woodville, 17 Swanmere Park, Ellesmere, Shropshire. Vyrnwy, lake and canal. Some tickets.

Elmore (Seal) Angling Club. L A Woods, 12 Beacon Way, Park Gate, Southampton.

Ely Highflyers Angling Club. D Jakes, 43 Station Road, Ely, Cambridgeshire. Great Ouse. Tickets.

Enton Fly-Fishers' Club. G R Porter, 62/64 Hartfield Road, Wimbledon, SW19. Trout lakes at Witley. No tickets.

Epsom Angling Society. E L Waters, 134 Miles Road, Epsom, Surrey. Mole. No tickets.

Esk and Liddle Fisheries Association. R J B Hill, Solicitor, Royal Bank of Scotland Buildings, Langholm, Dumfriesshire. Border Esk and Liddle. Tickets.

Esk Fishery Association. H B Thomas, Angrove House, Great Ayton, Teesside. Yorkshire Esk. Tickets.

Essex Fly-Fishers' Club. D A L Birrell (chairman), High Hedges, Little Waltham, Chelmsford, Essex. Reservoir. Trout. Members only.

Exeter and District Angling Association. D Beavan, 46 Hatherleigh Road, Exeter. Exe, Culm, canals, ponds, etc. Tickets.

Exmouth Sea Anglers' Association. Mrs P Moffat, 13 Lawn Road, Exmouth, Devon, EX8 1QJ.

Exmouth Deep Sea Fishing Club. J H R Lethbridge, 6 Lower King's Avenue, Exeter.

Fakenham Angling Association.

Falmouth and Penryn Angling Association. David Johns, 32 Old Hill Crescent, Falmouth, Cornwall (sea only).

Falmouth Shark and Big-Game Angling Club. W Lane, 4 Railway Cottages, Falmouth, Cornwall.

Farnborough Angling Society. J Raisin, 2 Park Road, Farnborough, Hampshire. Trout and coarse fish.

Farnham Angling Society.

Faversham Angling Club. A P Baldock, 5 Kennedy Close, Faversham, Kent. Pits. Tickets.

Felixstowe Sea Angling Association. P G Borley, 2 Oak Close, Felixstowe, Suffolk.

Ferryhill and District Angling Club. A Roxley, 60 Linden Road, West Cornforth, Co Durham. Wear, Tyne, Swale, Ure, ponds. Members only.

Filey Brig Angling Society. K C Carpenter, 18 Ash Grove, Filey YO14 9LZ, N Yorks.

Folkestone Sea Angling Association. H King, Little Mead, Brewers Hill, Sandgate, Kent.

Fordingbridge Angling Club. A Lynn, 10 Penny's Crescent, Fordingbridge, Hampshire. Avon, Stour. Members only.

Foston Fishing Club. A T Unwin, Treetops, Upper Poppleton, Yorkshire. Foston Beck. Members only.

Fowey Angling Club. D Johnson, c/o Club Headquarters, Safe Harbour, Fowey, Cornwall.

Frome and District Angling Association. B L Neale, 29 Avenue Road, Frome, Somerset. Frome. Tickets conditional.

Frome Vale Angling Club. R G Parsons, 5 Badminton Road, Kendleshire, Gloucestershire.

Frosterley Angling Club. G W Lee, Frosterley, Co Durham. Wear. No tickets.

Galgate Angling Association. Inquire R Johnson, 5 Main Road, Galgate, Lancashire. Condor. No tickets.

Game Fishers' Club. L L Jackson, 53 Frankley Beeches Road, Northfield, Birmingham. Fly-fishing on streams in Worcestershire and Welsh border. Guest permits only.

Garstang and District Angling Association. D E Irvin, Market Place, Garstang, Lancashire. Wyre. Some wt for resident holiday visitors.

Gillingham and District Angling Association. P J Rolfe, 12 Butts Mead, Shaftesbury, Dorset. Stour. Tickets.

Gipping Angling Preservation Society. George Alderson, 19 Clover Close, Chantry, Ipswich, Suffolk. Gipping. Tickets.

Glaston Manor Angling Association: R J Dickens, 36 Underwood Road, Glastonbury, Somerset. Brue. A few tickets. Apply K Hansford, 28 Bove Moor Road, Street, Somerset.

Gloucester Angling Club.

Gloucester United Anglers' Association. P Farnsworth, 10 The Butts, Newent, Gloucester. Severn. Tickets.

Goathland Angling Club. Ph. Skelton, Darnholme, Goathland, Whitby, Yorkshire.

Godalming Angling Society. R Richardson, 87 Summers Road, Farncombe, Godalming, Surrey.

Godalming and District Angling Society. A G Johnson, 86 Peper Harow Road, Godalming, Surrey. Wey and lake. Tickets.

Godmanchester Angling and Fish Preservation Society. B P Doherty, 5 Kisby Avenue, Godmanchester, Huntingdonshire. Great Ouse.

Golden Hill Club. A O Harland, Manor Lodge, 9 Woodgates Lane, North Ferriby, East Yorkshire. No tickets.

Golden Valley Fishing Club. R Hunt, 9 Bellifants, Farnborough, Bath. Boyd Brook, Frome, Avon, Axe, ponds. Tickets to members' friends only.

Goole and District Angling Association. David Whitaker, 39 Westbourne Grove, Goole, Yorkshire. Derwent. Some tickets.

Gorleston Sea Anglers. G Baker, 7 Pier Walk, Gorleston, Great Yarmouth, Norfolk.

Gosforth Anglers' Club. G H Brough, Holme Lea, Gosforth, Cumbria. Irt. Members only.

Grantham Angling Association. C E Yearle, 87 New Beacon Road, Grantham, Lincolnshire.

Great Yarmouth Gorleston and District Amalgamated Angling Association. W Platten, 1 Audley Street, Great Yarmouth, Norfolk.

Greenall Whitley Angling Association. Jack Robinson, "Rose Villa", 6 Birch Polygon, Rusholme, Manchester M14 5HX. Weaver, Dane, reservoir, lake. Some dt.

Greenwich Angling Society. A Cole, 1 Bexhill Road, London SE4.

Greet Fishing Club. H J Messer, 23 Cavendish Road East, The Park, Nottingham. Trout water on R. Greet. No tickets.

Gretna Angling Association. G Graham, 126 Currock Park Avenue, Carlisle, Cumbria. Esk, Kirtle. Tickets.

Grimsby and District Society of Anglers. B J L Todd, Wold View, Mount Pleasant, Holton-le-Clay, Lincolnshire. Pond at Cleethorpes. Tickets.

Grizedale Angling Association. W E Coates, Grizedale, Hawkshead, Ambleside, Cumbria. Grizedale Beck. Tickets.

Groe Park and Irfon AC. A Van Hees, c/o S G Thomas & Co, West Street, Builth Wells, Powys. Irfon. Tickets.

Guernsey Sea Anglers' Club. J Oakley, "Ridgeway", Point's Lane, St Andrews, Guernsey, Channel Islands.

Guernsey 30-Fathom Club. T W Rowe, Carantec, Rue du Marnis, Vale, Guernsey, Channel Islands.

Guildford Angling Society. B A Yarrow, 32 Litchfield Way, Onslow Village, Guildford, Surrey. Wey.

Hadleigh and District Angling Society. J S Hill, 18 Highlands Road, Hadleigh, Ipswich, Suffolk. Brett. No tickets.

Hailsham Angling Association. A W Bates, "Analan", Sandy Cross, Heathfield, Sussex. Cuckmere. Tickets.

Halifax Fly-Fishers' Club. L Stott, 6 Craven Court, Hopwood Lane, Halifax, Yorkshire. No water.

Halstead-Hedingham Angling Club. M Hardy, 87 Mount Pleasant, Halstead CO9 3NZ, Colne. Some tickets only.

Haltwhistle and District Angling Association. J Mason, 2 Castle Hill House, Haltwhistle, Northumberland. Tyne. Some tickets.

Hants and Sussex Alliance (inc Portsmouth, Bognor Regis, Petworth and Petersfield clubs). L G French, 27 Locarno Road, Copnor, Portsmouth PO3 5DG. Rivers, canal, lakes. Weekly ticket and some daily tickets.

Harleston, Wortwell and District Angling Club. C Saye, 20 The Common, Harleston, Norfolk. Pits. Tickets.

Harlow Angling Society. W J Pegram, Burnside, 5 The Hill, Harlow, Essex. Stort. Tickets.

Harrogate and Claro Conservative Angling Association. G Taylor, 14 Craven Street, Harrogate, Yorkshire. Ure. Tickets.

Harrogate Flyfishers' Club. J Darby Tredger, 18 St Catherine's Road, Harrogate. Water on Nidd. No Tickets.

Hartlepool and District Sea Angling Club. W Colling, 6 Wilson Street, West Hartlepool, Co Durham.

Hastings and St Leonards Sea Angling Society. G. Wall, 3 Marine Parade, Hastings, Sussex.

Hastings, Bexhill and District Freshwater Angling Association. J Gutsell, 14 Jameson Crescent, St Leonards, Sussex. Trout and coarse fisheries (good carp) Members only.

Hastings Flyfishers' Club Ltd. D Clarke and W R Beswick, 2 West Terrace, Eastbourne, Sussex. Trout fishing in reservoirs. Waiting list for membership. Daily ticket at reservoirs.

Hatfield and District Angling Society. E F Denchfield, 44 Stockbreach Road, Hatfield, Hertfordshire.

Hawes and High Abbotside Angling Association. Miss M Thwaite, Mount View, Hawes, Yorkshire. Yore. Tickets.

Haywards Heath and District Angling Society. S F Whetstone, 2 West View Cottages, Lindfield. Sussex. Ouse.

Hebden Bridge Angling Society.

Henfield and District Angling Society. Honorary Secretary, The Bungalow, Coombe House Lane, Bolney, Sussex RH17 5SG.

Hereford and District Angling Association. H Webb, 96 East Street, Hereford. Wye and Lugg. Tickets.

Herne Bay Angling Association. Hon Sec c/o HQ, 59 Central Parade, Herne Bay, Kent.

Hertfordshire Anglers' Consultative Association. E F Banfield, 14 Catham Close, St Albans, Hertfordshire.

Herts-Chiltern Anglers. Peter Frost, 28 Garden Road, Dunstable, Bedfordshire.

Hexham Anglers' Association. H Watson, 25 Beaufront Avenue, Hexham, Northumberland. Tyne. No tickets.

Higham Ferrers Angling Club. M Haynes, Elmhurst, Roland Way, Higham Ferrers, Northamptonshire.

Highflyer Fishing Club. H R Page, 35 Old School Lane, Milton, Cambridgeshire.

Hinckley and District Angling Association. G E Swarbrick, 49 Butt Lane, Hinckley, Leicestershire. Soar, Sence, Thames and Avon, canals, lakes and reservoirs. Permits.

Histon and District Angling Society. R Cooper, 236 Histon Road, Cottenham, Cambridgeshire. Old West River. Members only.

Hitchin and District Angling Association. L G Day, 14 Thatcher's End, Hitchin, Hertfordshire. Ouse, Arlesey Lake. Members only.

Holbeach and District Angling Club. S H Bowell, 67 Battlefields Lane, Holbeach, Lincolnshire.

Holland Anglers' Society. G S Mankelow, 51 Warren Lane, Holland, Oxted, Surrey. Eden (Kent). Members only.

Holmesdale Angling Society. S Banks, 1 Bessels Way, Bessels Green, Sevenoaks, Kent. Lake at Sevenoaks.

Horncastle Angling Club. F Bryan, 15 North Street, Horncastle, Lincolnshire. Pts. Tickets.

Horsham and District Angling Association. G R and L T Kempson, 11 Clarence Road, Horsham, Sussex.

Houghton and Wyton and Hemingfords Angling Society. A Rout, The Haven, Fenstanton, Huntingdonshire. Great Ouse. Daily ticket.

Houghton Bridge and District Angling Society. W G Charman, 27 South Lane, Houghton, Sussex.

Houghton Fishing Club. P K George, The Old Parsonage, Shorne, Gravesend, Kent. Test. No tickets.

Hounslow Piscatorials. P Bowden, 7 Denbigh Drive, Hayes, Middlesex. Wyrardisbury and Colne.

Hove Deep Sea Anglers. J Greenfield, Club House, Western Esplanade, Hove, Sussex.

Howden and District Angling Club.

Huddersfield Angling Association. C A Clough, 38 Holly Bank Avenue, Upper Cumberworth, Huddersfield, Yorkshire. Water on reservoirs.

Hull and District Amalgamated Angling Association. K Bone, 151 Steynberg Street, New Bridge Road, Hull, Yorkshire HD8 8NY.

Hull Rock Angling Club. S Medcalf, 237 Portobello Street, Holderness Road, Hull, Yorkshire.

Humber Sea Angling Club. J W Gennery, 66 Coronation Road, Cleethorpes, S Humberside.

Hungerford Canal Angling Association. A A Chandler, 27 Bockhampton Road, Lambourn, Newbury, Berkshire. Hungerford and K and A Canals. Tickets.

Huntingdon Angling Society. W Wallis, 8 Clayton's Way, Huntingdon. Great Ouse. Tickets.

Hutton Rudby Angling Association. B Milburn, 11 South Side, Hutton Rudby, Yarm-on-Tees, Yorkshire. Tees, Leven. Limited st.

Ilchester Angling Club. L Purchase, 28 Telis Cross, East Coker, Somerset.

Ilford and Wanstead Angling Society. H Mead, 6 Windsor Road, Ilford, Essex.

Ilford Piscatorial Society. R S Oughton, 31 Fowey Avenue, Roding Lane South, Redbridge, Ilford, Essex.

Ilfracombe and District Anglers' Association. Messrs Labbetts, 61–2 High Street, Ilfracombe.

Ilkley and District Angling Association. J A Cockerill, 31 Grange Estate, Valley Drive, Ilkley, Yorkshire. Wharfe. Tickets.

Ilminster Angling Association. Mrs S C Jobson, 25 West Crescent, Ilminster, Somerset. Isle. Tickets.

Ingatestone and Fryerning Angling Club. E B Quale, 45 Willow Green, Ingatestone, Essex.

Ingleton Angling Association. R Gowland, 86 New Village, Ingleton, via Carnforth, Lancashire. Greta (Lune). Tickets.

Ipswich Sea Angling Association. H D Ellwood, 105 Wallace Road, Ipswich, Suffolk.

Irthlingborough, Raunds and District Angling Club. C E Crawley, 20 Palmer Avenue, Irthlingborough, Northamptonshire.

Isfield and District Angling Club. Mrs Mary Inman, 24 Selby Rise, Uckfield, Sussex. Uck, Ouse and lakes.

Isis Angling Club. D A C Horsman, 9 Noredown Way, Wootton Bassett, Wiltshire. Avon, Marden, Thames, lakes. No tickets.

Isle of Wight (Freshwater) Angling Society. W Kingswell, 12 Manor Road, Lake, Sandown, IoW, PO36 9JA.

Isle of Wight Federation of Angling Clubs. R E Winship, Robreena, West Hill Road, Ryde, IoW.

Ivel Protection Association. R Hitchcock, 10 The Crescent, Beeston, Sandy, Bedfordshire. Ivel. No tickets.

Izaak Walton (Stafford) Anglers' Association. R Wilton, Brook House, Brook Lane, Brocton, Stafford. Sowe. Penk and canal.

Jersey Sea Fishing Club. HQ, 16 Broad Street, St Helier, Jersey, CI.

Jolly Anglers. R Dell OBE, Brookside, Winterbrook, Wallingford, Berkshire. Thames. Tickets.

Keighley Angling Club. L Brocklesby, 11 Eelholme View Street, Keighley, Yorks. Aire and reservoir. Tickets for reservoir only.

Kelvedon and District Angling Association. J L Joyce, 32 Glebe Crescent, Broomfield, Chelmsford, Essex. Blackwater, pits. Dt for pits only.

Kent, Bela, Winster, Leven and Duddon Fisheries Association. O R Bagot, Levens Hall, nr Kendal, Cumbria. Advisory body.

Kent (Westmorland) Angling Association. J C Parkin, 11a Blea Tarn Road, Kendal, Cumbria. Kent, Mint, Sprint and reservoir. Tickets.

Keswick Angling Association. W Ashcroft, Spring Haven, How Lane, Portinscale, Keswick, Cumbria. Greta (Cumberland) and Derwentwater. Tickets.

Kettering, Thrapston and District Angling Association. L R Garrett, 10 Naseby Road, Kettering, Northamptonshire. Nene. Tickets.

Keynsham Angling Association. B Veale, 117 Wellsway, Keynsham, Avon. Chew, Avon. Tickets.

Kibworth and District Angling Society. H Taberer, 11 Weir Road, Kibworth-Beauchamp, Leicestershire. Canal. Tickets.

Kidderminster and District Angling Association. S Lewis, 94 Coventry Street, Kidderminster, Worcestershire. Severn. Members and associates only.

Kilnsey Angling Club. J A Croft, Throstles Nest Farm, Conistone, Skipton, N Yorks. Wharfe and Skirfare. Members only.

Kingfisher Angling and Preservation Society. P D Stewart, Heathfield House, Bourne Road, Crayford, Kent.

King of French Angling Club. W E West, 31 Listowel Crescent, Clifton, Nottingham. Trent. No tickets.

King's Lynn Angling Association. G T Bear, 63 Lynn Road, Downham Market, Norfolk. Great Ouse. Tickets.

Kintbury Angling Association. Brian Culley, Bray Cottage, Kintbury, Berkshire. No tickets.

Kirkby Fleetham Angling Club. S Schofield, 1 Colstan Road, Northallerton, Yorkshire.

Kirkby Lonsdale and District Angling Association. G Clough, Keepers Cottage, Burrow, via Carnforth LA6 2RN. Lune. Tickets.

Kirkby Stephen and District Angling Association. J B Owen, 22 Market Street, Kirkby Stephen, Cumbria. Eden. Members only.

Kirkham and District Fly Fishers' Club. J H Boulton, 8 Preston Street, Kirkham, Lancashire. Reservoir. Tickets.

Knaresborough Anglers' Club. C Jesper, "Hall Mead", 20 Woodlands Drive, Harrogate, Yorkshire. Nidd. Tickets for members' friends only.

Knaresborough Piscatorials. G E Farrer, 11 Manor Orchards, Knaresborough, Yorkshire. Nidd. Tickets.

Knowle (Bristol) Angling Association. A R J Riddell, 43 Highworth Crescent, Yate, Bristol. Chew, brooks. Tickets.

Ladykirk and Norham AA. J Blythe, 14 St Cuthbert's Square, Norham, Berwick-upon-Tweed.

Lakenham Angling Club. C F Wickham, 2 Robin Hood Road, Norwich.

Lamb Angling Club. G C Mulvey, 82 Watling Street, Wilnecote, Tamworth, Staffordshire.

Lancashire Fly-Fishing Association. R Hill, 161 Blackburn Road, Accrington, Lancashire, Ribble, Hodder, Lune, Wenning, Dean Clough Reservoir. Day ticket for members' friends only.

Lancaster and District Angling Association. C T Preston, Greenacre, High Biggins, Kirkby Lonsdale, Cumbria. Lune. Tickets.

Lancing Anglers. Gilbert A Ramsey, Elinor Lodge, East Street, Lancing, Sussex.

Langley Park Angling Association. T B Fishwick, 5 West Cross Street, Langley Park, Co Durham. Water on Browney.

Langport Angling Association. Mrs E J Close, 2 Ducks Cottage, Thorney, Langport, Somerset.

Lansil Angling Association. J Clayton, Lansil Sports Club, Caton Road, Lancaster, Lancashire. Water on Lune. Tickets.

Launceston Anglers' Association. R Tomkins, 38 St Leonards Road, Lanstephan, Launceston, Cornwall. Tamar, Ottery, Kensey. Permits.

Lavington Angling Club. M Gilbert, Gable Cottage, 24 High Street, Erlestoke, nr Devizes, Wilts. Semington Brook.

Lawford Angling Society. R W Nunn, Mistley Hall Cottage, Clacton Road, Mistley, Manningtree, Essex.

Leamington Spa Angling Association. E G Archer, 9 Southway, Leamington Spa, Warwickshire. Avon and canal. Some tickets.

Leatherhead and District Angling Society. R J Boychuk, 22 Poplar Avenue, Leatherhead, Surrey. Mole, ponds. Private.

Ledbury and District Angling Association. C F Davies, The Wren, Banit Crescent, Ledbury, Herefordshire.

Leeds Angling Association. H Wigglesworth, 84 Westfield Road, Wrose, Shipley, Yorks. Private club. Swale. Members and guests only.

Leeds and District Amalgamated Society of Anglers. G Copley, Anglers Club, Becket Street, Leeds 9. Ouse and tributaries. Tickets.

Leek and Morlands Fishing Club. D White, 20 Campbell Avenue, Leek, Staffordshire. Churnet, canal.

Leicester Angling Club. V D Coles, 60 Chadwell Road, Leicester. Grand Union Canal. Tickets.

Leicester Angling Society. C F Turner, 213 Walnut Street, Leicester. Soar, Grand Union Canal. Tickets.

Leicester and District Amalgamated Society of Anglers. R Green, 52 Skampton Road, Leicester. Wreake, Nene, Eye, Soar, Grantham and Grand Union Canals. Tickets.

Leigh Angling Association. J Scotson, 26 Glover Street, Leigh, Lancashire.

Leighton Buzzard Angling Club. F Groom, Nancegollan, 29 Albany Road, Leighton Buzzard, Bedfordshire. Great Ouse, Ouzel, Claydon Lakes, pits, etc. Tickets for members' friends only.

Letchworth Angling Club. F Young, 224 Rushby Mead, Letchworth, Hertfordshire.

Leven Lower Fishery. J Lightfoot, Hill Rise, Haverthwaite. Ulverston, Cumbria. Restricted membership. No tickets.

Lewisham Piscatorials. D Bresnahan, 30 Charldane Road, New Eltham, London, SE9. Beault. No tickets.

Licensed Victuallers' Deep Sea Angling Club (South-Eastern). E D Goodwin, 15 Greenhill Bridge Road, Herne Bay, Kent. London and South: E E Doree, 1 Norfolk Court, Rustington, Sussex.

Lincoln and District Angling Association. T McCarthy, 33 Chiltern Road, Brant Road, Lincoln. Lake. Tickets.

Lincolnshire Anglers' Federation. J D McGuire, 6 Churchill Drive, Boston, Lincolnshire.

Lincolnshire Rivers Anglers' Consultative Association. J D McGuire, 6 Churchill Drive, Boston, Lincolnshire.

Linesmen Angling Club. Andrew Wilson, 30 Baker Street, London W1. Fisheries in eight counties.

Linton, Threshfield and Grassington Angling Club. N M Dennis, Low Mill Cottage, Grassington, Skipton, Yorkshire. Wharfe. Tickets.

Liskeard and District Angling Club. B G Wilson, The Bruff, Rila Mill, Callington, Cornwall. Fowey, Camel, Lynher, Seaton, Looe, Inny. Tickets.

Littleborough Angling Society. H Ingham, 86 Whalley Avenue, Littleborough, nr Rochdale, Lancashire. Canal. No tickets.

Littlehampton and District Angling Club. R Christian, Lynhay, Cherry Walk, High Salvington, Worthing, Sussex.

Littleport Angling Club. D Clarke, 41 Forehill, Ely, Cambridgeshire. Great Ouse and Lark.

Liverpool and District Anglers' Association. J Johnson, 97 Liverpool Road North, Maghull, nr Liverpool, Lancashire. River Dee. Tickets.

Llandrindod Wells Angling Association. A H Selwyn, Anglers' Depot, Llandrindod Wells, Powys. Ithon. Tickets.

Llanfair Fishing Club. Hon Sec, Llanfair-Caereinion, Powys. Banwy. Some tickets.

Llanidloes Angling Society. I Glyn Tilsley, Foundry House, Llanidloes, Powys. Severn, Clywedog, Dulas. Tickets.

London Anglers' Association. H J Wilson, 32 Stroud Green Road, Finsbury Park, London, N14 (LAA offices), or 60 Park Lane, Waltham Cross, Hertfordshire. Thames, Lee and tributaries; Hampshire

Avon, Arun, Gt Ouse, Suffolk Stour, canals, lakes, etc. Day ticket for some waters.

London Brick Co (Angling Section). R Peake, Phorpres Club, London Road, Fetton, Peterborough. Brick pits; members only.

London Catchers Club. Dave Lawrence, 57 Knightsbridge, SW1. Offers service to anglers. Tickets for many waters.

Long Eaton and District Angling Federation. D L Kent, 18 Collingwood Road, Long Eaton, Nottinghamshire. Trent. Tickets.

Long Eaton Victoria Angling Society. D L Kent, 18 Collingwood Road, Long Eaton, Notts NG10 1DR. Soar, Trent, Erewash and Cranfleet canals, ponds. Tickets.

Long Preston Angling Club. J Bowker, Pendle View, Long Preston, Skipton, N Yorks. Ribble. Tickets.

Looe and District Sea Angling Association. V Sneed, c/o Cotton's Tackle Shop, The Quay, E Looe, Cornwall.

Lostwithiel Fishing Association. S E Brewer, Avery House, Bodmin Hill, Lostwithiel, Cornwall. Water on Fowey. Tickets.

Loud and Hodder Angling Association.

Loughborough Soar Angling Society. B A Hull, 40 Chapel Street, Shepshed, nr Loughborough, Leicestershire. LE12 9AG Soar and canal. Tickets.

Louth Cawacs Angling Association. G Allison, 15 Florence Wright Avenue, Louth, Lincolnshire.

Lower Teign Fishing Association. J Michelmore, Market Street, Newton Abbot, Devon. Teign. Tickets.

Lowestoft Freshwater Angling Club. David Shreeve, 52 Highland Way, Lowestoft, Suffolk.

Lowestoft Sea Anglers. E Weaver, Waterloo Road, Lowestoft, Suffolk.

Lowestoft (South Pier) Angling Club. S G Hok, 132 Bevan Street, Lowestoft, Suffolk.

Ludlow Angling Club. A J Carter, 26 Housman Crescent, Ludlow, Shropshire. Teme. Tickets.

Luton and District Anglers' Association. J R Bird, 115 Stopsley Way, Luton, Bedfordshire. Upper Ouse, Linford Lakes. Members only.

Luton Angling Club. A G Norn, 134 Alexandra Avenue, Luton, Bedfordshire.

Lychnobite Angling Society. P Kemp, 25 Fulbourne Road, Walthamstow, London, E17.

Lydney and District Angling Club. M G Nash, 42 Templeway West, Lydney, Gloucestershire.

Lymington and District Sea Fishing Club. B Greenwood, 2 Boldre Lane, Lymington, Hampshire.

Lymm Angling Club. K J Fraser, 45 Highfield Road, Lymm, Cheshire. Lake. Tickets.

Lytellton Angling Association. E Wilkes, 31 Mostyn Rd, Stourport, Worcestershire. Severn. Tickets.

Mablethorpe, Sutton-on-Sea and District Angling Club. V A Hardy, 33 Alford Road, Sutton-on-Sea, Mablethorpe, Lincolnshire. Great Eau.

Macclesfield Amalgamated Society of Anglers. P W Nevitt, 50 Roewood Lane, Macclesfield, Cheshire.

Macclesfield Flyfishers' Club. A H Ashness, School House, Langley, nr Macclesfield, Cheshire. Dane and Clough, lakes. No tickets.

Macclesfield Victoria Angling Society. A Jackson, 8 Barton Street, Macclesfield, Cheshire. Canal. Tickets.

Maidenhead Angling Society and District Association. A Brocklebank, 39 Francis Way, Slough, SL1 5PH. Thames. Members only.

Maidstone Victory Angling and Medway Preservation Society. P Makin, 174 Brompton Farm Road, Strood, Kent. Medway. Tickets.

Maldon Angling Society. R Revill, Langford Limes, 94 Crescent Road, Heybridge, Maldon, Essex. Blackwater. No tickets.

Malton and Norton Angling Club. M Foggin, Westwood, 123 Welham Road, Norton, Malton, Yorkshire. Derwent. Tickets.

Manchester Anglers' Association. Dr P J Mellor, 126 Boothroyden Rd, Blackley, Manchester M24 4RW. Ribble and Lune. No tickets.

Manchester Federation of Anglers. David Lloyd, 10a Reddish Road, South Reddish, Stockport, Cheshire.

Mansfield and District Angling Association. M Straw, 27 King Edward Avenue, Mansfield Woodhouse, Nottinghamshire. River Devon, pits. Members only.

Mannin Angling Club. A Pennington, 10 Lhag Beg. Port Erin, I.O.M.

March and District Federation of Anglers. M H White, King William (HQ), High Street, March, Cambridgeshire. Fen waters. Tickets.

Manx Game Fishing Association. Hon Sec, 5th Floor, Victory House, Douglas, I.O.M.

March Working Men's Angling Club. H Davis, North Drive, March, Cambridgeshire. Twenty Foot. Permits.

Marconi Angling Society. Hon Sec, Marconi Athletic Social Club, Beehive Lane, Chelmsford, Essex. Canal. Tickets.

Margate Fishing Club. Hon Sec, Club HQ, Saracens Head, High Street, Margate, Kent.

Market Harborough and District Society of Anglers. J W Ashton, 16 Connaught Road, Market Harborough, Leicestershire. Canal. Tickets.

Marlbrough and District Angling Association. M Ellis, 8 South View, Marlborough, Wiltshire. Kennet and Avon Canal. Tickets limited.

Marlow and District Angling Association. F Warwick, 2 Elizabeth Road, Marlow, Buckinghamshire. Thames. No tickets.

Marsden Star Angling Society.

Masham Angling Club. W P Todd, Greenways, Fearby Road, Masham, Yorkshire.

Matlock Angling Club.

Melton Mowbray Society of Anglers. R W Benskin, 24 Chetwynd Drive, Melton Mowbray, Leicestershire. Eye and Wreake (Trent). Tickets.

Mere Angling Club (Derwent Sector). W H Smith, 1 Cecil Court, Ryndleside, Scarborough, Yorkshire. No tickets.

Middlewich Angling Society. J F Hulme, 20 Hightown, Middlewich, Cheshire.

Midland Angling Society. W Oldham, 57 Albury Drive, Aspley Estate, Nottingham. Trent.

Midland Flyfishers. A D Clark, 5 Deansway, Worcester WR1 2JG. Onny, Welsh Dee. Tickets.

Mid-Northants Trout Fishers' Association. T Broughton, 52 Bush Hill, Northampton.

Millhouse Beck Fishing Club. D J Broady, Ings Lane, Dunswell, Hull, Yorkshire. Beck. Members only.

Millom and District Angling Association. D Myers, 29 Bowness Road, Millom, Cumbria. Members only.

Milnthorpe Angling Association. A R Park, Hawkshead House, Priest Hutton, Carnforth, Cumbria LA6 1JP. Bela. No tickets.

Minehead Sea Angling Club. R Tudball, The Beacon, Beacon Road, Minehead, Somerset.

Monsal Dale Fishery. C A Roose, Estate Office, Edensor, Bakewell, Derbyshire. Wye (Trent). No tickets.

Monmouth and District Angling Society. Fred Hughes, Brook Cottage, Monmouth. Monnow.

Montgomeryshire Angling Association. Stuart J Harding, 29 Rhoslan, Guilsfield, Welshpool, Powys. Severn and tributaries, canal, lakes. Tickets.

Moor Hall and Belhus Angling Society. M Tilbrook, 46 Mill Road, Aveley, Essex. Stour, Ham River, pits. No tickets.

Morecambe Bay Angling Club. J Smith, 17 Barnes Road, Morecambe, Lancashire.

Moss Side Social AS. A Jones, 10 Purley Avenue, Northenden, Manchester 22. Dee. Members only. Bosley Reservoir. Tickets.

Mounts Bay Angling Society. D Cains, 29 Treassowe Road, Penzance, Cornwall.

Myddelton Angling Club. J B Harland, Barradene, 57 Grove Road, Ilkley, Yorkshire. Wharfe. Tickets.

Nantwich Angling Society. J Haighton, The Bungalow, Worleston Road, Reaseheath, Nantwich, Cheshire. Weaver. No dt.

NETA Angling Society. F Rye, 42 Northfield Road, Laleham, Middlesex.

Newark and District Piscatorial Federation. J N Garland, 58 Riverside Road, Newark, Nottinghamshire. Newark Dyke. Tickets.

Newbrough and Fourstones Angling Association. C Telford, Newbrough Hall Lodge, Newbrough, Fourstones, Hexham, Northumberland. S Tyne.

Newbury and District Angling Association. T A Collins, 43 Valley Road, Newbury, Berkshire. Kennet, canal. No tickets.

Newhaven Deep Sea, Anglers' Club. D F Wood, Lakri, 56 Slindon Avenue, Peacehaven, Sussex.

Newport Pagnell Fishing Association. F J Read, 19 Chicheley Street, Newport Pagnell, Buckinghamshire. Great Ouse, gravel pits. Tickets.

Newquay Angling Association. J Waller, 3 Higher Tower Road, Newquay, Cornwall.

New Studio Angling Society. W Dexter, 62 Battersby Road, London, SE6. Medway. Members only.

Newton Abbot Fishing Association. P Goss, Flat 1, 3 Orchard Park, Dartington, nr Totnes, Devon. Lakes. St only.

Nidderdale Angling Club. Mrs J Dalton, Bracken House, Princess Road, Ripon, N Yorks. Nidd. Tickets.

Northallerton and District Angling Club. G Easby, 24 Quaker Lane, Northallerton, Yorkshire. Swale. Tickets.

Northampton Nene Angling Club. E M Love, 103 Charnwood Avenue, Weston Favell, Northampton. Ouse, Nene. Tickets.

North Buckinghamshire Angling Association. F Mayo, 145 Church Street, Bletchley, Buckinghamshire.

Northern Anglers' Association. General Secretary: G Wilson, 11 Guildford Ave, Chorley, Lancashire. Ribble, Dee, canals, etc. Tickets.

Northern AA (Preston Centre). G Jones, 1 Carnarvon Road, Preston, Lancashire. Ribble and tributaries. Tickets.

North Oxford Angling Society. G E Brown, 72 Islip Road, Oxford. Water north of Oxford. No tickets.

North Somerset Association of Anglers (Embracing old Highbridge, Clevedon and Weston-super-Mare clubs). M White, 26 Walrow Road, Highbridge. Axe, Brue, drains and ponds. Tickets.

North Walsham Kingfishers. P Hooker, 21 Fairview Road, North Walsham. Lake. Dt.

Northumbrian Anglers' Federation. C Wade, Glen-Turret, 2 Ridge Villas, Bedlington, Northumberland. Salmon and trout water on Coquet, Tyne. Tickets.

North-West Durham Angling Association. J W Geddes, Snook Acres Farm, Witton Gilbert, Durham DH7 6TQ. Tyne & Wear. Trout reservoirs. Tickets.

Northwich and District Angling Association. E Moore, Struma, Gadbrook Road, Rudheath, Northwich, Cheshire. Weaver. Tickets.

Norwich and District Angling Club. J C Braithwaite, 4 Cranage Road, Mansfield Lane, Norwich. Thurne, Bure, Broads. Tickets.

Norwich Sea Anglers. D Mundford, 68 Heath Road, Norwich.

Norwich City Supporters' Angling Club. R Stolworthy, 595 Earlham Road, Earlham, Norwich, Norfolk. Broads. Members only.

Nottingham Anglers' Association. Eric Collin, 224 Radford Boulevard, Nottingham, NG5 3E8. Trent. Tickets.

Nottingham and District Anglers' Joint Council. N A Cade, 82 Broxtowe Lane, Nottingham, NG8 5NJ.

Nottingham and District Federation of Angling Societies. W Beeshaw, 17 Spring Green, Clifton Estate, Nottingham. For matches contact Mrs M Whitmore, 47 Criftin Road, Nottingham. Trent. Tickets.

Nottingham Fly Fishers' Club. H J Messer, 23 Cavendish Road E, The Park, Nottingham. Lakes and river. No tickets.

Nottingham Piscatorial Society.

Oakham Angling Society. R Taylor, 8 Beech Road, Oakham, Rutland. Welland, Glen canal and ponds. No tickets.

Offord and Buckden Fishing Society. A Plumb, 8 Latin Close, Offord Cluny. Huntingdonshire Great Ouse, Limited tickets.

Oldham United Anglers' Society. A Benney, 2 Chelwood Street, Manchester 9. Reservoirs. Tickets.

Old Windsor Angling Club. A F Heather, 8 Newton Lane, Old Windsor, Berks. Thames. Tickets.

Ongar and District Angling Society. D F How, 85 Moulsham Lodge Estate, Chelmsford, Essex. Roding and pit. Members only.

Orpington and District Angling Association. R Bright, 133 The Drive, Bexley, Kent. Lakes. No tickets.

Oswestry Angling Society. W Jones, 55 Laburnum Drive, Oswestry, Salop. Tickets for holiday visitors.

Otley Angling Club (Trout Preserves). D B Hall, 20 The Gills, Carr Bank, Otley, Yorkshire. Wharfe. Members only.

Ottermouth Trout Association. W K H Coxe, Council Chambers, Budleigh Salterton, Devon.

Oulton Broad Piscatorial Society. O Lay, 205 Victoria Road, Oulton Broad, near Lowestoft, Suffolk.

Oundle Angling Association. G Colver, 48 Springfield Road, Oundle, Northamptonshire. Nene. Members only.

Ouse Angling Preservation Society. Dr J L Cotton, Down End, Kingston Road, Lewes, Sussex. Sussex Ouse. Limited season tickets.

Over and Swavesey Angling Society. M D Cook, 70 High Street, Over, Cambridgeshire. Great Ouse. Members only.

Oxford Alliance Angling Society. G Wilkinson, 54 Evans Road, Eynsham, Oxfordshire. Thames. Tickets for members' friends.

Oxford and District Anglers' Association. F Jones, 20 Merlin Road, Littlemore, Oxford.

Paignton Sea Anglers' Association. C Holman, 61a Higher Polsham Road, Paignton, Devon.

Palmers Green Angling Society. B Bailey, 7 College Court, Cheshunt, Herts. EN8 9NJ. New River, Mimram, Avon, and lake.

Pangbourne and Whitchurch District Fishing Club. Mrs Lusted, 74 Radstock Road, Reading, Berkshire.

Peel and Dist Angling Association. W Clagne, West View, Peel, IOM.

Penrith Angling Association. R F Allinson, 7 Scaws Drive, Penrith, Cumbria. Eden, Eamont, Petterill (Eden), and Lowther. Tickets.

Penshurst Angling Society. M Mills, 3 Montgomery Road, Tunbridge Wells, Kent. Medway and Eden (Kent). No tickets.

Peper Harow Flyfishers' Club. Miss M E Hide, Tanglewood, Mouse Mill Lane, Milford, Nr Godalming, Surrey. Private club with trout water on Wey and two ponds; rods limited.

Peterborough and District Angling Association. W Yates, 75 Lawn Avenue, Dogsthorpe, Peterborough. Nene.

Peterborough Jolly Anglers' Society. C Graves, 8 Saxon Road, Peterborough.

Petersfield and District Angling Club. G A McKee, 25 North Lane, Buriton, Petersfield, Hampshire. Rother. No tickets.

Petworth Angling Club. D A Pugh, 1 Station Road, Petworth, Sussex. Rother, Chichester Canal. Some tickets.

Petworth, Bognor and Chichester Amalgamated Anglers. A W Pascoe, 53 Wesley Lane, Copnor, Portsmouth. Western Rother. Tickets.

Pewsey Angling Club. B R Euston, 86 Broadfields, Pewsey, Wiltshire. K & A Canal. Tickets.

Pickering Fishery Association. C Hardy, 3 Westbourne Grove, Pickering, Yorkshire. Pickering Beck, Costa Beck, Oxfolds Beck and trout lake; members only, but hon secretary will help visitors.

Piscatorial Society. R A A Moore, 38 Grosvenor Road, Petts Wood, Kent. Itchen, Lambourn, Kennet and Wylye. No tickets.

Plowden Club. R H P Kidson, Westgate, 1 Westland Avenue, Wolverhampton. Onny. Private.

Plymouth and District Freshwater Angling Association. Hon Sec, Spring Cottage, Hemeradon, Plympton, Devon. Plym. Members only.

Plymouth Federation Sea Angling Club. Roy Drew, Sea Angling Centre, Vauxhall Quay, Plymouth.

Plymouth Sea Angling Club. Allen Higginson, Sea Angling Centre, Vauxhall Quay, Plymouth, Devon.

Poole Dolphin Sea Angling Club. Mrs I Wright, 9 Buckland Grove, Highcliffe, Christchurch, Dorset.

Portsmouth and District Angling Society. L G French, 27 Locarno Road, Copnor, Portsmouth, Hampshire. Trout and coarse fishing. Tickets.

Portsmouth Services Fly Fishing Association. Surgeon Captain J W Walker, OBE, Royal Naval Hospital, Haslar, Portsmouth.

Potter Heigham and District Angling Club. W Platten, 1 Audley Street, Great Yarmouth, Norfolk.

Preesall Angling Club. C Rowe, 24 Sandy Lane, Preesall, Lancashire. Wyre. Members only.

Prestwood and District Angling Club. A G Hall, 5 Orchard Close, Wendover, Buckinghamshire.

Pride of Derby Angling Association. A Miller, 16 Mercia Drive, Willington, Derby. Trent. Members only. Waiting list.

Prince Albert Angling Society. C Sparkes, High Lodge, Upton, Macclesfield, Cheshire. Rivers, streams, lakes, pools.

Pulborough Angling Society. W H Dean, 7 Rivermead, Pulborough, Sussex. Arun.

Quorn Angling Society. W Boyd, 28 Beaumont Road, Barrow-on-Soar, Leicestershire. Soar, canal. Tickets.

Radcot Angling and Preservation Club. C R Neville, Clanville House, Bampton Road, Clanfield, Oxfordshire. Thames. Tickets.

Ramsey Angling Club. J Hall, Martrooan; Brookfield Ave, Ramsey, Isle of Man.

Reading and District Angling Association. F Newman, 907a Oxford Road, Reading. Kennet. No tickets.

Redditch Angling Club. G W Blundell, 99 The Meadway, Redditch, Worcestershire B97 5AE. Avon. Tickets.

Redditch and District Anglers' Federation. C Wright, 16 Cyprus Avenue, Ashwood Bank, Redditch, Worcestershire.

Red Spinner Angling Society. Honorary Secretary. Brook House, Woolhampton, Berkshire. Evenlode, Stour (Dorset), Ebble, Hampshire Avon, Cheshunt Reservoir, Bearwood Lake. Members only.

Remenham Angling Society. B R Hughes, 11 St Mary's Close, Henley-on-Thames, Oxfordshire. Thames. Tickets.

Retford and District Angling Association. H Oxby, 104 Moorgate, Retford, Nottinghamshire. Chesterfield Canal. Tickets.

Rhayader Angling Association. G H Roberts, Belmullet, Rhayader, Powys. Wye, Marteg and lake.

Ribble and Wyre Fishing Association. G Jones, 1 Carnarvon Road, Preston, Lancashire. Tickets.

Richmond (Yorks) and District Angling Society. J Legge, 9 St John's Road, Hipswell, Catterick Garrison, N Yorkshire. Swale. Tickets.

Ringwood and District Anglers' Association. M D Winslade, 87 Lake Road, Verwood, Dorset.

Ripley and District Angling Club. R Turner, 2a Argyll Road, Ripley, Derbyshire. Amber, reservoirs. Tickets.

Ripon Angling Club. A R Trees, 13 Skellfield Terrace, Ripon, Yorkshire. Yore, Laver, Skell, reservoir. Tickets.

Ripon Piscatorials. P Godden, 3 Oak Road, Ripon, Yorkshire. Yore. Tickets.

Ripponden Fly-Fishers. H Hamer, The Hollies, Greetland, Halifax, Yorkshire. Reservoir.

River Glaven Fishery Association. T G Bird, Newgate Green, Cley, Holt, Norfolk. Trout fishing in Glaven.

Rochdale and District Angling Society.

Rochdale Walton Angling Society. D Gent, 6 Alpine Drive, Milnrow, Near Rochdale.

Ross-on-Wye Angling Club. V R Hepburn, 23 Claytons Bridstow, Ross-on-Wye. Wye. Tickets.

Rother Angling Club. C Boxall, 4 Half moon Cottages, Petersfield Road, Midhurst, Sussex. Western Rother. Tickets.

Rother Fishery Association. P T Hyland, 151a Mount Pleasant Road, Hastings, Sussex. Rother. Dt.

Rotherham and District Limited Anglers' Federation. F Dickens, 18 Burns Road, Herringthorpe, Rotherham, Yorkshire.

Rowley and District Angling Society. H F Hambridge, 29 Hollydale Road, Rowley Regis, Warley, Worcestershire. Severn. No tickets.

Royal Ramsgate Invicta Angling Association. B A Kirkaldie, 67 Boundary Road, Ramsgate, Kent.

Royal Tunbridge Wells Angling Society. Clifford C Lupini, 25 The Drive, Hedge Barton, Fordcombe, Kent. Rother, Teise, Medway. No tickets except to members.

Rugby Federation of Anglers. Mrs O Cave, 165 Alwyn Road, Bilton, Rugby. Avon, canals. Permits.

Rugeley and Brereton Angling Society. S J Cubley, 141b Wolseley Road, Rugeley, Staffordshire.

Rushden and Higham Ferrers Angling Association. Enquiries to Jack Leach, Anglers Depot, Rushden, Northants.

Ryburn Angling Society. L Kitching, 44 Sellerdale Avenue, Wyke, Bradford, Yorkshire. Ouse. Tickets.

Rye and District Angling Society. J Fiddimore, Iden Boarding Kennels, Coldharbour Lane, Iden, Rye, Sussex. Rother. Tickets.

Ryedale Angling Club. H M V Wright, Rose Cottage, Lund, Driffield, Yorkshire. Rye. Members only.

Sabrina Angling Club. W G Smart, Sunny Hill, Lyth Bank, Bayston Hill, Shrewsbury. Severn and Roden. Members only.

St Helens Angling Association. J Powell, 49 Eskdale Avenue, St Helens, Lancashire. Welsh Dee, canal, lakes. Limited weekly tickets.

St Ives and District Fish Preservation and Angling Society. P Keepin, 2 New Road, St Ives, Huntingdon, Cambs. Great Ouse. Tickets.

St Leonards Sea Anglers. HQ, 16 Grand Parade, St Leonards, Sussex.

St Mawgan Angling Club. G Booker, St John's Lanherne, St Mawgan, Newquay, Cornwall. River Menalhyl.

St Michael's Angling Association. A J Moss, West Bungalow, St Michael's, Preston, Lancashire. Wyre.

St Neots and District Angling Society. S E Smith, 10 River Terrace, St Neots, Huntingdonshire. Great Ouse. Tickets.

Salcombe and District Sea Anglers' Association. M Durrans, Quay House, Union Street, Salcombe, Devon.

Salisbury and District Angling Club. G W Tedd, Yarmley Lane, Winterslow, Salisbury, Wiltshire. Avon, Bourne, Nadder, pits. Some tickets.

Salopian Fly Fishing Association. Donald Jones, 56 Wrekin View, Madley, Shropshire.

Saltaire Angling Association. Wm Troman, 10 Maddocks Street, Shipley, Yorkshire. Wharfe and Aire. Tickets.

Saltburn and District Sea Anglers' Association. Mrs E M Vickery, 3 Wardsman Crescent, Redcar, Yorkshire.

Sandgate Sea Angling Society. R J Piddock, "Kerry Vale", West Street, New Romney, Kent.

Sandown and Lake Angling Society. Mrs V Withers, 74 Station Avenue, Sandown, Isle of Wight.

Sandwich and District Angling Association.

Sawbridgeworth Angling Society. R Edwards, 41 Lawrence Avenue, Sawbridgeworth, Hertfordshire, Stort. Tickets.

Scarborough Boat Angling Club. J A Martin, 26 Ling Hill, Newby, Scarborough.

Scarborough Mere Angling Club. W Scott, Cemetery Lodge, 30 Dean Road, Scarborough, Yorkshire.

Scarborough Rock Anglers. H Dobson, 1 Uplands Avenue, East Ayton, near Scarborough, Yorkshire.

Scunthorpe and District Angling Association. P Gilliat, 15 Crowdland Avenue, Scunthorpe, Lincolnshire.

Seabrook Sea Anglers' Association. R Perrin, 74 Horn Street, Hythe, Kent.

Seaford Angling Club. Mrs I Hopkins, "Alaska", 28 Cinque Ports Way, Seaford, Sussex. Freshwater section: L Tucknott, 77 Stafford Road, Seaford.

Seaham Sea Angling Club. K B Fox, 41 Burnhall Drive, Seaham, Co Durham.

Sedbergh and District Angling Association. J P Lowis, Yarlside, Sedbergh, Yorkshire. Trout water on Lune. Tickets.

Selsey Tope Fishers Specimen Club. R G Horrod, 28 Beach Road, Selsey, Sussex.

Services Dry Fly Fishing Association (Salisbury Plain Area). Major D H Scarfe, Hon Sec SFFA, Airfield Camp, Netheravon, Salisbury, Wilts. Avon. Private.

Settle Anglers' Association. M G Riley, Rock House, Giggleswick, Settle, Yorkshire. Ribble. Tickets.

Seven Angling Club. P Stansfield, Sun Seven, Sinnington, Yorkshire. Seven. Members only.

Shanklin Angling Society. T Heath, 17 Hope Road, Shanklin, Isle of Wight.

Sheffield Amalgamated Anglers' Society. A D Baynes, Lansdowne Hotel, Lansdowne Road, Sheffield 1. Trent and tributaries, canals, etc. Permits.

Sheffield and District Anglers' Association. J W Taylor, 12 West Lane, Aughton, near Swallownest, Sheffield. Trent and tributaries, canals, etc. Permits.

Shefford and District Angling Association. J Anderson, 44 Ampthill Road, Shefford, Bedfordshire.

Sheringham Sea Angling Club. R Sitters, Holway Road, Sheringham, Norfolk.

Shiplake and Binfield Heath Fishing Club. K Willmott, 35 Albany Road, Reading, Berks., Thames. Members only.

Shipston-on-Stour and District Angling Club. E Draper, 37 Station Road, Shipston-on-Stour, Warwickshire.

Shrewsbury Angling Society. D Clarke, 5 Albert Street, Castlefields, Shrewbsury, Salop.

Shropshire Union Canal Association. F A Allwood, 73 Church Street, Leigh, Lancashire. Canal. Permits.

Sidmouth Sea Angling Club. A C Thorne, 25 Coleridge Road, Ottery St May, Devon.

Sinnington Angling Club. J D Wattersley, 2 Willow Rise, Kirkby Moorside, N Yorks. Seven. Occasional tickets.

Sittingbourne Angling Club. C Brown, 5 Sunnybanks, Murston, Sittingbourne, Kent. Pits. Dt (restricted).

Skegness Angling Association. L H Dent, 11 High Street, Skegness, Lincolnshire.

Skegness Sea Angling Club. S Kinning, Everingtons Lane, Skegness.

Skerton and Morecambe Angling Society. C Boswell, 16 Slyne Road, Skerton, Lancashire.

Skipton Angling Association. J W Preston, Hill Crest, Beech Hill Road, Carleton, Skipton, Yorkshire BD23 3EN. Aire. Tickets.

Slaithwaite and District Angling Club. A Bamforth, 43 Binn Road, Marsden, near Huddersfield, Yorkshire. Trent, Rye, canals and reservoirs, etc. Tickets.

Somerfords Fishing Association. M J Stoodley, The Old Orchard, Lower Stanton Street, Quinton, Chippenham, Wilts. Frome, Loddon. Tickets to members' friends only.

South Coast Sea Angling Association. R G Horrod, 28 Beach Road, Selsey, Sussex.

South Molton Angling Club. Inquire Thompson's (tackleist), The Square, South Molton. Tickets for Taw, Mole.

Southampton Piscatorial Society. W I Gibbs, 4 Deacon Close, Bitterne, Southampton. Dorset Stour. No tickets.

Southampton Sea Angling Club. R Trent, 49 Lytham Road, Bitterne Park, Southampton SO2 2BW.

Southend Amateur Angling Society. G Kirby, 25 The Meads, Vange, Pitsea, Essex.

Southern (IOM) Angling Club. A A Kelly, 19 Seafield Ave, Port St Mary, IOM.

Southern Counties Angling Federation (31 member clubs). Douglas Richardson, 117–121 Rose Green Road, Rose Green, Bognor Regis, Sussex.

Southsea Sea Angling Club. 42 Granada Road, Southsea, Hampshire.

South Tyne Angling Association. J O Moore, 24 Struther Close, Haydon Bridge, Northumberland. S Tyne. Tickets to local residents only.

Spalding Angling Association. H E Parkinson, 76 St Thomas Road, Spalding, Lincolnshire. Glen (Welland). Tickets.

Spilsby Angling Association. G Matthews, 57 Ancaster Avenue, Spilsby, Lincolnshire.

Staines Angling Society. G H Brown, 134 Page Road, Bedfont, Middlesex.

Stalbridge Angling Association. W Steward, 27 Grosvenor Road, Stalbridge, Dorset.

Stamford Welland Angling Association.

Stanhope Angling Association. J J Lee, 1 Eastcroft, Stanhope, Co Durham. Wear. Tickets.

Stapleton Angling Association. F Ives, 4 Frome Terrace, Stapleton, Bristol. Avon, Chew, Frome.

Staveley and District Angling Association. D A Taylor, 18 Rawes Garth, Staveley, Cumbria. Kent, Gowan, lake. Tickets.

Stevenage Angling Society. W J Lewis, 54 Stonycroft, Stevenage, Hertfordshire. No water.

Steyning and District Angling Club. E G Spence, 42 Undermill Road, Upper Beeding, Sussex. Adur. Tickets.

Stockport Waltonians' Angling Society.

Stockton Angling Association. R Corner, 120 Station Road, Billingham, Cleveland. Tees. No tickets.

Stoke City and District Anglers' Association. P Johansen, 31 East Crescent, Sneyd Green, Stoke-on-Trent, Staffordshire. Canal.

Stokesley Angling Club. K W Foggin, 6 Busby Lane, Kirby in Cleveland, Stokesley, Yorkshire.

Stoke-sub-Hamdon Angling Association. M Prescott, Homemead, Rimpton Road, Marston Magna, Yeovil, Somerset. Parret. Members only.

Stony Stratford Angling Club. T R Valentine, 34 Mallets Close, Stony Stratford, Wolverton, Buckinghamshire.

Stour Fishery Association. L G Holtom, Barton Mill, Canterbury. Kentish Stour. No tickets.

Stowe Angling Club. C Hawkins, Homelea, Dadford, Buckingham MK18 5JX.

Stowmarket and District Angling Association. J Eade, 37 Windermere Road, Stowmarket, Suffolk.

Sturminster and Hinton Angling Association. T J Caines, Coombe Gate, The Bridge, Sturminster Newton, Dorset. Stour. Restricted permits.

Sudbury and District Angling Society. W T Gabbey, 13 Lambert Drive, Acton, Sudbury, Suffolk. Stour. Tickets.

Suffolk Fly Fishers' Club. J Bird, 27 Norbury Road, Ipswich.

Sussex County Angling Association. George Jenner, 31 Weald Close, Hurstpierpoint, Sussex.

Sussex Piscatorial Society. D G Ham, 5 Bavant Road, Brighton, Sussex. Ponds and lakes. Tickets for members' friends only.

Sutton Coldfield Angling Society. E C Curnock, 2 Homestead Drive, Sutton Coldfield, Warwickshire. Lakes. No tickets.

Swaffham Angling Club. Honorary Secretary, 30 Kings Street, Swaffham, Norfolk and Trout lake. St.

Swanage and District Angling Club. S J Mason, 8 Ancaster Road, Swanage, Dorset.

Swindon Golden Carp Angling Association. K Hale, 11 Elmina Road, Swindon, Wiltshire. K and A Canal. Tickets.

Tadcaster Angling and Preservation Society. D Wilkinson, 10 Sandfield Terrace, Tadcaster, Yorkshire. Wharfe. Tickets.

Talbot Angling Society. R W Griffin, 11 St Richards Gardens, Droitwich Spa, Worcestershire. Severn. Tickets.

Tamworth Working Men's Club. M Stokeheld, 14 Bridge Street, Amington, near Tamworth, Staffordshire. Tickets.

Tanfield Angling Club. J Whitfield, 7 King Street, Mirfield, W Yorks WF14 8AP. Tickets to guests of members only.

Tarporley Angling Club. R W Cross, 25 Burton Avenue, Tarporley, Cheshire. Oulton Mill Pool. Tickets.

Taunton Angling Association.

Taunton Fly-Fishing Club. J S Hill, 21 Manor Road, Taunton, Somerset.

Tavy, Walkham and Plym Fishing Club. D F S Giles, "Woodcote", Crapstone, Yelverton, Devon. Tickets.

Taw Fishing Club. A R Smith, Rathlin Lympstone, near Exmouth, Devon. Taw. Restricted tickets.

Tebay and District Angling Club. H Riley, White Cross House, Tebay, via Penrith, Cumbria. Lune. Tickets.

Teignmouth Sea Angling Society. Mrs R Treacher, 26 Deer Park Avenue, Teignmouth, Devon.

Teise Anglers' and Owners' Association. M E Sutton, 2 Marle Place Cottages, Brenchley, Kent. Teise. Tickets.

Tenbury Fishing Association. J Weston, Berrington Mill, Tenbury, Worcestershire. Teme. Limited tickets.

Tenterden and District Angling Preservation Association. N E Sharp, 123 High Street, Tenterden, Kent. Rother. No day or period tickets. Membership covers Rother Fishing Association waters.

Test and Itchen Fishing Association. Mrs M F Baring, Well House, Malshanger Green, Basingstoke, Hampshire. Register compiled of rods to let; apply Honorary Secretary.

Tewin Fly-Fishing Club. K F Atkins, 9 Warren Way, Digswell, Welwyn, Hertfordshire. Mimram. Members only.

Tewkesbury Angling Association. R A Smith, 10 Tretawn Gardens, Newtown, Tewkesbury. Severn. Tickets.

Thames Angling Preservation Society. A E Hodges, The Pines, 32 Tile Kiln Lane, Bexley, Kent. (Crayford 25575). Voluntary body concerned with fishery improvement.

Thatcham Angling Association. R Strange, 134 Park Avenue, Thatcham, Berkshire. Kennet. No tickets.

Thirsk Angling Club. R W Stephenson, 76 New Estate, Norby, Thirsk, Yorkshire. Cod Beck, Thirsk and Swale. Tickets.

Thornaby Angling Association. A G Butler, Melsonby Grove, Hartburn, Stockton-on-Tees, Cleveland TS18 5PF. Tees, Eden, Swale, Ure. Members only.

Thurrock Angling Club. D Nutt, 94 Eriff Drive, South Ockendon, Essex. Lakes. No tickets.

Tisbury Angling Club. P Lever, 1 Maypole Bungalow, Ansty, Tisbury, Wiltshire. Nadder. Tickets to members' friends only.

Tiverton Fly Fishing Club. H H Lewis, 2 New Place, Bakers Hill, Tiverton, Devon. Exe. Limited tickets.

Todmorden Angling Society. D Howorth, 42 Hallroyd Crescent, Todmorden, Lancashire.

Tonbridge Angling and Fish Preservation Society. A S Wolfe, 59 Hunt Road, Tonbridge, Kent. Medway. Day tickets (limited).

Torbay Association of Sea Anglers. J C Stevenson, 48 Padacre Road, Torquay.

Torquay Sea Anglers' Association. C F Finch, 14 Clifton Road, Paignton.

Torridge Fly Fishing Club. F J Witt, 35 Fore Street, Northam, nr Bideford, Devon. Reservoirs.

Towcester and District Angling Association. P Kimbell, 53 Newcombe Road, Northampton. Tove. No tickets.

Tring Anglers. J A Smith, 67 Lower Icknield Way, Marsworth, Tring, Hertfordshire. Grand Union Canal. Tickets.

Twickenham Piscatorial Society. C Etherington, 49 Muswell Park Gardens, Hounslow, Middlesex. Kennet, Thame, pits. Tickets.

Two Mills Flyfishers' Club. J V Borthwick, Mills Platt, Box Hill, Chippenham, Wiltshire SN14 9EZ. By Brook. No tickets.

Twyford Angling Club. G L Addy, 16a Woods Road, Caversham, Reading, Berkshire. Thames. No tickets.

Ulverston Angling Association. H B Whittam, 29 Lyndhurst Road, Ulverston, Cumbria. Lakes, becks and canal. Tickets.

Upper Alde and Ore Angling Club. R C Foster, Maltings Farm, Aldham, Ipswich, Suffolk. Alde. Trout tickets.

Upper Coquet Angling Club. A C Dixon, 7 Douro Terrace, Sunderland. Coquet. No tickets.

Upper Culm Fishing Association. T A Blackhore, 'Sunset', Clayhidon, Cullompton, Devon. Culm. Tickets.

Upper Tanat Fishing Club. George Lewis, c/o Crampton Pym and Lewis, The Poplars, Willow Street, Oswestry, Shropshire. Tanat. No tickets.

Upper Teign Fishing Association. A J Price, Gibbons Meadow, Chagford, Newton Abbot, Devon TQ13 8DS,. Teign. Tickets.

Upper Weardale Angling Association. G Hughes, Golden Lion, St John's Chapel, Bishop Auckland, Co Durham. Wear. Tickets.

Upton-on-Severn Angling Association. R Tainton, 136 Poolbrook Road, Malvern, Worcs.

Uttoxeter Angling Association. I E Davies, The Coppice, Sunnyside Road, Uttoxeter, Staffordshire. Dove.

Vectis Boating and Fishing Club. M T Sawyer, 27 Salters Road, Ryde, Isle of Wight.

Ventnor Angling Club. Mrs O Spanner, Hillhurst, Mitchell Avenue, Ventnor, Isle of Wight.

Wadebridge Angling Association. E J Renals, Coppins, Whitebrook Close, Wadebridge, Cornwall.

Walton-on-the-Naze Sea Angling Club. T Chalk, c/o Metcalfes, 15 Newgate Street, Walton-on-the-Naze, Essex CO14 8TD.

Walton-on-Thames Angling Society. A C Wyatt, 12 Rivermead Close, New Haw, Weybridge, Surrey. Mole, lake. No tickets.

Wangye Angling Society. N Smith, 7 Sherwood Road, Barkingside, Ilford, Essex.

Wansbeck Angling Association. D J Bell, 9 Bilton's Court, off Newgate Street, Morpeth, Northumberland. Wansbeck. Members only.

Wansford, Yarwell, Nassington and District Angling Club. C W J Howes, 43 Elton Road, Stibbington, Wansford, Peterborough.

Wareham and District Angling Society. E J Kendall, Cypress Ridge, Wareham, Dorset. Frome, Piddle. No tickets.

Warmington Angling Club. I G W Brudenell, 10 Church Street, Warmington, Peterborough PE8 1TE. No tickets.

Warminster and District Angling Club. D M Vickers, 113 Westleigh, Warminster, Wilts. Wylye, lakes. No tickets.

Warrington Anglers' Association. J S Jackson, 23 Nora Street, Warrington, Lancashire. Dee, Severn and tributaries, Ribble, Dane, canal, lakes, etc. Members only.

Watchet FC. c/o The Gardeners Arms, Bishops Lydeard, Taunton, Somerset.

Wath Brow and Ennerdale Angling Association. D F Whelan, 11 Crossing Close, Cleator Moor, Cumberland. Ehen. Tickets.

Watford Piscators. P J Lambourne, 8 St James Road, Watford, Hertfordshire. Gade, canal, lakes.

Wellingborough and District Nene Angling Club. D Kelly, 21 Ruskin Avenue, Wellingborough, Northamptonshire. Nene, Great Ouse. No tickets.

Wellington (Somerset) Angling Association. J Hayes, 1 Tonegate, Wellington, Somerset. Tone. Tickets.

Wellworthy Angling Club. I H Dibble, 28 Longstone Avenue, Bridgwater.

Welshpool Angling Association. F Eakins, Westwood Park Hotel, Salop Road, Welshpool, Powys. Severn, Mule, Rhiew and Banwy. Some permits.

Wem Angling Club. D Trow, 40 Eskdale Road, Telford Estate, Shrewsbury, Shropshire. Lake. Tickets.

Wensleydale Angling Association. H G Leyland, Millgarth, Bainbridge, Leyburn, N Yorks. Yore. Tickets.

Wessex Federation of Anglers. J Mathrick, 31 Drake Road, Wells, Somerset. Parret, Isle; affiliated clubs share rights.

West Bay Sea Angling Club. Mrs H Pettet, Home Farm View, Bothenhampton, Bridport, Dorset.

West Beck Preservation Society. C W G Derrick, 3 Link Road, Cottingham, E Yorkshire. West Beck. Members only.

West Country Fly Fishers. J W Hamilton Roberts, 64 Hampton Park, Redland, Bristol BS6 6LJ.

West End Angling Association. R A Richardson, 68 Raby Street, Byker, Newcastle-upon-Tyne.

West Ham Angling Society. A E Mileham, 43 Avenue Road, Forest Gate, London, E7. Lee. Some tickets.

Westminster Angling Society. H H Bone, 52 Tothill House, Vincent Street, London, SW1. Club fishes Calpac Waters.

Weston-super-Mare Angling Association. J Morgan, 57 Earlham Grove, Weston-super-Mare, Avon.

Weston-super-Mare Sea Angling Association. W Letts, 21a Brean Down Avenue, Weston-super-Mare, Avon.

Wetherby and District Angling Club. P L Burnett, 10 Calder Close, Wetherby, Yorkshire. Wharfe. Tickets.

Weybridge Angling Club. P Daymon, 61 Byron Road, Addlestone, Weybridge, Surrey, Wey. Members only.

Wey Navigation Angling Amalgamation. Ian Fraser, 4 Elm Grove Road, Weybridge, Surrey. Wey. Tickets.

Weymouth Angling Society. L Thomas, Angling HQ, Commercial Road, Weymouth, Dorset.

Wheelock Angling Society. A Darlington, Overland House, Moss Lane, Elsworth, Sandbach, Cheshire.

Whitby Sea Anglers' Association. T G R Sleightholme, 2 Crescent Avenue, West Cliff, Whitby, Yorkshire.

White Hart Dagenham Angling Society. D Brown, 100 Crescent Road, Dagenham, Essex.

White Swan Piscatorial Society. R G Dutton, 8 Rushbrook Drive, Parklands, Sutton Coldfield, Warwicks.

Whitmore Reans Angling Association. R H Hughes, Star Chambers, Prince's Square, Wolverhampton. Severn, Roden, Tern, Penk, Sowe, and local canals. Tickets.

Whitstable and District Angling Society. Mr Foyle, 48 Albert Street, Whitstable, Kent.

Whitstable Sea Fishing Association. H S Noel, 34 Grimshill Road, Whitstable, Kent.

Whittlesey Angling Association. P O Frost, 80 Mayfield Road, Eastrea, Whittlesey, Peterborough PE7 2AY. Nene, Twenty Foot, Cock Bank, pits. Tickets.

Wigan and District Angling Association. T Blackledge, 16 Florence Street, Wigan, Lancashire. Ribble, Wyre, Winster, Lake Windermere, reservoirs, flashes, ponds. Tickets.

Wigston Angling Society. G C Bray, 23 Kent Crescent, South Wigston, Leicester. Canal tickets.

Willington Angling Club. J Clark, 7 High Street, Howdon-le-Wear, Co Durham. Wear; dt.

Wilmslow and District Angling Association. P H Curbishley, 16 Alderdale Grove, Wilmslow, Cheshire. No tickets.

Wilton Fly-Fishing Club. M H A Fraser, Grey Gables, Pilton, Shepton Mallet, Somerset. Wylye. Limited membership.

Wimborne and District Angling Club. J M Bass, 16 Tennyson Road, Walford, Wimborne, Dorset BH21 1NT. Members only.

Windermere, Ambleside and District Angling Association. J B Cooper, 'Rylstone' Limethwaite Road, Windermere, Cumbria LA23 2BQ. Rothay, Troutbeck and Rydal Water. Tickets.

Windsor Angling Society. G E Johncey, 2 Bradshaw Close, Windsor, Berkshire. Thames.

Winsford and District Angling Association.

Wisbech and District Angling Association. E G Baker, 11 Orchard Drive, Wisbech, Cambridgeshire.

Witham Joint Angling Committee. R Hobley, 30 Gunby Avenue, Lincoln.

Witham Sea Anglers Club. Leonard Harding, 65 Chelmer Road, Witham, Essex.

Witney Angling Society. W R Ward, 17 Perrott Close, North Leigh, Oxfordshire. Thames and Windrush, pits. Members only.

Woking and District Angling Association. B C Tunnell, 2 Hartland Cottages, Broadmeads, Send Road, Send, Woking, Surrey. Wey. Tickets.

Wolsingham Angling Association. J L Peart, 37 West End, Wolsingham, Co Durham. Wear. St.

Wylye Fly-Fishing Club. Commander P D Hoare, RN (Retd), Monks Farm House, Corsham, Wiltshire. Members and guests only.

Yarm Angling Club. F. Flynn, 12 Varo Terrace, Stockton-on-Tees, Cleveland. Tees. Tickets.

Yeovil-Sherborne Angling Association. M Dash, 11 Orchard Street, Yeovil, Somerset. Trout and coarse fish on Yeo and tributaries; two ponds.

York and District Amalgamation of Anglers. Eric Woodward, 204 Salisbury Terrace, Leeman Road, York. Ouse, Foss, Derwent, Nidd, becks and ponds. Tickets.

York Angling Association. H White, (Chairman), 21 Linton Street, Poppleton Road, York, Derwent, Pocklington Canal. Tickets and match bookings.

York Flyfishers' Club. Major L M Stansfield, MBE, Miles Croft, Thornton-le-Clay, Yorkshire. Trout lakes. No tickets.

York Tradesmen's Angling Association. J R May, 1 Neville Drive, Bishopthorpe, York. Various becks. Members only.

Yorkshire Flyfishers' Club. Hon Sec, Oakwood House, 637 Roundhay Road, Leeds LS8 4BA, Yorkshire. Eden, Eamont, Lyvennet, Ribble and Yore. No tickets.

Woodbridge and District Angling Club. B G Gray, 12 Conach Road, Woodbridge, Suffolk IP12 4HN.

Woodford Angling Society. Hon secretary, 22 Evanrigg Terrace, Woodford Green, Essex. Roding. Members only.

Wootton Bassett Angling Club. A Fairbanks, 22 Whitehill Lane, Wootton Bassett, Swindon, Wiltshire. Lake, Brinkworth Brook. Members only.

Worcester Angling Society. H L Cull, 49 The Hill Avenue, Worcester. Teme. No permits.

Worcester and District United Anglers' Association. C J Baker, 10 Dilmore Avenue, Fernhill Heath, Worcester. Avon, Severn, Teme, Canal. Some tickets.

Workington Angling Association. G E Craswell, 26 Calva Brow, Seaton, Workington, Cumbria.

Worksop and District United Angling Association. R Whitehead, 72 Dryden Dale, Worksop. Canals and Trent. Tickets.

Worthing and District Piscatorial Society (Freshwater). R P Tunnicliffe, 79 North Lane, Portslade BN4 2NF, Sussex.

Worthing Sea Anglers' Association. S C Montgomery, 71 Galsworthy Road, Worthing, Sussex. Headquarters. Worthing Pier, Worthing, Sussex.

Note: *Every effort has been made to ensure accuracy in these lists, but club secretaries come and go. Where difficulty is encountered, the local tackleists can often help. Apologies are offered for gaps in this club-list. The National Federation of Anglers (see p 202) which holds the relevant information on file, was obliged by its rules of procedure to decline an invitation to make disclosures.*

WELSH FISHING STATIONS

IN the pages that follow, the catchment areas of Wales, are given in alphabetical order, being interspersed with the streams and the lakes of the Principality under headings such as "Powys (streams)"; "Gwynedd (lakes)," etc. The rivers of each catchment area are arranged in the manner described under the heading "English Fishing Stations", on p 47 and the other notes given there apply equally to Wales. The whole of the Wye, it should be remembered, is included in the section on England, while the Usk and the Dee are listed among the Welsh rivers.

Note: *Sea trout are commonly referred to as "sewin" in Wales, although some associations define sewin as immature sea trout returning to the river for the first time.*

AERON

(For close seasons, licences, etc, see Welsh Water Authority, p 43)

Rises in Llyn Eiddwen, 7m north-west of Tregaron, and flows about 17m to sea at Aberaeron. Excellent run of sewin from June onwards with smaller salmon run. Brown trout plentiful but small.

Aberaeron (Dyfed). Trout, salmon. Tickets obtainable for Aberaeron AA waters. Booking advised in March for season permits (£25); weekly tickets in July and August (£15) cannot be booked in advance. Dt £2. SAE requested. No dt July–Aug. **Wyre** and **Arth,** two streams to north, hold brown trout and have small runs of sewin. Fishing mostly held by farmers, who often give permission.

ANGLESEY (streams)

(For close seasons, licences, etc, see Welsh Water Authority, p 43)

ALAW: Rises above Cors y Bol bog and flows some 7m to sea beyond **Llanfachraeth,** opposite Holyhead. Fishes well (trout) for first three months of season and again in September when good run of small sea trout expected; usually too low in summer. Permission of farmers.

BRAINT: Small stream which flows almost whole width of the island, parallel with Menai Straits, to sea at Aber Menai, beyond **Llangeinwen.** Trout, some sea trout, but usually fishable only first three months of season. Permission of farmers.

CEFNI: Rises above Llangwyllog, flows through Llyn Frogwy *(see Anglesey Lakes)*, on to **Llangefni** and Cefni Reservoir *(see Anglesey Lakes)*, and then to sea in 6m. Lower reaches canalised. Only fair-sized river in island. Brown trout and chance of late salmon or sea trout. Permission of farmers. Hotel: The Bull.

CEINT: Small stream entering sea at Red Wharf Bay; some trout; permission of farmers; summer conditions difficult. Fishing station: **Pentraeth.**

FFRAW or GWNA: Under name of Gwna rises 4m above Bodorgan and waters Llyn Coron *(see Anglesey Lakes)* just below village. Stream then takes name of Ffraw and runs to sea at **Aberffraw** in 2m. Little more than brook. One or two pools fishable early on, but overgrown June onwards. Trout, some sea trout. Hotels: Prince Llewellyn, Crown, both Aberffraw; Merrick Arms, Bodorgan Arms, **Bodorgan.**

WYGYR: Small stream falling into sea at **Cemaes Bay.** Trout; restocked. Wygyr AA has about 2m (both banks); st wt and dt. Tickets from Cefn Glas Inn, Llanfechell; or Gwynfa Stores; fly only: Good sea fishing in bay.

Note: *Many hotels issue visitors' permits, but where numbers are limited, guests naturally have prior claim.*

Fishing a man-made reservoir. In Wales these often augment the natural beauty.
Photograph: John Tarlton.

ANGLESEY (lakes)

Cefni Reservoir. Llangefni. 173 acres. Brown trout (average 12 oz); fly only; good wading; boats. Leased by WWA to Cefni AA. Dt £2.50, wt £10, st £16, from hon sec and Millsports, Bridge Street, Llangefni.

Coron Lake. Bodorgan. Trout, sea trout; fly only. Dt and boats from Bodorgan Estate. Hotels: Meyrick Arms; Bodorgan Arms. RD licence from Malltdraeth Post Office.

Dinas Lake. Valley. Mainly roach; permission of farmers. **Penrhyn Lake:** mainly perch; permission of farmers; **Traffwll Reservoir;** roach, perch, trout; inquire locally.

Geirian Lakes. Llanfechell. No longer open for angling. Mr Mountfield now deceased; widow should not be troubled with enquiries.

Fodol Lake, Rhosgoch. Fishery ruined by damage to dam. Future uncertain.

Hendref Lake. Gwalchmai. No fishing at present, due to WWA drainage scheme works. Rights owned by Mrs E Hughes, Hendref Farm.

Llyn Alaw. Llantrisant. 770-acre reservoir offers about 9m of bank fishing for brown and rainbow trout (fish over 8 lb taken). Also boats with or without outboards. Season: March 20–Oct 17 (b) Oct 31 (Rb). Dt £3.50, wt £15, st £90.

Boats: rowing £3, motor £5. Self-issue of permits in operation at Alaw Fishing Office. Boats and N. shore; fly only. Worming and spinning allowed on S. shore. Reservoir office (Tel no Llanfaethlu 323).

Maelog Lake. Rhosneigr. Roach, perch, trout; free; boats. Hotel: Maelog Lake

(advt p 229). Tackle, licences from Balkin's Antique shop.

Mynydd Badafon Lake. Roach and perch; free. No licence required for coarse fishing.

Hotels in Anglesey: Dinorben Arms, Amwlch; Faraway, Cemaes Bay; Bull, Valley; Tysilio Guest House, Rhosgoch.

CLEDDAU (Eastern and Western)

(For close seasons, licences, etc, see Welsh Water Authority, p 43)

East Cleddau rises on east side of Mynydd Prescelly and flows 15m south-west, partly along old Carmarthenshire border, to north branch of Milford Haven. West Cleddau rises on west side of mountain and flows about 20m south-east to same creek of Haven. Rivers hold salmon, sewin and trout. Sewin fishing good in June, July and August.

WESTERN CLEDDAU: Salmon, trout.

Haverfordwest (Dyfed). Pembrokeshire AA has water; wt (8 days) £15 dt £3 from Toms Sports Outfitters (also RD licences), Market Street, Haverfordwest; County Shooting Supplies, Old Bridge; and Mr Harries (chemist), Bridge Street. R K Lucas & Son, Victoria Place, issue RD licences. Further information from hon sec. Riparian owners may give permission elsewhere. Sewin fishing good June to August. At **Llysyfran** (8m NE) is 187 acre reservoir with good trout fishing; Rb and B trout. Season April 1–Sept 30. Boats available at extra charge. St £40, dt £2.60 from reservoir.

St also from authority, Meyler House, Thomas Green, Haverfordwest. Fly, spinning and worming. Hotels: Mariners, County, Red House, Llawhaden, Nr Haverfordwest, Dyfed.

Rose Bush (Dyfed). Martel Brook Syfnau. Gwaen, 2m. **Prescelly Reservoir.** Brown trout. St £10 from Authority at Meyler House, Thomas Green, Haverfordwest; dt £1, at reservoir.

EASTERN CLEDDAU: Salmon, trout. Fishing station **Clynderwen** (Dyfed).

Clarbeston (Dyfed). Eastern Cleddau, 3m off. Farmers may give permission *(see Haverfordwest).* Sewin good, May to August.

CLWYD

(For close seasons, licences, etc, see p 43)

Salmon runs in summer and autumn, but mainly sea trout river with some heavy fish; June to August. Good below Ruthin and Llanfair on tributary Elwy. Trout numerous (average 9 in) but better in Wheeler and Elwy.

Rhyl (Clwyd). Tidal; fishing free to RD licence-holders from sea up to Rhuddlan, 3m away; salmon and sea trout, but fish tend to run straight through; no holding pools. Also flounders, bass and eels (no licence required). Rhyl AA has water on Clwyd, **Elwy** and **Prion Reservoirs.** Members only. Permits from Information Centre, Llyn Brenig, Cerrig-y-Drudian, Corwen, Clwyd for following lakes; **Aled** and **Aled Isaf,** coarse, dt 70p, st £6.50. **Plas Uchaf** and **Dolwen,** trout; limited dt £2.70. Permits available on site. Trout and coarse fishing at **Alwen Reservoir** on Denbigh moors; St £18, dt (t) £1.60 (c) 90p from Llyn Brenig Information Centre. *(See below.)* Coarse

fishing in Cefndy Brickworks pool; permits from caretaker. Sea fishing from river mouth, foreshore and boats. Tope, skate, plaice, mackerel, etc. Tackleists: Wm Roberts (Rhyl) Ltd, 131 High St; The Anglers Den, 29 Queen St.

LLYN BRENIG. Cerrig-y-Drudion. 919-acre reservoir opened for trout fishing in 1978. Fly only, brown and rainbow trout. St £90, dt £3.50, motor boats £10, rowing boats £5.50. Season: bank—April 1 to Oct 17, boat—May 1 to Sept 30. Tickets from Information Centre at reservoir.

Rhuddlan (Clwyd). Salmon, sea trout, brown trout. Bodrhyddan Estate owns fishing on both banks of Clwyd from Rhuddlan Bridge upstream to St Asaph and also River **Elwy** upstream from junction with Clwyd (1m above Rhuddlan) upstream to old Pentre railway bridge. Season permits to local anglers only, but dt sometimes available Rhyl AA and St Asaph AA have water on Elwy. *(See Rhyl.)*

St Asaph (Clwyd). **Rhyl AA** *(see Rhyl)* waters ½m below St Asaph.

Bodfari (Clwyd). Wheeler. Clwyd, 1m W; Salmon, trout. Mold & Dist Kingfishers have stretch of **Wheeler** and **Alyn;** members only. Hotel: Pwllgwyn, Afonwen, Flints.

Denbigh (Clwyd). Clwyd, 2m E; salmon, sea trout, brown trout. Denbigh AC has water on Clwyd, Ystrad and Elwy; members only, but membership open to non-residents. Lakes: **Aled,** 11m SW; coarse; dt and st from Water Authority Offices, Plastirion, Russell Road, Rhyl. Alwen Reservoir 11m SW; trout; permits at site. *(see Rhyl)* Hotels: Bull and Crown. Licences and trout tackle from Mr Bradley, Joyces (jewellers).

Ruthin (Clwyd). Trout, salmon, sea trout. Ruthin Castle Hotel has ½m free to guests. Clwyd AC has about 5m from

Ruthin to junction of Clwyd and **Clywedog** below Llandrynog. Members only. Salmon and sea trout only late in season and very few; more run up Clywedog. Clywedog practically all private, and where not private very overgrown. Both rivers shrink to low levels in mid-summer. Other hotels: Bridge Inn, Bontuchel, near Ruthin, which has short stretch at back of hotel.

Tributaries of the Clwyd

ELWY: Sea trout (June onwards), some salmon, small brown trout.

Llanfair-Talhaiarn (Clwyd); ns Abergele, 6m. Trout, sea trout, salmon; preserved by Llangerniew AC; members only. Other water strictly preserved and no permits obtainable. For other clubs with water see Dee. Melan 2m SW. Aled, 2m E. Hotels: Tarhodes, Black Lion, which has 1½m of water, wt £8, dt £2, but hotel guests given preference. Early and late water.

CLYWEDOG: Trout, preserved. Salmon and sea trout (very late), trout. All water strictly preserved. Clwyd AC, Capenhurst AC and Llay AS have water; members only.

WHEELER: Trout. Mold and District Kingfishers have water on Wheeler and Alyn; members only. *(See also Clwyd.)*

CONWAY

(For close seasons, licences, etc, see Welsh Water Authority, p 43)

Rises on Migneint, in Gwynedd and flows between the old Caernarvonshire and Denbighshire boundaries for much of its course, emptying into the Irish Sea near Conway. The upper part of its valley is noted for its beauty. Spate river with salmon runs throughout season (May and June usually best); grilse early July; sea trout late June to September.

Conway (Gwynedd). Tidal; sea fishing only. Codling, dabs, plaice, bass and mullet above and below suspension bridge. Boats available. Tackleists: Cambrian Supplies, Castle St. Hotels: Castle, Erskine Arms.

Dolgarrog (Gwynedd). Salmon, sea trout; deep tidal pools. Dolgarrog FC has 2½m of tidal water. Dt and salmon and sea trout are issued. St £8, wt £4, dt £1. Brown trout on upland watershed, including **Llyn Eigiau** and **Llyn Coedty** and connecting rivers.

Tal-y-Cafn (Gwynedd). Salmon, sea trout; deep tidal water. Ferry Hotel has short length. Dolgarrog FC has 2½m tidal Conway; visitors welcomed. Guests can obtain other fishing on Llanrwst AC waters.

Llanrwst (Gwynedd). Salmon and good sea trout; brown trout poor. Llanrwst AC has ¼m, both banks. Limited st (covering also one reservoir and ¼m of Conway at Trefriw) £30 and wt £14 (to Sept 12 only) from T J Jones, The Library, Bridge Street (who stock some tackle). Sunday fishing allowed. Permits (25p day) from Forestry Commission, Gwydyr Uchaf, for left bank of **Machno** from junction with Conway and portion of right bank. Tickets also from Mrs Jones, Pandy Mill and Post Office, both **Penmachno.** Hotels: Maenan Abbey, Victoria (both have salmon and trout fishing).

Bettws-y-Coed (Gwynedd). Conway; Lledr; Llugwy; trout, salmon, sewin. Gwydyr Hotel (pro. Miss V L Connell Smith) has about 15m on Rivers **Conway, Lledr** and **Llugwy**, from near semi-tidal Trefriw Quay upstream to Plantation Pool near Pontypant on Lledr and to Mymbyr Lake at Capel Curig on Llugwy; 55 pools, some semi-tidal, flats, and well-known "The Rocks" stretch of Lledr are included. Hotel waters also include Elsi Lake (stocked with Loch Levens), another trout lake (Siabod) and semi-tidal stretch called Belmont, about 1m down river from Trefriw Quay. Charges: Residents only, from £60 to £100 per week according to stretch. Other water available to residents and non-residents alike from £170 to £360 per rod—or rod/day—per season. Dt £1.15 and wt £5 for R Llugwy, brown trout. St £40, wt £10, dt £2.50, for Elsi Lake, Moel Siabod. Night sea trout ticket £7. Dt (inclusive) £14.50. Sunday fishing. Tickets and details from hotel

(advt p 231). Bettws-y-Coed AC has 1m of Conway (left bank only) and 3m of Llugwy (both banks). Wt only. Swallow Falls Hotel, via Bettws-y-Coed, has trout lake *(see Capel Curig)*.

Ysbyty Ifan (Gwynedd). Trout (half-pounder, good fish). About 11m of National Trust water. Conway river in Ysbyty Ifan area, st £10, from Conway Falls Bridge to Rhydlanfair Bridge, £5. Parts of **Machno** and **Glasgwm** rivers owned by National Trust, £3. Tickets from The National Trust, Dinas, Bettws-y-Coed and Caradog Evans, 3 Trem Afon, Ysbyty Ifan.

Tributaries of the Conway

ROE: Trout.
Roe-Wen (Gwynedd) ns Talycafn. Upper reaches now form part of Dolgarrog FC waters and are included in club permit. Accommodation at Ty Gwyn Hotel. Fly fishing impossible on lower reaches.
DDU: Trout.
Pont Dolgarrog (Gwynedd). Trout. Ddu enters Conway ½m below village; drains Llyn Cowlyd. River Dolgarrog FC water; lake free to licence-holders by permission of Conway Valley Water Supply Unit, 50 Mostyn Street, Llandudno; no boats.
CRAFNANT: Trout.
Trefriw (Gwynedd). Ns Llanrwst. Crafnant drains **Llyn Crafnant** and joins Conway just below village. Lake is Llanrwst water supply; trout; dt; boats and RD licences from Lakeside Cafe.
LLEDR: Trout, sewin, salmon.
Dolwyddelan (Gwynedd). Dolwyddelan FA water is most of both banks from village to Pont-y-Pant. Resident visitors, not campers or caravanners, wt for salmon and sewin (late summer and early autumn best) March–June £2, July–Oct (m to f) £10 from newsagents. Gwynedd RD licence required. Prince Albert AS has stretch here; enquire hon sec. Lakes: Diwaunedd (two) 3m W; trout; pre-served. Hotels: Gwydyr, Ellen's Castle. *For Conway water below Dolwyddelan see Bettws-y-Coed and Llanrwst.*
LLUGWY: Trout.
Capel Curig (Gwynedd). Trout; right bank preserved from Bettws-y-Coed to Capel Curig (Llynau Mymbyr) and left bank to Miners' Bridge by Conway FA which

issues tickets *(see Bettws-y-Coed)*. Gwydyr Hotel has water *(see under Conway)*. Hotels: Tyn-y-Coed and Cobden's Snowdonia (joint fishing on 2m of river and numerous lakes in neighbourhood; boats can be had on several; dt issued). Tickets and tackle available locally. *(See also under Dolwyddelan for FC waters.)*
GWRYD (trib of Llugwy): Trout.
Pen-y-Gwryd (Gwynedd) ns Llanberis or Bettws-y-Coed. Trout. Gwryd runs to Llynau Mymbyr, near Capel Curig. Fishing on river has improved with re-stocking and 3m are available to guests at Pen-y-Gwryd Hotel (left bank only). Wt £5, dt £1. Llynau Mymbyr belongs to Sports Council, Plas-y-Brenin, Capel Curig. Llyn-y-Cwm Ffynnon; trout. Lly-nau Diwaunedd, 2m SE; trout; Free. Gwynant 3m S; boats. Edno, 7m S; large trout; free.
HWCH: Trout.
Gwynedd RD issues tickets for this river and **Arddu.**
MACHNO: Trout.
Penmachno (Gwynedd). Tickets (60p day) from Mrs Jones, Pandy Mill, and Post office for one stretch. Good free trout fishing for RD licence-holders; National Trust has fishing on Machno and **Glasgwm.** St £5, wt £2.50, dt £1.25 from NT Office, Dinas, Bettws-y-Coed, Gwynedd.
NUG: Trout.
Pentre Voelas (Gwynedd). Mrs Edwards, Bank House, issues permits for **Merddwr** and **Conway** (trout, fly only); charges on application. **Alwen Reservoir:** trout; permits from Superintendents office on site.

DEE (Welsh)

(For close seasons, licences, etc, see Welsh Water Authority, p 43)

Usually has a spring run of fish up to 30 lb. Grilse enter in June and there is a run of grilse and summer fish until the end of the season as a rule. In spring most fish are taken from Bangor to Corwen. Trout from Bangor upstream and grayling above Llangollen.

Coarse fish predominate downstream of Bangor. River holds good bream, roach, dace, perch and pike.

Chester (Cheshire). Coarse fish. Little permit-free fishing, but rod licence only needed from Suspension Bridge up-stream to Kissing Gates. No licence for coarse fishing in tidal waters. Most fishing controlled by Chester Assn of Anglers; permits for trout and coarse fishing only from hon sec. Dt from tackleists. Assn also has fishing on **R Llafar** and **Shropshire Union Canal.** Dee AA issues salmon permits (limited) for **Sutton Green** stretch; separate trout and coarse fish permits. St Helens AA also has water at Sutton Green; members only. Other clubs with fishing on lower river: Lavister AC, Warrington AA, Northern AA, Liverpool AA; all members only except Warrington, which may allow visitors. **River Gowy,** which runs into Mersey, passing by Mickle Trafford about 3m from Chester: Warrington AA has water. Trout and coarse fish. Tackleists: E P Martin, The Tackle Box, 53 Lower Bridge Street, H Monk, 77 Foregate Street, D Gibson. Upper Northgate St: Mrs I M Williams, 316 High Street,

Connah's Quay. G Boddy, Westminster Road, Hoole, Chester. Hotels: Grosvenor, Queen, Blossoms.

Holt (Clwyd). Salmon, pike, bream. Alyn, 2m NW; trout. Dee AA, Chester, rents a number of stretches in the Holt, Farndon, Sutton Green area. St for salmon or trout. Northern AA and Warrington AA rent stretches at **Shocklach, Berwyn, Lower Hall** and **Churton.**

Bangor-on-Dee (Clwyd). Salmon, trout, coarse fish. Bangor-on-Dee AA rents long stretch downstream. Permits for salmon and trout fishing from S Adams, The Stores, High Street. Hotel: Buck.

Overton (Clwyd). Salmon, sea trout, trout, coarse fish; dt £1 from V Guest, Bryn Hovah, Bangor-on-Dee, for Bryn-y-Pys AA water; trout only (about 8m in all). Boat Inn, Erbistock, has salmon and trout beat.

Trevor (Clwyd). Trout, salmon, coarse fish (including pike and grayling). Very good salmon and trout fishing on dt from S Diggory, Cambrian Fly Fisheries *(advt p 235),* Pontcysyllte. Mr Diggory also has

tackle shop 50 yards from Dee. Maelor AA has water. Wt £3, dt £1 for trout and coarse fish only on 1½m (both banks). Coarse fishing good September onwards. Tickets from hon sec. Newbridge AA issues tickets for trout and coarse fishing. Accommodation (and permits) at Dee House.

Llangollen (Clwyd). Trout, grayling, salmon, pike. Llangollen AA preserves about 6m below bridge to village of Rhewl. Trout and coarse fish; st, wt and dt for salmon and trout. Wading necessary. March to end of June best. No coarse fishing allowed in close season for salmon and trout. Tickets from W N & H A Elbourn (tackleist), Chapel Street. Wt (S) £25, dt (S) £6, wt (T) £10, dt (T) £2. Dt for coarse fishing in canal, 50p. Maelor AC has water from here to Pontcysyllte; members only. Warrington AA has good stretch. Ceiriog, 3m S. Alyn, 7m N, at Llandegla; trout. Hotels: Golden Pheasant, Llwynmawr (Salmon beats on Dee and Severn, and trout and grayling fishing on rivers and lakes; several miles free to guests). Hand, Ponsonby, Bryn Howel (all have fishing for guests), West Arms, Llanarmon.

Berwyn, for Llantysilio (Clwyd). Salmon fishing all preserved; trout, grayling. Llangollen AA water: permits for left bank only *(see Llangollen)*; fly only. Former Glyndyfrdwy Preserve now divided between three private owners. Lower third all preserved. Middle third preserved by Glyndwr Preserve, who now have salmon water from Glyndyfrdwy Bridge downstream for about 4m, on which water limited trout tickets (fly only) are available from local sources: details posted by water, which is strictly keepered. Upper third owned by Berwyn Arms Hotel, Glyndyfrdwy, Corwen (1¾m, mainly single bank). Salmon and trout dt issued, £6 and £2, fly only. Tel: Glyndwr 210).

Corwen (Clwyd). Corwen and Dist AC controls most of trout and grayling fishing on Rhug Estate (about 4m), Dee and **Alwen.** Association also has fishing on **Cynwyd Reservoir** (trout) and trout lake. Members only (long waiting list). St to visitors £12, Crown Hotel, **Llanfihangel,** issues permits for 1¼m on **Alwen** (trout). Tackleist: C Williams, Waterloo House (licences).

Cynwyd (Clwyd). Trout, grayling, salmon. Corwen and Dist AC has ½m above Cynwyd: members only. Inns: The Blue Lion and Prince of Wales.

Llandrillo (Clwyd). Salmon, trout, grayling, perch and pike. Strictly preserved by executors of Duke of Westminster's Palé Estate. Hotel: Dudley Arms.

Llandderfel (Gwynedd). Salmon, trout, grayling, perch and pike. Strictly preserved by Palé Estate. Lakes: Caereini (3½m); also Mynyllod and Maesclawdd, strictly preserved by private landowners. No permits. Hotels: Bryntirion Inn (which has two rods for guests on 1¼m; trout and grayling, fly only).

Bala (Gwynedd). Salmon, trout, perch, pike and grayling. From confluence with Tryweryn to Bala Lake it is Bala AA water. Members (non-residents £10) may fish another stretch of Dee and lake itself. Assn also has water on **Tryweryn, Lliw, Llafar,** (dt), **Cwm Prysor Lake** (trout; fly only; dt) *(see also Llanuwchllyn)*; Sunday fishing allowed; visitor's wt £5 and dt £1 and £1.50, issued, inquire hon sec or tackleists. Block permits for small clubs for Bala AA waters. **Lake Bala** itself (trout early on, coarse fish) owned by County Council; dt 70p, wt £2 from tackleists W E Pugh, High Street and R E Evans, Bradford House; also from Lake Warden. **Llyn Celyn:** (4m); brown trout; tickets from tackleists. Hotels: White Lion, Royal, Plas Coch, Goat, Ye Olde Bulls Head, Ship. *(See Gwynedd Lakes.)*

Llanuwchllyn (Gwynedd). Trout and grayling. Permits from Post Office, Llanuwchllyn and Bala tackleists; for stretches of Dee, Lliw and Twrch. No Sunday fishing or ground baiting. Clubs: Llanuwchllyn AC; Prince Albert AS (trout and grayling fishing on Little Dee, Twrch and Lliw; members only).

Tributaries of the Dee

ALYN: Trout.

Rossett (Clwyd). Trout and dace, Rossett and Gresford AA restock 4m annually with Loch Levens; fly only; st £12, entrance fee £3.50.

Gresford (Clwyd). Trout *(see Rossett).* Llay AA has The Flash; tench, carp, pike, rudd; members only *(see Llay).*

Wrexham (Clwyd). Wrexham and Dist AA has water on Alyn (permits to members'

guests only from hon sec). Other clubs: Caergwrle AA (trout; st only); Llay Hall AA (st only); Bradley FC (members only); Llay AS (dt from bailiffs etc); Rossett and Gresford AA (members only); Cerrig-y-Drudion AA (members only). Bryn y Pys AA. Permits from East Denbighshire Water Supply Unit, 21 Egerton Street (Wrexham 2259) for upper and lower **Penycae Reservoirs** (trout). Tackleists: H Jones, 2 Ruabon Road, who supplies tickets for local club waters.

Hope (Clwyd). Trout. Wrexham and Dist AA has about 5m of Alyn; annually stocked with trout up to 10 in; members only. Annual sub £20. Fly only.

Llay (Clwyd). Llay AS has trout water on Alyn and **Cegidog** and good coarse fishing in **The Flash, Gresford** tench, carp, pike, rudd; **Llay Reservoir** tench, carp, rudd, perch, pike; **Brymbo Pools** tench, rudd, perch; on **Severn, Vyrnwy, Dee** and **Barog, Wyche Brook, Overton Pools,** the canal above **Welshpool.** All waters members only. Memberships from hon sec.

Mold (Clwyd). Clwyd County Council hold fishing rights in **Loggerheads** area, leased to local clubs. Cilcain FFA has five trout reservoirs nearby. Dt (two only) from hon sec (enclose s/a envelope); fly only. Tackleists: Blundells, 1–2 The Cross.

SARN:

Whitchurch (Salop). No stream fishing. Coarse fishing in lakes: **Brown Moss Lakes** 1½m SE; pike, bream, roach, tench; apply N Shropshire RDC for permits. Quoisley Big and Little Meres, 3m N; boats. Marbury Mere, 3m NE; dt Blakemere, 1m NE; pike, perch, bream, roach; dt; boat from A W Hiles, Yockingsgate; Osmere, 2m NE; good bream, tench, pike, rudd, roach; dt (bank only) from J E Windsor, Black Park. Tackleist: Mr Speed, Watergate Street.

CEIRIOG: Trout, sea trout (Aug onwards).

Chirk (Clwyd). Good coarse fishing on **Shropshire Union Canal.** Chirk Fishery Co Ltd, *(see p 32)* has hatchery here. Chirk AA has trout fishing on Ceiriog and Dee; Limited wt and dt by advanced booking.

Llwynmawr (Clwyd). Golden Pheasant Hotel has stretch of Ceiriog. Guests may also fish 5m of **Dee** for trout and salmon

and beats on **Severn** and **Tanat.** Sewin run late August. Lake fishing for trout and coarse fish within few miles. Licences and flies available.

Glyn Ceiriog (Clwyd). Farmers sometimes give permission. Golden Pheasant Hotel has water in this area *(see Llwynmawr)*.

Llanarmon DC (Clwyd). Ceiriog, 2½m, brown trout. Hotels: West Arms, Llanarmon DC, near Llangollen, which has free fishing on 1½m (both banks) for hotel guests. Hand Hotel has trout and coarse fishing for guests (both hotels issue RD licences).

ALWEN: Flows out of large reservoir (trout, perch) on Denbigh Moors and enters Dee near Corwen. Very good trout fishing and some salmon. For **Alwen Reservoir** permits apply Dee and Clwyd Division of WWA. Dt from office at reservoir. Cerrig-y-Drudion AA has river fishing; members only. Crown Hotel, **Llanfihangel** issues permits.

TRYWERYN: Joins Dee below Lake Bala. Good trout fishing. Bala AA has 4–5m and mountain lake **Cwm Prysor.** Tickets from Bala tackleist. *(See Bala.)*

DOVEY

(For close seasons, licences, etc, see Welsh Water Authority, p 43)

Rises on east side of Aran Fawddwy and flows 30m south and south-west to Cardigan Bay at Aberdovey. Has long estuary and provides splendid sport with sewin (sea trout) and salmon. Many large sea trout taken. Salmon run in small numbers from May to October; sea trout from May on. Best months: July, August, September. Small tributaries hold many little trout, and leave can generally be obtained from owners.

Aberdovey (Gwynedd). At estuary mouth; surf and estuary fishing. Free trout fishing in Happy Valley on permission of farmers; stream; trout small.

Machynlleth (Powys). Salmon, sea trout. New Dovey Fishery Association controls 15m (both banks) of river between Llyfnant stream and Nant Ty-Mawr on the L bank, from opposite Llyfnant mouth to Abergwybedy brook on R. An extremely restrictive and highly complex form of fishery-management is in force under which very few permits indeed are issued to anglers neither born, brought up nor resident in the district. They cost £32, entitling the holder to fish four days in one week, once in a season. There is a more generous allocation of £5 dt to fish a part only of the water. These are available from D G Evans, Garage,

Cemmaes Road; Mrs E Jones, PO, Cemmaes and E Francis, Nant Nest Stores, Dinas Mawddwy. Other enq to Hon Sec, D Morgan Jones, Plas, Machynlleth, Powys. Tel Machynlleth 2721. Hotels: Wynnstay (Trust House), Glyndwr and Lion Hotel, Machynlleth, Ynyshir Hall, Eglwysfach, Penrhos Arms, Cemmaes, and Riverside Hotel, Pennal. Permission from farmers for **Pennal Stream;** rapid water; trout small but plentiful. Corris AC controls 3m of **N Dulas.** Llugwy Hotel, Pennal *(advt p 237)* has half-mile on **S. Dulas** free to guests.

Cemmaes (Powys). Trout, sea trout, salmon. For details of permits, *(see Machynlleth)*.

Llanbrynmair (Powys). 5m from Cemmaes Road. On **Twymyn;** sewin, salmon, fair trouting. 3m of **Twymyn** controlled by

Prince Albert AS; inquiries to hon sec. Llanbrynmair and Dist AC has water from Twymyn Village to confluence with Dovey apart from one stretch held by Prince Albert AS; good trouting; dt and wt from hon sec.

Dinas Mawddwy (Gwynedd). Sewin, salmon, trout; fishing good. Brigands Inn, **Mallwyd,** has some of the best pools on upper reaches and stretch of **Cleifion** wt £27.50, dt £5.50. A dt at £2.20 available in April and May to residents. 245 sea trout to 12 lbs taken in 1980. Buckley

Arms hotel has water from the **Cowarch** down to **Cleifion**. Montgomeryshire AA has water on **Cleifion;** inquire hon sec. Sea trout runs (water permitting) May, July, Sept; best July to October. Licences and further information from hotel. **Twrch,** 8m E; good trouting. Prince Albert AS has 2½m stretch of Dovey at Gwastad Coed, **Gwerhefin.** Inquire hon sec for details of society's rights, which include **Lyn-y-Foel** (south half) and stretch of **Lledr** *(see Conway).* Other hotel: Dolbrawmaeth Hall (½m on Dovey; dt issued).

DWYRYD

(For close seasons, licences, etc, see Welsh Water Authority, p 43)

Rises in small, nameless pool 3m above Tan-y-Grisiau and flows into Cardigan Bay through estuary north of Harlech. Holds trout, sewin and salmon. Salmon and sea trout run up as far as the falls on the main river and its tributaries, Teigl and Cynfal. Connected with Dwyryd is Trawsfynydd Lake. Best months April, May, June and Sept for trout; late June to Oct for sea trout and salmon.

Tan-y-Bwlch (Gwynedd). Sewin, salmon. For local possibilities, consult tackleist in High Street, Portmadoc.

Maentwrog (Gwynedd). Grapes Hotel has about 3m of River Dwyryd; trout, sewin and salmon (June to Sept best); Tickets issued. Other stream and lake fishing for trout available **Tecwynuchaf** and **Tecwynisaf Lakes,** 2m SW Talsarnau AA; st from hon sec. River Prysor, 5m, controlled by Prysor AA, Trawsfynydd; tickets from H E Lewis (newsagent), Trawsfynydd. Licences and tickets for Talsarnau AA and Cambrian AA waters can be obtained at Grapes Hotel *(see Ffestiniog).*

Ffestiniog (Gwynedd). Sewin and salmon fishing on Dwyryd, £1.50 day from local tackleists (see below). Principal trout

lakes controlled by Cambrian AA as follows: **Gamallt** (3m E), sport excellent; **Dubach** (3m N), **Manod** (2m NE), **Morwynion** (2m E), **Cwmorthin** (3m NW). **Llagi** and **Adar.** Full information from hon sec. Visitors' tickets: st £8, wt £4.50, dt £1.50. Cambrian AA has also some trout fishing on tributaries of Dwyryd. **Tan-y-Grisau Reservoir** (season Apr 1–Oct 31) (2m NW), 95 acres, stocked with 12 in brown and rainbow trout; Dt from local tackleists. Spinning and bait fishing allowed. **Trawsfynydd Reservoir:** trout (4m S) (season Feb 1–Sept 30), perch and rudd all the year round. CEGB waters *(advt p 233).* Tackleists: Geoff Payne (tackle hire, information, live bait), Ffestiniog; J F Davies, Bl. Ffestiniog. Hotels: Abbey Arms, Pengwern Arms. Brynllydan.

Tributaries of the Dwyryd

PRYSOR (and Trawsfynydd):
Trawsfynydd (Gwynedd). **Prysor, Cain** and **Trawsfynydd Lake** controlled by Prysor AA. Trout, but also many perch and rudd. Assn also has 3m on **Eden** (salmon, sewin). Permits for lake, dt £2.50, boat extra. River permits: dt £2.50, wt £12.50, dt and licences from

H & P Lewis (newsagent), Trawsfynydd and hon sec. Hotels: Cross Foxes, Trawsfynydd; Oakley Arms and Grapes, Maentwrog, Abbey Arms and Pengwern Arms, Ffestiniog *(see also Gwynedd Lakes).* Tackleists: C Davies, Portmadoc; H & P Lewis, Trawsfynydd.

DYFED (streams)

(For close seasons, licences etc, see Welsh Water Authority, p 43)

ALLAN. Fishing station: **St David's;** ns Haverfordwest, 18m. Allan (6m long); 4m suitable for fishing, mostly on private property on owners permission; trout good quality but small.

BRAWDY BROOK. Fishing station: **Brawdy;** ns Haverfordwest, 10m. Brook is 7m long. Small trout.

CARN. Fishing station: **Loveston;** ns Templeton, 3m. Carn rises 1½m W from Templeton station, runs 3m to Loveston, and 1m down, 3m from Begelly, is joined on left bank by Langden Brook, 3m long. Carn runs 2½m to Milford Haven. Small trout.

CAREW BROOK. Fishing station: **Carew;** ns Pembroke, 4m. This brook, which rises by Redberth, is 4m long, joining sea water at Carew which is an inlet from Milford Haven. Small trout.

CLARACH. Enters sea 1m N of **Aberystwyth.** Holds trout, sewin and occasional salmon; preserved; permission from farmers.

COWIN. Fishing station: **Sarnau.** Sea trout, occasional salmon. Only worth fishing June onwards. Permission from farmers.

DISSILIO. Fishing station: **Llandissili-Gogo;** ns Lampeter, 20m. Dissilio is 6m long. 1m W runs Tydi, 6m long. Small trout.

GARNAS BROOK. Fishing station: **Cronware;** ns Whitland, 5m. This brook rises 1m above here, and joins the sea 3m down. Small trout.

GWAUN. Fishing station: **Fishguard.** This 8–9m trout stream rises on lower slopes of Prescelly Mountains, and runs through a beautiful wooded valley. Trout not large but provide excellent sport with fly, and sewin also caught in season. A few salmon. Permission freely given by landowners and tenants. Dt. Further information from hon sec, Fishguard AA (enclose sae). Tackleists: Mr Birch, West Street, and Mr Evans (saddler), West Street, RD licences from Boots (Chemists), Fishguard. Hotel: New Inn at Rose Bush. Guest houses: Glyn-y-Mel, Fishguard, and Pentower, Tower Hill, Fishguard.

GWENDRAETH FACH. Fishing station: **Kidwelly.** Carmarthen and Dist AC has 5m; very good trout fishing; occasional sea trout in lower reaches. *(See also Towy–Carmarthen.)* Gwendraeth Fawr runs 1m E from Kidwelly; trouting fair. Hotel: White Lion. Tackleist: F M and H E Davies, Bridge St.

KILRELGY BROOK. Fishing station: **Begelly.** This stream, 5m long, runs 1m E. Carn, 3m. Langdon Brook, 3m. Small trout.

LLANDILO BROOK. Fishing station: **Maenclochog.** Gilfach Brook, 1m. Syfynfy, 2m. Corwyn, 4m. Crynanich, 4m. Small trout.

LLETHI. Fishing station: **Llanarth;** ns Lampeter, 13m. Llethi Gido rises 3m above Llanarth, and 2m down is joined on left bank by brook 4m long. Llethi runs to Llanina and sea, 1m. One mile NE runs Drowy to sea, 4m long. Small trout.

MARLES. Fishing station: **Narberth.** Gwaithnoak, 2m. Eastern Cleddau, 2m. Taf, 5m. Small trout. Pembrokeshire Fly Fishers *(advt p 251).* Hotel: Robeston *(advt p 251).*

MULLOCK BROOK. Fishing station: **St Ishmael's;** ns Milford, 5m (small trout), 6m long, joining the sea at Dale Road.

NEVERN (Dyfed): Rises near Crymmych and flows to sea at **Newport:** ns Fishguard and Goodwick, 7m. Cardigan, 10m. Night fishing for sewin excellent; river also holds some salmon. Overgrown in parts, but many improvements recently carried out. The Coach House, Newport, has ½m; dt 20p. Below Nevern, Newport and District AA has water (st £6, mt £5, wt £3). Permits from hon sec, Lloyds Bank, B Williams, tackleist, or E Harvard (ironmonger), Main St, all Newport. Other tackleists: H T Birch and M Evans, both Fishguard.

PERIS. Fishing station: **Llanon;** Peris is 6m long. Llanon, 4m long, runs ½m. Small trout.

RHEIDOL. Fishing stations: **Aberystwyth** and **Devil's Bridge.** Salmon, sea trout, brown trout; Rheidol recovering as salmon river but hydro-electric scheme governs flow. River almost entirely Aberystwyth AA water. Assn also has stretch of **Ystwyth** and several lakes: *(See under Dyfed, lakes).* Non-residents' permits for whole fishery from B Jones, tackleist, Aberystwyth. Llanilar AA has 14m of trout and sewin fishing on Ystwyth; tickets from B Jones, tackleist,

3 Queen's St, Aber Gun Supplies, Terrace Road (both Aberystwyth) and E H Evans, Erwyd Garage, Ponterwyd, Dyfed.

WYRE. Fishing station; **Llanrhystyd;** Aberystwyth, 9m. Trout (small), some salmon and sometimes good for sewin. Permits, licences at Post Office. Hotel: Black Lion.

DYFED (lakes)

Devil's Bridge. Aberystwyth AA has the Penrhyncoch lakes in the hills between Devil's Bridge and Nant-y-Moch Reservoir; **(Llyn Craig-y-Pistyll, Llyn Syfydrin, Llyn Rhosgoch, Llyn Blaenmelindwr** and **Llyn Pendam) Llyn yr Oerfa** and **Llyn Llywernog** 2m SW of Ponterwyd, and the Trisant lakes **(Llyn Frongoch, Llyn Rhosrhydd** and **Llyn Glandwgan)** 2m SW of Devil's Bridge. Some are stocked, others self-stocking. Several contain trout up to 2 lbs. Some are fly only; spinning and restricted bait fishing on others. The Assn also has water on **Rheidol.** St (full) £55, (lakes and part of Rheidol fishery) st £40. Wt £24. Dt £5. Concessions for OAP and juvs. Boats extra. Tickets from Aberystwyth tackleists and Erwyd Garage, Ponterwyd. Full details of fishings from hon sec. Hotel: Hafod Arms.

Llysyfran Reservoir. (8m NE **Haverfordwest).** (Trout. For details inquire WWA, Meyler House, Haverfordwest. St £25, dt £1.50.

Nant-y-moch and Dinas Reservoirs. CEGB waters *(advt p 233)* in the hills N of the A44 Aberystwyth–Llangurig road at Ponterwyd. Dinas, 68 acres, stocked frequently with 12 in–13 in B and Rb trout. Spinning and ledgered worm allowed. Nant-y-Moch, 860 acres, fly only for wild brown trout av 8 ozs. Six-fish bag limit; size limit 9 in. Wt and dt from Aberystwyth Sports Centre, Hubbards Tackle Shop, Borth, Evans Garage, Ponterwyd.

Pembroke. Pembroke Town Mill Pool; mullet, bass, flatfish; also trout and sewin higher up. **West Orielton Lake,** 3m; coarse fish, no pike; permission sometimes obtainable; inquire at West Orielton Farm. **Bosherston Lily Ponds,** Stackpole (6m). Pike, perch, tench, roach. Pembroke and Dist AC. Wt £2, 50p from the café, Bosherston; tackle, permits and licences from Sports and Leisure, 29 Main Street, Pembroke and Frank Donovan, 61 Bush Street, Pembroke Dock (sports outfitters). Hotels: King's Arms, Royal, George, Lion, Castle Inn. For sea fishing, *see Pembroke Dock.*

Prescelly Reservoir, Rosebush. 11m NE of Haverfordwest. WWA, Meyler House, Haverfordwest. Permits from Unit, or from bailiff at reservoir. St £25, dt £1.50. Licence required. Boat-hire at reservoir.

Strata Florida. Tregaron—Nearby are **Teify Lakes,** at headquarters of Teifi (new road from Tregaron). Dt £2 from South West Wales RD and Post Office, Pontrhydfendigaid. **Llyn Egnant** (3m), and Llyn Hir fly only: Llyn Teifi a mixed-method fishery. **Llyn Gorlan** rented by Prince Albert AA, Macclesfield *(see under Teifi).* **Llyn Fyrddron Fawr** hold big fish, but access difficult; no permits required.

Talybont. Forestry Commission issues permits for Anglers Retreat Lakes; trout. Talybont AA has water on **Lerry** and **Einion** and four stocked lakes. Wt £12, dt £3.

Tregaron. Berwyn, 5m; trout; peaty water; Tregaron AA; permits from Barclays Bank. *For river fishing in neighbourhood see Rivers Teifi and Aeron.*

DYSYNNI

(For close seasons, licences, etc, see Welsh Water Authority, p 43)

Rises in Llyn Cau, on steep southern side of Cader Idris, then falls rather rapidly via Dol-y-Cau. Falls into Tal-y-llyn Valley about half a mile above well-known Tal-y-llyn Lake. Emerging from lake, flows westwards as typical upland stream to Abergynolwyn where, joined by the Gwernol, it turns north through narrow valley until it enters upper end of broad Dysynni Valley. At Peniarth it becomes deep and sluggish and finally enters Cardigan Bay 1½m north of Towyn. Trout along whole length and tributaries, and sea trout (sewin) and salmon travel beyond Tal-y-llyn Lake and up to Dolgoch on Fathew. In lower reaches good sport may be had, early and late in season, with trout and sewin; August generally best. Also excellent grey mullet and bass in estuary.

The Dee at Corwen.

Towyn (Gwynedd). Dysynni; salmon, sewin, trout, with grey mullet in tidal parts and excellent bass fishing at mouth and from adjacent beaches. Some free fishing to licence-holders and three main stretches for which permits may be had. Latter are: **Peniarth,** st £8, wt £4, dt £2. **Peniarth Uchaf:** 2½m both banks held by Prince Albert AS; details from hon sec. **Estimaner** (Estimaner AA has 8m and restocks annually); st £8, wt £4, dt £2 (no Sunday fishing on Estimaner water). Tickets from Mrs Rowlands, the Post Office, Abergynolwyn; Sports Shop, Jones Bros (boot stores), and J Roberts, barber, all Towyn; and from Mrs Rees Wern, Llanfihangel.

Tal-y-llyn (Gwynedd). Good trout fishing in **Tal-y-llyn Lake;** owned by Tyn-y-Cornel Hotel and reserved for guests but few dt available £3.50; fly only *(advt p 236).* For river fishing *see Towyn.* Fishing also available at Llanfihangel-y-Pennant; fast stream, trout; fly or worm; permits from cottages in Llanfihangel *(see also Gwynedd Lakes).*

GLAMORGAN (West, Mid and South)

(For close seasons, licences, etc, see Welsh Water Authority, p 43, unless otherwise stated)

AFAN. Fishing station; **Aberavon.** Small trout stream (with sewin on lower reaches) on which Afan Valley AC has water from Aberavon to Cymmer; wt £5, dt £1 from tacklists. Association has improved sport; regular stocking. Fly only in March; worming allowed rest of season; spinning June–Aug. RD licences and tackle from The Sports Shop, Station Road, **Port Talbot;** all types of fair fishing allowed. River Nedd 4m away; trout, sewin. Ogmore easily accessible. Hotels: The Twelve Knights; Berni Inn, Beach.

CADOXTON STREAM. Fishing station: **Cadoxton.** Cadoxton Stream rises 6½m from Cardiff and enters the sea 2m below Cadoxton. Small trout; permission from farmers (Glamorgan RD).

EGLWYS NUNYDD near Margam, British Steel Corporation (Port Talbot) reservoir. Excellent trout fishing, brown and rainbow; fish run large (9 lb record). March 20–Oct 17. Dt £3, wt £10, st £25 (VAT incl). No boats. Apply company Sports Club, Groes, Margam, Port Talbot. (Port Talbot 883161 Ext 3368 during day).

KENFIG. Small stream entering sea between Port Talbot and Porthcawl. Trout (av ¾ lb). Fishing station: **Kenfig Hill.** Club: Kenfig Hill and Dist AA. Kenfig Pool (90 acres) holds pike, carp, bream, tench, roach, rudd; rainbow and brown trout successfully introduced. No visitor's tickets.

NEATH. Rises in the Brecon Beacons and flows 27m to sea. Salmon, sewin, brown trout. Fishing station: **Neath.** Neath Canal, which holds a head of coarse fish, stocked with trout by Neath and Dulais AA, which also has water on both Neath and **R Dulais.** St £4.50, wt £3 and dt £2. Regular re-stocking with 8–10 in trout. Tributaries of the Neath are **Dulais** and **Pyrddin.** Glynneath and Dist AA has 17m on Neath and tributaries; trout only above Pontneathvaughan; good fly-fishing. Wt £4 and dt £2 from hon sec; water restocked. Pyrddin AS (10m from Neath) has water; dt and wt (also RD licences) from hon sec; water restocked. Two hotels in Neath. In headwaters of the Neath is Ystradfellte Reservoir. Tackleists: B Bevan, 36 Windsor Road, and 'Fishing Tackle', 63 Old Road.

OGMORE. Fishing station: **Bridgend.** Rivers Ogmore, **Ewenny** and tributaries; trout, sewin, salmon. Ogmore AA stocks and controls about 20m on these rivers. Mt, wt and dt; no Sunday fishing. Licences (Glamorgan RD) and tackle from W E Watts, 1 Adare Street, Bridgend. Hotels: Wyndham, York, Dunraven, all Wyndham Street. Another tributary is **Llynfi.** Fishing station: **Maesteg.** Club: Llynfi Valley AA, which has 8m excellent trout fishing and coarse fish pond; wt and dt from hon sec. Tackleist (and licence distributor); C Gow, Sports Shop, 59 Commercial Street, Maesteg.

RHYMNEY. About 30m long, rises above town of **Rhymney,** Gwent. Polluted in lower reaches, but some trout fishing higher up. Fishing free to licence-holders from Rhymney Bridge to New Tredegar. Caerphilly AA has stretch from Llanbradach to Bedwas; wt, dt. Rhymney and Dist AS has rights on two ponds: **Butetown** and **Rhos-las.** Both well stocked with coarse fish of all usual species; pike in Rhos-las. Dt 50p for both ponds from hon sec or H James, Tackle Shop, High Street. For details of fishing on **Pontsticill, Pentwyn** and **Upper** and **Lower Neuadd Reservoirs,** apply to Taff Division, WWA, Medallion House, Crwys Road, Cardiff. Tel 399961. Llangorse Lake *(see Brecon, on Usk)* and Talybont Reservoir *(see Talybont and Newport, on Usk)* are accessible. Caerphilly and Dist AA has coarse fishing in three large lakes at **Caerphilly:** mirror carp, bream, tench, roach, perch, pike (restocked). Dt issued. Association also has stretch on **Taff** at Taffswell. Members only.

TAWE. Centres: **Swansea, Pontardawe** and **Ystradgynlais.** River is polluted from Swansea to Clydach, about 7m, but much improved; salmon and sewin more numerous than ever; clear from Pontardawe to source. Upper reaches noted for scenery. Tawe and Tributaries AA has 7m; headquarters at Ystradgynlais; st and dt from Mrs M A Williams, Pontardawe; D Watkins Sports Shop, Ystradgynlais. Sunday fishing allowed. From Pontardawe to Morriston about 6m, is largely Pontardawe AS water; good trout fishing. Permits, licences, information about association waters from Linnards Sports, Swansea and Lea Davies, Morriston. St £14, dt £2. Trout fishing on **Cray Reservoir,** near Trecastle, Powys. Apply Glamorgan RD, 86 Kingsway, Swansea SA1 5JL, or reservoir keeper. Llangyfelach and Dist AA has water on **River Llan** (sewin, brown trout, wt £2), Sunday fishing permitted. Swansea Amateur AA has water on **Cothi;** (visitors to be accompanied by member). D Watkins, Ystradgynlais issue permits for Usk fishing. Good sea fishing (especially bass) from **Swansea** at **Mumbles** and all along Gower Coast. Advice and tackle from Capstan House, Beach Street, P E Mainwaring, 9 Dillwyn Road, Sketty, and Keith Pryer & Co, 31 Kings Road, Mumbles. Hotels: Gwyn Arms (above Craig-y-nos) (permits). Ancient Briton (Penycae); Dynevor Arms (Pontardawe); and Gough Arms and Yniscedwyn Arms (Ystradgynlais).

GLASLYN

(For close seasons, licences, etc, see Welsh Water Authority, p. 43)

Rises in Llyn Glaslyn, 3m south-west of Pen-y-Gwyrd, and flows through three lakes to Beddgelert then along Pass of Aberglaslyn to lower reaches and Portmadoc, where it enters sea. Noted sea trout river and efforts are being made to increase salmon run. Best trout fishing in upper reaches, mountain lakes and tributaries. Best spots for salmon and sewin are: Glaslyn Hotel Bridge; Verlas; and above the pass.

Portmadoc (Gwynedd). Salmon, sewin, brown trout, Glaslyn AA water, Portmadoc to Beddgelert except two private stretches; st, wt, dt from Mr Jones, 27 High Street, and Coffee Bar, Beddgelert. Lakes: Cwm Ystradllyn, 4m. N; trout; good fly fishing: ¾ lb to 4 lb. Tackleist: R Davies, High Street. Hotels: Queen's, Royal Sportsman. Brynllydan at Llanfrothen.

Beddgelert (Gwynedd); ns Portmadoc, 7½m. Trout, sewin, salmon, Glaslyn AA has river from Beddgelert to Portmadoc (both banks, except two private stretch-es). Best months are: April and May for trout; April to Oct for salmon; May to Oct for sewin. Association tickets available *(see Portmadoc)*. Fishing rights on left bank from Beddgelert to and including **Dinas Lake** and stretch above lake belong to R H Williams, Beddgelert; wt, dt and boats. Permits (salmon, sewin, trout) for part of **Gwynant Lake** (boats only) also available from Beddgelert and Nantgwynant Post Offices. Sunday fishing on river and lakes. Hotels: Royal Goat and Saracen's Head (both can provide fishing on several miles of river).

GWENT (lakes, streams)

Aberbeeg. Pound-y-Coed-Cae, 2m Trout; let to Blackwood AC; members only.

Afon Llwyd. Cwmbran AA controls 2½m running through new town of **Cwmbran;** stocked annually with brown trout; fly or worm; dt £1 from D H Powell (ironmongers), Chapel Street, Pontnewydd. Assn also has fishing on **Blaen Bran Reservoir** for members only, Lower Bigsweir on the **R Wye** and issues dt 50p for stretch of **Monmouthshire Canal;** general coarse fishing. Pontypool AA has several miles of trout fishing; st from Jayeff Sports, 48 Windsor Road, Griffithstown, both Pontypool. Hotel: King's Head, Pontnewydd.

GWYNEDD (streams)

(For close seasons, licences, etc, see Welsh Water Authority, p 43)

ABER. Fishing station: **Aber.** Aber rises in Llyn-Anafon, runs to Aber and sea in 2m. Trout (average 7–8 in). Now a Nature Reserve. No fishing. Hotel: Aber.

ARTRO. Rises in Lyn Cwmbychan, 6m E of Harlech, and enters sea 1m below Llanbedr. In tidal waters is good bass fishing. Noted for night fishing for sea trout but has suffered in past from poaching and neglect; overgrown in places and little fly fishing done. Conditions now improving. Fishing station: **Llanbedr.** Sewin, occasional salmon. 4m (both banks) leased by Artro FA; tickets at Post Office, Llanbedr; wt and dt. Good free trout fishing in tributary **Nant-col.** This has been dammed to form lake in which trout up to 3 lb taken (mostly on minnows). Several lakes also free (trout), while permission can be had for others. Lakes include: **Eiddewbach** (trout); **Fedw** (trout); **Eiddewmawr** (trout); **Graigddrwg** (trout); **Cwmbychan** (sewin, trout; preserved); **Gloywlyn** (good trout); **Pryfell** (trout); **Twrglas** (trout); **Hywell** (trout). Hotel: Victoria *(see also Gwynedd—lakes).*

DARON. Fishing station: **Aberdaron:** ns Pwllheli, 17m. Daron and Cyll-y-Felin run down two valleys and join at Aberdaron; restocked and hold good-sized trout. Sea fishing for mackerel, pollack, lobsters, crab, etc, from rocks or boat. Tackle and licences from Jones, Spar Stores, Aberdaron.

DWYFAWR and DWYFACH. Fishing sta-tion: **Criccieth.** Best part of river lies in 1m W of Criccieth, where there is length of 12m unobstructed and good for fly fishing. Salmon fishing has greatly improved owing to restrictions on netting. Sewin very good; late June to Oct; night fishing best. Criccieth, Llanystumdwy and Dist AAA controls about 10m both banks; st £41, wt £16 and dt (member's friend) £3. Sunday fishing. Association also has about 2m on Dwyfach; shorter river than Dwyfawr (about 10m) and rather heavily wooded but good for brown trout and sewin (mid-July onwards). RD licences and assn permits from R T Pritchard, Sheffield House. High Street. Hotels: Marine, Lion; Ranch Hotel, Llanystumdwy.

ERCH. Fishing station: **Pwllheli.** Trout, sewin. Some good fishing here and on **Soch, Rhydhir** and tributary (11m) in hands of Pwllheli and Dist AA; wt and dt. Association also has good trout fishing on Rhydhir. **Cwymystradlyn Lake,** approx 10m NW; 95 acre lake stocked with brown and rainbow trout by WWA. St £35, dt £2. Tickets on site. For Assn water tickets apply D Hughes, Walsall Stores, Penlan Street, Pwllheli. Hotels: Rhyllech Mansion (1m on Rhydhir), Tower, West End, Crown.

GEIRCH. Fishing station: **Nevin,** ns Pwllheli, 8m. Geirch, 2m W, 5m long; good sea fishing at Morfa Nevin. RD licences and tackle from D Chapman, High Street, Pwllheli.

GWYRFAI. Issues from Llyn Cwellyn,

near Snowdon, and flows into Menai Strait through **Bettws Garmon** and **Llanwnda.** Salmon, sea trout, trout. Seiont, Gwyrfai and Llyfni AS controls much of river; wt £12, dt £4. Llyfni 1m NW of Rhyd-ddu trout.

LLYFNI. Rises in Llyn-y-Dywarchen, 1m NW of Rhyd-ddu and runs through Nantlle Lake; salmon, sea trout (good), trout. Seiont, Gwyrfai and Llyfni AS controls nearly all right bank downstream of Llyfni Bridge to sea (4m) *(see Seiont)*.

SOCH. Fishing station: **Llangian** ns Pwllheli, 7m. Trout and rudd; an early stream; dry fly useful; weeds troublesome later; some sewin, late; plenty of sea fishing, bass, pollack, whiting, flatfish, at Abersoch (ns Pwllheli, 7m), from which this stream can be fished. Licences at Abersoch and Llangian post offices.

WEN. Fishing station: **Afon-wen.** Wen rises 4m above Llangybi station, runs 1m to Chwilog, and sea at Afon-wen, 1m; sea trout and brown trout; permission from farmers.

YSGETHIN. Fishing station: **Talybont.** Small trout; free to Gwynedd RD licence holders. River rises in Llyn Bodlyn (trout, char, free) **Llyn Irddyn** and **Llyn Dulyn** also provide free trout fishing (3 or 4 to lb).

GWYNEDD (lakes)

(For close seasons, licences, etc, see Welsh Water Authority, p 43)

Bala (Llyn Tegid). Owned by Gwynedd County Council, Caernarvon. Permits from Lake Warden, Warden's Office on foreshore and Bala tackleists. Charges for visitors as follows: st £6, wt £2, dt 70p incl VAT with concessions to clubs and parties. Salmon may sometimes be taken and trout early in season. Pike, perch, roach, grayling, eels. Bala is largest natural lake in Wales 4m long, 1m wide. Here, too, is found that rare and interesting fish called gwyniad. Coarse fishermen will find all their wants more than provided for; pike up to 25 lb; perch and good roach. RD licence required. Hotels quite close to fishing in Bala town. Llanuwchllyn AC issues tickets for Lower Lliw and Twrch; wt and dt from Post Office at Llanuwchllyn. Bala AA has stretch upstream of Bala New Bridge (dt) and winter fishing for members only

on another stretch, both banks. Assn also has water on **Tryweryn** (members only), **Lliw, Llafar** (dt) and **Cwm Prysor Lake** (dt). St £10, wt £5 and dt £1 and £1.50 from Bala tackleists.

Bethesda. Ogwen Valley FA has trout lakes for which permits are available. **Ogwen,** 5m; boats. **Idwal,** 7m SE; a large lake, well known for rugged scenery; trout; fly only. **Ffynnon Lloer Lake,** also fishable on Ogwen VFA permits. Wt £10, dt £3. Other lakes: **Melynllyn,** 5m E. **Dulyn,** 6m E; **Cowlyd** (5m W Llanwrst); all trout reservoirs belonging to Water Authority; free to licence holders. Tackle, licences and Ogwen VFA permits from T Jones, 29 High Street. Association also has river fishing *(see Ogwen).*

Beddgelert. Dinas, 2m NE; abundant trout, sea trout and salmon; permits for fishing

The Wye at Erwood – a typical mid-Welsh prospect. *Photograph: John Tarlton.*

from village to and including **Dinas Lake** and river above lake from Post Offices at Beddgelert and Nantgwynant; best for sea trout mid-May to early Sept; salmon May–Oct; wt, dt and boats. Also part of **Gwynant Lake** (4m NE); apply hotels: Royal Goat, Saracen's Head, Prince Llewellyn. Permits for **Cwmystradllyn Lake** (trout, £2 day) from Treatment works at lake. Yr Arddu, 3m SE; deep lake amid fine scenery; trout; Cerig-y-myllt, 3m SE. Llagi, 4½m E; trout numerous good size. Yr Adar, 5m E; trout; fishing sometimes good; Edno, 6m NE near Llagi; trout large but difficult.

Llyn Celyn near **Bala**. Reservoir near Bala (4m) managed by WWA, Shire Hall, Mold, Clwyd. Trout. April 1–Sept 30. Visitors' permits: st £40, dt £2.30 (evening after 5 pm, £1.50 from local tackleists. All prices include VAT. Concessions for juvs. and OAP. Sunday fishing (*see Bala under Dee*).

Llyn Crafnant, Trefriw; 3m W of Llanrwst. One of the most beautiful lakes in Wales. Trout only (av 2 lbs) tickets from lakeside cafe. St £25, wt £7.50, dt £2. Boats, rod licences and information from café. Sunday fishing.

Llyn Cwellyn, nr Caernarvon. Salmon, sewin, brown trout. St £20, wt £7 and dt £2 from Mrs Davies, Castell Cidwm Hotel, Betws Garmon.

Dolgellau. Tal-y-llyn, 8m S; a well-known trout lake with hotel accommodation (*see River Dysynni*). Gwernan, 2m SW; trout and coarse fish. Cynwch, 2m N; trout and coarse fish; fishing generally leased. Aran, 3m S; trout, fishing free. Cregennan, 4m SE; trout. Gader, 4m SW; trout; free fishing, but rather poor. Y-Gafr, 4m SW; trout; near Gader, free, not very good. *For stream fishing see River Mawddach.* Permits and tackle from Celfi Diddan, Eldon Square.

Dolwyddelan. Llyn-y-Foel, 3m NE Diwaunedd, 3m W. Free trout fishing. **Llyn Bychan** and **Llyn Goddionduon** nr Capel Curig, are leased by Betws-y-Coed AA. Dt from Tan Lan Café.

Y Dywarchen, Rhyd Ddu, ½m S of Llyn Cwellyn. Seiont, Gwyrfrai and Llyfni AS water. Open 1977, fly only. *See Seiont.*

Y-Gader, 4m on main road to Caernarvon; trout; reputed good fly lake; boats obtainable at village (*see Gwyrfai—streams).*

Llyn Gwynant, 3m S; salmon, trout, sea trout; part private, part Glaslyn AA

water (*see Glaslyn*). Lockwood's Llyn; trout; dt at petrol station; boat available.

Harlech. Good centre for Llanbedr and Talsarnau Lakes, and Artro and Glyn rivers. **Hafod-y-llyn** Lake, coarse fish, is private. 2m SE. **Craigddrwg,** 5m NE. **Dywarshen,** 8m NE. Du, 8m NE. **Eiddewfach,** 8m NE. **Eiddew-mawr,** 8m NE. These last-named lakes are free.

Llanberis. Llyn Peris no longer a fishery; **Llyn Padarn** stocked with wild brown trout and arctic char. Spinning and worm permitted. St £20 and dt £1 from WWA Bangor and D Jones, The Shop, Llanberis.

Llanbedr. Cwm-bychan Lake. Trout and sewin; good fishing. Apply Cwmbychan Farm, Glouwln (dt, wt and st). For **Glouwlyn Lake** apply Cwmrafon Farm. Apply Artro FA, Llanbedr, for **Llyn Hywel;** trout; good fishing. **Llyn Perfeddau,** trout, good fishing; free. For stream fishing, *see River Artro.* Apply Artro FA.

Maentwrog: ns Tany-y-Bwlch. **Y-Garnedd,** 1m N (trout) and **Hafod-y-Llyn** 1m NW (pike, coarse fish) are both private. **Tecwyn-Uchaf,** 2m SW and **Tecwyn-Isaf,** 2m SW, are under Talsarnau AA; trout; st issued. Other lakes under Cambrian AA are: **Morwynion, Gamallt, Cwmorthin, Manod, Barlwyd, Dubach, Dubach-y-bont. Trawsfynydd** is accessible. For stream fishing, *see River Dwyryd.*

Manod. Manod, 1m E; trout fishing often good; tickets from Cambrian AA, Blaenau Ffestiniog who have a number of mountain lakes around Blaenau Ffestiniog, some producing large fish. St £7.50, wt £4.25, dt £1.25. Tickets from Blaenau Ffestiniog tackleists. *For stream fishing, see River Dwyryd.*

Penmaenpool. Trout, sewin, and salmon; **Mynach Gadr,** 1m S Llechan, 2m W. Lake: **Cwmmynach,** 4m N (preserved).

Pen-y-Gwryd. Lyn Cwm Ffynnon. Excellent fly lake, trout plentiful but very small; free: **Teyrn,** ½m SW; RD experimental lake; strictly preserved. **Diwaunedd,** 2m SE; good trout on occasion; free (*see Dolwyddelan, above*). Llydaw, 2m SW.

Talsarnau. Glyn Group Lakes: Fedw (good-sized trout numerous) **Caerwych** (small trout), **Eiddew Bach** (numerous free-rising trout, 4 to 1 lb). **Eiddew Mawr** (small trout). Tecwyn group lakes: **Tecwyn-Isaf** (good quality trout; wading not advised). **Tecwyn-Uchaf** now stocked annually with 12–14 in rainbows, some larger native fish. Glyn river and tributary hold numerous small trout. Talsarnau AA issues wt £3 and dt £1. Licences and tickets at Post Office, Talsarnau; The Pharmacy, Harlech; Mr Pierce (ironmonger), Penrhyndeudraeth; and The Grapes Hotel, Maentwrog.

Tal-y-llyn. Tal-y-llyn; trout, reserved for guests at Tynycornel Hotel but few dt available. £3.50 fly only *(advt p 236)*. For river and stream fishing, *see Dysynni.*

Trawsfynydd Lake. 3m long and 1m wide. Brown and rainbow trout (average 1½ lb). Also many perch and rudd (coarse fishermen welcomed in winter to reduce stocks). Sport controlled by Prysor AA; st, wt and dt, extra for boat. Fly only from boat. Assn controls 5m of **Prysor River;** provides good sport with trout, especially towards end of season when lake trout run up. Assn also controls about 3m of upper **Eden;** salmon and sewin June onwards. Assn has own hatchery. Membership inquiries to hon sec. Dt and licences from H & P Lewis (newsagent), Trawsfynydd. Hotels: Cross Foxes, Trawsfynydd; Grapes, Maentwrog; Abbey Arms and Pengwern Arms, Ffestiniog.

LLWCHWR (or LOUGHOR)

(For close seasons, licences, etc, see Welsh Water Authority, p 43)

Rises some 3m east of Llandybie on Taircarn Mountain and flows 15m south-west through Ammanford and Pontardulais to Burry Inlet, north of Gower Peninsula. Fishing good for brown trout and sewin, and some salmon (April–July; August–October best). Salmon and sewin runs reported to be increasing. Most fishing controlled by clubs, from whom tickets are available.

Pontardulais (Glamorgan). Trout and good run of sea trout; some salmon. Pontardulais and Dist AA has 6m good fishing; limited permits from hon sec. Ammanford AA has water on middle and upper reaches and tributaries; st issued. No dt or wt, but visitors' permit for 14 days issued. Swansea AAA and Llangyfelach AA also have water. Hotels: Gwyn; Penrhiw Guest House. Ammanford; Wernolau Hotel, Pontamman. Tackleist: R Thomas, Stepney St, Llanelly.

Tributaries of the Llwchwr

AMMAN. Trout, sewin, few salmon. Very fast running; fishes well in spate. Fishing stations: **Garnant, Bryn-Amman, Ammanford, Pantyffynon** (all Dyfed). Llwchwr, 1m; Marlais Brook 1m; Lash, 1m. Ammanford and Dist AA has water on Llwchwr tribs and on **Cennen** and **Gwili.** Sea trout run from August onwards. St £10, wt £5 and £2.50, dt £3 and £1.50, according to conditions; hon sec or D Chiswell, Amman Sports, Wind Street, Ammanford. Accommodation: West End Guest House, Pen-Rhiw Guest House.

MARLAIS BROOK. Sewin, July onwards. Fishing stations: **Llandybie.** Llwchwr, 3m. Gwendraeth Fawr, 5m W. Lake: Llyn Lechowen, 5m W. **Derwydd Road.** Marlais Brook. Cennen (tributary of Towy).

MAWDDACH

(For close seasons, licences, etc, see Welsh Water Authority, p 43)

Rises in hills between Bala and Trawsfynydd Lakes and flows 10m south to confluence with Wnion, 2m below Dolgellau, and thence through long estuary to sea at Barmouth. River holds salmon, sea trout and brown trout and is all preserved, although permits can be had for some stretches. Successful stocking with locally hatched salmon fry. Salmon and sea trout may be taken up to Pistyll Mawddach.

Barmouth (Gwynedd). Within radius of 10m from Barmouth angler can have every variety of fishing. Rivers: Mawddach and **Wnion;** trout, sea trout and salmon. Run of sea trout and salmon is from beginning of June to end of season *(see Penmaenpool).* Other nearby streams are Arthog, Gwril, Bontddu, Glandwr, Artro, Scethin, Afon Cwm Mynach and Ardudwy; permission can usually be obtained from landowners; trout, not large, but very plentiful. Lakes: Dilyn, Bodlyn, Urddyn, Cwmbychan, Glawlyn, Llyn Howell, Llyn Cwmmynach and Ubi. Trout; also some char.

Penmaenpool (Gwynedd). Sewin, salmon, few trout; tidal. Tickets for Hengwrt Estate water, which extends 2m down and 1m up from Llanelltyd Bridge now rented by Macclesfield Prince Albert AS from Post Office, Llanelltyd. Mynach Gadr, 1m S, Llechan, 2m W. Lake; Cwm-mynach, 4m N (preserved). Hotel:

George. *For licences and tackle, see Dolgellau.*

Llanelltyd and Ganllwyd (Gwynedd). Salmon, sewin, trout (small); preserved. Best months for salmon, June onwards; for sea trout, June to Sept. Hengwrt Estate water now rented by Prince Albert AS, Macclesfield. Cefndeuddwr Fishing Syndicate has water on **Eden** and Mawddach; tickets from Post Office, Ganllwyd, Dolgellau; wt and dt. Various small streams and lakes holding trout for which permission may be given. Hotels: Tyn-y-Groes *(advt p 248)* (1½m salmon and sea trout fishing on river; 8m on **Wnion**), a stretch on the **Conway** and a lake above the hotel. Dolmelynllyn Hall (1¼m on Mawddach; dt 75p).

Tributary of Mawddach

WNION: Salmon, sewin, brown trout.

Dolgellau (Gwynedd). Wnion and Mawddach rivers. Wnion runs by Dolgellau and joins Mawddach 2m below town. Mawddach, 1m NW. Dolgellau AA owns rights on Wnion, also Mawddach and **Clywedog** at Dolserau Hall, 1m from

town. Dt £3, wt £10, st £30 from Don Sports, Bridge Street and D Stuart, Store House Cottage, Barmouth Road. Assn also has trout fishing on **Llyn Cynwch** (£2 day). **Tal-y-llyn** 8m S; good trouting for residents of Tynycornel Hotel *(advt p 236)*. Free lakes nearly all

containing trout, some of them coarse fish also, are: Arran, 3m S; Gafr 4m SW; Cyri; Cader; Cau; Gwernan (half only), 2m SW. Best months for salmon: April, Sept and Oct; for sea trout, June to Sept, for brown trout, April, May, late August, Sept. Tickets may be available for Nannau Estate water. Tackle and licences from Celfi Diddan, The Square. Hotels: Dolmelynllyn Hall, Ganllwyd (salmon, sea trout fishing on Mawddach), Tyn-y-Groes *(see Llanelltyd);*

Cross Foxes (3m on Wnion; also mountain streams and fishing by arrangement at Trawsfynydd).

Bont Newydd (Gwynedd). Wnion; trout, sewin. Permits, wt and dt, from Celfi Diddan, Dolgellau.

Drws-y-Nant (Gwynedd). Wnion; trout, sewin; preserved by owners. Hallog, Cwm-ochr, Ciddow, 1m W. Fiddow, 1½m W. Dovey, 3m. Mawddach, 4m N; trout, sewin, salmon. Lakes: Dyfi, 3m W. Crych-y-wayen, 4m N.

OGWEN

(For close seasons, licences, etc, see Welsh Water Authority, p 43)

Rises in Ogwen Lake, half way between Bethesda and Capel Curig, with tributaries running in from Ffynnon Lloer and Bochlwyd Lakes, and runs from lake to outlet at Menai Straits, near Bangor, about 10m in all. Excellent trout fishing; leased by Ogwen Valley AA from Penrhyn Estate. Extensive restocking programme, with trout, sea trout (sewin) and salmon. Catches improving. Autumn good for salmon.

Bangor (Gwynedd). Ogwen, 2m E; Salmon, sewin, trout. Parts of river leased by Ogwen Valley AA, which also has lake fishings *(see Bethesda).* Sea trout run starts about mid-June. Salmon best Aug–Oct. Salmon: wt £15, dt £6. No Sunday fishing *(see Bethesda).* Sea fishing very good in the Menai Straits, near suspension and tubular bridges;

bass, whiting, pollack, etc. Hotels: Waverley, British Castle, Railway.

Bethesda (Gwynedd). Ogwen Valley AA has water on main river and tributaries and on three lakes: **Ogwen, Idwal** and **Ffynnon Lloer.** Charges for river under **Bangor** *(this page)* wt for lakes £10, dt £3, with concessions for juniors. Tickets from T Jones, Windsor House, High Street.

POWYS (lakes)

Llyn Clywedog. Llanidloes (3m); 615 acres; Llanidloes and Dist AA. Reservoir shared with sailing club; western half is fishery area, but fishing permitted in much of eastern half, also by arrangement with sailing club. Well stocked with brown and rainbow trout averaging 1¾ lb. Fly only. £2.80 day (£1.80 evenings). £15 week, £30 (concession rate for residents) season from hon sec, local tackleists and hotels. RD licence required. *See also Llanidloes.* Tackleists: Dallas Sports, Grapple Tackle Box.

Lake Vyrnwy, nr Llanwddyn. Naturally-bred brown trout, stocked rainbows and brook trout. Annual catch nearly 2,000 fish av 15 ozs. A brown of 5½ lbs taken in 1979. Limit: ten brace. Season: March 1 to Oct 15. Dt £3.50 (£2.50 after July 15) boats, for which residents have priority, £3.50. Rowing boats only. Apply to Lake Vyrnwy Hotel, via Oswestry, Salop SY10 0LY (Tel Llanwddyn 244) to which fishing rights are let. Hotel also has 3m

on river, dt £1.50. Bodfach Hall Country House Hotel, Llanfyllin has use of boat on Lake Vyrnwy (10m) and stretch of **River Cain.**

Llanrhaiadr-ym-Mochnant; ns Llanfyllin, 7m. Llyn-y-cawg, 6m NW; trout; free.

Llangorse Lake. Brecon 6m. Holds good pike, good bream, perch, roach, eels, etc. Boats from Mr R P B Davies at lake side caravan park. Fishing free but Wye rod licences required. Llynfi runs from lake to Wye at Glasbury and holds a few trout; overgrown in places; requires short rod. Hotel at Llangorse: Red Lion.

Blaentawe. Fan Fawr, 1m. Fan Fach, 3m; many small trout; small charge made.

Talybont. 6m SW of Brecon. WWA reservoir, continuously stocked with brown and rainbow trout. St £40, dt £1.50, from reservoir or Div Office, Gwent Water Div, WWA, Station Buildings, Newport, Gwent. One boat available, £5 per day. *(See Talybont, Usk).*

SEIONT

(For close seasons, licences, etc, see Welsh Water Authority, p 43)

Rises in two tarns in Cwm-glas, under crest of Snowdon, and runs to Llanberis, 3m, where it enters the Llanberis Lakes, Llyn Peris and Llyn Padarn. Flows thence to Menai Straits at Caernarvon. Attractive river with long flats, nice runs and excellent pools holding salmon (May onwards), sea trout (June onwards), and brown trout. Trout rather small, but in faster water can give good account of themselves.

Caernarvon (Gwynedd). Salmon, sea trout, trout. Seiont, Gwyrfai and Llyfni AS control the following: bank fishing on **Llyn Gadair,** with boat-fishing rights; and 23 miles of salmon and sea trout fishing on **Seiont, Gwyrfai** and **Llyfni.** St £18, wt £12, dt £4. Permits from hon sec. Tackleists: Mrs D Huxley-Jones, 1 and 3 South Penrallt. Hotels: Eagles, Prince of Wales, Castle, Royal, Black Boy.

Llanberis (Gwynedd). Trout, salmon sewin; preserved (as Caernarvon) Hwch, 2m NW; trout. Mar, 3m NE **Llanberis Lakes:** L Peris no longer fished: L Padarn stocked brown trout and arctic char. Fly, worm and spinning. St £20 and dt £1 from D Jones, The Shop, Llanberis. Marchllyn-mawr and Marchllyn-bach, 5m NE, preserved by Lord Penrhyn. Hotels: Padarn Lake (on lakeside); Victoria, Dolbadarn, Castle.

TAF

(For close seasons, licences, etc, see Welsh Water Authority, p 43)

Rises on Mynydd Prescelly and flows about 25m south-west and south-east to Carmarthen Bay at mouth of Towy. Has reputation for sea trout (sewin) and also holds salmon and brown trout. Sewin run from June onwards.

St Clears (Dyfed). Salmon, sewin (brown trout poor). April, May, Sept best for salmon, sewin July onwards. Some open waters. Carmarthen and Dist AC have water on Taf and stretch on **Dewi Fawr** (for charges *see Towy*). St Clears and District AA has good water; tickets from hon sec. Glynin; trout, sewin. Cowin, 3m; trout, sewin. Permission of farmers. Hotels: Railway, Yelverton, Fisher's

Arms. RD licences from Post Offices at St Clears and Meidrim.

Whitland (Dyfed). Salmon, sea trout, brown trout. Whitland AA has 6m of fishing. St £20, wt £5 and dt £3 from hon sec and Station Garage. Waungren Mansion and Farm has ¾m. Tackle and RD licences from Walters & James, Gerald Jones, both of St John St. Hotels: Waungren, Farmers Arms, Yelverton, Taf.

TAFF and ELY

(For close seasons, licences, etc, see Welsh Water Authority, p 43)

Taff has its source in two headstreams on the Brecon Beacons and flows about 40m south-east to the Bristol Channel at Cardiff. Trout and sea trout, but river hard-hit by pollution and clubs fighting uphill battle; one club dissolved. Ely joins mouth of Taff at Penarth.

Cardiff (Glamorgan). Brown trout (stocked) and run of sea trout but sport marred by pollution. Glamorgan AC (membership 400) has headquarters at Old Arcade Hotel, Church Street, and preserves about 6m on **Trothy** at Dingestow and Mitchel Troy (trout), 5m on Ely at Llantrisant (trout), and 8m coarse and trout fishing in Taff from Canton Bridge, centre of Cardiff, north to Radyr station (not continuous). Club also holds rights on freshwater reservoir at Barry Docks

(see Barry, under Sea Fishing Stations) and on the St-y-Nyll ponds at St Brides. Also has sea-angling section. Tickets from hon sec, but no dt for trout issued from May 1 to Aug 1 inclusive. Trout season March 1 to Oct 1. **Bute AA** has fishing at **Marshfield Reens;** good carp, tench, etc. St £3 from hon sec. Also coarse fishing on Wye and Usk. **Monmouthshire and Brecon Canal** (roach and perch). Controlled by B W'ways Board, which has leased stretches to clubs. Tick-

ets from Inspector of Waterways, Railway Buildings, Govilon. Centres: **Cwmbran, Pontypool, Newport.** Roath Park Lake (Cardiff Corporation) holds rudd, roach, carp, tench. Many good sea fishing stations are within reach. Tackle and advice from Bale's *(see below)*. Local sea-angling organisation is Cardiff Sea AA. **Cardiff Reservoirs.** Managed as "fly-only" trout waters by the Cardiff Unit of Taff Water Div, WWA, Crwys House, Crwys Road, Cardiff CF2 4YF. **Taf Fawr Group,** *Beacons Reservoir* (52 acres) Brown trout, fly only; *Cantref Reservoir* (42 acres) rainbow & brown trout, fly, spinning and worm fishing; *Llwynon Reservoir* (150 acres) rainbow trout & brown trout, fly fishing only, all located in Brecon Beacons National Park adjacent to A470(T) road, 3 miles North of Merthyr Tydfil and 15 miles South of Brecon. **Taf Fechan Group,** *Pontsticill Reservoir* (253 acres) Rainbow & brown trout, fly, spinning, worm, maggot and cereal baits on hook only; *Dolygaer Reservoir* (96 acres) rainbow & brown trout, fly fishing, and spinning zone on West bank; *Lower Neuadd Reservoir* (12 acres) fly only, stocked with 2 lbs plus rainbows; *Upper Neuadd* brown trout & brook trout, fly only all located in Brecon Beacons National Park 4 miles North of Merthyr Tydfil. Day permits available for all above Reservoirs from Self Issue Vending Machines at Llwynon and Pontsticill Works (machines will accept 50p, 10p & 5p coins only—please tender the correct amount). **Cardiff Group,** *Llanishen* (59 acres) and *Lisvane* (19 acres) Reservoirs, rainbow trout, fly fishing only. Located within Cardiff City

boundary, approach via B4562 road. Day permits available from site staff. Charges: The reservoirs are graded and season tickets, conferring the right to fish more than one, range from £30 to £72. These are obtained from Taff Division of WWA. Dt, obtainable on site, range similarly from £1.50 to £3.50. Tackleists: A Bale, 3 Frederick Street (information, bait, licences); W Powell, Grangetown; Luxton's, Custom House Street; Norrie's, Arcade, Newport Road; Anglers Supplies, 172 Penarth Road. Cardiff hotels: Alexandra, Angel, Central, Grand, Park, Queen's, Royal.

Llandaff (Glamorgan). Taff: river unfishable due to pollution.

Pontypridd (Glamorgan). At junction of Taff and Rhondda. Club: Pontypridd and DAA, which has water here holding trout (av $\frac{1}{2}$ lb); which includes 4m on **Honddu** (Powys) and small lake.

Treharris (Glamorgan). At junction of Taff and **Taff Bargoed.** Clubs: Treharris AA and Bedlinog AA, which has 7m of **Taff Bargoed,** mountain stream holding brown trout. Also two ponds; coarse fishing. Inquire hon sec for details.

Merthyr Tydfil (Glamorgan). Merthyr Tydfil AA has rights on practically whole of Taff, Taff Fechan and Taff Fawr from Merthyr Vale to Pontsticill about 13m in all also a stretch on the **Tarrell** at Libanus, 4m from Brecon. Excellent trout fishing (browns and rainbows) after improvement work by RD and club members. Assn also has coarse fishing in Penywern Ponds, Bryn-Cae-Owen Pond (carp up to 16 lbs) and lakes in Cyfarthfa Park. Tickets available for all assn waters from hon sec. *(For details of reservoirs in vicinity, see Cardiff p 250.)*

Tributaries of Taff

RHONDDA FAWR and FACH:

Pontypridd (Glamorgan). At Junction of Rhonddas Fawr and Fach and Taff. Club: Pontypridd and Dist AC.

Treorchy (Glamorgan). Rhondda; trout; Upper Rhondda AA control river from Blaencwm to Treorchy and **Llyn Fawr Reservoir.** Annual stocking with 10/13 in fish. St for river, but no vacancies except for local people. Dt for reservoir.

Tonypandy (Glamorgan). Glyncornel AA has 6m of Rhondda between Porth and Treorchy; restocked annually with brown trout. St £5 from local tackle

dealers. Club holds rights on Rhymney Bridge Reservoir. Fly only. Inquiries to hon sec. Permits for Rhondda and Darran Lake from local sports shops.

CYNON:

Aberdare (Glamorgan). Cynon joins Taff between Treharris and Pontypridd. Aberdare and Dist AA has trout fishing on Cynon, **Aman, Dare, Lliw** at **Ystradfellte, Cilenni** at **Pentrebach,** near Sennybridge, **Yscir,** near Brecon, and **Taff** at **Cefn Coed-y-Cymmer.** Dt and wt from local tackleist, Leather Stores, Cannon Street.

ELY:
Peterson (Glamorgan). Trout, Glamorgan AC has coarse fishing in St-y-Nyll ponds at St Brides. The river fishing in Taff and Ely FA. *(Tickets, see Cardiff.)*
Llantrisant (Glamorgan). Trout. Glamorgan AC has 5m (not continuous), beginning at Miskin Weir (upstream limit of Taff and Ely water) and total length of **Clun Brook**. *For tickets see Cardiff.* Local club: Llantrisant and Dist AC, which has about 5m trout fishing upstream of Miskin Weir on Ely.

TEIFI

(For close seasons, licences, etc, see Welsh Water Authority, p 43)

Rises in Lyn Teifi, near Strata Florida, in NE Dyfed, flows south-west and then west, entering Cardigan Bay below Cardigan Town. Association water provides salmon, sea trout (sewin) and brown trout fishing. April and May are the best months of spring salmon; summer salmon fishing depends on floods. Sea trout run from July onwards. Coracle and draft nets come off September 1.

Cardigan (Dyfed). Salmon, sewin, trout. Bass, mullet and flounders below bridge to sea, 2m; boats available. Tackleists: R Squibbs, High St (who will supply licences) and M & A Williams, 10a Pendre, who will both supply information about district. Hotels: Black Lion, Angel, Grosvenor.
Llechryd (Dyfed). Castle Malgwyn Hotel has 1m free to guests. Llwyndyris Mansion Hotel has 650 yards; wt issued. Teifi Trout Assn water *(see Newcastle Emlyn).*
Cenarth (Dyfed). Salmon, sewin, trout. Famous falls; last site of historical coracle fishing for salmon. Teifi Trout Assn water *(see Newcastle Emlyn).*
Newcastle Emlyn (Dyfed). Salmon, sewin. Good centre for Teifi Trout Association has 10m of water in and around Newcastle Emlyn and including Cenarth. St and rod licences from tackleists. Cawdor Estates have single-bank fishing here; salmon and sewin. Available for long- or short-term lets. Apply Estate Office, Broad Oak, Dyfed, and D G Evans, Gelligatti Farm (also accommodation).

Tackleists: Cliff Jones, Emlyn Boot Stores. Hotels: Emlyn Arms (AA), Cawdor.
Llandyssul (Dyfed). Salmon, sewin, brown trout. Popular centre; fishing good. Best April–May and Aug–Sept for salmon; sewin July onwards. Llandyssul AA has about 27m of fishing in all. St £45, wt (SMT) £30 (NT) £15, dt for members' guests only. Permits from hon sec. Cerdin Twelli; trout (good). Clettwr, 2m; trout (good). Bargoed, 5m. Hotels: Porth (2 rods on association water for residents; details on request) and County Gate, Llanfihangel-ar-Arth, **Pencader** (on river bank, several miles of private water; dt issued; other fishing by arrangement).
Llanybydder (Dyfed). Salmon, sewin, brown trout. Llanybydder AA has salmon and trout water. St £6, dt £1 from hon sec. Black Lion Hotel has four excellent beats totalling about 3m; Highmead Arms has 1½m including eight pools. Other hotel: Cross Hands.
Lampeter (Dyfed). Salmon (April onwards), some sewin, brown trout (3 to

lb, good for dry fly). Dulas: trout. Gran-nell, 3m trout. Aeron, 6m W, salmon, sewin, trout. Cothi, 8m E; salmon, sewin, trout. Llandyssul and Llany-bydder clubs have water. Tickets from tackleists: Rees, 56 Bridge Street; Megicks, Harford Square, Cwmann AA has 6m starting within five minutes' walk of town. Hotels: Black Lion, Falcondale, Royal Oak, Castle.

Tregaron (Dyfed). Good fly fishing for brown trout. Salmon fishing also good when conditions right. Tregaron AA has 12m of Teifi from Penybont Bridge to Gogoyan Bridge. Assn also controls fishing on **Brianne Reservoir** and stream and on **Berwyn Lake** (4m); trout. Per-mits from Barclays Bank, Tregaron and W Rees, London Shop, Llandewi Brefi. Permits for **Teifi Pools**, 8m; £2 dt, from M Morgan, Post Office, Pontrhydfendi-gaid *(see also Strata Florida).* Other good fishing on Aeron, 6m. Hotels: Talbot (1m on Teifi) *(advt p 254);* Sunny Hill; Red Lion, Brynawel and Aberdwr Guest Houses. Licences from Caron Stores *(see also Dyfed lakes).*

Strata Florida (Dyfed). Strata Florida AA has 6m stretch of Teifi in the vicinity of the village. St £6, wt £2, dt £1, from R Rees & Son, Florida Shop, Pontrhydfen-digaid. Tackleist: D Jones, Rhydteify, Pontrhydfendigaid. Near Strata Florida are **Teifi Lakes,** on headwaters of river. *(See details under Tregaron and p 240.)*

Llyn Gorlan and **Llyn Bach** belongs to Earl of Lisburne, who also owns 3m of double bank fishing and 1⅝m of single bank fishing on Teifi. Inquire at Talbot Hotel, Tregaron and Hafod Arms Hotel, Devils Bridge; also Belle Vue Royal, Aberystwyth. **Llyn Gynon,** 7m; difficulty of access, but is well stocked with trout. Permits from Post Office, Pontrhydfen-digaid. Hotels: Red Lion, Black Lion, Llysteg.

TOWY

(For close season, licences, etc, see Welsh Water Authority, p 43)

Rises in the Cambrians, near source of **Teifi,** and enters seaward end of Bristol Channel by small estuary. Lower reaches near Carmarthen are tidal holding trout, salmon and sewin in season (June and July best); association waters. Above this Towy mostly preserved, but some fishing by leave, ticket or from hotels. Salmon average 12 lb and sea trout up to 8 lb are taken; brown trout generally small.

Carmarthen (Dyfed). Salmon, sewin, trout. March and April good for spring salmon and large sewin. Tidal up to Carmarthen and 3m above. Carmarthen Amateur AA has three stretches on Towy (one tidal) and other good water on **Gwili, Cothi** and **Gwendraeth Fach** (15m in all); salmon, sea trout, brown trout; wt issued for all or part of fishings; all fishing within about 6m *(see Nant-garedig Gwili).* Permits from Lyric Sports, King Street. Carmarthen and Dist AC has useful waters within 2 or 3m of town and extending for 2m of Towy. These cover tidal reaches, which give sport with salmon, sewin and trout. Club has water also on **Cothi, Gwili;** sea trout, trout, some salmon; **Gwendraeth Fach** (6m to 8m away; sea trout lower, trout only upper); **Taf** (10m away) and **Dewi Fawr.** St and wt issued. Trout only (aver-age ¼ lb) in Gwendraeth Fach and Dewi Fawr. Permits and RD licences from tackleists: J M Dark, Chapel St, Sports Depot, Lammas St, Jones-Davies, King St (all Carmarthen), Towy Sport, 9 King St, Llandeilo; R Thomas, Stepney St, and Anglers Corner, Robinson St, Llanelli; Davies, Bridge St, Kidwelly and PO, Nantgaredig. Broadsheet giving full details of all waters issued by hon sec. Hotels: Falcon, Boar's Head, Gol-den Lion, Ivy Bush, Park. Hon secs of Carmarthen associations will be pleased to give information.

Nantgaredig (Dyfed). Salmon, trout, sewin; fishing private. Cothi; salmon, sewin. Carmarthen AAA has water on Towy and Cothi. Assn also has lower reaches of Cothi; inquire of hon sec. For middle reaches inquire of Forest Arms, Brechfa, and Black Lion Hotel, Aber-gorlech. *(See also Pumpsaint and Car-marthen.)*

Llanarthney (Dyfed). Hotel: Golden Grove Arms. Salmon, sewin, trout; mostly preserved.

Golden Grove (Dyfed). Preserved by Mill-bank Dyfed Estates and well keepered. Upper Water: Runs from Llandeilo Bridge to Myddfai Brook (Cilsane); 1m single bank, 1⅝m double bank; fly only.

Middle water runs from the old footbridge at Glantowy to Rofawr boundary post (about 4¼m, both banks); fly whenever conditions permit. Lower Water: from Bremenda-isaf boundary to old footbridge at Glantowy (about 1⅞m, single bank). Season tickets on all beats £172.50 including VAT. No weekly or daily tickets issued. Full details from Estate Office, Llangathen, Carmarthen, Dyfed, SA32 8QF. Tel: Dryslwyn 494.

Llandeilo (Dyfed). Salmon, sewin; Llandeilo AA preserves 8m on Towy, about 1m on Lower **Dulais** and about 1m on Lower **Cennen**; wt £20, dt £8 (limited), £5 (brooks only) from hon sec. Juniors half-price. Fishing good when water in condition. Black Lion Inn, Llansawel, has 2½m on Towy; rods also available on **Teifi** and **Cothi** *(see under Brechfa)*. **Cennen** good trout stream; Hotels: Morfa King's Head, Cawdor Arms, Castle. Edwinsford Arms.

Llangadog (Dyfed). Salmon, sewin, trout. Swansea Piscatorials and Llangadog AA have water. Wt £15, dt £4 and limited night-fishing tickets, £4, issued. **Bran, Marles, Sefin, Sawdde;** salmon, sewin, brown trout; mostly preserved by landowners; Hotel: Red Lion, which issues dt for 2m.

Llandovery (Dyfed). Salmon, sewin (best June–Sept), trout. Day and weekly tickets for visitors on Llandovery AA waters; 2m on **Gwydderig**, 3m on **Bran** and 8m on Towy. Tickets and licences from tackleist: C Bancroft, 11 Stone Street. **Usk Reservoir** (11m), trout tickets from keeper. Swansea Amateur AA has water at Tonn Farm, above Llandovery Bridge, both banks; dt and wt (8 days) from hon sec (visitors must be accompanied by member). Hotels: Castle, King's Head, North Western, Royston, Picton Court and Llwyncelyn (last three private).

Tributaries of the Towy

GWILI. Small river of 12 ft to 16 ft in width which joins Towy 1m north of Carmarthen. Sea trout (sewin) river, fish running from early June onwards, averaging 2 lb and attaining 6 lb. Brown trout fishing poor. Occasional salmon caught. Carmarthen Amateur AA has about 6m; Carmarthen & Dist AC, a shorter stretch; tickets *(see Carmarthen)*.

Bronwydd Arms (Dyfed). Sewin, trout, occasional salmon; Carmarthen Amateur AA has about 6m of water *(see Towy—Nantgaredig)*; accessible by bus. Carmarthen and Dist AC has 6m *(see Carmarthen)*.

Conwil (Dyfed). Trout, sewin mostly preserved by Conwil AA; mt, wt and dt available for **Conwil;** best June onwards. **Duad** and its tributary, Cochen, give good trouting. Cowin, 7m; trout, sewin.

COTHI. Larger stream than Gwili, but rocky and difficult to fish. Excellent sport with sewin (June onwards); salmon quite good. Some fly water middle and upper reaches. Spinning most popular, but worm also much used.

Carmarthen (Cothi, 6m). Swansea Amateur AA has two stretches of about 1m each. Apply hon sec. Hotel: Cothi Bridge.

Llanfynydd (Dyfed). Penybont Inn has 2m; Cresselly Arms, Cothi Bridge, has short stretch for residents. Tickets from hotel for Assn water: st £25, wt £10 and dt £3.

Brechfa (Dyfed). Salmon, sea trout, good; fishing available from Brechfa Fishing Lodge (Brechfa 212). Black Lion Inn has short stretch at **Abergorlech;** and a longer stretch lower down the river; dt issued *(see Llandeilo).*

Pumpsaint (Dyfed). Cothi and **Twrch.** Trout, sea trout (June onwards); salmon from early July. Dolaucothi Arms has 4½m stretch running through National Trust property; fishing reserved for guests; limited dt if guests not fishing.

SAWDDE; ns Llangadock (Dyfed). Small trout; free. Inn: Cross, Llandeusant.

BRAN. Fishing station: **Cynghordy.** Towy, 3m; trout; fishing preserved. Rhaiadr, 3m. Crychan, 3m. Gwenffrwd 6m.

USK

(For close seasons, licences, etc, see Welsh Water Authority, p 43)

Good salmon river and first rate for trout. Geological formation is red sandstone, merging into limestone in lower reaches. Trout average from about ¾ lb in the lower reaches to ¼ lb towards the source. Some tributaries also afford good trout fishing; Ebbw,

The sport of angling, with the First Gentleman at its summit, unites all classes and sections of society. HRH Prince Charles shows his elegant paces at Glanusk. *Photograph: John Tarlton.*

Afon Llwyd and Sirhowy are recovering from pollution and providing good sport in places. Salmon fishing mostly private, but several opportunities for trout.

Newport (Gwent). Newport AA has stretch of **Monmouthshire Canal** and leases Liswerry Pond; coarse fish; good tench in pond. Dt 50p, juvs ½ price; apply hon sec. Trout fishing in the WWA **Reservoirs; Llandegfedd** (429 acres) **Wentwood** (42 acres) **Upper and Lower Ynysfro** (totalling 26 acres). Well stocked with brown and rainbow trout. Season: April 4 to Oct 14. St (Llandegfedd) £85: others; £70, from Usk Div. WWA. Dt (Llandegfedd) £3: others, £3, on site. 22 boats on Llandegfedd (mb £10 per day, rowing, £5) one rowing boat only, £5 on others. Price concession for juvs and OAP. **Tredegar House Lake** now open for fishing. Good tench and roach. Dt from Leisure Services Dept, Borough of Newport, Baneswell, Newport. Personal callers only. Islwyn AC and Risca Fly FA have trout fishing on **Sirhowy;** inquire hon secs. Tackleists: Dave Richards, 8 Caerleon Road; Fussell's, 194 Dock St. Hotels: King's Head, Queen's, Westgate, Tredegar Arms.

Pontypool (Gwent). Usk private. Tributary **Afon Llwyd,** once heavily polluted, now provides good trout fishing in parts.

Contact Cwmbran AA and Pontypool AA for details. Latter club has rights on **Pen-yr-Heol** reservoir, 3½ acres. B & Rb trout. Fly only. No tickets. Dt for **Olway Brook** from Greyhound Inn, Usk. Water on Monmouth Canal and coarse fishing on **Usk. Glyn Ponds,** upper and lower, provide fair trouting; inquire tackleists: Noel Trigg Sports, Osborne Road, Pontypool; Jayeff Sports, 48 Windsor Road, Griffithstown. Both issue permits for local fishing. Hotel: Clarence.

Usk (Gwent). Usk Town Water FA holds about 2m mostly above Usk Bridge, from Llanbadoc church to Garcoed. Trout tickets only are issued. Charges st £35 (incl. coarse fishing in winter) wt £10, dt £3.50; fly only. Usk RD licences required. Wading advisable. Permits, tackle and licences from Sweet's Fishing Tackle, Porthycarne Street. Hotels: Three Salmons, Castle, Cross Keys, Davington Guest House, Glen-yr-Avon and Bridge Inn, Kemys.

Abergavenny (Gwent). Salmon, trout. Abergavenny Town Council holds left bank from Llanfoist Bridge to Cae Kenfy Brake and right bank from Llanfoist Bridge to below Sewer Bridge. St and dt for salmon and trout. Rods available for short and long terms for Chain Bridge Fishery (salmon and trout), from Mrs M Longsdon, Ty Pengam, Llanfair and Vaughan & Marshall, 2 Bridge St, Usk. Tickets for various waters from PM Fishing Tackle. **Gavenny;** trout. **Mynachdy Brook,** 3m. **Trothy,** 4m; trout. **Full Brook,** 5m. **Honddu,** 5m; trout. **Monnow,** 6m; trout. Hotels: Angel (Trust House); Great Western, Clytha Arms (salmon and trout fishing); and Bell, Glangrwyney (salmon and trout fishing). Tackleists: PM Tackle, 12 Monk Street; Fussells Sports, 53 Cross Street, both Abergavenny; Brutens, Market Street, Ebbw Vale.

Crickhowell (Powys); ns Abergavenny, 10m. Salmon, sea trout, brown trout. Gliffaes Country House Hotel (Tel 0874 730371) has water (2¼m); first-class brown trout and salmon fishing, some sea trout; dt £5 (S £7.50) available *(advt p 253)*. Bridge End Inn has short length below bridge. For stretch of about ½m upstream of Llangynidr Bridge (south bank), Major Llewelyn, Hill Crest, Llangynidr, issues tickets, £5 day. Trecastle

and Talybont Reservoirs are within reach. Crickhowell AC has water. Dt for salmon and trout from Vine Tree Inn, Llangattock. Tackleist: Kirkland's, High Street.

Glangrwyney (Powys). Salmon, sea trout, brown trout. Bell Hotel has water here and issues tickets to residents and non-residents for salmon and trout fishing. Hotel stocks Usk flies.

Talybont (Powys). River privately preserved trout fishing in **Talybont Reservoir** (318 acres) well stocked with browns and rainbows; st £50, dt £2. From reservoir or Div Office, Usk Division, WWA, Station Buildings, Queensway, Newport, Gwent, Hotel: Usk (trout and coarse fishing arranged).

Brecon (Powys). Usk: salmon, trout av ¾ lb. Tributaries: **Honddu, Tarell, Bran.** Brecon AC has 2m above Llanfaes bridge, limited dt £1.50. Brecon Fishery Assn has approx 1¼m, both banks, below the bridge. 3 day tickets for salmon (£8) and trout £4. **Llangrose Lake,** 5m from Brecon, contains pike, perch, roach and bream. Boats and caravans for hire at lakeside from Mr Davies. WWA licence required for all waters. Tackleist: D Spilsbury, Watergate. Hotels: Castle of Brecon, Nythfa, Uskview GH.

Sennybridge (Powys). Trout, salmon. Sennybridge FA has about 1m on one bank of Usk and about 2m on left bank of Senny Brook; dt £2 and £1. A private stretch, about 2¼m just below Sennybridge on one bank of the Usk (site of capture of Usk record brown trout—9¼ lb); dt £1.60. Tickets and licences for this and other trout water on Usk from W J Davies (tackleist), Drug Stores, Sennybridge. Mr H Morgan, Ynysyrwyrddfa Farm, issues st and dt for 1m each bank of Usk. Details of other Usk fishings between Sennybridge and Brecon from Woosnam & Tyler, Builth Wells. Permits for Usk tributaries from farmers. At **Trecastle** is **Usk Reservoir;** 280 acres: Trout; mixed method fishery. St £70, dt £3. Two motor boats available £10 per day. Season: March 20–Oct 17. Rods also available on **Crai Reservoir.** Tickets from reservoir keeper. Glyncornel AA has 1½m on river in Trecastle area; apply hon sec for st. Hotels: Usk, Railway, and White House (1½m on river), all Sennybridge and Castle, Trecastle (trout fishing; £1.50 day).

WELSH SEA FISHING STATIONS

Those given in the following list are arranged from south to north. Sea fishing is available at other places also, but those mentioned are included because they cater specially for the sea angler. Further information may be had from the tackleists and club secretaries (whose addresses will be found in the club list). When writing, please enclose stamped addressed envelope for reply. Local authorities will help with accommodation.

Swansea and Gower. Bass, flatfish from beaches and rocks (Worm's Head). Fish baits cast from Llanmadoc take conger, tope, thornbacks and monkfish. Mackerel caught in warmer months. Bass, mullet and flounders in estuary at Loughor Bridge. Excellent boat fishing in Carmarthen Bay and off Worm's Head, but boats difficult to obtain. Welsh Tope, Skate and Conger Club charters boats leaving Swansea riverside quays and fishing the bay and Pwlldu. Bookings through clubs and skippers. Club membership made through qualifying fish. HQ: Rock and Fountain Inn, Skewen. Small bass, mullet, flatfish and mackerel off Mumbles Pier; no night fishing. Docks permit required for Queens Dock breakwater; good for cod in winter. Bait can be dug in Swansea Bay and estuary; squid, herring, sprats and mackerel from Swansea Market. For details of charter-boats, apply to Derek Jones, 24 Cilonen Road, Three Crosses. Tackleists: Capstan House Pro-Angling Centre, Beach Street; Mainwarings, Dilwyn Road, Sketty. Other clubs: Swansea Sea AC; Mumbles Motor Boat and Fishing Club.

Fishguard (Dyfed). Main captures from shore and breakwaters are flatfish, codling, conger, pouting, mackerel and some tope. Sea trout and mullet near mouth of Gwaun. Tope, mackerel, conger, skate, etc. from boats. Boats from Fishguard Yacht & Boat Co, Main Street, Goodwick, Tel Fishguard 873377. Club: Fishguard & Goodwick SA, annual membership: £1. Tackleists: Collins, 46 West Street; Thomas, 21 West Street; Johns, The Square, Goodwick. Hotel: Fishguard Bay.

Tenby (Dyfed). Good sport from Old Pier; whiting, pollack, bass, codling and grey mullet; good bass fishing from south and north sandy beaches, and spinning from rocks. Fine mackerel fishing most seasons, and tope off Caldey Island as early as April. For boats inquire Morris Bros

(tackleist see below) and D Bowler, 1 Lexdem Terrace. Shark trips also arranged; inquire of Mr Harries, Cambrian Hotels, Saundersfoot. Tackleist: Morris Bros, St Julian Street.

Milford Haven and Pembroke (Dyfed). Fine surf-fishing and spinning from rocks for bass from Freshwater West and Broad Haven (Bosherton); best late summer and autumn. Kilpaison good for bass, flatfish early on; also codling and coalfish. Stone piers and jetties inside Haven provide deepwater sport for pollack, skate, rays, whiting, codling, dogfish and coalfish. Hobbs Point (Pembroke Dock) excellent for conger and skate. Mackerel from rocks and boats (Stackpole Quay good). Tope from boats in Barafundle Bay and mackerel and bass from rocks. Other useful venues are Nab Head, Martins Haven and Angle Bay, Thorn, Rat and Sheep Islands and Harbour Rock. Mackerel from boats at harbour entrance. Lugworm and razor fish may be dug in several places, esp mudflats at Kilpaison and Angle Bay. Pennar Gut and Pembroke River. Tackleists: Sports and Leisure, Main Street and F Donovan, Bush Street, Pembroke; Humbers, Diamond St, Pembroke Dock; F Powell, 84 Charles St, Milford Haven. Boats (for tope fishing) from Sinclair Bros and D V Howells at Hakin Point. Clubs: Pembroke and Dist AC and Milford Haven Sea AC.

Aberystwyth (Dyfed). Shore and boat fishing, principally for bass, pollack and mackerel, tope and skate, with cod and whiting in winter. Stone Pier, harbour and Castle Rocks good shore marks. Borth and Ynyslas Beach for bass: bass and mullet also from estuaries. For boat trips apply Jack Hicks, Bryn Villa, Bryn Road. Tackleists: J Rosser, 3 Queen's Street and E & L Reddington, 23 Chalybeate St. Club: Aberystwyth SAC.

Barmouth (Gwynedd). Bass (large), flatfish, mullet in Mawddach estuary and from nearby beaches; also codling, mackerel, flatfish, etc. Ynys y Brawd island good for bass and flounders from shore and boats. Tackle, bait and boats (6-hour trip £7): All Sports, Beach Road. (Tel 280240.)

Pwllheli-Criccieth (Gwynedd). Dogfish, dabs, plaice, skate, pollack and a few

sole the year round: mackerel, tope and monkfish from June to September. October to January; whiting. Boats and bait available. Tackleists: Walsall Stores, 24 Penlan Street, Pwllheli; R T Pritchard, Sheffield House, High Street, Criccieth.

ANGLESEY

Holyhead and Holy Island. Fishing off Holyhead Breakwater, 1¾m long, good on any tide; summer and winter fishing, many species caught. Very food fishing also on Stanley Embankment, at Cymran, Rhoscolyn, Trearddur Bay, Porthdafarch and Holyhead Mountain. Bull huss, dogfish, pollack, wrasse, mullet, plaice, dab, flounder, conger, whiting, codling, thornback ray and bass all taken in season from the various shore-marks. Boat-fishing, possible in all but the worst of weather, yields also shark, tope, ling and smoothhound. Bait readily available. Excellent boat fishing; thornbacks, tope, etc. Bait in harbour or from tackleists: County Sports, Stanley Street; R P Owen, 35 Market Street. Thos Owen, 19/20 Cybi Street, J's Fishing Parlour,

Newry Street, which acts as agency for charter-boat hire. Hotels: County, Holborn, Scimitar, Queen's. Club HQ: Valley-of-the-Rocks, Porthdafarch.

Amlwch. Tope taken to 40 lb, skate, conger, herring, mackerel, etc, from boats; obtainable at Amlwch and at Bull Bay (1½m). Hotel: Dinarban Arms.

Beaumaris. Plenty of good flatfish and small codling opposite Beaumaris and along the Straits. Between Menai and The Tubular Bridge fair-sized bass and conger are caught. Boat trips daily from Menai Bridge to deep water off Puffin Island. Good catches of Pollack, cod and lobsters. Tackleist: Messrs G and L Whiffin, 46 Castle Street; K Johnson, Water Street, Menai Bridge.

Bangor (Gwynedd). Centre for Menai Straits and Anglesey. Excellent bass and plaice in Menai Straits, but thornbacks and tope more often taken by boat anglers. Good beaches between Bangor Pier and Menai Bridge; bass, flatfish, conger, etc. Boats: inquire piermaster. For parties and clubs apply A J Regan, 106 Orme Road, or J Evans (Bangor 3854). Tackleists: Edwards, 6 Dean Street; Davies, High Street.

Deganwy (Gwynedd). Wide variety of fish taken from boats in Gt Orme, Menai Straits and Puffin Island areas. Bass in estuary and off Benarth, Bodlondeb and Deganwy Points and Beacon Light. Bait from shore and estuary. Many boats. Tackleists: H L Bayley, Station Road; Conway.

Llandudno (Gwynedd). Excellent codling, pollack, bass, mackerel, plaice, whiting, conger, coalfish, etc. Rocky beach at corner of Little Orme good for bass; so is west shore, especially Black Rocks area.

Bait plentiful. Fishing from pier, beach, rocks and boats. Tope and mackerel taken by boat fishers. Boats from M Davies and J F Jones, both of Tywyn Hill, Deganwy. Tackleists: The North Wales Boat Shop, The Bridge, Llandudno Junction; R Lyon, 13 Gloddaeth Street.

Colwyn Bay (Clwyd). Bass off Rhos Point and Penmaenhead. Whiting, codling in winter from beach. Dabs, whiting, some plaice from pier (dt available all year). Tope and skate from boats. Tackleists: Duttons, 52 Sea View Road (bait); R D Pickering, 60 Abergele Road; Pet Stores, Market Hall.

Rhyl (Clwyd). Bass, flatfish from shore. Tope, dabs, plaice, whiting, turbot, skate, cod, bass, etc from boats. (Boats (in season) from Blue Shark, Quay Street; Marina Service Station, Wellington Road. Tackle and bait: Wm Roberts, (Rhyl) Ltd, 131 High Street and Anglers Den, 29 Queen Street.

FISHING CLUBS & ASSOCIATIONS IN WALES

I NCLUDED in this list of fishing clubs and associations in Wales are some organisations which have their water on the upper reaches of the Wye or Severn, details of which are contained in the English section of *Where to Fish*. The secretaries of the clubs are usually pleased to supply further information. but they appreciate the inclusion of a stamped addressed envelope with postal inquiries.

NATIONAL BODIES

Welsh Anglers' Council. Hubert T Gwynne, 87 Shirley Drive, Heolgerrig, Merthyr Tydfil, Mid. Glam.

Welsh Salmon and Trout Association. M J Morgan, The Post Office, Pontrhydfendigaid, Ystrad Meurig, Dyfed.

Welsh Tope, Skate and Conger Club. Colin Delfosse, 4 Heedland Terrace, Mumbles, nr Swansea.

CLUBS

Aberaeron Angling Association. J H Evans, 1 Alban Square, Aberaeron, Dyfed. Aeron. Tickets.

Aberdare and District Angling Association. J Bebb, 40 Ynyscynon St, Cwmbach, Aberdare, Glamorgan. Cynon and Usk tributaries. Tickets.

Aberystwyth Angling Association Ltd. PO Box 15, Aberystwyth, Dyfed SY23 1AA. Rheidol, Ystwyth and lakes. Tickets.

Aberystwyth Sea Angling Club.

Afan Valley Angling Club. R Hope, 1 Wellington Place, Port Talbot, W Glamorgan.

Amlwch and District Angling Club. J Davies, Ty'n Giat Garage, Amlwch, Anglesey..

Ammanford and District Angling Association. A Usherwood, 49 High Street, Ammanford, Dyfed. Llwchwr, Amman, Cennen, Marlais and Lash. Members only.

Artro Fishing Association. G Pierce, Lluest, Llanbedr, Gwynedd.

Bala and District Angling Association. D M Rees, 21 Tremyffridd, Bala, Gwynedd. Dee and tributaries and Lake Bala. Tickets.

Bangor City Angling Club. M Partridge, 1 Lon Isaf, Menai Bridge, Anglesey.

Bangor-on-Dee Angling Association. R Johnson, High Trees, Dean Road, Rhosnessney, Clwyd. Dee. Tickets.

Barry Angling Society. J Slatter, 3 Vere Street, Cadoxton, Barry, Glamorgan.

Bedlinog Angling Association. E Jones, 52 Hylton Terrace, Bedlinog, Treharris, Glamorgan.

Betws-y-Coed Angling Club. Ernest Jones, 7 Bro Gethin, Betws-y-Coed, Gwynedd.

Birchgrove (Cardiff) Angling Association. E Parry, 13 Westmorland Street, Canton, Cardiff.

Bishopston Angling Club. E C Roberts, "Croydon", 10 Heal Lane, Pennard, Gower.

Blackwood Angling Club. D B W Lewis, 4 Brynglas Avenue, Pontllanfraith, Gwent.

Bradley Fishing Club. F Hughes, 39 Heol y Waen, Bradley nr Wrexham. Alyn. Members only.

Brecon Angling Society. W L Peters, 53a Ffynnon Dewi, Llanfaes, Powys.

Bryn-y-Pys Angling Association. V Guest, Bryn Hovah, Bangor-on-Dee, Wrexham, Clwyd. Dee. Tickets.

Buckley Angling Association. R Lewis, 31 Padeswood Rd, Buckley, Clwyd. Lake permits.

Bute Angling Association. L V Powell, 176 Clare Road, Grangetown, Cardiff, Glam.

Caergwrie Angling Association. R Mathers, 29 Hawarden Rd, Hope, Wrexham, Clwyd. Alyn; st only.

Caerphilly and District Angling Association. J E Lintern, 74 Station Terrace, Nelson, Treharris, Glam. Lakes. Tickets.

Cambrian Angling Association. E Evans, Garth, Tyddyn Gwyn Manod, Blaenau Ffestiniog, Gwynedd. Lakes. Tickets only.

Cambrian Fly Fisheries. S Diggory, Pont-cysyllte, Clwyd. Dee. Tickets.

Cardiff Sea Anglers' Association. H Allen, 10 Clareston Road, Cardiff.

Cardigan and District Angling Club. W H McManus, Cheriton, Aberporth, Dyfed. Teify. Tickets.

Carmarthen Amateur Angling Association. R Jones, 1 Francis Terrace, Carmarthen SA31 1EY. Towy. Tickets.

Carmarthen and District Angling Club. H Evans, 25 Maple Crescent, Carmarthen. Towy, Gwili, Taf, Gwendraeth Fach, Cowin and Cennen. Tickets.

Cefndeuddwr Fishing Syndicate. c/o Post Office, Ganllwyd, Dolgellau. Mawddach and Eden. Tickets.

Cefni Angling Association. W J Williams, Gronant, Gaerwen, Anglesey.

Ceri Angling Association. J E Morgans, Gwynfryn Beulah, Newcastle Emlyn, Dyfed.

Cerrig-y-Drudion Angling Association. W M Roberts, 4 Cae Lwydd, Cerrig-y-Drudion, Clwyd. Alwen. Members only.

Chester Association of Anglers. R Pritchard, 67 Durham Rd, Blacon, Chester.

Chirk Angling Association. T L Davies, 76 Longfield, Chirk, nr Wrexham. Dee. Tickets to local residents only.

Cilcain Fly Fishing Association. D S Jones, Bryn Hyfryd, Cilcain, Clwyd. Trout reservoirs. Permits.

Clwyd Angling Club. B J B Roberts, 4 Bryn Goodman, Ruthin, Clwyd. Clwyd; limited membership.

Conway Fishing Association. Miss Connell Smith, Gwydyr Hotel, Betws-y-Coed, Gwynedd. Conway. Tickets.

Conwil Angling Association. Hon Sec, c/o Rock and Fountain, Conwil Road, Carmarthen. Gwili. Tickets.

Corwen and District Angling Club. M J Green, 69 Clawdd Poncen, Corwen, Dee and Alwen; members only.

Criccieth, Llanystumdwy and District Angling Association. G Hamilton, Morawell, Llanystumdwy, Criccieth, Gwynedd. Dwyfawr. Tickets.

Crickhowel Angling Club. V H Hesketh, Brick House, Church Lane, Crickhowell, Powys. Usk. Tickets.

Cwmbran Angling Association. P M Gulliford, 16 The Circle, Cwmbran, Gwent. Afon Lwyd. Tickets.

Dee Anglers' Association. H C Wickham, 12 St John Street, Chester. Dee. Tickets.

Denbigh Angling Club. A T Hirons, Tydrawllan, Cyffylliog, Ruthin. Clwyd. Clwyd. St only.

Dolgarrog Fishing Club. F A Corrie, 3 Tayler Avenue, Dolgarrog, Conway, Gwynedd. Conway and Roe. Tickets.

Dolgellau Angling Association. W E Roberts, 2 Muriau, Cader Road, Dolgellau, Gwynedd.

Dolwyddelan Fishing Association. T V Jones, Dolawel, Dolweyddelan, Gwynedd. Lledr. Tickets.

Estimaner Angling Association. W G Humphrys, 2 Pandy Square, Abergynolwyn, near Towyn, Gwynedd. Dysynni. Permits.

Fishguard and Goodwick Sea Anglers. F J Poole, Shangrila, Feidr-Dylan, Fishguard. Dyfed.

Glamorgan Anglers' Club (and Cardiff Piscatorial Society). A Seager, 55 Heol-y-Ffynon, Efail Isaf, Pontypridd, Glamorgan. Taff, Ely, and Trothy. Tickets.

Glaslyn Angling Association. O W Jones, 5 Britannia Terrace, Portmadoc, Gwynedd. Glaslyn. Tickets.

Glyncornel Angling Association. J M Evans, 126 Ystrad Road, Ystrad, Pentre, Glamorgan.

Glynneath and District Angling Association. R Cole, 24 Woodlands Park Drive, Cadoxton, Glamorgan.

Gowerton Angling Association. G Thomas, 10 Elba Street, Gowerton, nr Swansea.

Grosvenor Angling Association. D E Whitehouse, 18 Knowsley Road, Chester. Dee. St only.

Gwent Angling Society. W Watkins, Deristone, 76 Monk Street, Abergavenny, Gwent.

Gwent Federation of Angling Societies. G Gurmin, 26 Railway Terrace, Hollybush, Blackwood, Gwent.

Holyhead and District Angling Club. G H Jones, 8 Moreton Road, Holyhead, Anglesey. Gwynedd LL65 2BG.

Isca Angling Club. B Evans, 22 Eton Road, Newport, Gwent.

Islwyn Angling Club. Dr M T Wade, Gardd y Graig, 106a Commercial Street, Risca, Gwent.

Kenfig Hill and Distict Angling Association. A Waite, 16 Marlas Road, Pyle, Glamorgan.

Kirkdale Angling Association. A C Hoer, 61 Baythorne Road, Liverpool. Dee. St only.

Lavister Angling Club. W A Smith, "Ulsterlea", 4 Hollyfield, Gresford, near Wrexham. Dee. Members only.

Liverpool AA. Water on Dee. *(See English list)*.

Llanbedr Fishing Association. H Warburton, Ty Mawr, Llanbedr, Gwynedd.

Llanbrynmair and District Angling Club. H Hughes, Bod Hyfryd, Llanbrynmair, Powys.

Llanbyther Trout Fishing Association. Mr Thomas, Lloyds Bank Ltd, Llanbyther, Dyfed.

Llandegfedd Fly Fishers. M Williams, Wellfield Farm, Coedypaen, Usk.

Llandeilo Angling Association. Regd. Office, Llystewydd, Ffairfach, Llandeilo, Dyfed. Towy. Tickets.

Llandovery Angling Association. Hon sec, c/o Barclays Bank, Llandovery, Dyfed. Towy. Tickets.

Llandrindod Wells Angling Association. A H Selwyn, 4 Park Crescent, Llandrindod Wells, Powys. Ithon. Tickets.

Llandudno and District Sea Angling Club. Miss C C Jones, 7 Gogarth Avenue, Penmaenmawr, Gwynedd.

Llandyssul Angling Association. A M Jones, The Alma, Llandyssul, Dyfed. Teify. Tickets.

Llanfair-p-g and District Sea Angling Club. S R Walburn, 97 Tan-y-Bryn Road, Rhos-on-Sea, Colwyn Bay. Clwyd.

Llangadog Angling Association. J O Slaymaker, Brynamelon Llangadog, Dyfed.

Llangerniew Anglers. S G Ronan, Wigfair Isaf, St Asaph, Clwyd. Elwy. Members only.

Llangollen Angling Association. S I Evans, "The Dingle", Abbey Road, Llangollen, Clwyd. Dee. Tickets.

Llangyfelach Angling Association. M L Griffiths, 3 Aldwyn Road, Cockett, Swansea, W Glamorgan.

Llanidloes and District Angling Association. I J Dallas Davies, Dresden House, Great Oak Street, Llanidloes, Powys.

Llanilar Angling Association. W M Jones, Bryn Ystwyth, Llanilar, Aberystwyth SY23 4PJ.

Llanrwst Angler's Club. Hon Sec, 30 Llwyn Brith, Llanrwst, Gwynedd. Conway. Tickets.

Llansannan Anglers. G W Owen, Glasfryn Stores, Llansannan. Tickets.

Llantrisant and Pontyclun Anglers. G H Davies, 2 Lanelay Road, Talbot Green, Llantrisant, Glamorgan.

Llanuwchllyn Angling Club. H E Morris, Plas Newydd, Llanuwchllyn, Dee. Tickets.

Llay Angling Society. J Keen, 15 Clarke Road, Borros Park, Wrexham, Clwyd, Alyn. Tickets.

Llay Hall Angling Association. N Griffiths, 26 Tan-yr-Allt, Cefn-y-Bedd, Wrexham. Alyn. St only.

Llynfi Valley Angling Association. G Ball, 2 Heol-y-Bryn, Llangynwyd, near Bridgend, Glamorgan.

Maelor Angling Association. K Bathers, Sunnyside, Hill Street, Cefn Mawr, Wrexham, Clwyd. Dee. Tickets.

Maerdy and Ferndale Angling Society. W H Blake, 7 Richard Street, Maerdy, Ferndale, Glamorgan. Reservoirs; tickets.

Merthyr and St Tydfils Angling Association. B D Walkley, 13 Alexandra Avenue, Merthyr Tydfil, Glamorgan.

Midland Flyfishers. A D Clark, 5 Deansway, Worcester. Dee. Tickets.

Milford Haven Sea Angling Club. G Betty, 113 Haven Drive, Milford Haven, Dyfed.

Mold Angling Association. A Sprake, Liverpool Road, Buckley, Clwyd. Alyn. Tickets.

Mold and District Kingfishers. Mold, Clwyd. Wheeler, Ayn, pools, St only.

Monmouth and District Angling Society. B Vickers, 13 Clwdd-y, Goldwire Lane, Monmouth. Monnow and Trothy. Members only.

Montgomeryshire Angling Association (including Llanfair Caereinion FC, Newtown FC, Welshpool AC). Stuart J Harding, 29 Rhoslan, Guilsfield, Welshpool, Powys. Severn and tribs, canal, lakes. Tickets.

Montgomeryshire Federation of Angling Associations (seven clubs). Edgar Spooner, Memorial Gallery, Newtown, Powys.

Moss-Side (Manchester) Angling Society. Water on Dee *(see English list)*.

Mountain Ash Flyfishers. I Glyn Jenkins, 10 Eul-y-Plwyf, Ynysbwl, Pontypridd, Glamorgan.

Mumbles Motor Boat and Fishing Club. Ron Edwards, 642 Mumbles Road, Mumbles, Swansea.

Neath and Dulais Angling Association. A Beasley, 10 Neath Road, Tonna, Neath, W Glamorgan.

Newbridge Angling Association. R Vanstone, Pen-y-Bont Farm, Newbridge, Wrexham, Clwyd. Dee. Members only.

New Dovey Fishery Association (1929) Ltd. D Morgan Jones, Plas, Machynlleth, Powys. Dovey; some tickets.

Newport (Mon) Angling Association. Peter Climo, 35 Claremont, Malpas, Newport, Gwent. Monmouth Canal and pond. Tickets limited.

Newport (Dyfed) Angling Association. G Tucker, Spring Hill, Newport, Dyfed.

New Quay and District Angling Club. D H Jones, Helybryn, New Quay, Dyfed.

Northern Anglers Association. Water on Dee *(see English list)*.

North Wales Federation of Anglers. G M Williams, The Fisherman's Cabin, 11–13 High Street, Bala, Gwynedd.

Ogmore Angling Association. C D John, 3 The Parc, Priory Avenue, Bridgend, Glamorgan.

Ogwen Valley Angling Association. Emlyn Jones J P, 5 Maes Coetmor, Bethesda, Bangor, Gwynedd LL5 73DS. Ogwen. Permits.

Pembroke Angling Association. J Price, 104 Haven Road, Haverfordwest, Dyfed.

Pembroke and District Angling Club. T Caveney, Kilnbac, Angle Village, Angle, Dyfed.

Pembrokeshire Anglers Association. M Gibby, 22 Greenfield Close, Haverfordwest, Dyfed.

Pencoed and District Angling Club. G D John, Railway Inn, Pencoed, Glamorgan.

Poncian Angling Society. W G Hughes, 2 Dover Terrace, Chapel Street, Poncian, nr Wrexham. Lakes. Permits.

Pontardawe and District Angling Association.

Pontardulais and District Angling Association. D J Davies, 23 James Street, Pontardulais. Llwchwr and Dulais.

Pontrhydfendigaid Angling Association. D Lloyd Jones, Rhyd Teify, Pontrhydfendigaid, Dyfed.

Pontypool and District Angling Association. A Wakeham, 7 St Hilda's Road, Griffithstown, Pontypool, Gwent. Usk. Tickets.

Pontypridd and District Angling Association. T Thomas, 3 Barry Road, Pwllgwaun, Pontypridd, Mid-Glam.

Porthcawl Sea Angling Association. A Burch, 171 New Road, Porthcawl, Glamorgan.

Prince Albert Angling Society. C Sparkes, High Lodge, Upton, Macclesfield. Dovey, Dulas, Dysynni, Dee, Twymyn. Some tickets.

Prysor Angling Association. D G Williams, Meirionfa, Trawsfynydd, Gwynedd. Prysor and Trawsfyrydd Lake. Tickets.

Pwllheli and District Angling Association. M R Ellis, Swn y Wylan, Golf Road, Pwllheli, Gwynedd. Erch, Soch, etc, tickets.

Pyrddin Angling Society. D M Jones, 4 Moorlands, Dyffryn Cellwen, Neath, Glamorgan. Neath. Tickets.

Rhayader Angling Association. G H Roberts, Belmullet, Rhayader, Powys. Wye, Marteg and lake. Tickets.

Rhostyllen Angling Club. J N Deary, 69 Henblas Road, Rhostyllen, Wrexham, Clwyd.

Rhyl and District Angling Association. Howell I Jones, 51 Pendyffryn Road, Rhyl, Clwyd. Elwy and Clwyd. Permits.

Rhymney and District Angling Society. G H Roper, 72 Penybryn Avenue, Cefn Forest, Blackwood, Gwent. Lakes.

Risca Fly Fishing Association. Dr M Wade, Gardd y Graig, Risca, Gwent. Sirhowy. Tickets.

River Wygyr Fishing Association. T Gillham, 2 Crown Terrace, Llanfechell, Anglesey.

Rossett and Gresford Angling Association. J F L Coates, 62 Daleside, Upton-by-Chester, Chester. Alyn. Members only.

St Asaph Angling Club. R C Baldwin, 6 Bryn Elwy, St Asaph, Clwyd. Clwyd. Members only.

St Clears and District Angling Association. T Jenkins, Fairfields House, St Clears, Dyfed. Taf. Tickets.

St Helens Angling Association. Water on Dee *(see English list)*.

Seiont, Gwyrfai and Llyfni Anglers' Society. H P Hughes, 11 Eryri Estate, Bethel, Caernarvon, Gwynedd. Seiont, Gwyrfai, Llyfni lakes. Tickets.

Sennybridge Fishing Association. W J Davies & Son, Sennybridge, Powys. Usk. Tickets.

South Wales and Monmouthshire Federation of Angling Societies. J E Palmer, 8 Caerau Park Place, Ely, Cardiff, Glamorgan.

Strata Florida Angling Association. D Lloyd Jones, Rhydteify, Pontrhydfendigaid. Ystrad Meurig, Dyfed. Teify. Tickets.

Swansea Amateur Angling Association. E R Coombs, Bryn Cothi Lodge, Brechfa, Dyfed. Towy, Cothi. Tickets.

Swansea Sea Angling Club. Roy Griffiths, 131 Rhondda Street, Mount Pleasant, Swansea.

Talsarnau and District Angling Association. C R Jones, 4 Cilfor, Talsarnau, Gwynedd. Lakes.

Talybont Angling Association. Hon Sec c/o Lerry Mill, Talybont, Dyfed.

Tawe and Tributaries Angling Association. K Jones, 21 St David's Road, Ystalyfera, Swansea.

Teifi Trout Association. Rev Clement Davies, Llyshywel, Newcastle Emlyn, Dyfed. Teifi. St only.

Trawsfynydd Lake Management Committee. H E Lewis, Castle House, Trawsfynydd, Gwynedd.

Tredegar Angling Society. A S Davies, 68 Queen Victoria Street, Tredegar, Gwent.

Tregaron Angling Association. G R Phillips, Barclays Bank, Tregaron, Dyfed. Teifi. Tickets.

Treharris Angling Association. D L Lewis, 4 Penlocks, Treharris, Glamorgan.

United Usk Fishermen's Assn. H J P Candler, 32 Monk Street, Abergavenny, Gwent.

Upper Rhondda Angling Association. D Rossiter, 71 Miskin Street, Treherbert, Glamorgan.

Usk Town Water Fishery Association. C E Brain, 56 St Julian's Road, Newport, Gwent. Usk. Tickets.

Warrington Angling Association. Dee *(see English list).*

Whitland Angling Association. R M Jones, Glenafon, Market Street, Whitland, Dyfed.

Wrexham and District Angling Association. G I Franks, 132 Oak Drive, Acton Park, Wrexham, Clwyd. Alyn. Members' guests only.

Wygyr Angling Association. T Gillham, Crown Terrace, Llanfechell, Anglesey. Wygyr. Tickets.

Ynysddu and Cwmfelinfach Angling Club. H P Hopkins, 2 Brynderwyn, Ridge Cafe, Cwmfelinfach. Sirhowy. Tickets.

Gratitude is owed to the Welsh Anglers Council for help freely given in the updating of this club list.

Check before you go

While every effort has been made to ensure that the information given in "Where to Fish" is correct, the position is continually changing and anglers are urged in their own interests, to make preliminary inquiries before travelling to selected venues. This is especially important with reference to prices quoted. Inevitably, the rate of inflation is affecting stability in this quarter. Angler's attention is also drawn to the fact that the hotels mentioned under the various fishing stations do not necessarily have water of their own. Any amendments or further data for inclusion in subsequent editions, and any criticism, will be welcome. All correspondence to the Editor.

FISHING IN SCOTLAND

District Boards and Close Season for Salmon and Trout

FISHING in Scotland is under the general jurisdiction of the Dept of Agriculture and Fisheries for Scotland, Chesser House, Gorgie Road, Edinburgh EH11 3AW.

The annual close season for **trout** in Scotland extends from October 7 to March 14, both days included. Trout may not be sold between the end of August and the beginning of April, nor at any time if the fish are less than 8 in long.

Visiting anglers are reminded that on Scottish rivers and lochs the owner of the fishing is the riparian proprietor, whose permission to fish should be obtained. The only public right of fishing for brown trout is in those portions of the rivers which are both tidal and navigable, but the right must not be exercised so as to interfere with salmon or sea-trout fishing and can be exercised only where there is a right of access to the water from a boat or from the banks.

Salmon. Provision is made in the Salmon Fisheries (Scotland) Acts, 1862–68, for the formation of District Boards, composed of representatives of proprietors of salmon fisheries in each district. These boards, the addresses of which are given on pages 270–1, are responsible for the administration and protection of the salmon fisheries in their districts, and boards have been formed for practically all the important salmon rivers. In districts in which boards have not been formed, the salmon fisheries, of which sea-trout fisheries are legally part, are under the direct control of the proprietors.

In the following list, the days fixing the start and finish of the annual close time for net fishing and for rod fishing respectively are in all cases inclusive, and, as in the case of the Add, the first river in the list, the first pair of dates are the limits of the net season and the second pair apply to rod fishing.

Add. Annual close time for net-fishing: From Sept 1 to Feb 15, both dates inclusive. Annual close time for rod-fishing: From Nov 1 to Feb 15, both days inclusive.

Ailort. Aug 27 to Feb 10; Nov 1 to Feb 10.

Alness. Aug 27 to Feb 10; Nov 1 to Feb 10.

Annan. Sept 10 to Feb 24; Nov 6 to Feb 24.

Awe. Aug 27 to Feb 10; Oct 16 to Feb 10.

Ayr. Aug 27 to Feb 10; Nov 1 to Feb 10.

Baa and Goladoir. Aug 27 to Feb 10; Nov 1 to Feb 10.

Badachro and Kerry (Gairloch). Aug 27 to Feb 10; Nov 1 to Feb 10.

Balgay and Shieldaig. Aug 27 to Feb 10; Nov 1 to Feb 10.

Beauly. Aug 27 to Feb 10; Oct 16 to Feb 10.

Berriedale. Aug 27 to Feb 10; Nov 1 to Feb 10.

Bervie. Sept 10 to Feb 24; Nov 1 to Feb 24.

Bladnoch. Aug 27 to Feb 10; Nov 1 to Feb 10.

Broom. Aug 27 to Feb 10; Nov 1 to Feb 10.

Brora. Aug 27 to Feb 10; Oct 16 to Jan 31.

Carradale (in Kintyre). Sept 10 to Feb 24; Nov 1 to Feb 24.

Carron (W Ross). Aug 27 to Feb 10; Nov 1 to Feb 10.

Clayburn Finnisbay, Avennangeren, Strathgravat, North Lacastile, Scalladale and Mawrig (East Harris). Sept 10 to Feb 24; Nov 1 to Feb 24.

Clyde and Leven. Aug 27 to Feb 10; Nov 1 to Feb 10.

Conon. Aug 27 to Feb 10; Oct 1 to Jan 25.

Cree. Sept 14 to last day of Feb; Oct 14 to last day of Feb.

Creed or Stornoway, and Laxay (Island of Lewis). Aug 27 to Feb 10; Oct 17 to Feb 10.

Creran (Loch Creran). Aug 27 to Feb 10; Nov 1 to Feb 10.

Croe and Shiel (Loch Duich). Aug 27 to Feb 10; Nov 1 to Feb 10.

Dee (Aberdeenshire). Aug 27 to Feb 10; Oct 1 to Jan 31.

Dee (Kirkcudbrightshire). Aug 27 to Feb 10; Nov 1 to Feb 10.

Deveron. Aug 27 to Feb 10; Nov 1 to Feb 10.

Don. Aug 27 to Feb 10; Nov 1 to Feb 10.

Doon. Aug 27 to Feb 10; Nov 1 to Feb 10.

Drummachloy or Glenmore (Isle of Bute). Sept 1 to Feb 15; Oct 16 to Feb 15.

Dunbeath. Aug 27 to Feb 10; Oct 16 to Feb 10.

Earn. Aug 21 to Feb 4; Nov 1 to Jan 31.

Echaig. Sept 1 to Feb 15; Nov 1 to Feb 15.

Esk, North. Sept 1 to Feb 15; Nov 1 to Feb 15.

Esk, South. Sept 1 to Feb 15; Nov 1 to Feb 15.

Ewe. Aug 27 to Feb 10; Nov 1 to Feb 10.

Fincastle, Meaveg, Ballanchist, South Lacastile, Borve and Obb (West Harris). Sept 10 to Feb 24; Nov 1 to Feb 24.

Findhorn. Aug 27 to Feb 10; Oct 6 to Feb 10.

Fleet (Kirkcudbrightshire). Sept 10 to Feb 24; Nov 1 to Feb 24.

Fleet (Sutherlandshire). Sept 10 to Feb 24; Nov 1 to Feb 24.

Forss. Aug 27 to Feb 10; Nov 1 to Feb 10.

Forth. Aug 27 to Feb 10; Nov 1 to Jan 31.

Fyne, Shira and Aray (Loch Fyne). Sept 1 to Feb 15; Nov 1 to Feb 15.

Girvan. Sept 10 to Feb 24; Nov 1 to Feb 24.

Glenelg. Aug 27 to Feb 10; Nov 1 to Feb 10.

Gour. Aug 27 to Feb 10; Nov 1 to Feb 10.

Greiss, Laxdale or Thunga. Aug 27 to Feb 10; Nov 1 to Feb 10.

Grudie or Dionard. Aug 27 to Feb 10; Nov 1 to Feb 10.

Gruinard and Little Gruinard. Aug 27 to Feb 10; Nov 1 to Feb 10.

Halladale, Strathy, Naver and Borgie. Aug 27 to Feb 10; Oct 1 to Jan 11.

Helmsdale. Aug 27 to Feb 10; Oct 1 to Jan 10.

Hope and Polla or Strathbeg. Aug 27 to Feb 10; Oct 1 to Jan 11.

Howmore. Sept 10 to Feb 24; Nov 1 to Feb 24.

Inchard. Aug 27 to Feb 10; Nov 1 to Feb 10.

Inner (in Jura). Sept 10 to Feb 24; Nov 1 to Feb 24.

Inver. Aug 27 to Feb 10; Nov 1 to Feb 10.

Iorsa (in Arran). Sept 10 to Feb 24; Nov 1 to Feb 24.

Irvine and Garnock. Sept 10 to Feb 24; Nov 1 to Feb 24.

Kannarid. Aug 27 to Feb 10; Nov 1 to Feb 10.

Kilchoan or Inverie (Loch Nevis). Aug 27 to Feb 10; Nov 1 to Feb 10.

Kinloch (Kyle of Tongue). Aug 27 to Feb 10; Nov 1 to Feb 10.

Kirkaig. Aug 27 to Feb 10; Nov 1 to Feb 10.

Kishorn. Aug 27 to Feb 10; Nov 1 to Feb 10.

Kyle of Sutherland. Aug 27 to Feb 10; Oct 1 to Jan 10.

Laggan and Sorn (Island of Islay). Sept 10 to Feb 24; Nov 1 to Feb 24.

Laxford. Aug 27 to Feb 10; Nov 1 to Feb 10.

Leven. Aug 27 to Feb 10; Nov 1 to Feb 10.

Liddle. Rod-fishing: Nov 1 to Jan 31.

Liddle (Newcastleton). Rod-fishing: Oct 1 to April 14.

Little Loch Broom. Aug 27 to Feb 10; Nov 1 to Feb 10.

Loch Duich. Aug 27 to Feb 10; Nov 1 to Feb 10.

Loch Luing. Aug 27 to Feb 10; Nov 1 to Feb 10.

Loch Roag. Aug 27 to Feb 10; Oct 17 to Feb 10.

Lochy. Aug 27 to Feb 10; Nov 1 to Feb 10.

Lossie. Aug 27 to Feb 10; Oct 16 to Feb 10.

Luce. Sept 10 to Feb 24; Nov 1 to Feb 24.

Lussa (Island of Mull). Aug 27 to Feb 10; Nov 1 to Feb 10.

Moidart. Aug 27 to Feb 10; Nov 1 to Feb 10.

Morar. Aug 27 to Feb 10; Nov 1 to Feb 10.

Mullanageren, Horasary and Lochnaciste (North Uist). Sept 10 to Feb 24; Nov 1 to Feb 24.

Nairn. Aug 27 to Feb 10; Oct 1 to Feb 10.

Naver and Borgie (see Halladale).

Nell, Feochan and Euchar. Aug 27 to Feb 10; Nov 1 to Feb 10.

Ness. Aug 27 to Feb 10; Oct 16 to Jan 14.

Nith. Sept 10 to Feb 24; Dec 1 to Feb 24.

Orkney Islands (river from Loch of Stenness, etc). Sept 10 to Feb 24; Nov 1 to Feb 24.

Ormsary (Loch Killisport), **Loch Head, and Stornoway** (Mull of Kintyre). Aug 27 to Feb 10; Nov 1 to Feb 10.

Pennygowan or Glenforsa and Aros. Aug 27 to Feb 10; Nov 1 to Feb 10.

Resort. Aug 27 to Feb 10; Nov 1 to Feb 10.

Ruel. Sept 1 to Feb 15; Nov 1 to Feb 15.

Sanda. Aug 27 to Feb 10; Nov 1 to Feb 10.

Scaddle. Aug 27 to Feb 10; Nov 1 to Feb 10.

Sheltand Islands. Sept 10 to Feb 24; Nov 1 to Feb 24.

Shiel (loch Shiel). Aug 27 to Feb 10; Nov 1 to Feb 10.

Sligachan, Broadford and Portree (Isle of Skye). Aug 27 to Feb 10; Nov 1 to Feb 10.

Snizort, Orley, Oze and Drynoch (Isle of Skye). Aug 27 to Feb 10; Nov 1 to Feb 10.

Spey. Aug 27 to Feb 10; Oct 1 to Feb 10.

Stinchar. Sept 10 to Feb 24; Nov 1 to Feb 24.

Sunart. Aug 27 to Feb 10; Oct 31 to Feb 10.

Tay (except Earn). Aug 21 to Feb 4; Oct 16 to Jan 14.

Thurso. Aug 27 to Feb 10; Oct 6 to Jan 10.

Torridon, Balgay and Shieldaig. Aug 27 to Feb 10; Nov 1 to Feb 10.

Tweed. Sept 15 to Feb 14; Dec 1 to Jan 31.

Ugie. Sept 10 to Feb 24; Nov 1 to Feb 9.

Ullapool (Loch Broom). Aug 27 to Feb 10; Nov 1 to Feb 10.

Urr. Sept 10 to Feb 24; Nov 30 to Feb 24.

Wick. Aug 27 to Feb 10; Nov 1 to Feb 10.

Ythan. Sept 10 to Feb 24; Nov 1 to Feb 10.

DISTRICT FISHERY BOARDS

The names, addresses and telephone numbers of the clerks of the various district fishery boards in Scotland are as follows: Please note that their duties are purely to operate the Acts and that they do not have fishing to let.

Add District Board. D M MacKinnon, Solicitor, British Linen Bank Buildings, Oban, Argyll PA34 4LN (Tel Oban 3014).

Alness District Board. W H Cormack, Solicitor, 20 Tower Street, Tain, Ross-shire IV19 1DZ (Tel Tain 2046).

Annan District Board. McJerrow and Stevenson, Solicitors, 55 High Street, Lockerbie, Dumfriesshire DG11 2JJ (Lockerbie 2123/4).

Awe District Board. J F Watt; Macarthur, Stewart & Orr, Solicitors, National Commercial Bank Chambers, Oban Argyllshire (Tel Oban 2215).

Ayr District Board. J Laurence Tait, Solicitor, 2 Wellington Square, Ayr KA7 1EN (Tel 65024).

Bervie District Board. R M Ross, SSC, 112 High Street, Montrose, Angus, DD10 8JH (Tel Montrose 2929).

Bladenoch District Board. R G Armstrong, Solicitor, 66 Victoria Street, Newton Stewart, Wigtownshire (Newton Stewart 13).

Broom District Board. Middleton, Ross and Arnot, Solicitors, Clydesdale Bank Buildings, Dingwall, Ross-shire (Dingwall 2214/5).

Brora District Board. N R ff Campbell, Sutherland Estates Office, Golspie, Sutherland KW10 6RR (Tel 268).

Clayburn District Board. D M Mackinnon, 7a Urgha, Tarbert, Harris. (Tel Harris 2356).

Conon District Board. Middleton, Ross and Arnot, Solicitors, Clydesdale Bank Buildings, Dingwall, Ross-shire IV15 9HQ (Dingwall 2214/5).

Cree District Board. R G Armstrong, Solicitor, 66 Victoria Street, Newton Stewart, Wigtownshire (Tel Newton Stewart 13).

Creed or Stornoway and Laxay District Board. Douglas N Kesting, Bank of Scotland Buildings, Stornoway, Isle of Lewis (Tel Stornoway 3356).

Dee (Aberdeen) District Board. J G Innes, 7 Golden Square, Aberdeen AB9 8EP (Tel Aberdeen 29065).

Dee (Solway) District Board. J W Campbell, New Cottages, St Mary's Isle, Kirkcudbright (Tel 242).

Deveron District Board. A Gibb, Solicitor, 29 Low Street, Banff AB4 1AX (Banff 2457).

Don District Board. G Alpine, 6 Union Row, Aberdeen AB9 89Q (Tel 0224 26262).

Doon District Board. H S Campbell, Solicitor, 8 Alloway Place, Ayr (Ayr 69131).

Dunbeath District Board. J W Doull, Estates office, Lybster, Caithness.

Esk (North) District Board. R M Ross, SSC, 112 High Street, Montrose, Angus.

Esk (South District Board. R M Ross, SSC, Montrose, Angus (Tel Montrose 2929).

Ewe District Board. Middleton, Ross and Arnot, Solicitors, Clydesdale Bank Buildings, Dingwall, Ross-shire (Dingwall 2214/5).

Fincastle District Board. D M MacKinnon, 7a Urgha, Tarbert, Isle of Harris (Tel Harris 2356).

Findhorn District Board. W A Taylor, Solicitor, Royal Bank Buildings, Forres, Morayshire IV36 0PD (Forres 2228).

Forss District Board. J Atkinson, 8 Sinclair Street, Thurso, Caithness KW14 7AG (Tel 0847 3291).

Forth District Board. Henry Robb, LLB, Solicitor, 3 Pitt Terrace, Stirling (Stirling 5178). Superintendent—Major C Fordyle-Burke (Doune 449).

Girvan District Board. T L Wilson; Murray & Tait, Procurator Fiscal's Office, Girvan, Ayrshire (Tel 3118).

Gruinard and Little Gruinard District Board. Messrs. Middleton, Ross and Arnot, Solicitors, Clydesdale Bank Buildings, Dingwall, Ross-shire (Dingwall 2214/5).

Halladale District Board. J Atkinson, 8 Sinclair Street, Thurso, Caithness KW14 7AG (Tel 0847 3291).

Helmsdale District Board. Lt. Cdr. A N Rickards RN (Retd) Fishery Office, Strathnaver, Kinbrace, Sutherland (Tel 064 16 2017). (Address between October and March, Kirkmichael Old Manse, Ballindalloch, Banffshire).

Hope and Polla District Board. Middleton, Ross and Arnot, Solicitors, Clydesdale Bank Buildings, Dingwall, Ross-shire (Dingwall 2214/5).

Kinloch District Board. Messrs. Condie Mackenzie & Co WS, 2 Tay Street, Perth PH1 5LJ (Tel 0738 25381).

Kyle of Sutherland District Board. W H Cormack, Solicitor, 20 Tower Street, Tain, Ross-shire IV19 1DZ (Tel Tain 2046).

Loch Roag District Board. Douglas N Kesting, Bank of Scotland Buildings, Stornoway, Isle of Lewis (Tel Stornoway 3356).

Lochy District Board. A L Falconer, 209 High Street, Elgin (Tel 0343 2623).

Luce District Board. I H A Mackay, FRICS, Stair Estate Office, Rephad, Stranraer, Wigtownshire (Tel Stranraer 2024).

Nairn District Board. A Laurenson, Solicitor, British Linen Bank Buildings, 73 High Street, Nairn IV12 4BB (Nairn 3395).

Naver and Borgie District Board. *(See Helmsdale District Board, above).*

Ness District Board. J O Waddell, Anderson, Shaw and Gilbert, Solicitors, 20 Church Street, Inverness (Inverness 36123).

Nith District Board. F A O'Brien & Co, 26 Castle Street, Dumfries DG1 1DZ (Dumfries 5555).

Spey District Board. C D R Whittle, 121 High Street, Forres, Morayshire (Tel 0309 72216).

Stinchar District Board. T L Wilson, Murrey & Tait, Procurator Fiscal's Office, Girvan (Tel 0465 3118).

Tay District Board. Condie Mackenzie & Co, WS, 2 Tay Street, Perth PH1 5LJ (Tel 0738 25381).

Thurso District Board. P J W Blackwood, Estate Office, Thurso East, Thurso KW1 8HP (Tel 3134).

Tweed Commissioners. A Muir Sturrock, 12 Market Place, Jedburgh, Roxboroughshire TD8 6AE (Tel Jedburgh 2391).

Ugie District Board. G T Macrae, Gray & Gray, Bank of Scotland Chambers, 32 Broad Street, Peterhead AB4 6BY (Tel 0779 2376).

Ullapool District Board. Middleton, Ross and Arnot, Solicitors, Clydesdale Bank Buildings, Dingwall, Ross-shire (Dingwall 2214/5).

Wick District Board. T D Buick, Solicitor, 22 Bridge Street, Wick, Caithness (Tel 2442).

Ythan District Board. Capt C A Farquharson, Estate Office, Haddo House, Aberdeen AB4 0ER (Tel Tarves 664/5).

SCOTTISH FISHING STATIONS

THE nature of Scotland with its many rivers and lochs, especially on the west coast, makes it impracticable in some cases to deal with each river's catchment area separately. Thus some fisheries on the west coast north of the Firth of Clyde are grouped under the heading "West Coast Rivers and Lochs".

The need again arises to decide whether a river should be included in England or Scotland. The Border Esk is dealt with in the English section, together with the Kirtle and the Sark, which happen to fall within the Esk's catchment area on the map. The Tweed and *all* its tributaries are included in this Scottish section. All the Scottish Islands, including Sheltand and Orkney, are considered as within one watershed, viz, "The Islands", in which, for convenience, Kintyre is included. The exact position in the book of any river or fishing station can, of course, readily be found by reference to the index.

ALNESS

Rises 4 miles west of Loch Morie and flows 12 miles to Cromarty Firth at Alness. Salmon, sea trout, brown trout.

Alness (Highlands). Highland and Islands Development Board has acquired water here, which is administered by Alness AC. Dt and wt. Worm and fly only. Hotels: Station, Novar Arms, Evanton.

Evanton (Highlands). Factor, Novar Estates Office, issues permits for two private beats; Fly only; fishing let by the day and the week. Dt from £2–£4, according to month.

ANNAN

Rises in Moffat Hills and flows about 30 miles to Solway Firth. Good spring salmon, sea trout in May and June. Good herling in July and August, and salmon in late autumn; brown trout.

Annan (Dumfries & Galloway). Newbie Estates water. River above bridge; limited dt from Newbie Mill. River south of bridge now let to Annan AC, which also has three small lochs and reservoir; members only. Hoddom Castle water: limited dt £4 (Feb 25 to Apr 30) £3 (May 1 to Sept 30) £5 (Oct 1 to Nov 15). Tickets from P Helm, river-watcher, 22 Fernlea Crescent, Annan; advance booking accepted. (Tel: Annan 2922.) Castle Milk water: particulars and permits from Caslte Milk Estates *(see also Lockerbie).* Dt (£5 and £3.50) for Hoddom and Kinmount Estate waters at Newbie Mill. Feb, March, April and Oct best for salmon; May, June, July best for sea trout and brown trout; herling in July and Aug. Full details from river watcher, Newbie Mill (Tel: 2608). Queensbury Arms can arrange permits.

Ecclefechan (Dumfries, & Galloway). Annan, 2m SW; salmon, herling (late July onwards), brown trout. River preserved from here to sea *(see Annan).* Dt for Hoddom Castle water (over 2m) may be booked from river watcher, P Helm, 23 Fernlea Crescent, Annan. Limited to 15 rods daily. Charge according to season. Fly only, except when river height is above white line at Hoddom Bridge, when spinning permitted. Worm fishing now forbidden. **Water of Milk,** 4m W *(see Lockerbie).* At a short distance is the **Kirtle Water** trout. *(See Border Esk in English section.)* Hotel: Ecclefechan, where permits are available for Hoddom and Castle Milk waters.

Lockerbie (Dumfries & Galloway). Annan 1½m W; salmon, sea trout, brown trout. Castle Milk Estate water: Two beats on Annan, one on **River Milk.** St £50–£5. Wt £7.50–£1. Dt £3 to 50p. Full details from Factor (Tel Kettle Holm 203). McJerrow and Stevenson, Solicitors, Lockerbie, issue permits for Halleaths water: wt £10, st £50; fly only. Hoddom and Kinmount Estates, Lockerbie, may have rods and fishing cottages to let; inquire of the Factor. **Black Esk Reservoir:** Boats. Apply Wm Thomson, Sandyford Filter Station, Boreland; fly only.

Applegirth Water on Annan, **Kinnell Water** and **Dryfe Water;** now taken over by upper Annandale AA. Limited st £25, wt £10, dt (until Sep 15) £2.50. Tackleists: T R Jackson and McCall, both High Street; permits from former for Upper Annan fishing. Hotels: Dinwoodie Lodge (can arrange fishing), King's Arms, Crown, Bluebell, Townhead, Somerton House, Lockerbie House, Queen's.

Lochmaben (Dumfries & Galloway). Salmon, sea trout, trout, chub (good). Royal Four Towns water, Hightae. Tickets: Restricted, (no parties) wt £10, dt £2. Salmon season. Feb 25 to Nov 15; trout, March 15 to Oct 6: from Clerk, William Graham, Glenelg, Hightae, Lochmaben. **Kinnell Water,** 3m trout, upper Annandale AA water. **Garrel Water,** 4m N. (trout); Small fee for boats. Coarse fishing in three lochs. Permits from local filling station, hotels, etc. Permits for **River Ae,** from Wilson, Esbie farm. No Sunday fishing in rivers. Hotels: Kings Arms; Balcastle; Crown.

Wamphray (Dumfries & Galloway). 4m of R Annan *(see Moffat)* controlled by Upper Annandale AA. Permits from hon sec and Red House Hotel: dt £1.50, wt £5 pre-Sept 15, £7 after. Limited st at £15.

Beattock (Dumfries & Galloway). Upper Annandale AA water on river. Auchen Castle Hotel can arrange fishing on river and has trout loch in grounds.

Moffat (Dumfries & Galloway). Upper Annandale AA controls ½m of **Little Annan,** 1m of **Moffat Water,** from Meeting of Waters; 4m **Annan** from Meeting of Waters. Salmon: dt £1.50, wt £5 (£7 after Sept 15) st £15. (no dt for salmon after Sept 15). Tickets from hon sec and other local sources; reductions for juveniles. Fly only for trout, sea trout and herling in April and Sept. Spinning allowed from Feb 25 to Sept 30 when water level is not below white lines marked on bridges. Salmon season best August onwards; sea trout July onwards. No Sunday fishing. Trout burns: Birnock Water. Frenchland Burn, 1m E. Cornall Burn, 1m. Moffat Water, 2m E. Evan Water, 2m S. Mere Burn, 3m W. Lochan Burn, 4m N. Auchencat Burn, 4m N. Blackhope Burn, 1m NE. Carifferan Burn, 7m NE. Harthope Burn, 8m. Fopperveck Burn, 9m NW. Bidhouse Burn,

9m NW. Midlaw Burn, 10m NE. Loch: Skene all private, 10m NE. Hotels: Elmhill (fishing arranged in Annan, and Moffat), Annandale Arms, Moffat House, Buccleuch Arms, Red House, Balmoral, Star, Moffat Mercury. Tackleist: T Porteous.

AWE and LOCH AWE and LOCH ETIVE

A short river, but one of best-known salmon streams of west coast. Connects Loch Awe to sea by way of Loch Etive, which it enters at Bonawe. River fishes best from July onwards.

Taynuilt (Strathclyde) Salmon, sea trout, trout; Taynuilt Hotel has fishing; non-residents £5 day for salmon and sea trout. Polfearn Hotel is convenient for Loch Etive. Inverawe Fisheries (Tel 08662 262) have 1m on river wt £50, dt £9; a boat on L Etive (dt £12) and three lochs stocked with rainbow trout. Dt £8, with part-day and father/son concessions. Tuition, tackle for hire and refreshments available. Dalavich, by Taynuilt. R Avich dt £2 (trout only £1 to Aug 31) bank fishing L Avich dt £1, boats £8 (outboard motor) £4 (rowing) also available on L Awe. Apply Forestry Commission, 21 Dalavich, Taynuilt, with SAE if booking by post.

Connel (Strathclyde). Ossian's Hotel, newly built, overlooks Loch Etive; salmon, sea trout, brown trout. Fishing also from Falls of Lora Hotel.

LOCH AWE:

Lochawe (Strathclyde). Free for salmon, sea trout, brown trout, perch and pike; boats. Fishing on Awe and **Orchy,** for guests at Carraig Thura Hotel. Dt on river for non-residents (as available) £7.

Lochaweside (Strathclyde). Taychreggan Hotel on lochside has salmon, sea trout, brown trout and coarse fishing on Lochs Awe and **Etive,** for guests. Fish run to good size. Boat with outboard; a few gillies available. Good sea fishing.

Kilchrenan. Bank fishing on L. Nant (two mile walk) bookable from Trading Post. £1 per day. Ardanaiseig Hotel arranges fishing. *(advt p 273).*

Portsonachan (Strathclyde). Portsonachan Hotel *(advt p 320)* on shore of Loch Awe has fishing in loch; trout, salmon, sea trout, perch, pike. Boats and gillies available to hotel guests. Fishing on hill lochs also.

Ford (Strathclyde). **Cam** and other hill lochs: bank fishing dt £1. **R Liever;** £2 (trout only £1, to Aug 31). Permits ; in office hours from Mrs Cameron, Ford PO.

Tributaries of the Awe

ORCHY: Good salmon, few large trout.

Dalmally (Strathclyde). River flows into Loch Awe here. excellent salmon fishing in May, June, Sept and Oct. Loch Awe holds salmon, trout, perch, pike, sea trout. Hotel: Dalmally *(advt p 275).* Craig Lodge *(advt p 290).*

Inveroran (Strathclyde). On Loch Tulla, and but 2m from the River Orchy, although 3m from available fishing; salmon, trout. The salmon fishing in the Orchy is good in the autumn, but given good water, July is the best month. Upper Orchy no good before mid-June. There are few trout in the river and those large. Hotel: Inveroran. Fishing in lake and 2m of Orchy for residents (April 1 to Oct 31) £7 per day.

AYR

Rises in Glenbuck and flows into Firth of Clyde through town of Ayr opposite south end of Isle of Arran. Good brown trout river (av ½ lb) with fair runs of salmon and sea trout.

Ayr. Mostly preserved, but tickets (wt £2.50, dt £1) can be had for ¾m water at Ayr from the Director of Finance, Kyle and Carrick DC, Town Buildings, Ayr, and from tackleists *(see below).* Up-river water privately held, but permission sometimes given by proprietors. Wading essential for good sport. Water restocked with brown trout by Ayr AC. About 3m N at Prestwick, dt can be had for Prestwick AC water on **Prestwick Reservoir;** trout, ¾ lb to 3½ lb; restocked annually; fishes best in evening. Tickets from A Sim, solicitor, 41 Main Street,

Prestwick, or tackleist, T G Morrison, 117 Main Street, Prestwick. Good and free pike and perch fishing can be had on various lochs within 10m of Ayr. At **Drongan** (10m ESE) Drongan Youth Group AC issues permits at small charge for **River Coyle** (sea trout, trout, grayling, few salmon). Trout fishing on **Lochs Bradan, Skelloch, Brechbowie** and **Dhu** (Ayr 20m) dt (bank) £1.50, boat from £2.50 extra. Pike fishing on **L Linfern:** dt £1.50. Apply Heany, Tallaminnoch, Straiton, Maybole, or Forestry Commission, Tel 0465 86223. **Penwhapple Loch,** near Barr, water of Penwhapple AC. Dt 75p, boats 50p per 4 hours, apply J Murray, 3 Dalrymple St, Girvan, or at loch. 3m S of Ayr is **River Doon,** at Alloway. Good salmon and sea trout (July onwards). Burns Monument Hotel, Alloway, has stretch. Otherwise private. Loch Doon is 20m S; 6m long; good free trout fishing early months; boats at Dalmellington village. Tackleists: James

Kirk, 25 Kyle Street, Gamesport, 60 Sandgate, from whom tickets for town and other waters on Rivers Ayr and Doon can be obtained and for coarse fish lochs.

Catrine (Strathclyde). Trout, grayling; some migratory fish. Club: Catrine AC; limited wt and dt.

Mauchline (Strathclyde). Permits from S Wallace, Kilmarnock Road, for fishing on Ayr and **Cessnock Water.**

Sorn (Strathclyde). Sorn AC has 5m on Ayr, both banks; trout, grayling, some salmon and sea trout late in season. Dt and wt to visitors staying in town. Accommodation at Sorn Inn.

Muirkirk (Strathclyde). Trout, grayling; tickets, from hon sec, Muirkirk AA and T Russell, Limerhaugh Farm; water restocked annually. Association also has fishing on **River Greenock;** trout and grayling; dt 30p. Hotels: Eglinton Arms, Mason Arms.

Tributary of the Ayr

LUGAR: Salmon, sea trout, trout, grayling.

Ochiltree (Strathclyde). Trout, grayling; some salmon and sea trout; Aug and Sept best. Ochiltree AA has Lugar and tributaries: limited membership. **Auchinleck** AA has 4m on **R Lugar** and 2m on **R Ayr.** Also **Tarmac Loch** (brown trout). Dt from hon sec.

Cumnock (Strathclyde). Cumnock and Dist AA controls several miles of Lugar

and its tributaries (Bello and Glaisnock) and two small lochs. Trout in Lugar and salmon and sea trout; restocked annually from association's hatchery. Tickets: from hon sec. Association also has **Boreland Reservoirs** (2), well stocked with trout; permit from hon sec or tackleists. Hotels: Dumfries Arms, Royal. Tackleists: B Black, Precinct, Thornton, Ayr Road.

BEAULY

Beauly proper is about 9m long, being formed by junction of Glass and Farrar. Flows into Beauly Firth and thence into Moray Firth. Good salmon and sea trout, April to October.

Beauly (Highland). All fishing on the Beauly is owned by Lovat Estates and let in various beats. The principal ones are the Home, Falls and the Downie on the lower reaches: salmon, grilse, sea trout, and finnock. Kilmorack Ex-

Servicemen's AA fish two days a week on the Tidal Beat. Day tickets from Lovat Estate Office for tidal, estuary, and other river and loch beats. Good sea trout from the beginning of the season.

Tributary of the Beauly

CANNICH:

Cannich (Highland). At confluence of Cannich and Affric. Guests at Glen Affric Hotel can have salmon fishing on 2m of **River Glass** and trout fishing on **Lochs Affric, Benevean, Mullardoch** and **Monar.** Permits for Loch Benevean (two

rods), also from J Macpherson & Sons, Sports Stores, Inglis Street, Inverness. Craigard Hotel, Boat of Garten, *(advt p 325)* issues permits (wt £10, dt £3) for 6m of **Spey,** both banks, Dt £6.50 for **Lochs Vaa** and **Dallas;** £2.25 for **Avielochan.**

BERVIE

Rises on Glen Farquhar Estate and flows 14m to North Sea near Inverbervie. Salmon, sea trout, autumn best for salmon and Aug–Sept for sea trout.

Inverbervie (Grampian). Trout, sea trout, salmon (best Sept–Oct) permits for fore-shore from Joseph Johnston & Sons, 3 America Street, Montrose, for fortnight-ly periods (restricted; advance booking advised). River permits from Burgh Office, Church St.

Fordoun (Grampian). Laurencekirk AA has full rights on river from here to Glenbervie; guest tickets available.

BRORA

After being joined by tributaries Blackwater and Skinsdale, Brora flows through Loch Brora and into sea at Brora. Blackwater enters Brora about two miles above loch (at Balnacoil Lodge) on Gordonbush Estate. All fishing rights on both banks, extending for about 10m, owned by estate. Other tributary, the Skinsdale, flows into Blackwater six miles above Balnacoil. Rights on this river also owned by Gordonbush Estate. Noted salmon and sea trout waters. Good throughout season for salmon; two runs of sea trout, large ones in June to July and finnock in August to Sept. Loch fishing best June to Sept. Brown trout small.

Brora (Highland). Salmon, sea trout. Gor-donbush Estate owns the sole fishing rights, both banks, between Loch Brora and Blackwater junction (2m). Salmon catch on this beat averages more than 400. Estate lets north bank from sea to loch and both banks from loch to Balnacoil; also both banks of Blackwater and Skinsdale, with or without Balnacoil Lodge. Also boats by day or longer periods on **Loch Brora** (Brora 345). Apply Gordonbush Estates Office, Brora, for salmon, sea trout, char and brown trout fishing. Hotels at Golspie and Brora have boats on loch. Suther-land Estates, **Golspie** (Golspie 268) owns south bank of Lower Brora from sea to Loch Brora and let four rods; also Upper Brora for about 5m (both banks) from Balnacoil Ford to Dalreavoch Lodge, let with or without lodge. Loch fishing avail-able. Estate also owns upper **Blackwater** at Benarmine, again let with loch fishing and with Benarmine Lodge. Golspie AC has salmon and trout fishing; permits from Lindsay's shop, Main Street. Tidal stretch of Brora open to public for sea-trout fishing; except in May. Loch Brora AC and Golspie AC have boats on Loch Brora. Salmon and sea trout. Also four estate and several hotel boats. Club also takes salmon beats on river. Dt for boat on loch: £3, dt for river (S) £13–£18. Golspie AC now has fishing on **Lochs Lundie, Horn** and **Farlary;** also the sea trout fishing on the estuary of **R Fleet.** Tackleist: Rob Wilson. Hotels: Royal Marine, *(advt p 286)* Links and Suther-land Arms, Brora; Sutherland Arms, Golspie.

CARRON (Grampian)

Rises in Glenbervie and flows about 9m to the North Sea at Stonehaven. Trout.

Stonehaven (Grampian). About 2½m brown trout fishing available to visitors from Stonehaven and Dist AA. Permits also issued for **River Cowie** (about 1¼m); sea trout, finnock. Best July, August and Sept;. Good sea fishing. Numerous hotels and boarding houses.

CLYDE

Rises near watershed of Tweed and Annan, and flows about 50m to the Atlantic by way of Glasgow. Once a famous salmon river, but long since spoiled by pollution. Trout and grayling fishing passable, especially in higher reaches. The Clyde's most famous tributary, the Leven, which connects with Loch Lomond, still has run of salmon and sea trout. In north-west corner of Renfrewshire is Loch Thom, linked by water spill with Loch Compensation, which, when water is high, drains into River Kip in Shielhill Burn. United Clyde Angling Protective Association Ltd, controls much of Clyde and Avon and tributaries. Association has hatchery and rearing pond, and restocks annually.

Greenock (Strathclyde). On estuarial Clyde. Greenock and District AC preserves **Loch Thom** (365 acres, trout—three to the pound). Also rights on **Compensation Reservoir** (38 acres, trout). **Yetts, No. 8 and No. 6** (Spring Dam); good trout. Dt £1, wt £1.50 from hon sec or waterman at Loch Thom, or farmers on loch side. Club membership restricted to persons resident in Greenock and district, but permits available to visitors; Sunday fishing; no parties. Fly only on all club waters during season (March 15 to Oct 6). Good sea fishing—cod, skate, dogfish, conger, haddock and plaice. Club: Firth of Clyde, Gourock, Renfrewshire. Tackleist: Findlay & Co, 29 West Stewart St, Greenock, who also issue tickets.

Port Glasgow (Strathclyde). On Clyde estuary. **Lower Loch Gryffe** (72 acres), **Knocknair** (10 acres), **Harelaw** (23 acres) preserved by Port Glasgow AC. Dt 50p from hon sec.

Glasgow (Strathclyde). Glasgow has excellent trout, sea trout and salmon fishing within a radius of 60m. Lochs Lomond, Dochart, Awe, Tay, Ard, Leven, Lubnaig, Vennacher, Lake of Menteith, etc, and Rivers Annan, Goil, Cur (head of Loch Eck), Clyde (trout and grayling only), Teith, Tweed, Allan, Dochart, Leven, Kinglass etc, all accessible from here. Coarse fishing in Forth-Clyde canal; roach and perch. United Clyde Angling Protective Association Ltd, issues season tickets £5 for a number of waters locally, apply hon sec or tackleists. **Lochend Loch, Coatbridge** (Monklands Dist water); trout and some perch; free to residents. Others apply to M M Barrow, Leisure and Recreation Dept, Monklands DC, Bank Street, Airdrie. Woodhead Loch, Coatbridge is private water. At **Kilsyth** Kilsyth FPA issue st £1.50 and dt 50p for **Birkenhead Reservoir, Townhead Reservoir** Banton Loch, **Corrie Reservoir** and **Garrel Burn;** boats on **Banton Loch** (trout); two sessions daily; permits and boats from Coachman Hotel, Parkfoot Street, Kilsyth. **Carron Dam,** 5m away; good trout; dt £2.25 (from boat only) **Carron Water;** free; good trout fishing. Dt for **Luggie Water;** trout; Waterside AIA. Coarse fishing on Black Loch. Strathclyde RC, Lower Clyde Div.—Water Dept, 419 Balmore Rd, Glasgow G22 6NU, issues permits at £4 per day (incl VAT) including boat, for **Loch Katrine; Picketlaw, Arklet** and **Glen Finglas Reservoir;** details from Division. At **Lennoxtown.** Campsie AC has trout fishing on **River Glazert,** burns and ponds. Dt and st from hon sec. Walton AC has water on **White Cart;** brown trout; members only. At **Airdrie** local club stocks two reservoirs—**Hillend** and **Lily Loch**—with Loch Leven and brown trout average 1 lb. Both waters shared with Blackridge AC; dt £2, st £5 from Auchengray Lodge, Forrestfield Hotel, Truff Inn and Eastercroft Hotel—all at lochside. Mrs Brown, "Wester Gavin", Howwood, issues dt 40p for **Whittlemuir Dam** (also from General Store, Howwood; fly only). At **Hamilton** (11m SE) are **Daer Reservoir** (trout) and **Roughrigg Reservoir** (pike and perch). Visitors' dt (£5) from Strathclyde Regional Council Water Dept, Hamilton ML3 0AL. Boats. Glasgow tackleists: Hardy Bros and John Dickson & Son, Royal Exchange Square; Cafaro Bros, 37 Cowcaddens Street; Arthur Allan, 3 West Nile Street; Robertson, 27 Wellington Street; Anglers Rendezvous, 24 Parnie Street; Lawrie Renfrew, 514 Gt Western Road; Scottish Angling Services, 367 Paisley Road; J Pitcher, 402 Dunbarton Road; McKendricks Sports, 8 Alexandra Arcade, East Kilbride.

Paisley (Strathclyde). Good trout fishing in **Glenburn** and **Muirhead Reservoirs.** £1, and in **Camphill Reservoir** (£4 per boat, 2 rods) **Rowbank** and **Barcraigs Reservoirs** (dt £3) all tickets from Strathclyde RC, Lower Clyde DIV—Water Dept, 19 Underwood Road, Paisley PA3 1TQ. Tackle and information from Pitcher's Sports Shop, Moss Street. Hotels: Brabloch and Rockfield, both Renfrew Road.

Strathavon (Strathclyde). Avon and Clyde; trout and grayling; st £5 from UCAPA for water on Clyde. Avon AC controls Avon. *(See also Carstairs.)*

Lanark (Strathclyde). Trout, grayling (trout av 6 oz, grayling ½ lb). Lanark AA has stretch from Kirkfieldbank Bridge to Upper Shoals. Permits from hon sec and water bailiffs, st £2, dt 50p. Trout and grayling.

Carstairs (Strathclyde). Trout and grayling; st £5 from United Clyde APA; good baskets of trout on minnow and fly. *(See also Thankerton.)*

Thankerton (Strathclyde). Permits for 9m of water from Thankerton to Roberton from hon sec, Lamington AA, or river watchers; st and dt; trout and grayling. UCAPA water below Thankerton; st £5. *(See Carstairs.)*

Biggar (Strathclyde). 1½m to Clyde; tickets from Lamington AA. Other Assn water at **Lamington, Symington** and **Roberton** *(see Thankerton).* Hotels: Hartree;

Toftcombs; Wyndales House, Symington; Shieldhill, Biggar. Tackleist: R E Watson, High Street.

Abington (Lanark). Trout and grayling; UCAPA water; st £5. Other Assn water at **Crawford** and **Elvanfoot.** Hotel: Abington.

Tributaries of the Clyde

LEVEN and LOCH LOMOND: Salmon, trout, pike and perch.

Loch Lomond (Strathclyde). Good trout, sea trout and salmon fishing (also perch and pike) can be had from various centres on loch. Under control of Loch Lomond Angling Improvement Assn, 224 Ingram St, Glasgow, G1 1HH (Tel: 041 221 0068). Fishing reserved for full members only (entrance fee £11.50, subscription £39.75) in Loch Lomond, Rivers Leven, **Fruin** and **Falloch** and some stretches of **Endrick.** Dt are issued for Leven and Loch Lomond (£3.16) at all local centres. St and wt also obtainable for Leven.Wt £8.20. No Sunday fishing. Dt from tackleists, boat hirers and hotels. Late April or May earliest for fly on Loch Lomond (sea trout and sal-

mon). Permits for pike, perch, roach and powan fishing are free during salmon and trout close seasons. Otherwise £3.16 per day, £8.20 per week. Apply Loch Lomond AIA. Hotels at **Tarbet** (Dunbarton), **Inversnaid** and **Rowardennan,** by Balmaha (Stirling) are convenient for loch; permits and boats.

Balloch (Strathclyde). Trout, good sea trout and salmon fishing on River Leven and Loch Lomond; large perch and pike in loch; fishing controlled by Loch Lomond AIA *(see Loch Lomond).* Hotels: Tullichewan, Balloch; boat available.

FRUIN: (tributary of Loch Lomond):

Helensburgh (Strathclyde). Trout, sea trout and salmon fishing; sub £39.75 + entrance fee, issued by Loch Lomond

AIA *(see Loch Lomond)*. Helensburgh AC has water; members only. Tackleists: Post Office, Cove. Hotel: Commodore. Boats and bait arranged.

Ardlui (Dunbarton). Trout, sea trout and salmon fishing in Loch Lomond. Hotel: Colquhoun Arms (boats).

ENDRICK: (tributary of Loch Lomond):

Killearn (Central). Good trout, sea trout and salmon fishing. Loch Lomond AIA has water; st £39.75 covers all assn waters; waiting list and entrance fee of £11.50 payable when vacancy notified. All prices incl VAT *(see Loch Lomond)*.

GRYFE (or GRYFFE): Trout and grayling.

Bridge of Weir (Strathclyde). Bridge of Weir River AC issue mt £1, wt 50p, dt 25p for 4m of water. Bridge of Weir Loch AC; no tickets.

Kilmacolm (Strathclyde). Strathgryfe AA has trout water here. Dt 40p/20p from Cross Cafe. No Sunday fishing for visitors.

CALDER and BLACK CART:

Lochwinnoch (Strathclyde). St Winnoch AC has stretch of Calder (brown trout). St £2 and dt 40p from hon sec. Sunday fishing. Castle Semple Loch (pike and perch) now taken over by Water Dept. Castle AC has water on Black Cart from Lochwinnoch Loch down to Milliken Park (2m); trout, some perch, occasional small pike; slow stream; good dry fly water; dt 50p from hon sec and general store, Howwood. Hotel: Mossend (½m Lochwinnoch).

CONON (including Orrin and Blackwater)

Drains Loch Luichart and is joined by Orrin and Blackwater before entering the Moray Firth and North Sea by way of Cromarty Firth. Spring fishing has declined and main salmon runs now take place from July to September. Sport then among best in Highlands.

Dingwall (Highland). Sea trout and brown trout. Dingwall District AC has beat on R Conon. Fly only, for sea trout and brown trout. Season; Jan 26 to Sept 30, best months May, Aug and Sept. Also fishing for brown trout, pike, perch and char on Loch Luichart. Season March 15 to Oct 6. Visitors' tickets from tackleist: J J Shanks, The Sporting Store, Tulloch. Mt £8, wt £3, dt £1. Salmon, sea trout and trout fishing on **Allt Graad River, Alness River** and **Loch Glass** near **Evanton** from Factor, Novar Estates office *(see under Alness)*. Alness AC also has water on river. Hotels: Conon at Conon Bridge and Aultguish (fishing on **Loch Glascarnoch**, boats).

Strathpeffer (Ross and Cromarty). Salmon and trout on **Rivers Conon & Blackwater;** trout in lochs. Loch Achonachie AC has beats on Upper Conon (April 1 to Sept. 30) and Upper Blackwater (ditto) also boats on **L Achonachie** and **L Meig.** Limited dt for all waters through bookings sec, M. Burr, The Tackle Shop, Strathpeffer. Both rivers fish best late in the season. Craigdarroch Hotel, Contin (by Strathpeffer) issues permits for Blackwater and lochs (brown and rainbow trout). Best July–Sept. Coul House Hotel, Contin, issues wt and dt (£12–£64 and £4–£12.50, according to date) for beats on **R Alness.** *(advt p 283)*.

Garve (Highland). Garve Hotel (Tel 205) has excellent fishing on Conon and **Loch Garve,** which holds large trout (fish up to 12 lb taken) also pike to 30 lb and perch. Fishing for rainbow trout on 1½m of River Blackwater within hotel grounds. Strathgarve Lodge has fishing on 7m of river (salmon and trout) and five lochs for guests. Own salmon beats April–Sept; other months by arrangement. Aultguish Inn, by Garve, issue wt and dt for trout fishing on **Loch Glascarnoch.**

CREE and BLADNOCH

Drains Loch Moan and flows about 25m to sea at Wigtown Bay. Has greatly improved as salmon river in lower reaches in recent years and now very good for salmon and sea trout in summer. **Minnoch,** tributary of Cree, is also a salmon river, joining Cree about six miles from Newton Stewart.

Creetown (Dumfries & Galloway). Hotel: Barholm Arms. Good river and loch fishing in the area; apply proprietor for particulars. Fishing on Cree mostly in hands of Earl of Galloway and available beats are let.

Newton Stewart (Dumfries & Galloway). Salmon, sea trout; best early in season. Newton Stewart AA has fishing for salmon, sea trout and brown trout in Cree. **Bladnoch, Minnoch** and **Penkiln Burn** and on **Kirriereoch Loch** (trout), **Palnure Burn** (salmon, sea trout, herling); **Bruntis Lochs, Lochs Ochiltree, Wee Glenamour** and **Kirriereoch** (all brown trout), and **Clatteringshaws dam** (trout and pike). Charges wt (including Cree) £20: (excluding Cree) £7.50. Dt £5 and £1.50. Tickets from R W McDowall, 4 Arthur Street, Newtown Stewart. Spinning and bait fishing allowed when river in flood. Creebridge House Hotel arranges fishing in River Cree and various lochs and burns. Galloway Arms Hotel can also arrange fishing. Corsemalzie House Hotel *(advt p 283)* between Wigtown and Glenluce, has fishing on Bladnoch, **Tarff** and **Malzie burn.** Fishing arranged on Cree and on nearby coast. Tackle and information from R W McDowall.

DEE (Aberdeenshire)

Second most famous salmon river of Scotland; for fly-fishing probably the best. Also holds sea trout and brown trout. Rises in Cairngorms and flows into North Sea at Aberdeen. Best months for salmon: February to mid-June. Best for finnock (small sea trout) mid-August to end of September.

Aberdeen.* Salmon, sea trout, brown trout; sea fishing. Many owners let for whole or part of season, but some good stretches held by hotels. Some hotel waters free to guests during summer. Lower reaches give good finnock fishing. Day tickets for various tidal reaches on Dee: Enquire of Aberdeen & Dist AA. Brown trout fishing in parts and good finnock fishing in spring and autumn in

Brochure on Fishing from Corporation Publicity Dept, 81 Nicholas House, Broad St, AB9 1DE (5p).

tidal part. Aberdeen and Dist AA has 10m of salmon and brown trout fishing on the **Don** (7m away), and trout fishing on **Loch Loirston** (3m away); dt £3 from J Somers & Son, (tackleist) 40 Thistle St, Aberdeen. Sea fishing is good in vicinity of Aberdeen *(see Sea Fishing Stations).* Other tackleists: Wm Brown & Co, 11 Belmont Street; John Dickson & Son, 35 Belmont St. Hotels: Station, Caledonian, Imperial, Royal, Marcliffe.

Drum (Grampian). Dee preserved. **Gormack Burn;** trout; heavily fished; permission of H Q Forbes Irvine, of Drum.

Banchory (Grampian). Salmon, sea trout and grilse. Fishing let at fortnightly periods on Ballogie stretch; 3m long; four rods allowed from Feb 1 to Sept 30; Carlogie stretch is 2m with three rods allowed; salmon and grilse caught Feb to Sept. Banchory Lodge Hotel by river can arrange salmon and trout fishing. Feughside Inn, Strachan, by Banchory, has 2 rods on 1½m of Dee and can arrange fishing on **Feugh;** salmon and sea trout. Other hotels: Potarch, Torna-Coille (fishing arranged on Dee and Feugh).

Aboyne (Grampian). Dee; salmon and sea trout. Hotels: Balnacoil (water on Dee); Huntly Arms (fishing arranged on river and lochs).

Ballater and Braemar (Grampian). Balmoral, Mar and Invercauld Estates preserve a great deal of the fishing. The latter lets the Crathie, Lower Invercauld and Monaltrie salmon beats, 20m of fishing in all, details from The Factor, Invercauld Estate Office, by Ballater. Tel: Braemar 224. Brown trout fishing on Rivers **Gairn** and **Clunie,** on **Lochs Nan Ean, Bainnie** and **Vrotichan.** St ranges from £3 to £5: dt from 50p to £1. Permits from the Estate Office. Hotels: Invercauld Arms; Mar Lodge; *(advt p 283)* which also reserve fishing for guests. Ravenswood Hotel *(advt p 282).*

DEE (Kirkcudbrightshire), including Lochs Dee and Ken

Flows through Loch Ken about 16m to Solway. Salmon, sea trout and brown trout. Netting reduced and river stocked with salmon fry.

Castle Douglas (Dumfries & Galloway). Dee private. **River Urr** (8m) holds salmon, sea trout and brown trout; Castle Douglas AA has 7m; re-stocked annually; good runs of sea trout and grilse starting in June. Permits from tackleists. Spinning and bait fishing in flood water only. Lidderdale and Gillespie issue permits for **Lairdmannoch Loch,** Twynholm. Several lochs may be fished from Milton Park Hotel *(see Deugh—Dalry).* Lochinvar Hotel also has fishing on loch *(see Dalry).* **Auchenreoch Loch** is 9m away on main Dumfries Road; good pike, some trout; permission from Galloway Arms, Crocketford. **Carlingwark Loch,** on outskirts of Castle Douglas (pike and perch) is free: boats available. Tackleists: As above and M McCowan & Son, 52 King Street. Culgruff House Hotel, Crossmichael has coarse fishing on **River Ken** and **Woodhall Loch** and caters especially for pike anglers in winter. Glaisters Lodge Hotel has fishing.

Boat o' Rhone (Dumfries & Galloway). Large pike in loch. Free fishing on Dee for perch and pike; good.

New Galloway (Dumfries & Galloway). Dee private. Fishing free in **Loch Ken** (1m); holds trout, large pike and perch, and some salmon. New Galloway AA issues permits for a stretch on the **R Ken**, **L Stroan** and **Clatteringshaws Reservoir.** Dt £1, wt £2.50 from hotels, the PO, Mossdale and from New Galloway Grocers. Ken Bridge Hotel has own stretch on R Ken and both this hotel and Cross Keys can arrange fishing on rivers and lochs. **Barscobe Loch;** trout; dt (incl boat) £1 from Hugh Wontner, Barscobe. For **Knockman Loch;** good trouting from bank; dt from Mrs D M Scott, Mersehead, Southwick, Dumfries but rights on **Lochinvar** now let to New Galloway AA for five years. **Clatteringshaws Dam;** large trout; dry fly good; dt 50p from local clubs.

Dalry (Dumfries & Galloway). Dalry AA has fishing on **River Ken** (left bank from Dalry to Boatknowe), **Carsfad** and **Earlstoun Reservoirs.** Tickets from Glenkens Cafe (wt only for river, dt for reservoirs).

DEUGH: (tributary of Loch Ken):

Dalry (Dumfries & Galloway). Trout. Permits from Dalry AA for **River Ken, Carsfad Reservoir** and **Earlstoun Reservoir;** boats on both. Milton Park Hotel (Tel Dalry 286). Trout fishing (brown and rainbow) on **Lochs Barscobe, Mossroddick, Brack** and **Howie** boats available with boat also on **Loch Earlstoun** at rear of hotel; all waters stocked with trout. Tickets for nonresidents, £2.50, incl boat, but guests have priority. Salutation Hotel (Carsphairn), can arrange fishing on Deugh. Lochinvar Hotel can arrange fishing in rivers, lochs and reservoirs (salmon, trout, pike and perch).

DEVERON

Rises in Cabrach and flows some 45m into the Moray Firth at Banff. A prolific, salmon river, but has, in particular, a reputation for its brown trout fishing. There are also some large sea trout, many of 8–10 lb. Sea trout run June to September; finnock mid-July to end of October. Best months: June and July.

Banff. Salmon, sea trout, brown trout. Hotels: Fife Arms and Banff Springs *(advt p 267)*, County Hotel *(advt p 285)* which can arrange fishings. Best months: salmon, March to Oct; sea trout June to Aug; brown trout, April, May and Sept. Sea trout improving. Local association: Banff and Macduff, which has about 1m both banks of tidal water; wt for visitors resident in Banff or Macduff; dt for others, from hon sec or tackleist *(see below)*. Sea trout fishing (July onwards) in **Boyne Burn,** 6m away. Tickets from Seafield Estate, Cullen (no charge, but limited).

Turriff (Grampian). Turriff AA has salmon, sea trout and brown trout fishing on Deveron; Dt (Mon–Fri) for resident visitors only, £20 from Ian Masson Sports Ltd, Main Street, Turriff. Fly only when level falls below 6 in on gauge. Best months July, August and Sept. Hotels: Union, White Heather, Royal Oak, Glenesk. Enquiries to Bell Ingram, 7 Walker Street, Edinburgh for Beldorney Castle Water. (£55 per rod per week).

Huntly (Grampian). **Bogie** and Deveron; salmon, sea trout and trout. **Isla;** trout. Enquires to Clerk to Huntly Fishings Committee, 27 Duke Street, Huntly. Kirkney, Bogie tributary (4m); small trout; permits from Forestry Commission. In late spring upper waters of rivers will be found best for salmon. Hotels: Gordon Arms, Castle *(advt p 286)* (rights on Deveron).

DIGHTY

Drains some small lochs and falls into the Firth of Tay not far from Dundee. Banks built up in lower reaches. Now clear of pollution. Trout, odd sea trout and salmon. Badly weeded and difficult to fish in summer.

Dundee (Tayside). Trout with occasional sea trout; free. **Lindores Loch:** holds brown trout over 3 lb and rainbows. Six boats. Apply F G A Hamilton, 18 Strathview Place, Comrie (Comrie 8221). **Rescobie Loch:** Large trout (brown and rain-

Note: *Charges given in this book may not include Value Added Tax unless otherwise Stated.*

bow). Bank and boat fishing through Mr
J Yule, South Lodge, Reswallie, Forfar.
Tel: Letham (Angus) 384. Tayside Regional Council Reservoirs: **Monikie and
Crombie Reservoirs, Lintrathen Loch.**
Good trout fishing in all three. For permits and boats for Crombie and Lintrathen, apply to the Tayside Council
Water Dept at 10 Ward Rd, Dundee
(Tel 21164). For Monikie, to Monikie
AC. Other trout waters within easy
reach include **Raith Lake,** Kirkcaldy (3
boats), **Loch Fitty** 16 boats and bank
fishing, tackle shop and fish farm to
which visitors are welcome. Apply Game
Fisheries Ltd, The Lodge, Loch Fitty,
Kingseat, Dunfermline (Tel 23162) for
both waters. **Ballo, Holl** and **Glenfarg
Reservoirs.** Morning and evening ses-
sions £1.15, boat extra. Permits from
Fife Regional Council Water Division,
Craig Mitchell House, Flemington
Road, Glenrothes, Fife KY7 5QH. Also
Tay, Eden, Lunan, N & S Esk and Loch
Leven *(see under separate headings).*
Tackleists: John R Gow & Sons, 12
Union Street, who will give advice on
fishing throughout Scotland and issue
permits for **Lunan** (Angus), **Eden** (Fife),
and Strathmore AIA water on **Isla and
Dean** (15m); restocked; st £6, dt £1.
Other Tackleists: Shotcast Ltd,
Whitehall Crescent.

DON (Aberdeenshire)

Rises near Ben Avon and flows for nearly 80m to North Sea at Aberdeen. Good salmon
river which is also noted as dry-fly trout water. Autumn salmon fishing falling off, but
spring fishing improving. Some sea trout.

Parkhill (Grampain). Now privately owned. No tickets.

Kintore (Grampian). 1m of salmon and
trout fishing on both banks of River
Don. Wt £8.50, dt £3.20 and £2.20,
according to date. Well stocked with
trout 10/12 ozs. Permits from Kintore
Arms and J Copland, Newsagent, Northern Road. Other hotel: Lorryburn. No
Sunday fishing.

Inverurie (Grampian). Burgh waters on **Urie** (4m; trout and salmon) and Don (2½m; salmon and trout and occasional sea trout); tickets from Town Hall or Inverurie AA (Tel: 2310): st £19, wt £8.50, dt £3.20 and £2.20, according to date. No Sunday fishing. Salmon best March, April, May and Sept–Oct. Hotels: Kintore Arms, Gordon Arms; Pitcaple (on Urie and near Don): fishing on Urie free to guests.

Kemnay (Grampian). Mrs F J Milton, Kemnay House, issues permits for Don, principally for trout.

Monymusk. Grant Arms Hotel has exclusive rights to 10m of trout and salmon fishing (13 beats) *(advt p 286)*.

Alford (Grampian). 26½m from Aberdeen.

Salmon and trout. Hotels: Haughton Arms, which has 6m of Don for guests only. Forbes Arms, Bridge of Alford, which has 6½m of Don for guests, wt £30, dt £5–£7. Some good trout burns (free) in vicinity.

Kildrummy (Grampian). Kildrummy Castle Hotel has good stretch of salmon and brown trout fishing. Trout best early, salmon late. Permits. Dt (S) £7 (T) £2, enquiries to J P Smith (Tel Kildrummy 264). Kildrummy Inn also issues permits.

Glenkindie (Grampian). Apply Glenkindie Arms for salmon and trout fishing. No Sunday fishing.

Strathdon (Grampian). Colquhonnie Hotel has 3m salmon water, 9m of trout fishing. Dt (S) £6.90, (T) £3.45 *(advt. p 286)*.

DOON

Drains Loch Doon on the Solway Firth's watershed and flows right through the old County of Ayr to the Firth of Clyde near Ayr Town. Good salmon, sea trout and brown trout water.

Ayr. On Doon and Ayr estuaries. Salmon and sea trout July onwards. Burns Monument Hotel has water on Doon *(see next entry)*. District Council issues permits for Ayr *(see p 274)*. Tackleist: Game Sports (Ayr) Ltd, 60 Sandgate.

Dalmellington (Strathclyde). Good salmon and sea trout (July onwards). Burns Monument Hotel, Alloway, has stretch. Dt from Doonfoot Store for tidal stretch; good finnock; otherwise private. **Loch Doon,** 6m; plenty of small brown trout and occasional salmon and char; fishing free; boats for hire. Craigengillan Estate has both banks of River Doon from **Loch Doon** to the Straiton Road Bridge. Permits are available for stretch from Loch Doon to Lynn bridge only. Brown trout and occasional salmon and sea trout. Prices on application to keepers at Mains

Farm, Craigengillan (Tel: Dalmellington 550 366). No fishing permitted below Lynn Bridge, but permits available for **Ladys Loch,** brown and rainbow trout (av 1 lb). Local clubs: Dalmellington AC; (fishes Lochs Doon, **Ballochling** and **Bogton.** Loch Doon free; dt for **Bogton** (salmon, sea trout, brown trout and pike) £3 boat; permits from hon sec); Brown trout fishing on Loch Bradon, dt £1.25, from R Hainy, Gamekeeper, Straiton. Ness Glen AC shares Bogton Loch. Hotels: Loch Doon, Eglinton.

LOCH DOON: Brown trout; free. Dalmellington AC fishes Doon, Ballochling and Bogton *(see Dalmellington)*.

LOCH FINLAS: (tributary of Loch Doon): Trout up to 1 lb. Rented by Loch Finlas FC; fishing is strictly for members and members' guests only.

EDEN (Fife)

Rises in Ochil Hills not far from Loch Leven and falls into North Sea in St Andrews Bay. Provides some very fair trout fishing. Slow-flowing stream suitable for dry-fly fishing. Some sea trout below Cupar.

St Andrews (Fife). **Cameron Reservoir** stocked by St Andrews AC (trout av 1¼ lb). Fly only. Details of permit and boat charges on application to the secretary. Permits and boat reservations from bailiff. (Tel Peat Inn 236), St Andrews

(Tel 2477). Kenly Burn (ticket water), inquire tackleists. Kinness Burn free. Tackleists: J Wilson & Son (as above); A Mackenzie & Son. Many hotels.

Cupar (Fife). Trout, sea trout, few salmon. Preserved by Eden AA. Dry fly much

used; trout average, $\frac{1}{2}$ lb to $\frac{3}{4}$ lb; sea trout run from tidal waters; st £5 from hon sec; dt (S and MT) £2; (T) £1 from Cupar railway station near river or John R Gow and Sons, Union Street, Dundee. Permits from Crawford Priory Estate, for trout fishing on **Clatto Loch**. St £40, wt £16, dt £4, from West Lodge, Crawford Priory. Boat extra. Hotel: Royal.

Ladybank (Fife). Fine dry-fly fishing; trout. Some free, but mostly preserved. **Lindores Fishery, Newburgh** (7m NW) opened in 1968; loch holding brown,

rainbow and American brook trout; fly only; no bank fishing. Day and evening tickets. Sunday fishing allowed. Applications to F G A Hamilton, 18 Strathview Place, Comrie, Perthshire (Comrie 8221).

Tributary of the Eden
MOUTRAY:
Kilmany (Fife). Trout; mostly free.

Note: *Trout fishing on several reservoirs in area available from Fife and Kinross Water Board* (see under Glenrothes, Loch Leven).

ESK (North)

Formed by junction of Lee and Mark, near Lochlee, and flows for nearly 30m to North Sea near Montrose. Good river for salmon and sea trout.

Montrose (Tayside). Sea trout, finnock (whitling) and brown trout. Joseph Johnston & Sons Ltd, 3 America Street, issue free permits for Morphie Beat (1m) for either Monday and Wednesday, Tuesday and Friday, or Thursday and Saturday from end of March to end of Aug (except May). Best April and Aug. Local club: Montrose AA (*see under Bervie and "South Esk—Bridge of Dun"*). Hotels: Links, new hotel, has four salmon rods for guests on N Esk; £12 week each; Park. Joseph Johnston & Sons issue dt £10 for Canterland beat. Salmon, sea trout, brown trout. Best early and late. Other tackleists: Hamilton, 122 Murray Street; Cobb, Castle Place.

Edzell (Tayside); ns Montrose. Salmon, sea trout, etc. Dt £3.50 to £8 for beat on S bank from Montrose and Dist AA. Contact Reid, 3 Meridian Street. Dt for Brechin and Arbroath AC water: £3 from Breans, Commission Agents, Lordburn, Arbroath. Tackleists: The Sports Shop, High Street, Brechin; A de Costa, Post Office, Edzell. Hotels: Glenesk, Central Panmure.

LUTHER WATER:

Laurencekirk (Grampian). Sea and yellow trout. Laurencekirk AA has full rights here; guest tickets available. Best Aug–Oct.

ESK (South)

Rises in Glen Clova and flows some 49m to North Sea near Montrose. Good salmon river with plentiful runs of salmon. Best months for salmon are February, March and April. Good autumn river (mid-September onwards).

Bridge of Dun (Tayside). Good for spring and autumn salmon and for sea trout. Grilse in June, July and August; finnock in February, March and April, and Sept-Oct. Wt and dt, £12 and £3, for visitors staying in Montrose from hon sec, Montrose AC. Hotel: House of Dun, with 1½m of first-class fishing for guests.

Brechin (Tayside). Salmon and sea trout; fishing good, but mostly preserved. Beats to let by week or longer periods on 2½m at Southesk Estates Office; Brechin. Dalhousie Estate Office, Brechin, issues permits for trout fishing on **Loch Lee** (Glenesk); fly only; also salmon beats to let by week or longer on N and S Esk. Justinhaugh Hotel has good salmon

stretch; 3m one bank, ¾m other; free to guests. Forfar AC have adjacent stretch. **Loch Saugh,** Fettercairn, is 12m; trout. Brechin AA water. Permits (dt £2) from Ramsay Arms Hotel, Fettercairn; Drumtochty Hotel, Auchenblae; and Sports Shop, 22/24 High Street, Brechin, who also issue limited dt (£3) for salmon and sea trout on Westwater. Hotel: House of Dun (two beats for guests).

Kirriemuir (Tayside). Kirriemuir AC has water. Salmon, sea trout, brown trout. Wt £20, dt £4. No dt on Saturdays. From J Norrie Ltd, High Street, Kirriemuir; P O Dykehead, Cortachy; or in advance from hon sec. Some fly only, but much unrestricted water. Strathmore AIA had

rights on Lower **Isla** and **Dean;** dt (T) £1, dt (coarse fish) 25p from tackleists in area. Ogilvy Arms has 3m of private

water on S Esk, dt £5, wt £20, mt £50 *(advt p 288)* Rottal Lodge, can also arrange fishing.

EWE

This river has good runs of salmon (best May onwards) and sea trout (end June onwards) up to Loch Maree. Fishing again excellent, after problems caused by disease.

Poolewe (Highland). Salmon, sea trout, trout. Shieldaig Lodge Hotel, by Gairloch, has salmon and trout fishing on **Badachro River** and loch, and hill lochs. Dt (S) £2–£5. (T—bank) £1.50. (T—boat) £2.30. National Trust, Inverewe Information Centre, has fishing on five lochs. Dt £2, boat £2.20. No Sunday fishing. Reduction for members.

LOCH MAREE (Highland). N.s. Achnasheen. Especially noted for sea trout (July to mid-October). Fish run large mostly taken on dap. Spring salmon season (trolling) April and May. Loch Maree Hotel, Achnasheen *(advt p 290)*, has fishing. Heavy demand for sea-trout season so early booking advised. Hotel owned by anglers' syndi-

cate which provides excellent facilities. Wt, including boat, £88. Gairloch Hotel, **Gairloch,** has boat on loch.

Kinlochewe (Highland). Kinlochewe Hotel has fishing on Loch Maree. Salmon April and May, sea trout July to Oct. Fly only after mid-June. *(advt p 291)* Pool House Hotel, Poolewe, has fishing on loch. Brown trout on Loch Rosque; bank only. At **Torridon** (10m SW) Torridon Hotel has fishing on **Rivers Balgy** and **Thrail** and **Loch Damb**—all salmon, sea trout and brown trout. Also hill lochs and hotel launch for sea fishing on **Loch Torridon.** Permit from Post Office for salmon and sea trout fishing on **Loch-an-Iasgaich,** and for **River Torridon.**

FINDHORN

Rises in Monadhliath Mountains and flows over 60m to Moray Firth. Good salmon river with many rock pools, mostly preserved by owners. Also sea trout and brown trout. Best months: July and August.

Forres (Grampian). Forres AA issues permits for visitors resident in town; wt £15 from Feb 11 to Sept 30. Good trout fishing on nearby lochs; **Loch of Blairs** (£3.25 day; boat); **Loch Dallas** (£2 day; boat); permits from Smokers, and Sports Shop, J Geddes, Tolbooth Street, Forres, issues permits for **River Nairn.** Permits for **Lochindorb** from Moray Estates, Forres. Tackleists: The Smokers, and Sports Shop, W Stuart & Son, both High Street; J Geddes, Tolbooth

Street (Findhorn permits). Hotels: Carisbrooke, Carlton, Park, Royal, Brig Motel, Ramnee.

Tomatin (Highland). Salmon and brown trout. Freeburn Hotel has salmon and trout fishing on river; permits: dt (S) £5.50, (T) £1.

Note: *Cawdor Estate Office, Cawdor, Nairn, lets beats on river. Apply to Factor. Moray Estates Development Co. Forres, may also have beats available.*

FLEET (Kirkcudbrightshire)

Formed by junction of Big and Little Water, empties into the Solway Firth at Gatehouse. Good sea trout and herling, and few grilse and salmon; best months July and August.

Gatehouse-of-Fleet (Dumfries and Galloway). N.s. Dumfries, 33m. Sea trout and herling early and some salmon and grilse. River fishing in Cally Estate Water of Fleet: Lower stretch (2½m both banks); middle stretch (2m both banks) (two rods); upper stretch (4½m both

banks). Details and tickets from Cally Estate Office DG7 2HX (Tel: Gatehouse 200) with priority for guests at Murray Arms. Lochs: **Whinyeon** (trout, 3 to the lb), boats; **Fleet** (trout, av ½ lb); **Grannoch** (trout av 5 oz), boat; **Skerrow;** trout (averaging 1¾ lb; best,

4½ lb); boat; **Bush Moss;** brown and rainbow trout; dt (limited to two) boat. Dts issued for lochs, Fly only on all lochs except Grannoch, Fleet and Skerrow (spinning). River stocked annually with sea-trout fry and lochs restocked as necessary. Gatehouse and Kirkcudbright AA controls **Lochenbreck** (6m; stocked annually with 12 in browns and large rainbows). Fly only. St £10, wt £6 and dt £2 from D & J Beswick, Gatehouse of Fleet, and McKinnel, St Cuthbert Street, Kirkcudbright. Hotels: Murray Arms, Gatehouse-of-Fleet; *(advt p 288)* sea trout and herling fishing on Fleet, brown trout on five lochs; Cally (own loch; fishing also arranged on Fleet and other lochs).

FLEET (Sutherland)

Rises east of Lairg and, after run of some 12m, flows into Loch Fleet at The Mound. Middle and lower half of river (northbank) owned by Morvich Estates; middle portion (south bank. by Rovie Lodge and lower portion (south bank) by Cambusmore Estates. Upper reaches owned by Tressady Lodge. Salmon and sea trout. Short leases sometimes available from Morvich Estates.

FORTH (including Loch Leven and Water of Leith)

Formed from juntion of Avendhu and Duchray not far from Aberfoyle, and thence flows about 80m to its firth at Alloa, opening into North Sea. Principal tributaries, Teith and Allan, flow above Stirling. A large salmon river, which at times, and especially on upper reaches, provides some good sport. Good run in lower reaches during February and March as a rule. This river and Teith, Balvaig, Leny water and Allan Water being extensively restocked with salmon and sea trout by Forth District Salmon Fishery Board. (Howietown and Northern Fisheries Co, Stirling, providing hatchery facilities.) Trouting in upper reaches and tributaries, particularly in lochs, where salmon also taken.

Stirling (Central). Forth, Allan and Teith may be fished from here. Herling in Forth in spring and autumn. Salmon fishing from Lands of Hood to mouth of Teith (7½m) including Cruive Dykes is controlled by District Council. Permits for residents and visitors from Chief Exec, Stirling DC; D Crockart & Son, tackleist, and McLaren's, 4 Allanvale Rd, Bridge of Allan, st £12.50, wt £8, dt £2.50. Sport on three miles of Teith from Blue Banks to Forth junction, Mon, Wed and Sat, dt for eight rods; salmon, sea trout, trout; permits from tackleist. Good trout lochs within reach by car. Loch Leven *(see under "Tributaries of Forth")*. **Loch Coulter;** Larbert and Stenhousemuir AC; limited dt and evening tickets at £3 and £2; fly only. **Carron Valley Reservoir;** controlled by The Central Regional Council; boat £4.50 pd (two rods). For permits see under *"Falkirk", (p 293).* **Lochs Ard** and **Chon:** dt (shore fishing) 50p. **Lake of Menteith:** brown and rainbow trout; boat £9.50 (9.30–5.30 or 6–11 pm) from Lake Hotel. **North Third Reservoir** is Sauchie Estate water *(see Devon-Alloa).* Tackleist: D Crockart & Son, 35 King Street (tickets for stretches on main river and tributaries, and information).

Aberfoyle (Central). Trout; a few salmon taken. GPO and Civil Service ACs control. Dt from Ferguson, Newsagent. Aberfoyle APA issues dt £1 for **L Ard,** brown trout, fly only. Tickets and boats from P O Kinlochard, newsagent and hotels. Dt for **L Chon,** Forestry Commission water, and boat-hire from C McNair, Frenich, Kinlochard. Hotels: Bailie Nicol Jarvie, Forest Hills, Altskeith. Among other accessible waters are **Lake of Menteith,** brown and rainbow trout, fly only (inquire of Lake Hotel) and Loch Lomond *(see Clyde).* Tackleist: D Crockart & Son, Stirling (permits) *(see Stirling).* Hotel: Inversnaid (fishing).

Loch Katrine (Central). Good trout fishing (fish av 6–8 oz). Permits (£4 per boat per day, VAT incl) from Strathclyde RC: Lower Clyde Div Water Dept, 419 Balmore Road, Glasgow G22 6NU. Season April–Sept *(see also Glasgow).*

FORTH—Tributaries

DEVON: Fair brown trout stream; sea trout and salmon lower down.

Alloa (Central). Devon AA has salmon and sea-trout fishing from one mile above Devonside Bridge to below Cauldron Linn. St and dt from hon sec or West's Sports Emporium, Primrose Street. Good centres include **Tillicoultry, Dollar, Rumbling Bridge** and **Crook of Devon,** and in **Glendevon.** Hotel accommodation at each of these places. Water within grounds of Castle Hotel, Glendevon. Rumbling Bridge Hotel and Blackhills Estate is private. Trout fishing on **Glenquay Reservoir,** sometimes available. Dt from Glendevon Hotels.

ALLAN: Fair trouting, with sea trout and grilse from July onwards.

Bridge of Allan (Central). Salmon and trout fishing on the river from junction with River Forth to Blackford, all under control of Allan Water Angling Improvement Association, which has rights on full stretch of River Allan, except where indicated by noticeboard. River stocked with both trout and salmon fry. Limited St £12, dt £2.50 and £1.50, according to date from hon sec, D Crockart, King Street, Stirling; McLarens Sports; or Allanbank Hotel, Greenloaning. Fishing much improved since closure in 1976 of mill with bad history of pollution.

Dunblane (Central). Trout. Several hotels. Allan Water AIA issues st £2.50, wt £1, dt 40p, but all charges under review. Apply hon sec; McLaren, tackleist, Bridge of Allan; or Crockart's, Stirling. Trout ½ lb to 1 lb; sea trout run from mid-April; grilse and salmon from mid-July on. Best stretches of river near Kinbuck and Greenloaning stations. Hotels: Allanbank, Greenloaning (permits for association waters); Stirling Arms, Dunblane Hydro, Ardleighton.

Blackford (Central). **Carsebreck Loch** (two boats), **Upper Rhynd and Lower Rhynd** (one boat on each). Very good trout fishing; fly only; boats from Simpson at Braco 218. Hotels: Gleneagles (see next entry), Braco and Blackford (trout and salmon fishing). **Frandy Loch** (Glendevon Reservoir) can be fished from here; brown trout; fly only; dt from reservoir keeper, boat extra.

Gleneagles (Central). Gleneagles Hotel can provide salmon, sea trout and brown trout fishing on **Rivers Tay** (20m); **Earn** (5–7m); **Braan** (20m); and **Machany River,** Sytathallen Castle Water (3–4m); boats on many. Other excellent lochs and reservoirs available. Charges on application. **The Laichloch** (brown trout), only 300 yards from hotel, free to guests. Visitors should give as long a notice as possible of their requirements.

AVON: Flows 18m to estuary of Forth near Grangemouth. Lower reaches polluted; good brown trout elsewhere (av ½ lb with few around 2 lb). River fishes best in late June, July and Aug.

Falkirk (Cental). Slamannan Angling and Protective Assn controls 5–6m of water; no permits. Long waiting list for membership. Central Regional Council, Water and Drainage Dept, Viewforth, Stirling, issues permits for **Carron Valley Reservoir** (£7.50 day per boat, ratepayers only on Saturdays. No bank fishing). Advance booking essential; apply Director of Finance. At **Larbert** (3m NW), Larbert & Stenhousmuir AC issue dt £3 for **Loch Coulter,** (Loch Leven, brown and rainbow trout). Other tackleist; W J Scrimgeour, 28 Newmarket Street (dt issued). Mrs J Jenkins, Northend Bar, and Mrs C Penman, Lochend Farm, issue st. *(For other reservoir and loch fishing in area, see Edinburgh.)*

TEITH: Noted salmon and brown trout fishery, with good sea trout in summer.

Callander (Central). Stirling District Council controls 3m of Teith, in which excellent salmon, sea trout and brown trout fishing open to visitors; st £12.50, wt £8, dt £2.50 (juvs ½ price), obtainable from James Bayne *(see below)*. Brown trout average ¾ lb. **Loch Vennacher** controlled by the Town Council; good salmon, sea trout and brown trout fishing: trout average 1 lb; fishing from bank permitted on parts of loch; st £10, wt £5, dt £1.50; boats available. Roman Camp Hotel has fishing on river (free to guests). Permits for **Loch Lubnaig** (trout av ¾ lb) from James Bayne (tackleist), 76 Main Street: st £8, wt £3, Dt £1. Boats on Loch Vennacher also from Mr Bayne at £2 day plus permit (two rods). Boats can be arranged too on **Linlithgow Loch** (trout; av 1 lb). Good and convenient trout fishing can also be had on the **Lochs Voil, Ard, Chon** and **Drunkie** (Post Office,

Brig o' Turk issues dt for Drunkie) *(see below)*. Further particulars from Town Clerk, Callander, or tackleist.

BALVAIG and CALAIR (Tributaries of Teith): salmon, trout.

Balquhidder (Central). Permits for 2m from Stronvar Farm. D Crockart & Son, Stirling, issue dt for short stretch. **Lochs Voil** and **Doine:** trout and occasional salmon. Boats from Stronvar Farm, and other proprietors on loch sides.

Strathyre (Central). Midland Counties APA issues st and dt, £2.50 and £1 for river. From hon sec or Strathyre Inn, Ben Sheann and Munro hotels. **Loch Lubnaig;** trout, also char, and some salmon by trolling; an early loch; wt and dt

from J Bayne *(see Callander)* or Strathyre hotels (Station, The Inn, Munro, Rosebank); have boats. Guests at hotels can fish Balvaig (ticket) and Lochs Vennacher *(see Callander)*, Voil, Doine, Ard, Dochart and Earn *(see Aberfoyle and Balquhidder)*.

LOCHS CHON and ARD

Aberfoyle. Trout, controlled by Aberfoyle APA *(see Aberfoyle under Forth)*.

Brig o' Turk (Central). Permits for Lochs **Drunkie** and **Achray** (trout and coarse fish) and for **Lochan Reoidhte** (trout, fly only) £1.50 from Forestry Commission W (S) Achray Forest, Aberfoyle, Stirling, and David Marshall Lodge, Aberfoyle.

Loch Leven

Famous Kinross-shire loch which produces quick-growing trout. Loch is nowhere deep so feed is good, and practically whole area is fishing water. Under efficient management, this has become one of the most notable trout-fishing lochs of Scotland.

Kinross. 16m from Perth, 25m from Edinburgh. Trout average 1 lb; annual catch in 1980, 13,877 trout. Trout up to 9½ lb have been captured on fly. Perch abundant, but pike rigorously exterminated, 40 boats. Charges: Boat (outboard motor), £10.50 (10 am–6 pm), £7 (2 pm–6 pm), £11.50 (6.30 pm–10.30 pm) including VAT. Fly only; three rods per boat only. All inquiries to the Manageress, The Pier, Kinross (Tel: 63407). Tackle can be bought at the pier. Fishing

also available on **Leven Cut** (Loch Leven sluices to Auchmuir Bridge) from River Leven Trust, Sluice House, Loch Leven (20p day, £1 season). At **Glenrothes** (12m) permits may be had from Fife Regional Council for reservoir trout fishing on **Glenfarg** and **Upper Glendevon, Ballo, Harperlees and Holl** morning and evening sessions. £1.15, boat extra. Enquire from Craig Mitchell House, Flemington Road.

Water of Leith

Local people who know river well get fair numbers of trout, but there is some pollution, which is being tackled.

Edinburgh. Water of Leith is only river quite close; restocked annually and controlled by Lothian Regional Council between Balerno and Redbraes; permits free and obtainable from Director of Administration, Lothian Regional Council, George IV Bridge, Edinburgh. There are ten reservoirs belonging to Lothian Regional Council's Department of Water Supply Services: **Gladhouse** (6m from Penicuik); **Talla** (about 40m, in the Borders); **Glencorse** (about 8m); **Harperrig** (6m SW of Balerno); **Clubbiedean** (¾m from Colinton); **Rosebery** (4m from Gorebridge); **Donnolly** (about 25m); **Hopes** (about 25m); **Whiteadder** (about 30m).

Season: April 1 to September 30, Sundays excepted. Fly only. Note: **Gladhouse** permits allocated by ballot; apply at least one week in advance.

Permits for **Donnolly, Hopes** and **Whiteadder** from Lothian Regional Council, Department of Water Supply Services, Alderston House, Haddington. Permits for all other reservoirs from Director of Water Supply Services, Lothian Regional Council, "Comiston Springs", 55 Buckstone Terrace, Edinburgh. Charges for all these waters under review as we go to press.

Linlithgow Loch, close to Linlithgow Palace, has been restocked with trout by Forth Area Federation of Anglers;

limited dt for bank and boat fishing; fly only. West Lothian County Club, Linlithgow, issues permits for **Belcraig's Reservoir.** West of Edinburgh is the **River Almond,** free from Harthill to Mid-Calder but fishing poor. **Blackridge** and Dist AC fish **Hillend Reservoir** and **Lily Loch;** st £5, dt £2 from Lodge House, Forrestfield Hotel, Eastercroft Hotel, Truff Inn and local tacklelists. **Avonbridge** and Dist AC has trout water on the Avon between Strathavon and Larkhall. Permits from hon sec and members. Near **Dunfermline** (17m NW) is **Loch Fitty,** good trout water. Permits at £11.50 day (including boat with outboard motor for three rods) from the Kingseat office of Game Fisheries Ltd, 3 Muirwood Place, Currie, Midlothian (Tel: Dunfermline 23162). **Raith Lake,** near Kirkcaldy, now fished by Raith Lake AC. **Craigluscar Reservoir and Dam** also provides sport with trout; no boat. Permit at reservoir. D Black, Hobby Shop, issues permits for **Broomhill.** Fishing on the **River Earn,** Forteviot, salmon and sea trout. Tackleists: John Dickson and Son, 21 Frederick Street *(advt p 281)*; E Miller, Field and Stream, Montrose Terrace; F and D Simpson, 28 West Preston Street, all Edinburgh. D Black, The Hobby Shop, 10–12 New Road, Dunfermline.

GIRVAN

Drains small loch called Girvan Eye and thence runs 25m to the Atlantic at Girvan. Good salmon and sea trout; fair brown trout. Salmon run March onwards; sea trout from July.

Girvan (Strathclyde). Salmon, sea trout, brown trout. Carrick AC issues ft and wt, available from John Murray (tackleist), 3 Dalrymple Street, who also issues dt for **Penwhapple Reservoir** (Penwhapple AC) which is 6m away; excellent trout loch; fly only; boats available; season opens April 1. At **Barrhill** (12m) are Drumlamford Estate fisheries, comprising 3m on **River Cree,** and three trout lochs (dt £5, boat £4 extra) and one loch stocked with coarse fish. Dt £2. Mr A Keand, The Lodge, Drumlamford Estate, Barrhill (Tel: 046 582 226). Excellent sea fishing; trips arranged by Girvan Sea AC; contact at harbour. Hotels: King's Arms, Hamilton Arms, Ailsa, Queen's, Royal. Turnberry Hotel is 4m N.

Maybole (Strathclyde). Salmon, sea trout, brown trout. Garpin AC has 1½m at Crosshill; permits from hon sec or T McCulloch, 50 High Street. Maybole AC has water; no tickets.

Straiton (Strathclyde). Salmon (late), sea trout, brown trout. Dt £3.50 (incl VAT) for Blairquhan Estate water from D Galbraith, The Kennels, Blairquhan Estate, Straiton. Apply R Rae, The Cottage for permit for Straiton club waters. For loch trout fishing fly only; boat available) apply R Heaney, Tallaminnoch, Straiton.

HALLADALE

Rises on north slope of Helmsdale watershed and empties into sea at Melvich Bay. Good and early salmon river. Trout average ¾ lb.

Melvich (Highland). Melvich Hotel, Melvich, by Thurso, 12m from Forsinard, offers trout fishing on a number of lochs, most of which have boats on them. Salmon fishing by arrangement on Halladale.

Bighouse (Highland). For salmon beats (wt £15–£120) and trout lochs (dt £5–£15) contact Mrs J Atkinson, Factor, 8 Sinclair Street, Thurso, or Milne, Home and Ballantyre, 27a Rutland Square, Edinburgh. Accommodation at Melvich Hotel, Melvich, by Thurso, or Forsinard Hotel, Forsinard. Both have rights in numerous trout lochs for guests.

Forsinard (Highland). Salmon sport good, especially after freshets. Application for beats can be made to the Forsinard Hotel, which is on the Helmsdale-Melvich road close to the railway station. Apart from beats on Halladale, dt £12, can arrange fishing on various trout lochs, most with boats, dt £3.45. Garvault Hotel, **Kinbrace,** has brown trout fishing on burns and lochs; free to guests; gillie, instruction available.

HELMSDALE RIVER

Formed by two headstreams near Kinbrace, this river flows 20m south-east through Strath Ullie to sea. Excellent salmon river, where there is now practically no netting.

Helmsdale (Highland). Salmon and sea trout beat lettings from Savills, 20 Grosvenor Hill, Berkeley Square, London *(advt p 30)*. Information from Lt Cdr A Rickards RN (Retd), Fishery Manager, Strathnaver, Kinbrace, KW11 6UA. Wt and dt (£25–£40: £5–£8) for Lower Helmsdale from A Jappy & Sons, Helmsdale. Navidale House Hotel issues dt, boat £3, bank £1, for brown trout, fly only, on **Loch-an-Ruathair** *(advt p 296)*. Other hotel: Belgrave.

INVER (including Kirkaig and Loch Assynt)

Draining Loch Assynt, this river flows into a sea loch on the west coast of Sutherland known as Lochinver (village and loch having same name), a little north of the old Ross-shire border. Holds salmon and sea trout but fishing is hard to come by.

Lochinver (Highland); ns Invershin, 54m. The Inver, running out of Loch Assynt (6m) is private. **Kirkaig**, 3½m off, goes with Culag Hotel and can be fished daily (upper, middle and lower beats) by guests; restocked annually with salmon; a short sporting river; small run of early fish, but main run begins with first spate in June. Hotel guests can also have sea trout fishing in **Manse Loch** (2m off), **Kirkaig Seapool** and **Loch Culag** (½m off; boat). Hotel waters open to public if not required by guests dt (S) £17, (T) £8 *(advt p 298)*. Brown trout fishing can be had on innumerable hill lochs (bank), **Loch Assynt** (boat), **Loch Fionn** (boat) and seven other lochs (boats). Sea fishing (good) arranged. Brown trout fishing closes Oct 7, salmon and sea trout Oct 15. Assynt AC has good trout fishing on about 30 lochs. Wt and dt issued for bank fishing; boat extra.

Drumbeg (Highland). 14m from Lochinver or 11m from Kylesku Ferry. Hotel has brown trout fishing for guests. Boats on six good lochs. **Loch Drumbeg,** in front of house, very good; fish average over ½ lb. Best months: May, June, July and Sept. Salmon fishing arranged. Good sea fishing (Hotel: Tel Drumbeg 236). Assynt AC controls **thirty-five lochs,** including **Loch Roe,** with a run of salmon and sea trout. Trout lochs: st £12, wt £8, dt £1.50. Loch Roe: dt £2. Boat £3 extra.

Altnacealgach Hotel (18m Ullapool, 25m Lairg, Highland). Fine trouting. **Loch Borralan:** trout, char; three boats. **Loch Urigill:** across Borralan by boat or 20 min walk; two boats. **Loch Cama,** 4m: trout, char; three boats. **Loch Veyatie,** 4m: trout; three boats. Trout at 3 to lb as a rule, but many big fish and ferox. Spinning allowed. No day tickets now for non-residents. Good trout streams nearby such as **Altnacealgach** and **Ledbeg;** fish well, with water, in August and Sept. Season: April to Oct. Tel 085 484 240 *(advt p 323).*

Loch Assynt

Inchnadamph (Highland). Salmon fishing (fair) from June on upper end of Loch Assynt and in **Loanan Water,** which runs into it out of Loch Awe. Loch Assynt now developing as sea trout water. Loanan Water holds salmon (good in spate) and brown trout averaging ½ lb, but also large ferox. Assynt AC controls 35 lochs, issuing st £12, ft £8 and dt £1.50 for trout lochs (boat £3 extra) £2 pd for salmon and sea trout on **Loch Roe.** Tick-

ets from hotels and Tourist Information Office. Permit from Inchnadamph Hotel for celebrated **Gillaroo Loch,** Loch Assynt and Loch Awe (£1.50 day). Season from May 1 till Oct 10. Best months for trout, mid-May to Mid-July, and Sept; for salmon, mid-June to mid-July, and Sept. Hotel: Inchnadamph; fishing free to guests on loch and on Loanan Water on alternate days. Nine boats available.

IRVINE (and Annick)

Rises near Loudonhill and flows about 20m to Firth of Clyde at Irvine Town. Main tributaries are Cessnock Water, Kilmarnock Water and Annick. Fishing controlled largely by clubs. Salmon and sea trout July onwards; brown trout average ½ lb; early season best.

Irvine (Strathclyde). Salmon, sea trout, trout; Irvine and Dist AA issues wt £4, dt £2 and £1 for 2m on Irvine and 3m Annick (no dt Saturdays). Irvine Water runs from estuary to Red Bridge, Dreghorn, on north bank and to Bogie Bridge on south bank. Annick Water is from confluence with Irvine to northern boundary of Annick Lodge Estate, except for one private stretch. Tickets from Currie Sports Shop, Townhead and R Gilmour, 58 Muir Drive, both Irvine.

Dreghorn (Strathclyde). Salmon, sea trout, trout; Dreghorn AC issues wt £5 and dt £2 for 12m water on both banks of Irvine and Annick; apply hon sec or A Lynch, 12 Sharpe Ave. July to Sept best for salmon and sea trout. Brown trout average ½ lb.

Kilmarnock (Strathclyde). Salmon, sea trout, trout. Salmon best Aug–Sept. St £5, wt £3, dt £1 from McCririck's, John Finnie Street; All Sports, Titchfield Street. Hotels: Ossington, Brodie's, Market.

Hurlford (Strathclyde). Salmon, sea trout, brown trout. Hurlford AC issues wt £7 and dt £1.50 for 3m of water. Salmon and sea trout best from June onwards. Apply J M McVey, Post Office, where tackle is obtainable.

Galston (Strathclyde). Good sport with salmon and brown trout; Aug to Oct for salmon. Galston AC issues dt for salmon and trout but not on Saturdays; 7m of water; Irvine and Cessnock Water.

Newmilns (Strathclyde). Salmon

(occasional; best Aug to mid-Oct), sea trout, trout; Newmilns and Greenholm AC has water and issues dt (Mon–Fri only), and wt; apply Valley Sports (tackleists), Main Street, who also issue tickets for Avon and Clyde and tributaries.

Tributaries of the Irvine

GARNOCK: Trout, sea trout, salmon.

Kilwinning (Strathclyde). Garnock and Irvine join in tidal water and have common mouth. Salmon, sea trout, trout. Kilwinning Eglinton AC has 9m on Garnock and **Lugton** Rivers; Tickets from hon sec, bailiffs and tackleists.

Dalry (Strathclyde). Salmon, sea trout, trout. Dalry Garnock AC has 6m plus tributaries (both banks) and **Third Part Reservoir** (trout only; fly only); mt, wt, and dt from hon sec. Hotels: King's Arms, Royal.

Kilbirnie. Kilbirnie AC has water on river and **Kilbirnie Loch** (trout, coarse fish) and two reservoirs; wt £3, dt £1, both excluding Saturdays. Tickets from hon sec, Glendale Inn, and D Lennie, Watchmaker, Main Street. Hotels: New; Dalry Inn.

ANNICK: Brown trout; small runs of salmon and sea trout Sept–Oct.

Stewarton (Strathclyde). Stewarton AC has water on Annick and tributaries, and **White Loch;** dt from hon sec. Kilmaurs AC has 7m on Annick and **Glaisart** at **Kilmaurs;** sea trout and brown trout, with salmon in autumn; dt and st. Dreghorn AC issues permits for 12m on both banks *(see Dreghorn)*. Permits for 12m of water on Irvine and Annick from hon sec and J Galt, 21 Maid Morville Ave. Wt and dt; no dt Saturdays. Salmon July onwards.

THE ISLANDS

The term "The Islands" include the Inner and Outer Hebrides, the Orkney and Shetland Islands and, for convenience, Kintyre.

ARRAN: For all streams and lochs, except Machrie and Iorsa Rivers and Loch Iorsa and Loch Garbad, apply secretary Arran AA. (Principal waters: Blackwater, Glenaskdale, Lagg, Slidderie, Rosa, Chalmadale, Arranton and Monamore Burns; Loch Urie.) Dt and wt. The Iorsa River and Loch, Tanna Loch and Kilmorie Water from Lagg Hotel *(see Kilmorie District)* to sea are reserved, but for Machrie River inquire of J T Boscawen, Land Agent, Killiechassie, Berfeldy, Perthshire.

Brodick. Best stream in Brodick district is Rosa. Brown trout in fair numbers, but very small. Cloy also fairly good for small trout. Small trout seem to be rule in all burns. During July, August and Sept there is good sea-trout fishing. Rods have got as many as 15 in a day, running from 1 lb to 5 lb or 6 lb. Machrie Water well spoken of. Rosa has early run of finnock; Feb to April. Arran AA permits (mt £5, wt £3, dt £1) from Messrs Currie Ltd. Hotels: Douglas, Ormidale.

Kilmorie District. Kilmorie and Slidderie Waters both good for salmon and sea trout in the autumn. Few brown trout to speak of, although Slidderie is better of two. Some very good sea trout are got in Slidderie in August and Sept. Arran AA permits at hotel and at A V C McKelvie (grocers), Corriecravie and Post Offices at Lagg and Machrie. Hotel: Lagg.

Lamlash. Good sea fishing *(see Sea Fishing Section)*. Two fair streams, Arranton and Monamore. Few brown trout worth speaking of, but in July, August and Sept fair number of sea trout can be got. Hill lochs contain numerous small trout, best being Loch Tanna in northern half of island. Hotels: White House; PH Trust; and Lamlash. Arran AA permits from Gordon Bros, Ship House.

BENBECULA: Lies between N and S Uist. Numerous lochs, giving good sea and brown trout fishing. Hotel: Creagorry, which has free fishing for guests on several lochs and three sea pools; boats available on some waters; waders useful; trout to 1 lb; farthest water 5m; June to

Sept best for brown trout and August and Sept for sea trout. Sea trout up to 8 lb in sea pools; no stream fishing. Hotel has right to fish two rods per day on Loch Bee in South Uist. Permits at small charge from South Uist AC for 15 lochs, four with boats.

BUTE: 5m from Ayrshire coast; 16m long and 3–5m wide. Burn fishing for sea trout, otherwise trout and coarse fish.

Rothesay. Loch Ascog, 1½m pike and perch. Permits: £1 season, 25p per day. **Loch Quien,** 5m, first-class trout fishing (fish averaging 1 lb); limited dt £1, bank only. Boat, if available, £1.50 extra. St available, £10. Fishes best early and late in season. Sea trout fishing on larger burns; st £2.50. Applications to Bute Estate Office. Rothesay (Tel 2627). Sea fishing from rocky shore popular and good: by boat regularly from Rothesay pier. Kyles of Bute AC and shops in Kames and Tighnabruaich, also Kilfinan Hotel, Kilfinan, issue dt for salmon and sea trout on **Kilfinan River.** Free to guests at hotel, otherwise £1. Arran AA issue tickets at small charge for all rivers on the isle except **Machrie** and **Iorsa Waters.**

COLL: 18,500 acres in extent, is owned by three proprietors, C K M Stewart, J de Vries and Mrs Erskine. Lies within easy reach of Oban and Tobermory (Mull). No stream fishing, but many inland lochs, all of which are now preserved for private fishing. Hotel: Isle of Coll, Arinagour; boats. Sea fishing excellent.

COLONSAY: Reached by car-ferry from Oban. The hotel shares fishing rights on East, West and Mid-Loch Fada; fishing and boats. Brown trout; best months, May, June and Sept; fish average 10–16 oz; sea fishing with fly and bait. Fishing free to residents of hotel and self-catering accommodation. Tel 09512 316 for full details.

CUMBRAE: Small islands lying between Bute and Ayr coast. Trout fishing in two reservoirs, wt £10 and dt £3 from A T Morton, 4 Mount Stuart Street, Millport. Sea fishing good from shore or boats. Boat hirers also provide tackle.

HARRIS: Southern part of the island of Lewis and Harris, Outer Hebrides. At **Tarbert,** good sea fishing for haddock, lythe, saithe etc in East Loch Tarbert. Position regarding salmon, sea trout and brown trout fishing uncertain as we go to press. Enquiries to Harris Hotel. Other hotel: Rodel. **Leverburgh,** South Harris, lets fishing on mill pond, Obbe and Steisavat Lochs, and several others, including Finsbay waters. Brown trout fishing during May and June inclusive. Good sea trout and occasional salmon; best months, July to Oct. Also good sea fishing close by. No stream fishing available. Borve Lodge, **Scarista.** Two salmon lochs and five sea trout lochs. Hatchery in operation. Fished by Tenants of Borve Lodge. Dt (fly only) sometimes available, from £3. Inquire The Factor, Borve Lodge Estate, Isle of Harris (Scarista 202). Horsacleit Lodge let furnished for six guests with fishing for salmon and sea trout in river; for brown trout on **Loch Drinishader.** Rents during fishing season run from £80 per week to £200. Bookings to Mr C J Lucas, Warnham Park, Horsham, Sussex. Limited dt from Manager N MacDonald; Tel Harris 2464. Harris AC issues dt from 50p for seven brown trout lochs. Tickets from hon sec or Tourist Information Centre, Tarbert.

ISLAY: Most southern island of Inner Hebrides. Lies on west side of Sound of Islay, in Argyllshire. Greatest length is

25m and greatest breadth 19m. Sport with salmon, sea trout and trout.

Bridgend. Loch Gorm, 9m from Bridgend, famous for trout. Bridgend Hotel has trout fishing in five good lochs, six boats at £4 per day, rest bank. Bank permits: wt £6, 3-day ticket £4, dt £2. River fishing, salmon and sea trout can be arranged. Islay Estates have boats on four good lochs, £4 per day, £3 per half-day. Dt for bank fishing £2. Tickets from Estate Office or head keeper, Islay House. Tel Bowmore 293.

Port Askaig. By staying at Port Askaig Hotel, trouting can be had in **Lochs Lossit, Ballygrant** and **Allan.** Dt (boat) £4; bank £1. Sport on other lochs by arrangement. Salmon fishing in River Laggan available. Best months: May, June and Sept.

Port Charlotte. Port Charlotte Hotel; trout fishing for guests; six lochs, incl **L Gorm.**

Port Ellen. Guests at Machrie Hotel can have brown trout fishing on Lochs Gorm, Ballygrant, Lossit, Finlaggan, Solon (salmon and sea trout also) and Glenastle, by arrangement with appropriate keeper. Machrie (salmon, sea trout) free to guests. May, June, July best for trout; Sept and Oct for salmon, sea trout. Also sea fishing.

KINTYRE: This peninsula is part of Argyll and lies between Islay and Arran.

Ardrishaig (Strathclyde). Guests at Auchendarroch and Argyll Arms hotels can have fishing in local lochs; trout. Fishing (trout) can be had in **Crinan Canal,** 2m N. *(See also Crinan and Lochgilphead.)*

Campbeltown (Strathclyde). Salmon and sea trout. Machrihanish Water free. Conie Glen and Glen Breckerie, st, wt, dt from Southend hotels and Campbeltown tackleists. Kintyre FP and AC has four trout lochs. Boats available on three. Permits from tackleists (A P Mac-Grory & Co, R Armour & Sons, and D Livingstone, all of Campbeltown) and Southend and Machrihanish hotels. Permits from Tangy Farm (A Black) for **Tangy Loch** (60 acres, boat and two rods, £3.50 day; £1.50 day from bank; trout to 2 lb). Sea fishing in harbour and Firth of Clyde. Hotels: Ardshiel, Royal White Hart and Argyll. Hon sec of club will be pleased to give further information (send sae). *(See also Machrihanish and Southend.)*

Carradale (Strathclyde). Excellent salmon and sea-trout fishing can be had on Carradale Water (subject to lettings). Dt. Fly only. Apply E Martindale, The Kennels, Carradale.

Crinan (Strathclyde). Near west end of Crinan Canal. Brown trout lochs controlled by Lochgilphead Dist AC. Canal (trout); no permits needed.

Lochgilphead (Strathclyde). At east end of Crinan Canal *(see Crinan and Ardrishaig).* Lochgilphead and Dist AC has rights on nine hill lochs; good brown trout; dt £1 from Hugh MacArthur (Sports), 37 Lochnell Street. Forestry Commission has brown trout fishing on **Lochs Coille Bhar, Barnluasgan, Lariche, Losgunn** and **Seafield.** Bank dt £1; boats £3–£4 + £1 per rod. Advance bookings from Forest Office, Knapdale Forest (Tel Lochgilphead 2304). Stag Hotel can arrange fishing on **River Add** and various lochs. Salmon and sea trout in river, brown trout in lochs. Permits for other waters. Ford Hotel can also arrange fishing on Add (8m away) and lochs. Wt £17 and dt £3.50 are available from Poltalloch Estate Office. Lochgair Hotel is good centre for Lochs Fyne and Glashan; boats available. Tackleist: K Milton, Lochnell Street.

Machrihanish (Strathclyde). Free salmon and sea trout fishing in Machrihanish Water. Permits for Kintyre FP and AC lochs from Ugadale Arms. Good sea fishing *(see Campbeltown)*.

Southend (Strathclyde). Salmon and sea trout fishing in Conieglen and part of Glenbreckerie; st £4, wt £2, dt 50p. Permits (and for Kintyre FP and AC lochs) from Keil Hotel, Argyll Arms and club hon sec *(see also Campbeltown)*.

LEWIS: Some salmon, much trout fishing on lochs and streams.

Stornoway. Little salmon fishing for visitors. For salmon and sea trout fishing in **River Creed, Loch Clachan** and **Loch an Ois** enquire of the Factor, Stornoway Trust, Estate Offices, Stornoway. For **Loch Valtos** and **Laxay River** enquire of Mr Victor Mackay, Valtos Cottage, Laxay. For Soval Angling Association enquire of Mr J M Macleod, 15 Balallan. Wt £2, dt £1. Sport with brown trout on numerous lochs within easy distance of Stornoway. Claitair Hotel, Sheildenish, has trout fishing. Uig Lodge Hotel has salmon, sea trout, brown trout fishing. The **Grimersta** belongs to Grimersta Estate Ltd; the river is let annually; inquiries to the Secretary, 7 Melville Crescent, Edinburgh. Best months July, August, September. Hotels: Country, Caledonian, Royal Lewis, Commercial. Caberfeidh Hotel has private beats for guests on loch or river for salmon, sea trout and brown trout.

Uig. Rods for guests at Uig Lodge on **River Fhorsa, Loch Slacsavat, Loch Bheannain** and **Loch Suainaval.** £89 per rod; dt £3.50 on Loch Suainaval. Contact Mr R Davis, Uig Lodge Hotel, Uig by Stornoway, I O Lewis. Tel Timsgarry 286 *(advt p 24)*. Scaliscro Lodge Hotel *(advt p 302)* also arranges fishings.

MULL:

Tobermory. Mishnish Lochs: 2m excellent brown trout fishing; Tobermory AA has three boats. Mt £8, wt £3.50, dt £1. Boats, £1.50 per 4 hours hire. **Loch Frisa:** good brown trout, some salmon and sea trout. 7m of fishing; boats. Good sea fishing. Permits for **Mishnish** from tackleist A Brown, 21 Main Street.

Accommodation: Mishnish Hotel, Macdonald Arms, Western Isles Hotel: Heanish Chalets and guest houses.

Salen. 10m south of Tobermory, is good centre. Salen Hotel has boat on Loch Frisa, 5m away; excellent trout fishing, best months May and June, with few sea trout and odd salmon later. For the **R Forsa**, a spate river, Glenforsa Hotel *(advt p. 302)* issues wt £24 and dt £6 when conditions suitable. 5m of fishing for salmon and sea trout. **Preferential terms for residents.** Mr W Mills, Killiechronan, **Aros,** issues dt £1 for salmon, sea trout and brown trout fishing on River Baa sea pool. Tel Aros 403.

At **Bunessan** Argyll Arms Hotel has good salmon, sea trout and brown trout fishing on Loch Assapool and brown trout fishing on Loch Poitee at £5 per day for non-residents. Work in hand to improve sea trout access to L Assapool.

At **Dervaig** is Bellachroy Hotel. Good trout and sea trout fishing on Loch Frisa (trout plentiful) free to guests. Quinish Estate and House *(advt p 303)*.

NORTH UIST: Island in Outer Hebrides, 17m long and 3–13m broad. Lochs and sea pools (numbering hundreds) well stocked with salmon, sea and brown trout. Lochs to north controlled by Department of Agriculture, and to south by North Uist Estates Ltd. Both issue permits. Main salmon lochs may be fished by visitors at Lochmaddy Hotel *(advt p 301)*. Fly only, except for sea pools holding sea trout. Twenty boats on lochs. Gillie for boat if required. Best months: March to May, and July to October. Apply Manager for permits. Hon sec, N Uist AC, which also issues permits for brown trout fishing, will be pleased to help visitors.

SOUTH UIST:

Lochboisdale. The hotel here offers 9/10 salmon/sea trout beats on seven lochs, dt £10 + ghillie's fee and fishing for brown trout of above average size on eight others. Boat (1–3 anglers) £5. Some free fishing for guests in April and Oct. Bank-fishing on brown trout lochs for non-residents by arrangement; wt £5, dt £1.50. Hon Sec South Uist AC will help visitors in respect of other waters.

ORKNEY

While sea fishing for skate, ling, halibut (British record), haddock, cod, etc, is general in waters about Orkney, and good fun may be had in the evenings with saithe

Fishing for trout as the storm gathers. *Photograph: John Tarlton.*

comparatively close to the shore anywhere, good quality trout fishing is confined to the mainland and Rousay for both brown and sea trout, but in the latter island the lochs are private, in contrast to the mainland, where all but one (Loch of Skaill) of the best lochs are "open" water. Sea trout, for which the east shores of the island of Hoy also have a good reputation, may be found at any point where fresh water enters the sea as well as in the Lochs of Stenness and Harray in March and April and from July to the end of October, and may be taken from a boat in the lochs. Wading trousers are useful in the estuaries.

Principal fishing lochs on the mainland are **Loch of Stenness,** 12m from **Kirkwall** and 3m from **Stromness,** which yields brown and sea trout, from March to October, the average weight being nearly 1 lb. The best part of the season for this loch is probably June to

August. **Loch of Harray,** 11m from Kirkwall and 4m from Stromness, is connected to Loch of Stenness and fishes well from April to end of September, the average being about 1 lb. The **Lochs of Swannay, Broardhouse** and **Hundland** are in close proximity to each other in the north of the mainland, about 20m from Kirkwall, and fish well, particularly Swannay, which yields good brown trout of more than 1 lb average weight. All three lochs are fairly early in form and good sport may be had from April until the end of September. Boats are available for hire on all of these lochs, in most cases without boatmen, though in certain cases this may be arranged. Free fishing is also available on the Lochs of Wasdale, Kirbister and Bosquoy.

Accommodation is available in Kirkwall at several hotels including the Kirkwall Hotel, and there are taxi services to fishing waters. Anglers might prefer to stay closer to the waters they want to fish, however.

Merkister Hotel is close to Loch of Harray (now the best of the Orkney Lochs) and affords excellent free loch fishing: boats, outboards, gillies (Tel 366) *(advt p 306)*. The Standing Stones Hotel, Stenness (fully licensed and under new management; boats, outboards, gillies) stands on the shores of the Loch of Stenness and is also convenient for Loch Harray, while Smithfield Hotel (Dounby) and The Barony (Birsay), are convenient for the Lochs of Boardhouse, Hundland and Swannay. In Hoy accommodation may be had at the Royal Hotel, Longhope. There are guest houses and cottages available and in Stromness at Keldroseed Guest House *(advt p 307)*.

Orkney Trout Fishing Association operates a trout hatchery. Restocking has yielded excellent results, notably in the Loch of Swannay. Information from hon sec R Windwick, 36 Quoybanks Crescent, Kirkwall.

RAASAY:
The Isle of Raasay is near Skye. Free trout fishing in lochs and streams; spare tackle and waders should be taken.

RUM:
The fishing in the streams and lochs of the Isle of Rum is all preserved by the Nature Conservancy.

SHETLAND

The following notes have been compiled mainly with the aid of *Manson's Shetland Guide* but help has also been sought from a booklet written by James Coutts and published by The Highlands and Islands Development Board (20p). They should be read in the light of the fact that reports from our local correspondent now underline the fears expressed by conservationists on the bearing oil-related development would have on the famous Shetland sea trout fishings. Now, it is suggested, visitors might do better to think in terms of loch fishing for brown trout. There is also a threat of unrestricted netting which the Shetland AA is fighting to the best of its ability.

The sea trout fishing season in Shetland extends from February 25 to October 31, and that for the brown-trout fishing from March 15 to October 6. Nearly all mainland waters are controlled by The Shetland Anglers' Association (Hon sec Andrew Miller, 3 Gladstone Terrace, Lerwick) and remainder are usually available on request or for a small fee. St for association waters £5.

Where the sea trout fishing so far remains unaffected, late March to early May, then July, August and September are the prime months. As regards size, fish up to 3 lb are not uncommon; fish up to 7 lb are not altogether rare; bigger fish are within the orbit of possibility, though perhaps scarcely within that of probability; but all these bigger fish are generally shy and difficult to capture.

Sea trout fishing, like all branches of this sport, cannot be made the subject of hard and fast rules, and both the methods and equipment used are entirely a matter for personal choice. It is not essential to have any special equipment apart from the ordinary outfit of a trout fisher, except perhaps such safeguards as are necessary against the corrosive effects of the salt water on certain types of aluminium reels and fitments of that nature. The sea trout takes a fly in salt water as readily as a brown trout takes it in the waters of a loch; and any of the standard types of sea-trout flies will, in favourable conditions, produce results until such time as the fisher develops those faiths and fancies to which all anglers are prone. He may then swear by his teal and red, or his blae and black, as his personal experience will no doubt have taught him to swear; or he may have become a disciple of the lure, which is often used to good effect, especially in weather which does not permit easy control of a lighter fly. He may even have recourse to bait-fishing to discover that the use of worm or strips of mackerel strip are not unproductive of good baskets.

There are two methods of fishing with mackerel. The easiest and most popular is to mount a strip of it on one of the hooks of the treble of any spoon or lure. The second approach is to use a rod of at least 12 feet, with fly-line and long tapered cast, and to attach a piece of mackerel strip to the hooks of Stewart or Pennel tackle. Fished in tidal water, allowing the current to work the bait as in salmon fishing, mackerel strip is the nearest thing to a live sand-eel.

The brown trout are more or less native to the freshwater lochs, of which literally thousands are populated by brown trout, most of them *under*-fished. Generally speaking, they average about ½ lb. There are bigger fish—in fact, there are individual lochs which occasionally produce exceptionally big ones; but most of the many lochs which have fish in any quantity rarely produce a higher average weight, and often a lower one, a re-stocking programme is in progress. Only in exceptional cases is a boat available for fishing the lochs; but almost in every case fishing can be done from the bank or shore, by wading. It is often desirable to wade, rather than to fish from the bank, in order to clear heather slopes which can so effectively wreck a light fly cast.

The failure of a fishing holiday in Shetland at the proper time of year can scarcely ever be attributed to lack of fish. Occasionally, as in all places, there are spells of weather which result in poor baskets; but as the Shetland weather is rather noted for its changeability, the day for the angler is usually not long to wait. At a time when trout fishing is becoming increasingly difficult to procure, Shetland has a hundred spots to offer the angler where he is more or less free to fish at will, and a hundred more when these are exhausted. It is true there is a growing tendency among landowners to regard these fishings as a possible source of revenue, but, with the habits of sea trout what they are, there will always remain in the islands the possibility of fishing untrammelled by the restrictions which have placed so many of Scotland's rivers beyond the reach of the average fisherman. Shetland regards her trout fishings as an attraction which will result in visitors discovering the islands for themselves, and the measure of freedom she has to offer in an age of increasing restriction may well be the measure of her future prosperity.

Sea fishing off the Shetlands is excellent—large skate, also ling, tusk, cod, haddock, pollack, etc. *(See under Sea Fishing Stations.)* The fishing is done invariably by boat, and the rock fishing, popular at some places on the mainland of Scotland, is practised only occasionally in the capture of young saithe (called "pilticks") which can be taken on fly from the shore. Boats and equipment are easy to obtain and comparatively inexpensive. The fish caught consist mainly of haddock and whiting, while at certain places the catch may include rock-cod, ling, flounder—in fact, a general assortment of fish which makes very interesting fishing indeed.

Generally speaking, the fishing grounds lie beyond the limits of the voes, but during July and August, in certain of the larger voes, good fishing can be had without going farther afield. Fishing is by rod or hand-line at a depth between 20/50 fathoms; and, when the fish are plentiful, big catches, numbering scores, are taken. Also generalising, early and late months provide the best fishing. Further information from ASA, Shetland Association of Sea Anglers, membership sub £2.50 pa. Tackleists on the island are J A Manson; Stove and Smith, both Commercial Street, Lerwick; and Hay & Co, Commercial Road.

NOTE: Anglers are recommended to bring their own cars, owing to the lack of public transport. Ferry services from Aberdeen and Leith. Shetland Tourist Organisation, Market Cross, Lerwick, will help with accommodation and other details. The association also issues a leaflet on angling. Shetland AA reports a disturbing decline in sport with sea trout and grilse following the advent of commercial fishing and fish processing. Association conducting vigorous campaign against netting.

Unst. Balta Sound Hotel, most northerly in British Isles, offers sea and trout fishing to guests.

Bressay. Loch and foreshore fishing leased from Garth Estate by Shetland AA; fishing by permit from hon sec; brown trout in Loch of Brough and Loch of Setter.

Delting. Lerwick 20m. Brown trout in lochs as follows: Mill Loch, Loch of Glen, Seawater, Loch of Voe. Sea trout at Dales Voe and Collafirth. Good sea trout fishing also at Garths Voe, Orka Voe, Voxter, Scatsta, Toft, Firth and Swinister Voes.

Dunrossness. Sea trout fishing at Spiggie, St Ninian's Isle, Channerwick, Cunningsburgh; also in Loch Spiggie during the fall fishing *(see also Scousburgh)*. Hotel: Spiggie.

Laxo. Laxo Voe, once one of the finest grilse and sea trout waters in the islands, now poached so heavily that Sumburgh Estates have given up the fishery.

Lerwick and District. The Shetland AA controls most of loch and sea trout fishing in Shetland (including Bressay). Best brown trout lochs (six in number) are located in valley of Tingwall. Tingwall is about 6m from Lerwick and 1 to 2m from Scalloway. Sea trout run into two of the above-mentioned lochs in season. Sea trout also obtained in nearby voes. Following voes (with distances from Lerwick) all contain sea trout. Full body waders are recommended. Laxo Voe (20m), Laxfirth (6m), Wadbister (8m). Hotels: Grand, Queen's Hotel, Lerwick Hotel, both Lerwick; Royal Hotel, Scalloway Hotel, both Scalloway. Information regarding other fishing readily given to visiting anglers by hon sec, Shetland AA Association issues seasonal, weekly and daily permits at extremely reasonable charges, plus extra charge for boats, for which key is issued enabling anglers to use them as desired. Fly only on most lochs. Accommodation from Information Centre, Lerwick. Tackleists: Stove and Smith; J A Manson & Son, both Commercial Street; Hay, Commercial Road.

Lunnasting. Poaching here now so severe a problem that attempts to preserve what was once excellent sea trout fishing have been abandoned.

Northmavine. Good brown trout fishing in Eela water, near Ollaberry and Bardister, and in many neighbouring lochs. In Pundswater, S of Hillswick, fish run larger. Good fishing and shooting over Lochend Estate. Sea trout in all lochs and numerous burns. Fishing and shooting can be rented with accommodation (contact A P Cromarty, Lochend House, Lochend). Sea trout also at Queyfirth,

Ronas Voe, Ollaberry, Bardister, Sullom, Mangaster, Hillswick. Also at Hamar Voe, Gunnister and Nibon. Good brown trout in numerous lochs between Nibon and Mangaster (Busta Estate). Limited but good accommodation at Mrs Mowat's Fair View, North Roe. Car advised. Close to Busta Estate brown and sea-trout fishing.

Sandness, Bridge of Walls, etc. Brown trout and sea trout in lochs and voes.

Scalloway. C Williamson, The Studio (Tel 242) issues permits for Shetland AA covering numerous lochs and voes. Hotel: Scalloway (excellent fishing in lochs and voes).

Scousburgh. Famous Loch of Spiggie holds good brown and sea trout in season. Permits, boats and accommodation at Henderson's Hotel, Spiggie. Best months: brown trout, May and June; sea trout, late Aug and Sept.

Weisdale. John White, Kergord (Weisdale, 6) gives permission to holders of assn permits to fish the Burn of Sandwater—reputed one of the best in the islands—when the fishing is not required by himself or his guests. Sea trout run through burn to reach Sandwater, 3m inland. Mr Winton should also be approached for permission to fish Weisdale Burn and the Burn of Strom.

SKYE

Trout and salmon fishing generally preserved, but some good free fishing for hotel guests. Sea trout especially good in places. Excellent sea fishing.

Bracadale. Stores at Struan will give information on excellent salmon, sea trout and brown trout fishing; river and loch.

Broadford. Broadford Hotel, Fishing on **Broadford River** (salmon, sea trout) free to hotel guests.

Duntulm. Hotel has salmon, grilse, sea trout, brown trout fishing on Kilmartin and Kilmaling Rivers and various lochs. Excellent sea fishing; boats available.

Dunvegan. Numerous streams in area can be very good for sea trout in May and June. Dunvegan Hotel *(advt p 301)* has rights and issues day and weekly permits for Caroy River, Claigan Lochs, Hamara River (Glendale) and Rivers Haulton

and Hinnisdale (also shooting over 23,000 acres). Best salmon months July through to mid-Oct. Sea angling excellent May to Sept. Capt Henderson, 17 Skinidin, Glendale (Tel 268) arranges boats.

Isle Ornsay. Hotel Eilean Iarmain (Isle-ornsay Hotel) has trout and sea trout fishing on a number of small rivers and lochs in the parishes of Sleat and Strath in the South of Skye. Boat also available for sea fishing. July–Sept best for sea trout and June for brown trout. St £20, mt £15, wt £7.50, dt £2. Toravarg House Hotel has trout fishing on Horavaig River; free to guests. Dt issued.

Portree. Lochs Fada and Leathan have good trouting (big trout occasionally); Storr Lochs are 4m away on good road. Bank fishing; seven boats. Mid-May to Mid-July best. Further information from hon sec Portree AA. There is salmon fishing in **Staffa River** and numerous small brown trout lochs in the north of the island. St and dt for these fishings. Enquries to hon sec Portree AA. Also sea fishing, for pollack and saithe in harbour. Sea trips from Portree daily, apply Tourist Office. Hotel: Cuillin Hills *(advt p 310).*

Skeabost. Skeabost House Hotel has 8m of salmon and sea trout fishing on Snizort River and trout fishing on Storr lochs; other sport arranged. Hotel launch available for trips on Loch Snizort. (Sea fishing.) Tackle and bait supplied.

Sleat. Kinloch Lodge Hotel has trout and sea-trout fishing by arrangement with Clan Donald Lands Trust.

Sligachan. Sligachan Hotel has salmon and sea-trout fishing in 2m Sligachan River and brown trout fishing in Loch-na-Caiplaich free for guests; salmon few, sea trout quite plentiful; best months, mid-July to end-Sept. Brown trout fishing by arrangement in Storr Lochs (15m); boats available; season, May to end Sept. Dt for non-residents £3.

Staffin. Dept of Agriculture and Fisheries for Scotland (Gamekeeper's Cottage, Staffin) issues tickets for rivers and lochs; salmon, sea trout, brown trout.

Struan. Ullinish Lodge has salmon, sea trout and brown trout fishing in three lochs (boats available on two of them) and 2½m of water on rivers **Ose** and **Snizort,** the latter reserved for hotel guests *(advt p 302).*

Uig. Uig Hotel can arrange fishing on north bank **River Hinnisdal** and **Storr Lochs:** also on various hill lochs on which Portree AS has rights.

LOCHAR

A sluggish stream, 15 to 16m long, which holds trout and some sea trout in season. Empties into Solway few miles east of Nith. Occasional salmon and herling caught near mouth during floods. River runs mostly through Lochar Moss. Fishing stations: **Ruthwell** (Dumfries). Near mouth: **Amisfield** (Dumfries). Trout: free on farmers' permission.

LOCHY (including Nevis)

Drains Loch Lochy and, after joining the Spean at Mucomir, flows about 8m to salt water in Loch Eil close to Fort William. Very good salmon and sea trout river but affected by hydro works at Falls of Mucomir. Best months: July, August and Sept. Inquire Manager, River Lochy Association, 5 Wellington Square, London, and for lower water and Spean apply to Rod and Gun Shop, Fort William. Permits also from Benmore Restaurant, **Crianlarich,** and A C Forster, tackleist, Killin. Fly only (see also Spean).

Tributaries of the Lochy

SPEAN: Flows from Loch Laggan. Sport with salmon can be very good after spates. Few sea trout. Best from mid-June onwards. Fishing above Spean Bridge and its tributaries, Roy and Treig, preserved by Bristish Aluminium Co., Fort William. For lettings and permits inquire at Rod & Gun Shop, 18 High Street, Fort William.

Spean Bridge (Highland). Beats available on dt £3 for left bank only, also for **Lochs Arkaig** and **Lochy**. Inquire of Spean Bridge Hotel or hon sec, River Lochy Association. Hotel: Spean Bridge. *(Advt p 311.)*

Kinloch Laggan (Highland). Trout fishing on loch controlled by Badenoch AA. Fish average ¾ lb. For possibilities on Spean, Roy, Treig and Cour inquire of hotel or Rod & Gun Shop, Fort William.

Roy (tributary of Spean): Salmon. A spate river; fishes best July onwards. Lower half let to Roybridge AC; and Glenspean Lodge. Upper half owned by Roy Fisheries, and managed by Mr R J Tapp,

Braeroy, Roybridge (Tel Spean Bridge 210). Wt £18 and dt £3 from Roybridge Hotel.

NEVIS: A short river flowing around south side of Ben Nevis and entering Loch Linnhe at Fort William, not far from mouth of the Lochy. Very good salmon and sea trout fishing.

Fort William (Highland). River Nevis; salmon, grilse, sea trout. Fort William AA has about 6m; dt from local tackleists (limited); no spinning; best June onwards. Good brown trout fishing on **Loch Lundavra** in Mamore Hills. Dt and boat from Mrs MacCallum, Lundavra Farm (Fort William 2582). For **Loch Arkaig** 15m away; sea trout and brown trout) apply West Highland Estate Office, Chartered Surveyors, 33 High St. St £92, mt £46.75, wt £19.55, dt £4.50. Tackleists: Rod & Gun Shop (licences and permits for town beat on River Lochy). Hotels: Imperial, Grand, Alexandra, West End, Milton.

LOSSIE

Drains Loch Trevie and flows about 25m to the Moray Firth at Lossiemouth. A good trout stream; salmon runs improving, July onwards. Provides good sport with sea trout from June onwards, especially near estuary.

Lossiemouth (Grampian). Salmon, sea trout. Lossiemouth AA has water; estuary and sea; sea trout and finnock only; st £2, wt £2 and dt 50p and information on other fishings available from hon sec or DIY, Queen Street; and Elgin Angling Centre. Hotels: Stotfield Laverock Bank, Rock House, Huntly House.

Elgin (Grampian). Lossie; salmon, sea trout and brown trout. Elgin AA has

15m of water; wt £4, dt £1, can be had from local tackleists: Kellas Estates office issues permits for stretch. Loch fishing for brown trout can be had on the Town Council's Milbuies Estate: dt £3.25 from Dept of Recreation 30 High St or on site. Loch fishing for brown trout may also be had by private arrangement at **Loch-na-bo** (3½m E). Numerous hotels.

LUNAN

Rises near Forfar and flows about 13m to North Sea between Arbroath and Montrose. Some good trout, dry fly good. Sea trout and finnock, and few salmon in autumn.

Arbroath (Tayside). Lunan and its tributary, the **Vinney,** about 8m of water, leased to Arbroath AC by riparian owners; restocked each year, holds good head of brown trout, ½ lb to 1 lb. St £5, dt £1 from T Clark & Son, tackleists, High Street. Good sea fishing.

West Water. A tributary of North Esk, leased to Arbroath AC for sea trout and salmon. Best months, Aug, Sept, Oct.

Brothock Burn, about 4m long, lies on east side of town. Holds good trout up to ½ lb. Free fishing; fly; spinning, bait.

Elliot Burn, also about 4m long, lies on west side of town. Holds good trout up to ½ lb and sea trout at mouth. Free fishing in town stetch; fly, spinning, bait.

Rescobie Loch, 250 acres, has been developed jointly by Arbroath and Canmore AC as high-class fly-fishing loch for brown and rainbow trout. Lies about 11m from Arbroath. Brown trout up to 3 lb and rainbows up to 2½ lb. Best months are Aug, Sept, Oct. Visitors' tickets for bank and boat fishing from T Clark & Sons, High Street; or bailiff at loch. Prices of tickets on application.

NAIRN

Rises in Monadhliath Hills and flows about 36m to Moray Firth at Nairn. Salmon, sea trout, finnock and yellow trout.

Nairn (Highland). Tickets for the lower reaches (estuary to Whitebridge, Cawdor, 7¾m) can be had from Nairn AA; ft £15, wt £10, dt £4. Best months: May to July for salmon. Permits from Pat Fraser, High Street; Clava Lodge Hotel, *(advt p 22)* Culloden Moor in Inverness, also issues permits for hotel stretch.

Lochs **Lochindorb, Allan, Flemington** and **Loch-an-Tutach** privately owned; brown trout; dt and boat. Tackleist: Sporting Stores. Other hotels: Meallmore Lodge, Daviot (private stretch of river); Newton (river and loch fishing by arrangement) *(advt p 313)*.

NAVER (including Borgie and Hope)

Drains Loch Naver and flows about 24m to north coast at Naver Bay. The Borgie, which also debouches into Naver Bay, drains Loch Laighal and has course of about 7m. Both are good salmon and sea-trout rivers; all preserved, but beats can be arranged, usually for fortnightly periods.

Bettyhill (Highland), via Lairg and Thurso. Bettyhill Hotel provides fishing for guests on River Naver and Loch Naver; on **Loch Rimsdale** (salmon, sea trout and brown trout, dt £3) and on nine smaller brown trout lochs, dt 50p to non-residents. No Sunday fishing; trout run to good size in several lochs; boats available on five, including Loch Naver (salmon, sea trout, brown trout; salmon very good March to June; sometimes July; sea trout good Aug/Sept) and Loch Rimsdale; trout; fishing free to hotel guests. Naver FC has sea trout and salmon fishing above Naver Bridge. Free

fishing for sea and brown trout in Naver estuary.

Altnaharra (Highland); ns Lairg. Hotel provides salmon fishing in Loch Naver and **River Mudale;** sea trout fishing in Loch Hope and brown trout fishing in a number of lochs, most of which have boats and are close to the road. Dt (S) £3, dy (T) £2. Permits for Loch Hope also from Tongue Hotel *(see Tongue).* Excellent sea trout water; also holds salmon. No bank fishing; fly only. Crask Inn; half-way between Lairg and Altnaharra, has rights on 6m of River **Tirry** and four lochs; brown trout.

Lochs Slaim and Craggie

Tongue (Highland). Tongue hotel has salmon fishing on Loch Slaim and River Borgie, and fishing for wild brown trout

(3 to lb) on Slaim, Craggie, **Loyal** and **Cormac.** Dt £5. Also excellent salmon and sea trout fishing on **Loch Hope.**

Boat: £9. Many small burns. Ben Loyal Hotel (Tongue AA HQ) offers trout fishing on 12 lochs. St £75, mt £5, wt £3, dt 75p, boat £2, motor £2.

NESS

Drains Loch Ness and flows to North Sea close to Inverness. Notable salmon and sea-trout river. Best July to October.

Inverness. Salmon, sea trout, brown trout. Leisurepay Ltd, 6/8 Inglis Street (Inverness 33168) issues permits for Inverness AC stretch from estuary upstream for about 2¾m and for **Loch Ruthven,** st £13, wt £10, dt £2.50. At **Fortrose** (10m NE) is good sea trout fishing from the seashore; fly and spinner; best June–July; Fortrose & Rosemarkie AC; tickets from A Gow, chemist, High Street, Fortrose. Other tackleists: J Graham & Co, 27 Union Street (permits for Ness and **Clunas Reservoir**). Hotels: Foyers (fishing in Ness by arrangement) and Clava, Culloden *(advt p 22)*.

LOCH NESS: Sea trout at Dochfour and Aldourie; salmon, especially out from Fort Augustus and where Rivers **Moriston, Enrick** and **Foyers** enter the loch. Brown trout all round the margins. Boats and boatmen from hotels at Fort Augustus, Drumnadrochit, Foyers, Lewiston and Whitbridge.

Drunmadrochit (Highland). Salmon, and brown trout, Lewiston Arms Hotel has boats for Loch Ness and free salmon and trout fishing for guests on 1m of **River Endrick,** which enters loch here; best months, April, May, June. Sea fishing on Moray Firth by arrangement. Further details from hotel. Glenurquhart Lodge can arrange fishing; Clansman Hotel, Lochness-side, has fishing; boats available. Ancarraig Chalets can arrange fishing on River Moriston, Loch Ness and several hill lochs. Tackle sale hire.

Foyers (Highland). Salmon and brown trout fishing in Loch Ness. River Foyers enters loch here; preserved. Foyers Hotel has fishing on Loch Ness. Boat with ghillie: £10 pd. Several other lochs

may also be fished, including **Lochs Bran, Garth** and **Farraline** (£3 day).

Invermoriston (Highland). River Moriston enters loch here. Permits from Estate Office for river and 7 hill lochs. Hotel: Knockie Lodge *(advt p 315)*.

Fort Augustus (Highland); ns Spean Bridge (bus service). Salmon and brown trout. Salmon season opens Jan 15. Trout season, March 15. Dt for River Oich (S) £6, (T) £3, for Fort Augustus AA Water (dt 50p) from The Outdoor and Garden Shop, Canalside. Hotels: Lovat Arms, Caledonian, Brae, Inchnacardoch.

Tributaries of Loch Ness

LOCH MHOR (Highland). 18m from Inverness. Loch is 4m long by ½m broad, and contains trout averaging ½ lb. Accommodation ½m away at the Old Manse Guest House, Gorthleck, and Whitebridge Hotel, Whitebridge (2½m); *(see Whitebridge)*. Boats available. **Loch Ruthven** can be fished, also **Loch Bran** and **River Fechlin.** Outlet from loch enters Loch Ness via River Foyers.

Whitebridge (Highland). Whitebridge Hotel has boats for use of guests on **Loch Knockie, Loch Bran** and **Loch Killin.** Daily charge £5. Arrangements also made for guests wishing to troll on **Loch Ness.** River and burn dried out in course of hydro-electric development. Other hotel: Knockie Lodge *(advt p 315)*.

MORISTON: Salmon; brown trout, occasional sea trout.

Glenmoriston (Highland). Glenmoriston Estates Ltd offer excellent salmon fishing on Loch Ness and River Moriston at prices from £3.00–£8.60 per rod, VAT included. Brown trout fishing is also available on 9 miles of Moriston, Loch Ness and 22 Hill Lochs, at prices from £1.80 for a bank dt to £8.00 for a boat. Discounts for occupants of the Glenmoriston Arms Hotel, Cluanie Inn and the Estate's Holiday Homes. Trout permits, salmon and boat bookings from Glenmoriston Estates Office Tel No: (0320) 51202. *(advt p 314)* permits also from Glenmoriston Arms Hotel and village shop. Glenmoriston Arms has boat and

bank fishing on 9m of river and numerous hill lochs.

GARRY: Rises in loch SW of Loch Quoich and runs into that loch at western end, thence to Lochs Poulary and Garry. Good salmon and trout river. Outlet to Loch Garry dammed by North of Scotland Hydro-Electric Board. At Loch Poulary are fish traps; at Invergarry, a hatchery.

Invergarry (Highland). As we go to press, Invergarry Hotel (under new proprietorship) is negotiating fishing rights River Garry, and on various lochs. Enquiries to hotel. Glengarry Castle Hotel also offers fishing. Dt £5 for **Loch Quoich**

(Hydro Board water) from Murdo Mackenzie (fishing tackle), Fort William. Glen Garry FC has fishing on river Garry and **Loch Inchlaggan;** boats on loch through hon sec or to guests at Garry Gualach Hostel or Tomdoun Hotel. Loch stocked with brown and rainbow trout, fly only *(see also Tomdoun)*.

Tomdoun (Highland); ns Invergarry. Free fishing on three miles of river and on Lochs **Garry, Poulary** and **Inchlaggan** (18 lb 4 oz trout taken in 1965) for guests at Tomdoun Hotel. Non-resident dt £1. Boats on **Loch Quoich** by arrangement. Best months: May and June.

NITH

Rises on south side of Ayr watershed and flows south and east to Solway, which it enters by an estuary with Dumfries at its head. Carries a good head of small trout and has runs of sea trout and salmon in spring, summer and autumn. Salmon fishing has improved since netting was suspended in 1947.

Dumfries (Dumfries & Galloway). Dumfires Town Water, 3m on Nith, 1½m on **Cairn** (tributary); salmon, sea trout, brown trout and grayling; best, March–May and Sept–Nov. Wt £11.50, st £28.75 (VAT incl) from Director of Finance, Nithsdale DC; Municipal Chambers. **Glenkiln Reservoir** (trout) now controlled by Directorate of Waters and Sewerage, Dumfries and Galloway Regional Council. St £13, dt (bank) £1.80, dt (boat) £4.60. Dumfries and Galloway AA has 3m on Nith and 20m on Cairn (brown trout, good; av ½ lb). Salmon and brown trout. Wt £17, dt £7. No visitors' tickets at week-ends. Tickets from McMillan, tackleist (see below). Mid-Nithsdale AA has 5m on Nith and tributaries **Scaur** and **Cample.** Salmon, sea trout, brown trout and grayling. Wt £26, dt £6 from hon sec. Upper Nithsdale AC

has 10m on Nith; tickets from hon sec. Dt £1 for fishing **Auchenreoch Loch** (10m) from Galloway Arms, Crocketford. Pike and perch only. Tackleists: W McCall and Co, 23 Castle Street; D McMillan, 6 Friar's Vennel; Malcolm Tathe, Queensberry Street. At **New Abbey** (Kirkcudbright), about 6m off, New Abbey AA has herling, sea trout and brown trout fishing in a small tributary of Nith; tickets from hon sec, Abbey Arms Hotel and Criffel Inn. Other hotels: Ashbank Guest House, Troqueer Rd (fishing arranged in Nith, Cairn and five lochs).

Auchencairn: Balcary Bay Hotel has 1½ miles sea-trout and salmon fishing on Nith.

Thornhill (Dumfries & Galloway). Salmon, sea trout, brown trout; some grayling. Mid-Nithsdale AA has 5m on main river and tributaries Scaur and Cample. Visitors' tickets, wt £26 (resident visitors only), dt (limited) £6; no dt on Saturdays; fly only in low water. Tickets from A Coltart & Son, shoeshop. Apply to The Factor, Queensberry Estate, Dabton, Thornhill, for wt and dt on salmon and sea trout beats. Hotels: Buccleuch and Queensberry (fishing arranged in Nith and Scaur), George *(advt p 316).*

Sanquhar (Dumfries & Galloway). Upper Nithsdale AC has several miles of Nith. Salmon, sea trout, brown trout and grayling. Monday–Friday wt for bona fide visitors, £20, dt £4. No visitors' tickets after November 30. Tickets from W & W Forsyth, solicitors, Council Chambers, 100 High Street, Sanquhar. Dt for grayling fishing, Dec–Jan, 50p from water bailiff. Hotel: Mennockfoot Lodge, Nithsdale (3m on **River Crawick**—salmon, sea trout, trout—and by arrangement in Nith). Glendyne; Drumbringan; Nithsdale House.

Crocketford (Dumfries & Galloway). Trout lochs; Corsock, Glenkiln and various others; boats available. Pike and perch fishing on Auchenreoch and Milton Loch, etc. River fishing on Nith and Cairn, all association water—*see Dumfries, Thornhill, etc*. Hotel: Galloway Arms (tickets for local fishing).

New Cumnock (Strathclyde). Salmon, trout, New Cumnock AA fishes the Nith, **Afton Water** and **Reservoir,** and other reservoirs and lochs (trout) and parts of **Rivers Deugh, Ken, Nith, Carsphairn Lane Burn.** Club also has some good coarse fishing, including grayling in Nith. St issued. No Sunday fishing.

OYKEL (including Carron, Cassley, Shin and Loch Ailsh)

Rises at Benmore Assynt, flows through Loch Ailsh and thence 14m to enter the Kyle of Sutherland at Rosehall. Excellent salmon and sea trout fishing. The Lower Oykel has produced an average catch of over 780 salmon in recent years. Much water managed by Renton Finlayson, Estates Office, Bonar Bridge, Sutherland and rods available.

Oykel Bridge (Highland). Lower reaches of Oykel are fished from Oykel Bridge Hotel which also has salmon beats on **Upper Oykel, Einig,** and boats on **Loch Ailsh, The Kyle of Sutherland,** and hill trout lochs. Apply Renton Finlayson, Bonar Bridge, Sutherland. Lower reaches fish very well for salmon early on and good grilse and sea trout run usually begins in the latter half of June. **Loch Ailsh.** Good sea and brown trout fishing with occasional salmon. Best months— Lower Oykel, March to September. Upper Oykel and Loch Ailsh, mid-Jun to September.

CARRON: Rises near Ben Dearg and flows 20m to enter Kyle of Sutherland opposite Bonar Bridge. Salmon, sea trout. Several beats, and occasional dt through Renton Finlayson *(see above)*.

Bonar Bridge (Highland). Caledonian Hotel has fishing in **Kyle of Sutherland** through Kyle AC; sea trout, trout. Best months: mid-July onwards for sea trout; June to Sept for Brown trout. For about 12m of sea-trout fishing above Bonar Bridge (Kyle of Sutherland) and 1m below bridge apply R L Henderson, East End. (Benmore Estates Water.) Apply hotel and Mr Henderson also for fishing on **Loch Migdale** (Skibo Estate) brown trout.

CASSLEY: Some 10m long, river is divided at Rosehall into upper and lower Cassley by Achness Falls. Below falls fishing starts early. Upper Cassley fishes well from May to Sept. Sea trout July and Aug. Rods let by week (av £80) on both banks. Sole agents: Bell-Ingram, 7 Walker Street, Edinburgh EH3 7YJ *(advt p 343)*. Hotel: Achness House, Rosehall.

SHIN (Loch Shin and Kyle of Sutherland): Outlet from Loch Shin controlled by hydro-electric works. River flows about 7m and empties into Kyle of Sutherland at **Invershin.** Salmon fishing privately let. Upper: Lairg Estates with some periods through Sutherland Arms and Aultnagar Hotels: Lower: under private ownership, but a 3-rod beat available via Sutherland Arms in mid-Aug and Sept. Trout fishings on Loch Shin and hill lochs. Fishing on Cassley also arranged. For Lairg AC fishing on Loch Shin, contact Mr J Ross, Lairg PO. Sea-trout fishing in Kyle from Dornoch AA. Other hotel: Invershin.

Lairg (Highland). Trout fishing in Loch Shin (av: ½ lb and up to 12 lb). This is largest freshwater loch in Sutherland— 16 miles long. Lairg AC issues wt £4 and dt £1 via local tackleists for bank fishing and for boat fishing, with or without outboard motor. Best mid-May to end of

The wild scenery of a middle beat on the Oykel. *Photograph: John Tarlton.*

July. Hotel: Sutherland Arms (salmon fishing on **River Shin,** sea and trout on Kyle of Sutherland, trout fishing on Loch Shin and hill lochs).

Overscaig Hotel *(advt p 315),* ns Lairg (16m). On shore of Loch Shinn. Hotel has boats on loch and others on Lochs **Ghriam** and **Merkland** with many hill lochs within walking distance. Facilities usually available for sea trout and salmon fishing on **Lochs Stack and More.** Hotel gillies, advice and instruction. Large brown trout caught on hotel waters in recent years. Fishing free to residents. Boats with OB motors. £7.50

per day. Wt for non-residents £5, dt £1.

DORNOCH FIRTH:

Dornoch (Highland). At entrance to Firth. Burghfield House Hotel has rights on **Lochs Migdale and Buidhe;** brown trout (av ¾lb) Dt. Sea trout fishing in **Kyle of Sutherland** from Creich to Cassley mouth; permits from local hotels; best mid-July onwards. Permits from Dornoch AA for sea-trout at **Little Ferry** and **Dornoch Beach;** also brown trout on **Lochs Lannsaidh, Buidhe, Laoigh** and **Migdale;** rainbow trout in **Loch Ghuibais.** Dt (bank) 50p, dt (boat) £3.

KYLE OF DURNESS

Durness (Highland); ns Lairg. Cape Wrath Hotel at Keodale has good salmon and sea trout fishing on **Rivers Dionard, Gru-** **die** and **Dall,** lochs and **Kyle of Durness.** Best for salmon and sea trout mid-June to mid-Sept. Big brown trout in Lochs

Calladale, Crosspool, Lanish and **Borley**—well-conditioned fish of 8 lbs in weight have been taken—and there are several hill lochs, four with boats. Lochs and rivers stocked with salmon, sea trout, brown trout fry. Good sea fishing. Lochs £4 per day, boat included. River £11.50 day per beat. Hotel open throughout year.

SCOURIE (including Laxford River and Lochs Stack and More)

Scourie (Highland, via Lairg). Excellent centre for sea-trout, brown-trout and salmon fishing. About 200 trout lochs. Scourie Hotel has extensive fishing rights on over 100; four with salmon and sea trout. Boats available on many. Gillies may also be employed. Good sea fishing; boats. Days on **Loch Stack** and **Lock**

More (by permission of Duchess of Westminster) available to guests during July, Aug and Sept. Salmon, sea trout (good), brown trout. Charges on application. Laxford River is preserved. Scourie AC has rights on seven lochs; trout around half-pound mark, but some larger fish; tickets from hon sec.

'Matting' salmon for dispatch at Oykel Bridge, Ross-shire. *Photograph: John Tarlton.*

SHIEL (Argyll/Inverness-shire) (including Moidart and Loch Shiel)

Short but good salmon river, only about 3m long, draining Loch Shiel. Moidart is a good spate river with excellent holding pools. Loch Shiel is fed by four major rivers, **Slatach, Finnan, Callop** and **Alladale,** which all tend to be spate rivers. The Loch is best for Salmon from April 1 till end May or early June. The Sea trout run from July onwards and fishing closes at the end of October.

Acharacle (Highland). River preserved. Loch Shiel, 17m long, holds salmon and sea trout, and a few brown trout; best mid-May to end of October; good late run. Boats from Loch Shiel, Salen, Sunart and Strontian Hotels. Good accommodation at Creel Cottage, two-bedroom cottage on edge of loch; tackle for hire; boat and gillie available; tuition arranged if required. Fishing also by arrangement on **Rivers Moidart, Strontian** and hill lochs; boat with OB motor £10 per day + petrol. Gillie £2. For full details apply to The Creel Fishing Facilties Co., Creel Cottage, Acharacle (Tel: 096 785 281). Lochshiel, Strontian and Sunart Hotels also have fishing.

Shiel Bridge (Acharacle, Highland). On loch and river. Loch fishing good for salmon, grilse, sea and brown trout. Lower end best. Sea-, brown- and rainbow-trout fishing. Glenborradale Farm. Tel 246. River Shiel strictly preserved.

Glenfinnan. Stage House Inn *(advt p 320)* (Kinlocheil 246) has 7 boats all with outboards available for hire and the hotel has recently been completely modernised and refurbished (see opposite). Glenfinnan House Hotel has two boats with outboard available and Glenalladale Estate occasionally has a boat available with chalet accommodation.

LOCH SUNART

Strontian (Highland). Salmon and sea-trout fishing on Lochs Shiel, **Doilet** and **Sunart;** Rivers **Carnoch** and **Strontian;** boats available from Strontian and Sunart Hotels. Loch Sunart Hotel *(advt p 321)* also has fishing on **River Pollach.** Sea fishing parties in Loch Sunart catered for. Best July to October. Kilcamb Lodge Hotel has fishing on Loch Sunart.

SPEY

Rises mile or two above Loch Spey and flows NE about 100m to North Sea, emptying between Banff and Elgin. One of great salmon rivers, which provides first-rate opportunities for visitors. Good sea trout and brown trout in places.

Fochabers (Grampian). Salmon fishing leased by Gordon Castle Estate; all beats privately let. Fochabers AA lease a stretch (1¼m) from May 16 to Aug 31; resident members only; limited number of permits for members' friends staying locally. Best months, July and Aug. Hotels: Gordon Arms (fishing arranged on **Spey, Deveron** and **Lossie**) Grant Arms; some permits for trout and finnock in estuary. Tackleist: Lipp & Son.

Craigellachie (Grampian). Salmon, sea trout, trout. Craigellachie Hotel has over 2m beat; £50 per week, residents only; best mid-April to mid-June; grilse, July to Sept.

Aberlour (Grampian). Salmon, sea trout, finnock. Burgh water for visitors here. Best season usually March till June but can be very good in July and August too. Hotels: Aberlour; Lour; Dowans. Fishings arranged on Spey, Avon and Lochindorb (14m). Dt £9 from tackleist: J A J Munro.

Grantown-on-Spey (Highland). Salmon, sea trout, brown trout. Strathspey Angling Improvement Association leases stretches on **Spey** and **Dulnain;** over 40m in all on both banks. Wt £12 and £1.50 (jun) for salmon and trout. Inquiries to hon sec. Private beats on Spey on daily or weekly basis from following: Seafield Estate Office, The Square; Tulchan Estate, Advie (10m from Grantown), Ballindalloch Estate, Ballindalloch (15m) and Pitchroy Estate, Ballindalloch (17m). Boats on brown trout lochs in the area from tackleists G G Mortimer, 61 High Street; Angus Stuart, (est 1879) 64/68 High Street; both Grantown on Spey. Twelve licensed hotels; twenty guest houses; see Seafield Lodge *(advt p 323)* and Haugh Hotel *(advt p 321)*; and excellent caravan site. Many hotel proprietors themselves keen anglers.

Nethy Bridge (Highland). Salmon, trout. Abernethy AIA has 6m of Spey and two good trout lochs. Best months, May, June, July. Courses for beginners run by Nethy Bridge Hotel in May and Sept *(advt p 324)*. *For Loch Garten see Grantown.* Mount View Hotel *(advt p 324)*.

Boat of Garten (Highland). Salmon, trout. Abernethy Angling Improvement Assn issues tickets for 5½ mile stretch of Spey (both banks) for those staying locally, wt £12, dt £3. Hotels: The Boat *(advt p 325)*. Craigard *(advt p 315)*, Nethybridge. Fishing schools spring and autumn. *For Loch Garten see Grantown.*

Aviemore (Highland). The principal Spey Valley tourist centre. Aviemore Osprey Fishing School, Chief Instructor James Cornfoot, provides courses and accompanied fishing outings on Spey, **Feshie** and a number of lochs. St £15, wt £8, dt £3. A leaflet is issued. Tel Aviemore 767.

Kingussie and **Newtonmore** (Highland). Badenoch AA has rights on more than 15m of trout and salmon fishing on Upper Spey, several lochs (brown trout), and **Spey Dam** (brown trout). Boat available on **Spey Dam** and **Loch Cuaich** (Dalwhinnie). Membership cards covering all waters. St for residents £5, non-residents £7.50. Visitors £1 day, £5 week from local tackle shops and hotels in Dalwhinnie, Newtonmore, Mains Hotel *(advt p 21)* and Kingussie, Scott's *(advt p 324)*. Trout protection order pending. Sport in Scotland Ltd, Inverness have several lets on Spey and tributaries.

Glenmore, by **Aviemore. Loch Morlich.** Permits at modest charge from Head Forester, Glenmore Forest Park.

Tributaries of the Spey

FIDDICH:
Dufftown (Grampian). Dullan, trout; free. Fishing arranged on Spey (4m) and Deveron (17m) for guests at Parkmore House Hotel. Other hotels: Fife Arms, Elms (temperance), Commercial.

AVON:
Tomintoul by Ballindalloch (Grampian). Sea trout, grilse and salmon. Richmond Arms has 6m of fishing on Avon and 2½m on **Livet** for guests. Wt £44. Gordon Arms guests can fish 5m of Avon and 1m of Livet. A beat on Avon (1m) is available for Tomintoul residents and visitors, and permits can be obtained from hotels and tackleists (see below). Permit includes trout fishing on **Conglass.** Permits also issued to guests at Delnashaugh Hotel, Ballindalloch. Free trout fishing on Avon and three streams; Conglass, Chabet and Brown or Lochy. Tackleist: J Ross, Main Street.

STINCHAR (and Cross Water of Luce)

One of west coast streams, rising on western slope of Doon watershed and flowing about 30m to Atlantic at Ballantrae. Has a very late run of salmon, lasting till middle of October. Also good sea trout and brown trout.

Ballantrae (Strathclyde); ns Girvan, 13m. Trout, sea trout, salmon. Beats readily obtainable. River rises and falls rapidly after rain. Barr Angling has water (salmon, sea trout, brown trout) on Stinchar; wt and dt: late July to Sept best. Dt for Knockdolian. Beat can be had from S Scobie, head gamekeeper, Colmonell (Colmonell 248) and other rods let by riparian owners. Kings Arms and Jolly Shepherds Hotels, **Barr,** arrange fishing on Stinchar, **Girvan** and various lochs. Salmon and sea trout in rivers, brown trout in lochs. Colmonella guest house, Colmonell, also arranges fishing in Stinchar and lochs. Daljarrock Hotel, Pinwherry (by Girvan) has fishing on Stinchar.

CROSS WATER OF LUCE

Dependent on flood water for good salmon fishing, but very good for sea trout after dark. Best July onwards.

Stranraer (Dumfries & Galloway). Excellent centre for river, loch and sea fishing **Loch Ryan** and open sea). Stranraer AA has about 8m of salmon and sea trout fishing on Cross Water of Luce, and on five trout lochs. Wt and dt issued. Waters are restocked. The lochs are: **Dindinnie, Knockquhassan** (boat), **Ree** (10m away), **Penwhirn Reservoir** and **Soulseat Loch** (rainbow and brown trout; av 1½ lb). Sunday fishing on lochs only. Tickets from hon sec, tackleists and numerous hotels. Boat bookings through the secretary. One of best lochs is at **Lochnaw Castle,** by Leswalt, where a dt (£5) is issued for boat-fishing on the loch. Brown trout, av 12 oz. Half-day sessions at £3. Refreshments available. Phone bookings to Leswalt 227. Tackleists: Sports Shop, George Street.

TAY

A prestigious salmon river. Tay proper runs out of Loch Tay, but its feeder, the Dochart, at head of loch, takes its head waters from slopes of Ben More. River fished mainly from boats, but certain beats provide also spinning and fly-fishing from banks. Notable in particular for run of spring fish, though autumn fishing often gives good results. After a course of some 120m it empties into North Sea by a long firth. Netting extends as far as Stanley, some miles above Perth. At least half a dozen of its tributaries are salmon rivers of little less repute than main stream. An excellent run of sea trout, big brown trout (less often fished for), grayling, and coarse fish (scarcely ever fished for).

Perth. Salmon plentiful in Tay from Jan 15 until Oct 15, when river closes, but best fishing is Feb to April and Sept/Oct. Permits (dt 50p non-residents) for river within city boundaries from City Chamberlain (roach increasing; no permits required). From Almond Mouth, some 2m above the town, to Aberfeldy, fishing strictly preserved. Many beats may be rented through Messrs P D Malloch (tackleist), of Perth. Another tackleist who issues permits is Bob Sime, 46 South Methven Street (tickets for Perth and Dist AA water on Earn). Dt for trout fishing on **Horn Loch** (8m) from Forester in charge, Glenalmond. Hotel: Isle of Skye, Queens Bridge.

Stanley (Tayside). Some of the best salmon pools are near here, such as Cat Holes and the famous Pitlochry Pool. In spring, preserved baits, devons and plugs, mainly used. All waters strictly preserved. Apply to Messrs Malloch, Perth, agents for principal proprietors. Beats always let in advance but occasional sub-lets available. Bell-Ingram, 7 Walker St, Edinburgh EH3 7JY, let Taymount Estate. Fishing by week; two beats, five rods each; 26 named pools. Gillie usually available. Hotels: Ballathie House (salmon fishing), Tayside.

Meikleour (Tayside); ns Cargill. The **Isla** here joins Tay; trout, salmon, pike and grayling; all preserved. Isla in upper water above Airlie Castle contains plenty of small trout; fishing free. From its junction with the Water of Dean, a few miles below Airlie Castle, to where it joins Tay, it is very sluggish, and full of pike, large trout, grayling and perch. **Water of Dean** contains capital trout.

Birnam (Tayside). By staying at the Birnam Hotel, 1m of salmon fishing can be had in Tay; (trout fishing only on Sundays); boat available. Best early and late in season. Other salmon fishing can be available from hotel proprietor or Mr Ian Redford, Homelea, Station Rd, Errol. Tel: 08212312.

Dunkeld (Tayside). Post Office and R Scott Miller, Atholl Street tackle shop, issue tickets. Mt £2.50, wt £1.50 and 50p from latter for trout fishing on **Braan**, a tributary entering the Tay here, the main river and lochs **Freuchie** (trout) and **Clunnie** (pike and perch). May and June are the best months. Permits for **Loch Marlee** from Marlee Hotel, by Blairgowrie. Dunkeld House Hotel (salmon fishing). Atholl Arms can arrange trout fishing for guests.

Ballinluig (Tayside). Salmon and trout, with good grayling Oct–March. Tummel here joins Tay. Fishing preserved. Hotel: Logierait, which has 2½m of the Tay near hotel and other stretches including Grandtully Castle beats, to let to residents (£5–£12); salmon (March to June best; mostly spinning), trout (wet and dry fly).

Aberfeldy (Tayside). Salmon reserved: trout fishing can be had on 3m of upper Tay, stocked annually. Tickets from secretary of Aberfeldy AC; dt 50p, wt £2. Tackleists: L Jamieson, Dunkeld Street; Carmichael and Campbell, The Square. Tickets from both for various fishings. Major Neil Ramsay, Farleyer, Aberfeldy, may have rods available on upper river. Hotels: Palace, Nessbank.

Weem (Tayside). Hotel: Weem, which has trout and salmon fishing available free to guests on Weem Water. Dt for others, £4.

Kenmore (Tayside). Tay here leaves Loch Tay. Salmon and trout fishing on river and loch for guests at Kenmore Hotel; boats available.

Killin (Tayside). **Dochart** and **Loch Tay;** salmon (Jan 15 to early May; average 18 lb; trolling on loch), trout (Mar 15 to Sept 30); average ½ lb; wet and dry fly and dapping). Apply H Anderson, Auchmore, for boat with outboard on Loch Tay. Hotels with boats and fishing rights on loch are: Killin (also Lochay River) Bridge of Lochay, Clachaig. Ardeonaig Hotel has 12m of fishing and

boats on loch. Dt (residents) £18, dt (non-residents) £20. Trout fishing can be had on 2m of Dochart, **River Lochay** and **Lochan-na-Laraig,** near Ben Lawers, from Kennell Estate. Permits at modest charge on these waters and Loch Tay west of Lawes from W Allan, Main Street.

Crianlarich (Central). Trout fishing on **Loch Dochart** (good early in the season),

Loch-an-Nubhair and **River Fillan.** In summer, salmon find their way into loch and up Fillan and tributaries. Best months: May, June, July and Sept. Ben More Restaurant issues permits. Hotel: Crianlarich (permits for Fillan and Dochart).

Tyndrum (Central). Fillan, Loch Lyon, Loch-na-Bhe (boats), Loch Tulla. Hotel: Royal.

Tributaries of the Tay

EARN: Salmon, sea trout, brown trout (av ½ lb) and excellent grayling.

Crieff (Tayside). Crieff AC has 4m of north bank and 6m of south bank available to visitors. Feb 1 to July 31: mt £22, wt £12, dt £3. 1 Aug 1 to Oct 15: mt £37, wt £20, dt £5 from tackleists, Wm Cook & Son, 19 High Street. No tickets on water. Limited number of st from hon sec. Best months: sea trout June to August; salmon, April, Sept and Oct. No Sunday fishing. No worms or gaffs before May 1. Gleneagles Hotel, Auchterarder, has loch fishing for guests. Inquire manager's office for details. For further water apply to Cook & Sons. Other hotels: Arduthie, Kingarth, Drummond Arms (St Fillans), George, Victoria, Star.

Comrie (Tayside). Salmon, sea trout, trout in Earn, **Ruchill** and **Lednock.** Salmon best Aug, Sept, Oct; sea trout best May and June. Rivers overfished and visitors' permits strictly limited. Tackleist: D McNaughton, Bridge Street. Hotels: Royal, Comrie, Ancaster Arms.

St Fillans (Tayside). Trout fishing for visitors in **Loch Earn** and river; boats. Whole of loch controlled by St Fillans & Loch Earn AA, which also has ¾m of trout fishing on River Earn and Glentarken Burn; mt £5, wt £3, dt £1 from post office (also tackle).

Lochearnhead (Central). **Loch Earn;** brown trout (½–¾ lb); permits from St Fillans and Lochearnhead Post Offices.

ISLA: Trout (av ½ lb and up to 3 lb) and grayling. Pike also in lower reaches.

Dundee (Tayside). Permits for trout and grayling fishing from Strathmore AIA; from local tackleists. Assn also issues permits for **Dean Water,** tributary of Isla; holds large trout and grayling, and is good for dry-fly. **Glamis** is useful centre. Assn also has short stretch of **Kerbet** and salmon fishing on **Isla;** members

only. Forfar Canmore AC has water on **Dean, Kerbet** and **Noran** waters and on **Forfar Loch** and **Glenogil Reservoir;** wt £1, dt 25p from C Kerr, West High Street. Other tackleist: E Mann, 44 Sheriff Park Gardens (permits for Glenogil Reservoir and Rescobie Loch; trout).

ALYTH (tributary of Isla):

Alyth (Tayside). Several streams in neighbourhood. Isla contains trout and grayling in lower reaches. Above Reekie Linn trout very numerous but small. Hotel: Lands of Loyal.

Glenisla (Tayside). Trout and grayling on Isla, **Melgum** and **Blackwater** from Glenisla Hotel.

ERICHT (tributary of Isla):

Blairgowrie (Tayside). Good trouting, esp April and May; tickets available from hon sec, Blairgowrie, Rattray and Dist AC, who will also give information on loch fishing in area; many lochs hold pike and perch (**Marlee** best; boats at Marlee Hotel). At **Kirkmichael** (13m NW) Edelweiss Hotel issues permits for **Ardle River.** Other hotels: Royal, Bridge of Cally.

Blacklunans (Tayside). Dalrulzion Hotel has trout and salmon fishing free to guests on **River Blackwater** and trout fishing on private loch.

BRAAN:

Dunkeld (Tayside). Several stretches of river free. Merryburn Guest House, Station Rd, Birnam, can arrange fishing on Braan and **Loch Craiglush.** Also own water on Tay (*see Birnam under Tay*) Loch Freuchie lies near.

TUMMEL: Salmon, trout and grayling.

Pitlochry (Tayside). The new loch formed here, **Loch Faskally,** has developed into good fishing water. Boats from P Williamson, Boat Station (Pitlochry 219), two rods in each case. Salmon fishing mainly trolling; no Sunday fishing. Bank

River Tay. Salmon fishing on the Kinnaird water near Ballinlung, Perthshire. *Photograph: John Tarlton.*

fishing (fly only), tickets also available; trout fishing April 15 to Sept 30; salmon fishing usually starts May 1, but not until 300 salmon have been counted through fish pass. **River Tummel below Pitlochry Dam.** Tickets can be had for Pitlochry AC water; salmon and sea trout on Port na Craig beat, limited dt (£12 and £6): trout and grayling in Tummel, st £10, wt £4, dt £1; **Lochs Bhac** and **Kinardochy,** trout, boat £6; **Loch Garry,** trout, bank dt 50p. Enquire for tickets from Pitlochry Tourist Office. Mostly fly only; limited salmon and sea trout £7–£10 a day, according to season. Postal bookings to AC c/o Tourist Office. Apply West Tempar Estate, Kinloch Rannoch, for other fishing on Tummel; **Loch Bhac;** trout; dt £3 (boat, two rods), £1 bank. Inquire hon sec, Pitlochry AC, for details. **Loch Moraig** available except Sat and Sun; excellent trout fishing; permits from W G Gordon, Lude, Blair Atholl. Permits for **Dunalastair Reservoir** (trout; boats) from J and H Mitchell, WS, 28

Atholl Road and Dunalastair Hotel *(see Kinloch Rannoch).* Other hotel: Pine Trees (Tummel fishing).

Strath Tummel (Tayside). **Loch Tummel** holds excellent brown trout, some pike and perch and occasional salmon and sea trout. Fishing from Loch Tummel Hotel; N Campbell, Ardgnalich Farm; and Mr Scott-May, Croft Douglas; boats.

GARRY (and Ericht): Ruined as fishery by North of Scotland Hydro-Electric Board scheme.

Blair Atholl (Tayside). Atholl Arms Hotel issues wt £2 and dt 50p, obtainable by non-residents from The Gun Shop, Blair Atholl.

Dalwhinnie (Highland). Fishing on **Loch Ericht** (22m long) and rivers. Hotel Loch Ericht.

LOCH RANNOCH: Trout, some large but averaging 9 oz; best May and June.

Kinloch Rannoch (Tayside). Struan, 14m Aberfeldy, 18m Rannoch Station, 17m Dunalastair Hotel *(advt p 21)* has

fishing free to guests on Tummel, on Loch Rannoch and on Dunalastair Reservoir. Dt to non-residents 75p on river, £6 on loch, incl boat. Bunrannoch Hotel has fishing on Loch Rannoch and **Tummel** (free to guests). Boats on **Lochs Finnart** and **Kinarochy** arranged. Moor of Rannoch Hotel, Rannoch Station, has fishing rights on **River Gaur** and **Loch Laidon** (trout) and can arrange fishing on Loch Rannoch. Rannoch AC has trout fishing on **Loch Eigheach,** Rannoch Station; dt £1 from hon sec or tackleists. Boat on Loch Rannoch for two rods, £3 per day; same price for boats on hill lochs **Finnart** and **Monogan** 7m west.
LYON (near Loch Tay): Good salmon and trout river in lovely valley.
Coschieville (Tayside); ns Aberfeldy. Tay, Lyon, Keltney Burn; much trout fishing on request; Contact Major N Ramsay; Farleyer, By Aberfeldy.

Fortingall (Tayside); ns Aberfeldy. Fortingall Hotel has 6m on **Lyon.** Salmon: wt from £19.20, dt from £4.50. Trout: dt £1, reduction for residents.
DOCHART (feeds Loch Tay):
Killin (Tayside). At confluence of Dochart and Lochay, near head of Loch Tay. Salmon fishing best in July, Aug and Sept. Trout numerous and run to a fair size. Water is very deep and sluggish down to Luib, but above and as far as Loch Dochart there are some capital streams and pools. Mr G Coyne, Keeper's Cottage, Auchlyne, issues wt £20 and dt £3.50 for Dochart. Trout fishing best April–May, good run of autumn salmon. Ardeonaig Hotel, **Ardeonaig,** has boat on Loch Tay. Morenish Lodge and Achray and Drummond Arms Hotel, **St Fillans,** can arrange fishing. W Allan, newsagent, Main St, issues permits for Kinnell Estate waters.

THURSO

A noted salmon river and one of the earliest in Scotland. However, the spring run has not been so good in recent times. Water level is regulated by a weir at Loch More on the upper reaches. The river is entirely preserved.

Thurso (Highland). Salmon fishing (fly only) can be arranged through Thurso Fisheries Ltd, Thurso East (Tel: Thurso 3134). Bookings usually by week, fortnight or month, but day lets arranged. Weekly charges, including accommodation, range from £140 to £240, according to date. Excellent accommodation at Ulbster Arms, Halkirk. Fishing and accommodation, £130–£175 per rod per week, according to date. Fishing improves progressively from opening on Jan 11 to close on Oct 10. First-class loch, burn and river fishing for trout from hotel at attractive terms *(advt p 328).* Thurso AA has one beat; members only, but possibility of permit if no members fishing. Hotels: Royal Hotel has rights on **Loch Calder;** free to guests; trout. Pentland Hotel has rights on **Lochs Watten, St John's** and **Stemster,**

and can arrange fishing on **Loch Calder;** boats available; trout. St Clair Arms Hotel, Castletown, has rights on all these lochs and **Loch Hielan.** Tackleists: A A MacDonald, 23 Sinclair Street (permits for Thurso (50p to £1.50 day) and permits, boats for Lochs Watten, Calder, St John's, Stemster, Toftingall); K Ferguson, 46 Galloway Street.
Halkirk (Highland). The Ulbster Arms Hotel has fishing on Loch Calder and many other hill lochs; trout; free to guests. Salmon fishing on Thurso River. Information from Secretary, Thurso Fisheries Ltd, Thurso East, Thurso, Highland.
Dunnet (Highland); ns Thurso. Hotels: Northern Sands—own boats on Lochs **St John's** and **Scarmelate.** Fishing arranged on most others; also some river fishing for salmon and sea trout.

Dapping for loch trout under the eagle's eye. Guilven dominates the back-drop.
Photograph: John Tarlton.

The Tweed below Kelso Bridge. *Photograph: Eric Chalker.*

TWEED

Rises in corner formed by watersheds of Clyde and Annan, and flows over 100m to North Sea at Berwick-on-Tweed, forming, for much of its course, boundary between England and Scotland. Tweed is second only to Tay in its fame as a Scottish salmon river. It contains over 300 named casts and its salmon harvest is considerable. Sport more affected by height of the water than most rivers. Tweed produces strain of sea trout which are remarkable both for size and distance they are known to travel in sea. Formerly called bull trout, they rise badly to fly. Excellent brown trout in main river and tributaries, and grayling.

Berwick-on-Tweed. Salmon, sea trout, trout, grayling, coarse fish. Tidal Tweed gives free fishing for roach and grayling. Berwick and Dist AA has fishing in **Whiteadder,** which joins Tweed 1½m from here; brown trout only. Good bus service on both sides of Whiteadder and to Norham from Berwick. St £4, wt £2, dt £1. **Till** enters Tweed 2½m above Norham, 9m from Berwick. A day or two's salmon fishing can sometimes be had from the lessees of the fisheries, on payment. Tillmouth Park Hotel, Cornhill, near mouth of Till and main Berwick–Cornhill road, has five beats on Tweed and two on Till; salmon and sea trout; boats and gillies available also holiday cottage with trouting, wt £115 and £172.50, according to date (Coldstream 2255). **Coldingham Loch,** near Great North Road, Ayton. Brown and rainbow trout. 7 boats, bank fishing for 6 rods. Dt (boat) £7; bank £5. ½ day and evening terms also. Permits from Dr E J Wise, West Loch House, Coldingham (Coldingham 270), who has chalets and cottages to let. Coldingham is noted for the quality and size of the trout caught there *(advt p 332)*. Berwick hotels: Castle, Kings Arms.

Norham (Northumberland). Salmon, trout; preserved. Ladykirk & Norham Angling Improvement Association has lot of water in the district—brown trout, grayling and coarse fish. Reputed to be one of best waters along border. St £5, wt £2, dt 75p from hotels. Hotels: Masons Arms, Victoria.

Coldstream (Borders). Tweed and Leet Water; salmon, trout. Permit from Tourist Information Centre, for trout and coarse fishing; £1 day. Hotel: Tillmouth Park, Cornhill *(see Berwick)*.

Kelso (Borders). Salmon and sea trout preserved, trout and grayling. Also excellent sport with roach (av ¾ lb). Kelso AA has about 8m of Tweed and **Teviot,** and water on **River Eden.** Tickets (trout, grayling, coarse fish) from hon sec. No Sunday fishing; size limit 9 in; restrictions on spinning; trout season, April 1 to Sept 30. Trout fishing good. St £6, wt £3, dt £1. Tackleists: Forrest & Sons, 35 The Square, and Redpath & Co, Horsemarket; from both tickets and information may be obtained. Sportswise, Roxburgh St, Kelso, also issues permits; others from river watchers. Trout fishing (brown and rainbow) on **Wooden Loch,** nr Kelso. Boat available. For reservations after April 10 Apply A H Graham, Gamekeeper's House, Eckford, Kelso. Hotels: Cross Keys *(advt p 332)*, Ednam House (fishing arranged in Tweed, **Teviot, Bowmont** and **Kale**), Woodside *(advt p 275)*, House on the Hill, Border (temp).

St Boswells (Borders). Salmon fishing mostly private. Permits for trout and grayling fishing can be had from the hotels or bailiffs (who are on the bank daily and are pleased to give local information) for 4½m of water belonging to St Boswells AA. Best: May–July. Concessions for parties of eight or more rods. Fishing, Shooting Services Ltd, 4 Weirgate Way (Tel: 22332) have rods on Tweed, **Teviot** and **Ettrick.** Hotels: Buccleuch Arms (trout fishing arranged), Dryburgh Abbey.

Melrose (Borders). Melrose and Dist AA has several stretches open to visitors for trout and grayling fishing. Fish average three to the pound. St £5, wt £3, dt £1, with concessions to juniors. No Sunday fishing; no spinning or use of natural minnow permitted. Tickets from hon

sec, Gibson Park caravan site or tackleist Anglers' Choice, High Street. Holders of these tickets eligible for dt 50p on new waters at Cowies and Ravenswood, but numbers restricted. Season: April 1 to Oct 6 (Sept 30 on new waters). Hotels: Bon Accord, Waverley Castle, Tweedmount. Guest House: Craig Friarshall, Gattonside.

Earlston (Borders). A good centre for **Leader** and Tweed trout fishing. Earlston AA controls about 5m of Leader adjacent to Earlston, with the exception of two small private stretches; st £2.50, dt £1, no salmon fishing; no Sunday fishing and Saturaday fishing for st holders only. Melrose AA has excellent trout water *(see Melrose)*. Other portions of Tweed are reserved. No salmon or sea-trout fishing is available on the trouting portions of Tweed. Hotel: White Swan. Tackleist: J Rutherford & Son.

Galashiels (Borders). Rods for Boleside beat from L Bald, Fisherman's Cottage, Boleside. Wt £110.40 and £82.80 VAT incl, according to date. Feb 1 to Sept 10. Tel: 2792. Salmon, brown trout and grayling. Gala AA has trout fishing on 10–12m of Tweed; st, wt and dt (no Sunday tickets; no spinning). Tickets from hon sec, river watcher, or J and A Turnbull (tackleist), Bank Street. April to Sept provides best daytime sport; mid-June to Aug best evenings. **Gala Water** is free trout fishing. Hotels: Douglas, Waverley, Royal, Kingsknowes.

Selkirk (Borders). Salmon fishing preserved. Good centre for Tweed, **Yarrow** and **Ettrick,** covering 80m of trout fishing. Selkirk and Dist AA restocks annually from own hatchery. Tickets from hon sec, any post office, hotel or river watcher in district. Trout average four to the pound and go up to 3 lb. spinning allowed. Tickets issued. Hotels: Shaws, Broadmeadows, Gordon Arms, Rodono, Tibbie Shiels, Fleece, Woodburn, Station, Philipburn, Heatheray Hill, Whitmuir Hall *(advt p 328)*. Some in the town, some in the surrounding countryside.

Clovenfords (Borders). Tweed here controlled by Gala AA *(see Galashiels)*. Caddon Water; trout. Gala Water; trout.

Thornielee (Borders). Salmon, trout. Peebles TFA has water *(see Peebles)*.

Walkerburn (Borders). Salmon, trout.

Peebles TFA has water. Also Peebles Salmon FA water *(see Peebles)*. Tweed Valley Hotel has fishing on 40m of Tweed (dt from £2) and stocked trout lochs *(advt p 335)*.

Innerleithen (Borders). Salmon, trout. Peebles TFA has water *(see Peebles)*. Leithen Water; trout; free. Quair Water; trout; preserved. Hotel: Traquair Arms.

Peebles (Borders). Salmon fishing on approx 10 miles of Tweed. Season Feb 21 to Nov 30. Tickets (some limited in number) issued by Peeblesshire Salmon Fishing Association. Enquiries 39 High

St, Peebles. Also salmon and trout on Town Water. Enquiries District Council Offices, Rosetta Road, Peebles. Limited st £35, dt £2.50 and £5, according to date. Trout and grayling on approx 25 miles of Tweed and 5 miles of Lyne. Restocked by Peeblesshire Trout Fishing Association. Season April 1 to Sept 30. No spinning or float fishing. Fly only April and Sept and all season on upper reaches. Fish under 9 in must be returned. Waders desirable. Good trout April/May on wet fly then dry best. Tickets issued by Peblesshire Trout FA. St £15, wt £6, dt £1.50. Enquiries 39

High Street, Peebles. Peeblesshire Salmon FA have very good water from Wire Bridge Cottage (1m below town) to county boundary. 60 only visitors' season permits at £40 available, allowing fishing on any week day from Feb 21 to Sept 14 and thereafter on odd or even dates only (excl Sats)—30 permits for each issued. Application in writing to Blackwood & Smith, WS, 39 High Street, Peebles before January 31. Day permits at £6 from Ian Fraser, Tackle Dealer, Northgate, Peebles (Tel: 20979) are limited after Sept 14 to 20 on weekdays and 30 on Saturdays. Bookable (and payable) in advance. Other hotels: Cringletie House (fishing arranged in Tweed and Eddleston Water); Tontine; Park; Green Tree; Cross Keys; Peebles Hydro.

Broughton (Borders). Trout; preserved. Holmes Water. Broughton Burn. Crook Inn, Tweedsmuir, by Biggar, convenient for Upper Tweed and **Talla Reservoir** £1 per day (bank), boat £2. Permits from Victoria Lodge, Tweedsmuir. Dt for river (S) £8, (T) £1.50, from Crook Inn *(advt p 328).*

Tributaries of the Tweed

WHITEADDER: Runs from Edrington Castle to Chirnside Bridge via Allanton Bridge. A good trout stream. Upper waters, from Ninewells (Chirnside) to source, including tributaries, are largely controlled by Whiteadder AA; st £3, dt £1 from hon sec. Concessions to ladies and juniors. Assn had restocked water with brown and rainbow trout. Trout av ¼ lb. Best months June–August. Many burns.

Allanton (Berwick). 1¼m Berwick and Dist AA water from ½m above Allanton Bridge to Cantie's Bridge; trout; visitors living outside 15m radius, wt and dt. St and dt for water above Allanton Bridge obtainable locally. Blackadder joins river here. Fishing reported good. Whiteadder AA has from above Allanton Bridge to source. Hotel: Red Lion, Allanton, Chirnside, Berwickshire *(see Chirnside).*

Duns (Borders). Trout. The following streams are within easy reach: Blackadder (preserved by private association), Whiteadder, **Fasney, Bothwell, Dye, Blacksmill, Monynut** and **Watch.** These, except Blackadder, are, with main steam, largely controlled by Whiteadder AA. Assn also has fishing on **Watch Reservoir;** bank dt £1, boat for two, £4; is stocked with brown and rainbow trout. Tickets from Rathbune Hotel, Longformacus *(see below).* Boats in advance from bailiff K Littlejohn, Langton Gate, Duns *(see Chirnside).* Riparian owners may grant permission. Tackleist: R Welsh, 28 Castle Street. Hotels: Bungalow, Blanerne, Duns. 2m both banks in Whiteadder reserved for hotel guests. White Swan, Bornikin.

Chirnside (Borders). Trout. Chirnside is good centre for Whiteadder, provided that angler has car. From here to source, except for small stretches at Abbey St Bathans House, Chirnside Paper Mills and Cumledge Bridge, river is controlled by Whiteadder AA, including all tributaries entering above Chirnside, except (1) the Monynut above Bankend; (2) the Fasney above Fasney Bridge; and (3) certain stretches of the Dye. Tickets from hon sec.

Longformacus (Borders). Some 7m from Duns. On Dye, Watch and Blacksmill burns. Whiteadder runs near Hotel: Fathburne (permits for Whiteadder AA fisheries), *(see Chirnside for fishing).*

BLACKADDER (tributary of Whiteadder): Very good for brown trout early in season.

Greenlaw (Borders). About 12m held by Greenlaw AC. Tickets from hon sec; st £3, dt 75p. Hotel: Castle.

TILL and BREAMISH: Trout, sea trout, salmon, good grayling, some pike and perch.

Etal (North'land). Accommodation at Red Lion. Millfield (about 3m), but all fishing round Etal strictly preserved.

Wooler (North'land). Good centre for Till (2m N) and **Glen,** which join below Wooler, running through Millfield Plain into Tweed, and are open for sea trout and salmon angling from Feb to Nov. Whitling early summer if conditions right; later on large fish numerous. Wooler and Doddington AA preserves 2m of the Till and 1m of **Wooler Water;** limited permits issued to visitors staying locally, but not for Sundays; fixed-spool reels prohibited; no maggot fishing; fly only, Feb–April inclusive and from Sept

14 to Nov 30. Tickets from hon sec. Some miles above Wooler, at Berwick Bridge, Breamish becomes Till. Wading in Till dangerous. White Swan Inn, Yetholm, can give details of fishing on **Bowmount** and **Kale Waters.** Trout (small), grayling, with good sea trout in wet season.

Chatton (North'land). Trout, grayling; and some fine roach: preserved by Chatton AA for 6½m. Limited number of associated members' tickets for visitors; st £5, dt £1; apply by Jan 1 to hon sec for st; dt from hotel. Other centres: **Lilburn, Chillingham.** Hotel: Percy Arms. *(See English section under Otterburn.)*

EDEN: Trout.

Ednam (Borders), ns Kelso, 2m. Trout: Kelso AA has water *(see Kelso).* Tweed 1m E.

TEVIOT: Good salmon spring and autumn, and first-class for trout and grayling.

Roxburgh (Borders). Kelso AA controls some miles of brown trout fishing on Teviot and Tweed *(see Kelso).* Tweed, 2m W.

Eckford (Borders). Eckford AA issues dt for Teviot (trout, sea trout autumn). Apply A H Graham, Gamekeeper's House, for trout permits for **Wooden Loch.** One boat only.

Nisbet (Borders). Salmon, bull trout, brown trout, pike, perch, grayling. Oxnam Water. Jed Water, 2m S: trout.

Hawick (Borders). St and wt (5 days) for many streams in district including Teviot (which flows through the town), **Slitrig, Borthwick, Rule** and **Ale** (tributaries) from hon sec, Hawick AC, Horse and Hounds, Bonchester and tackleists *(see below).* Club has jurisdiction over 100m of water, several trout lochs: and a reservoir; own hatchery. Limited st for visitors (trout only). Salmon fishing for visitors on Teviot (Mon–Fri only) if vacancy, from D Stothart *(see below).* Eckford AA has water on **Kale;** permits from hon sec. Dt and wt for **Williestruther, Alemoor, Acremoor** and **Hellmoor Lochs,** and **Acreknowe Reservoir** (boat on latter from I Rennie, Bourtree Place), from D Stothart (tackleist), 6 High Street, Burnett's Pet Stores, Union St, and hon sec, Hawick AC. Hotel: Buccleuch (fishing arranged on Teviot, reservoir and lochs).

Jedburgh (Borders). St £8, wt £4 and £2.50, dt £5, £1 and 75p for visitors (salmon and trout) for Rivers Jed and Teviot through Jed-Forest AA, Jedforest Hotel has stretch of **Jed Water,** which runs by hotel (brown trout). Royal Hotel can arrange fishing in Jed Water and Teviot. Tackleists: Jedburgh Gun & Sports Shop.

LEADER: Trout (4 to lb).

Lauder (Borders). Lauderdale AA controls 6m of Leader and 20m of tributaries upwards from Whitslaid Bridge to Carfraemill with the exception of waters in Thirlestane Castle policies. Tickets may be had from hon sec, bailiffs and Post Office. Earlston AA has water *(see Earlston under Tweed).* Hotels: Tower, Oxton; Carfrae Mill (4m from Lauder); Lauderdale; Black Bull; Loanside, Eagle.

Oxton (Borders). Lauderdale AC has burns; small trout *(see Lauder).*

GALA WATER: Popular trout water; fish average about 5 to lb.

Stow (Borders). Edinburgh is 26m distant by rail. There is a good hotel (Royal Hotel) standing on banks of Gala. Fishing on 5m below Stow, and 4m above. Ludgate Water, 1½m; trout; 6m off is the Leader; trout.

Fountainhall (Borders). Gala Water; trout. Armet Water. Within easy reach of Edinburgh.

ETTRICK WATER (and Yarrow): Salmon fishing preserved. All trout fishing in Ettrick and Yarrow by ticket; water being restocked with brown trout by Selkirk AA. Good fishing on some 50m besides many burns. Association tickets (£1 day, (£1.25 Saturdays) wt £2, mt £3.50, st £5) from Tushielaw Hotel (Ettrick), Gordon Arms (Yarrow), Rodono, Tibbie Shiels *(see Megget Water)* and bailiffs, and hotels and tackleists in Selkirk.

St Mary's Loch (Selkirk). Rights on Megget Water (7m long) held by Rodono Hotel. Trout; chance of a salmon. Fishing free to guests. Ticket charges for non-residents: mt £12, wt £4, dt 75p. Loch (into which Megget Water runs) leased and stocked by St Mary's Loch AC. Trout, pike and perch. Residents at Rodono and Tibbie Shiels hotels have free fishing. Boats available. **Loch of the Lowes** is also St Mary's AC and Rodono Hotel water; also feeder burns; brown and rainbow trout (few pike and perch); permits from bailiffs, hon sec, Gordon Arms Hotel and The Glen Cafe.

EDDLESTON WATER: Situated near Eddleston village on bus route. Equal distance from Peebles and Leadburn (5m). Trout; but of little account; fishable also from Peebles.

TYNE (Lothian)

Rises on north slopes of Lammermuir Hills and flows about 25m to North Sea a little south of Whitberry Ness. Has some sea trout but is known mainly as a brown trout stream—hard fished—and now badly polluted in parts. River also provides sport with roach, but less than it did a few years ago.

Haddington (Lothian). Trout; East Lothian AA controls most of water in county. St £3 and dt £1 from J Main, High Street, and L Walker, 3 Bridge Street, East Linton; also river watchers. No Sunday fishing; no spinning. *Note:* Roach fishers must comply with trout season and rules, and remove all roach caught. Permits for **Whiteadder Reservoir** (trout) from Water Engineer, Alderstone House, Haddington. Fishing on two other reservoirs—**Donnally** and **Hopes**—also available. Good sea fishing at **North Berwick** (10m).

UGIE

A small river entering the sea at Peterhead. Salmon, good sea trout, some brown trout. Salmon and sea trout best from July to October; good run of finnock in February and March.

Peterhead (Grampian). Permits available for approx 13m of fishing owned by Capt Curzon, Daluaine, Huntly. Apply G Morrison, c/o Bruce, Ironmonger, Chapel Street, Peterhead; Gavin Milne, Newsagent, 3 Ugie Street, Peterhead; or Dick's Sports, 54 Broad Street, Fraserburgh. St £25, wt £10, dt £3 + small Angling Assn surcharge. Juniors and OAP half-price. 12m N of Peterhead is **Loch of Strathbeg;** Loch Leven trout (av ¾ lb); for tickets (and boats) apply J Moir, Gamekeeper, The Kennels, Crimonmogate Estate, Lonmay (Lonmay 367) or Brown & McRae, solicitors. At **Fraserburgh** (17m NW) is **Red Loch** (rainbow and brown trout) for which the Pet Shop, Cross Street, issues dt £2 for bank fishing. Hotels: Alexandra, High St, Royal and Station, Broad St.

Tributary of the Ugie

STRICHEN (or North Ugie):
Strichen (Grampian). Free trout fishing (subject to permission of riparian owners). Salmon fishing strictly preserved.

URR

Drains Loch Urr and flows to Solway. Late run of salmon; also sea trout, herling and brown trout.

Rockcliffe (Dumfries & Galloway). On Urr estuary. Baron's Craig Hotel can arrange fishing on river and hill lochs (7m from hotel).

Dalbeattie (Dumfries & Galloway). Dalbeattie AA has 3½m both banks; salmon, grilse, sea trout, herling, brown and rainbow trout (re-stocking has improved trout fishing; av 1 lb). Visitor's tickets issued for river and **Dalbeattie Reservoir.** Prices still to be settled as we go to press. Assn also has 1m on Glenshalloch Burn (trout), **Dalbeattie Reservoir** is stocked with Loch Leven trout (Sunday fishing allowed). Applications for st (limited) to hon sec. Wt and dt from N Parker, The Cafe, 30 High St, Dalbeattie. Southwick AS has fishing on **Southwick Water;** sea trout, brown trout, herling; dt 25p and wt 40p from the hon sec. Hotels: Maxwell Arms, Galloway Arms, Kings Arms. Glaisters Lodge. Corsock. The Pheasant, Dalbeattie. At **Castle Douglas** (5m W) the Angling Assn has about 5m of Urr. Dt and wt from The Galloway News Office, 146 King Street. Tackleist: Tommy's Sports Goods, 20 King St, Castle Douglas.

WEST COAST STREAMS AND LOCHS

Some complex fisheries and one or two smaller—though not necessarily less sporting—streams are grouped here for convenience. Other west coast waters will be found in the main alphabetical list.

AILORT

A short but very good sea trout river which drains Loch Eilt and enters sea through salt-water Loch Ailort. One of very few rivers where run of genuine spring sea trout takes place.

Lochailort (Highland). 27½m from Fort William. Salmon and sea trout fishing on **Loch Eilt** and River Ailort preserved. For details apply to Morar Hotel or Rod & Gun Shop, Fort William. **Loch Morar,** a few miles north, provides excellent sport with salmon, sea trout and brown trout. Fishing from banks free. Boats £5 day from Morar Hotel when not wanted by guests.

LOCH BROOM (including Rivers Broom, Dundonnell, Garvie, Oscaig and Ullapool)

Achiltibuie (nr Ullapool). Sea trout, brown trout and sea fishing. Summer Isles Hotel has much fishing for guests on rivers and lochs in the vicinity. Sea trout, brown trout Loch Oscaig: boat £11, River Garvie, dt £6, brown trout lochs, dt £3. Own boats for sea fishing *(advt p 300)*. Permit from Badentarbat Lodge for salmon, sea trout and trout fishing on local lochs (salmon, sea trout £2 day, brown trout 50p).

Ullapool (Highland). **Ullapool River** and **Loch Achall.** Inquiries to Angie Allan, Warehouse Buildings, Ullapool. Ullapool AC controls fishing on lower river. No tickets. Royal Hotel has fishing for guests on **River Polly** (20m away) and on **Garvie** salmon and sea trout; **Loch Sionascaig** (20m), brown trout; **Loch Lurgain** (12m); sea and brown trout fishing arranged on Ullapool River and **Lochs Dubh** and **Achall.** "Tir-Aluinn", Leckmelm, arranges fishing on Rivers **Broom** and Ullapool, and several lochs—Salmon, sea trout, brown trout; boats. For salmon and sea-trout fishing on **Polly Lochs** apply to J Macdonald, Inverpolly. Tackleist: Angie Allan, Warehouse Buildings. Hotel: Royal *(advt p 20)*.

Dundonnell (Highland). Two rods available on 1½m (both banks) of **River Dundonnell;** salmon and sea trout. Inquire of D P Morrison, 30 Walker Street, Edinburgh.

Inverbroom. River Broom; best July and August. Also hill lochs. Beats sometimes available on Inverbroom Estate water; inquiries to Sharpe or Matheson, Inverbroom.

CARRON

Salmon and very good sea trout. Strathcarron Hotel (Lochcarron 228) controls 3m beat; £2 day. Best months June, July and August.

LOCH DUICH, including Shiel and Croe

Glenshiel (Highland); ns Kyle. Salmon and sea trout. Fishing available on **River Croe,** a spate-river with late runs. Dt £3.20 and £4.50, according to season from Nat Trust for Scotland, Morvich Visitor Centre, Inverinate, By Kyle. Reductions for members. Sea fishing on Loch Duich.

ECHAIG (Loch Eck and to Holy Loch)

Drains Loch Eck and flows about 5m into Atlantic by way of Holy Loch and Firth of Clyde. Salmon and sea trout.

Kilmun (Strathclyde). On Holy Loch and Firth of Clyde. Echaig enters sea here. Salmon, sea trout in Loch Eck (5m), where Whistlefield Inn has boats for guests; fly best at head of loch where **River Cur** enters. Other hotel: Coylet.

Dunoon (Strathclyde). River fishing now preserved. Coylet and Whistlefield Hotels have salmon (mainly trolling), sea trout and brown trout fishing on **Loch Eck** for guests (preferential terms for residents); boats available at hotels. Loch Eck is about 7m long. No good for salmon until early June; best in August, Sept. Whistlefield Inn also has fishing by arrangement in Rivers **Cur, Finnart** and

Masan. Permits from The Tackle Shop, Queens Hall buildings, Dunoon, for Dunoon AC water on **River Cur** and **Loch Tarsan. Small Echaig,** salmon, sea trout. **Dunoon Reservoirs** hold brown and rainbow trout. Charges under review. Permits from The Tackle Shop, address above. Permits for **River Finnart,** sea trout and occasional salmon, £1.50 per day from Forest Office, Benmore Forest, Kilmun by Dunoon. Glendaruel Hotel at **Glendaruel** (18m) has salmon, sea trout and trout fishing on **River Ruel** (best July to Sept). Permits £1 day.

LOCH FYNE (including Rivers Douglas, Shira, Garron, Kinglas, Fyne and Dubh Loch)

Large sea loch on west coast of Argyll, which provides good sea fishing and first-class salmon and sea trout in streams. These are spate rivers; best from June to September.

Inverary (Strathclyde). Argyll Estates, Cherry Park, Inverary (Inverary 2203) issue dt £1.25 for hill lochs.

Knipoch by Oban (Strathclyde). **Dubh Loch** and **Loch Seil** dt £2 with boat. L Leven and brown trout. River Euchar, salmon and sea trout; dt from J T P Mellor, Barndromin Farm.

Cairndow (Strathclyde). **River Fyne** tidal water: Dt (May–June) £10, (July–Oct) £12 from Ardkinglass or Cairndow Estate Offices (Tel: Cairndow 217 and 284 respectively). **River Kinglas** and **Loch Restil:** Dt from Cairndow Estate Office.

GAIRLOCH

A sea loch on the west coast of Ross. Gairloch Hotel has salmon and trout fishing on Loch Maree and other lochs. Shieldaig Lodge Hotel has trout fishing on lochs and salmon fishing on one loch and short stretch of river. Limited permits for visitors. Salmon and sea-trout fishing on **River Kerry** from Creagmore Hotel, dt £5. Dt £1 for hill loch brown trout fishing from tackle shops.

GLENELG

Rises in Glen More and flows about 10m to the sea at **Glenelg.** Salmon and sea-trout fishing preserved by owner of Scallasaig Lodge. Rod occasionally let for the day at owner's discretion.

LOCH INCHARD

Kinlochbervie (Highland). Garbet Hotel has extensive rights of high standard; over 40 lochs; sea trout (July to Sept), brown trout (April to Sept) and small spate river (the **Shinary**). Stock of flies and casts at hotel. Fishing free to guests. Boats from £1.10 day. Trout average 1 lb.

LOCH LONG (including Rivers Finnart and Goil)

A sea loch opening into the Firth of Clyde. Good sea trout, some salmon in streams. Finnart good in spates.

Ardentinny (Strathclyde). Finnart, 1½m fishable, enters Loch Long here. Salmon, grilse and sea trout, season July to mid-October: a few brown trout, but of good size, May–September. Permits, limited to 10 rods, can be obtained through Forestry Commission, Benmore Forest Office, Kilmun by Dunoon. Tel: Kilmun 308. Dt £1.50 VAT incl. No Sunday fishing.

Arrochar (Strathclyde). Arrochar House hotel (Tel 238) overlooks Loch Long, where good sea fishing obtainable. Hotel has trout fishing on **Loch Lomond** (1½m). North of Scotland Hydro Electric Board issues permits for trout fishing on **Loch Sloy** (33p day). Apply to Warden, Loch Lomond Caravan Park, Inveruglas.

Carrick (Strathclyde). Carrick Castle Hotel has salmon, sea trout and brown trout on River and **Loch Goil,** free to guests. Boat on loch.

Lochgoilhead (Strathclyde). Dt issued for about 3m on **River Goil** above where it flows into **Loch Goil** (a branch of **Loch Long**). Grilse, sea trout, some brown trout. Limited tickets from Mon to Sat, £3.45, bookable in advance, June 1 to Oct 15, from Forestry Commission, Arrochar (Tel: 243). For fishing on **Lettermay Loch,** brown trout, contact D Campbell, Faillte, Lochgoilhead. Sea fishing in **Loch Goil.** Hotels: Lochgoilhead, Drimsynie House (private stretches free to guests).

FIRTH OF LORN (including Loch Nell)

Forming the strait between Mull and the mainland on the west coast. Lochs Linnhe and Etive open into it. Good sea trout and a few salmon.

Oban (Strathclyde). Loch Nell (4m). Good sea trout, occasional salmon, July–Sept. Heavier sea trout run towards end of June, and later on finnock appear in numbers. Boats from Mrs MacIlwraith, Torinturk, Glenloan (Kilmore 212) by Oban. **Oban Reservoir,** at Loch-na-Gleanna Bhearraidh, 1½m of Ardrishaig Road, gives reasonable sport with brown trout (av 1 lb). Brown trout fishing in **Black Loch;** dt from halfway House, Caravan Site, Dunbeg, Connel. At **Kilninver** on **Euchar** estuary (10m south of Oban on A816), good salmon, sea trout and some brown trout fishing may be had from Mary McCorkindale, Sca-

madale, or Lt-Col P S Sandilands, Lagganmore. Dt £1.50. As the Euchar is a spate river, bookings are not accepted more than a week in advance. Boat on **Loch Scammadale** dt £2 + £1 per rod. J T P Mellor, Barndromin Farm, Knipoch (by Oban) has 1m, for which permits are issued three days a week only. Sea trout best mid-June to end of Sept; salmon first week of July to early Oct. Tackleist: D Graham, 9–15 Combie Street and 123 George St. Hotels: Alexandra; Shieling Guest House, Kilmore; Cuilfail, Kilmelford; Tighantruish, Clachan Bridge.

LOCH MELFORT

A sea loch opening into the Firth of Lorn south of Oban. Sea trout, mackerel, flounders, etc.

Kilmelford (Strathclyde) 15m from Oban. Cuilfail Hotel has the fishing on Lochs **Nan Drimnean** (10 min walk. trout; March–May, Aug–Sept best; fly only; 10 in limit), **A'Phearsain** (15 min walk; trout, char; fly only; April–June, Aug–Sept best), **Avich** (5m by road; trout; May–Oct best), **Na Sreinge** (8m by road and 35 min walk; trout; May–Oct best,

Scammadale (8m by road; sea trout, salmon; end June–Sept), Melfort (10 min walk; sea trout, mackerel, flounders, skate, etc; June–Aug best), and five hill lochs (hour's walk and climb; trout; June–Oct). Fishing free to residents, but a charge made for boats. Season: March 15 to Oct 15 *(advt p 343).*

Family fun on the Conon. History fails to record whether the man so tenacious of his plastic beaker was winning a bet or merely caught at a disadvantage (as so often happens) by a taking fish. *Photograph: Eric Chalker.*

MORVERN

Lochaline (Strathclyde). At mouth of Loch Aline; sea trout in loch and **R Aline,** whiting, mackerel etc, in Sound of Mull. Ardtornish Estate has fishing on river and boats on lochs. **L Arienas;** brown and sea trout: **L Tearnait;** brown trout av 12 ozs. Dt from 57p to £5.75 VAT incl. Inquiries to factor.

LOCH MUDLE

Ardnamurchan (Highland). Kilchoan Hotel, on the Ardnamurchan peninsula, by Fort William, issues dt (boat) £5 and (bank) £1 for **Loch Mudle. Glen Lochs,** about ½m from Kilchoan free of charge (brown trout).

WICK

Good salmon and sea-trout fishing on Wick River controlled by Wick AA *(see Wick).* All information from secretary. Famous Loch Watten (trout) is 7m from Wick. Also many other excellent trout lochs, including St John's Calder, and Stemster. Apply to Pentland and Royal Hotels (both Thurso), Northern Sands Hotel (Dunnet, by Thurso), Ulbster Arms (Halkirk) *(advt p 328)* John O' Groats House Hotel *(advt p 20),* and Loch Watten Hotel, Watten.

Wick (Highland). Wick AA permits for visitors. Wt and dt. River well stocked from association's own hatchery. Trout fishing on several lochs.

Lybster (Highland). Lybster is 12m S of Wick at mouth of Reisgill Burn. Guests at Portland Arms Hotel can have salmon and sea trout fishing on **Berriedale River**

and trout fishing on six lochs by arrangement. Best months for loch: May and Sept. Permits for (**Loch Watten** also from Lochview Farmhouse and for **St John's** from Northern Sands Hotel, Dunnet St

Clair Hotel, and A A MacDonald, both Sinclair St, Thurso. Thrumster Garages, Thrumster, issue permits for **Hempriggs** and **Sarclet** *(see also Thurso)*.

YTHAN

Rises in "Wells of Ythan" and runs some 35m to North Sea at Newburgh. Late salmon river which used to fish best in autumn, but now has good spring run (February, March, April). River of no great account for brown trout, but noted for sea trout and finnock, which run up from June through to September, with some fish in October. Ythan has very large estuary for so small a river and is markedly tidal for lower five miles or so of its course.

Newburgh (Grampian). 14 miles from Aberdeen, sea trout, finnock and salmon. Fishing the large estuary here controlled by Udny and Dudwick Management Ltd, close to the river (Tel: Newburgh 035-86 273). Sea trout average 2–2½ lb and run up to 12 lb; finnock May onwards with large ones in September. Fly fishing and spinning only; spoons, Ythan Terrors and devons fished on a 7–8 ft spinning rod with 8–12 lb line as most usual tackle. Worm, maggot, bubble float and other bait not allowed. Lead core lines, sinking lines and floating lines with sinking tips not allowed.

Much fishing from bank, but boats and gillies available. Fishery Office and Post Office stocks tackle. Best months June to September.

Methlick (Grampian). Still some spring fish, but the main run now Sept/Oct. Good early run of finnock; a second, smaller, run in the autumn. Sea trout; June–Oct. Fishing on Haddo Estate water; dt Sept 16–Oct 31 £3. June 1–July 50p, other times, £1.50 from Estate Office or S French & Son, Methlick (tackleists). For st apply estate office. The fishing extends for 3½ to 4m. No worm or maggot fishing allowed; no gaff before May 1; limit, 10 finnock. Hotel: Ythanview.

Ellon (Grampian). Salmon, sea trout, trout. Tickets for Ellon Castle water from Buchan Hotel; or John Dickson & Son (tackleists), Aberdeen. Water extends to 1½m, both banks, on backwater and Macharmuir Pool (last is tidal); Spring good for finnock (to mid-April) and Aug to Oct good for sea trout.

Tributaries: Ebrie *(see Auchnagatt)*. Forvie; trout; free. Loch of Strathbeg stocked with Loch Levens (av ¾ lb) *(see Ugie—Peterhead)*.

Fyvie (Grampian). Sea trout, finnock, salmon, brown trout. Sept and Oct best months for sea trout. Fyvie AA issues st £6 and dt £1.50, obtainable from hotels and Sheiling Tor Cafe.

Tributary of the Ythan

EBRIE:

Auchnagatt (Grampian). Parts of the river are free; sea trout, finnock, trout. Sea trout fishing fairly good in the back end when there is plenty of rain; fly or lure. Hotel: Baron's Inn.

SEA FISHING STATIONS IN SCOTLAND

IT is only in recent years that the full sea angling potential of the Scottish coast, indented by innumerable rocky bays and sea lochs, has come to be appreciated. Working in conjunction, tourist organisations and local sea angling clubs smooth the path for the visiting angler. He is well supplied in matters of boats and bait, natural stocks of the latter remaining relatively undepleted in many areas.

Note: The local name for coalfish is "saithe" and for pollack "lythe".
Further details on sea fishing in Scotland may be had from the Scottish Tourist Board, who provide a useful guide.

Stranraer (Dumfries & Galloway). Loch Ryan, the W coast of Wigtownshire and Luce Bay offer first-class sea fishing, boat and shore. Loch Ryan: codling, whiting, plaice, flounders, dabs, skate and dogfish. Other species found in Luce Bay and off Irish Sea coast include pollack, mackerel and tope. Detailed notes for visitors obtainable from hon sec, Lochryan SAA. Tackleist: Sports Shop, George St, Stranraer.

Girvan (Strathclyde). Mostly saithe, haddock, cod, pollack and mackerel, which run quite heavy towards Ailsa Craig; July onwards best. Shore fishing and boats from harbour; inquire of Harbourmaster. Tackleist: J H Murray, 42 Dalrymple Street. Six boats take out parties.

Ayr (Strathclyde). Saithe, haddock, whiting, skate, cod, mackerel, conger, eels, flounders; from pier, shore, or boats which can be hired in the town. Good mackerel fishing (trolling) in July and August. Tackleists: James Kirk, 25 Kyle Street; Game-sport, 60 Sandgate; J A Newbiggin, 19 Aitken St, Largs.

Saltcoats and Ardrossan (Strathclyde). Cod, haddock, conger, saithe, flatfish. Good beach fishing in Irvine Bay and small bay between Saltcoats and Ardrossan. Boatmen include: A Gibson, 1 Fleck Avenue, Saltcoats. Tackleist: D Barr, Hamilton Street. Clubs: Saltcoats SAA and Ardrossan and District SAC.

Lamlash (Isle of Arran). Growing centre. Horseshoe Bay popular. Good cod, haddock, whiting, flatfish, etc. Boats at St Molios Boatyard, Old Pier, or Pier Cafe. N C McLean, Torlin Villa, Kilmory, will answer inquiries. Angling festivals at Whitsun and in August.

Campbeltown (Strathclyde). Good sport with cod, haddock, flatfish, etc, in Kildalloig Bay and from The Winkie, causeway between Davaar Island and mainland. Some boats; trips arranged. Further details from the Tourist Information Office. Tackleists: R Armour & Sons, Longrow; A P MacGrory, Main Street.

Oban (Strathclyde). Accessible beaches overfished, but good sport in Firth of Lorne and tidal waters near Kerrera Island with saithe, pollack, mackerel, huss, conger and flatfish. D McLeod, 2 Castle Road, runs fishing trips. Several other boat hirers. Tackleists: D Graham, Combie Street.

Mallaig (Highland). Good centre in beautiful area. Flatfish, pollack, conger, mackerel, coalfish in bay and from rocks and new piers. Boats from John Henderson & Son. Tackleists: Johnston Bros; D W Maclean, The Pier.

Shieldaig (Highland). Perhaps best known for large whiting, including British record of 6 lb, but also holds haddock, cod, conger, saithe, ling, huss, dabs, sole and mackerel. Fishing in sea lochs of Shieldaig, Torridon and Upper Torridon; sheltered water nearly always. Outside lochs conditions can be dangerous. A Grant, merchant, has boats for hire.

Gairloch (Highland). Cod, haddock, whiting, pollack, saithe and flatfish in sea loch here, especially around Longa Island. Many boatmen catering for anglers. Hotels: Gairloch; Gairloch Sands; Myrtle Bank; Millcroft; Old Inn. Tackleists: Anglers' Aid, Gairloch Pier; Gairloch Sands Holiday Centre; Gordon of Alford, Clifton, Strath; The Wild Cat, Achtercairn; K Gunn, Strath. Gen information from Wester Ross Tourist Organisation (Tel: Gairloch 2139).

Ullapool and Summer Isles (Highland). Noted for large skate, fish over 100 lb have been landed from boats. Also haddock, whiting, codling, pollack, coalfish, mackerel, gurnard, flatfish, thornback ray, conger, dogfish, turbot and wrasse.

Excellent sport inshore from dinghies and in charter boats around the Summer Isles. Good shore fishing at Morefield, Rhu and Achiltibuie. Charter boats from Golden West Co and Ullapool Charter Co, Ullapool; I McLeod, Achiltibuie. Rowing boats and bait from Golden West Co. Club: Lochbroom SAC, who hold international sea angling festivals annually. Tackleists: A McKenzie, Warehouse Buildings, Ullapool; Ullapool and Loch Broom SAC.

Lochinver (Highland). Cod, halibut, skate, tope, saithe, codling, lythe, mackerel. N A Mackaskill, Cruimer, operates launches; other boats available. Tackleist: M B Turnbull, newsagent and Lochinver Fish Selling Co. Bait available from pier: Hotel: Lochinver. Tourist information centre. Supplies details of accommodation.

Portree (Isle of Skye). Good sport in harbour, loch and shore, with great variety of fish. Boats available. Most hotels will arrange facilities *(see Skye freshwater section)*.

Stornoway (Lewis). Cod, haddock, whiting, saithe, skate, etc. Fastgrowing centre with local club, Stornoway Sea AC, South Beach Quay, whose secretary will gladly help visiting anglers. Tackleist: The Sports Shop, 6 North Beach Street; and C Morrison and Son, Point Street. Hotels: County, Caledonian, Royal, etc.

Kirkwall (Orkney). Sheltered waters in Scapa Flow hold variety of fish (record skate; halibut over 150 lb; ling over 30 lb; large cod and pollack). Boats available. Orkney Tourist Board, Broad Street, Kirkwall, will supply further details.

Lerwick (Shetland). Superb skate fishing: Nearly 200 skate over 100 lb taken. Also excellent mixed fishing for ling, cod, tusk, haddock, pollack, etc, and chance of halibut. Area holds British records for tusk, homelyn ray, grey gurnard and Norway haddock. Also Scottish hake record. For boat hire contact Kennie Manson, Mizpah House, Bressay, Shetland. Hotels: Lerwick Hotel, Kveldsro House, Grand, Queens, etc. Club: Ler-

wick and Bressay Sea AC. Other centres in Shetland include **Whalsay, Unst** and **Burra.** Boat: H Smith, Buness, Baltasound, Unst and Berry Road, Scalloway. Hotels: Springfield, Maundeville (Unst) and Scalloway: Further details from R H Johnson. Hon Sec, Sheltland ASA (address in club list).

Wick (Highland). Mainly rock fishing for conger, pollack, saithe, cod, haddock, mackerel and flatfish. Good points are: Longberry, Boathaven, Sandigoe and Helman Head. Excellent cod fishing off Noss Head. Best months: June to Sept. Tackleist: H Banks (chemist), Bridge St. Hotels: Rosebank, Nethercliffe, Mackay's, Station, Queen's. Club: Wick Sea AC. Tourist Information Office, Whitechapel Road.

Lossiemouth (Grampian). Notable centre for sea-trout fishing off east and west beaches; spinning into breakers provides splendid sport. Also mackerel, saithe, flatfish from beach, pier and boats. Tackleists: Lofts, DIY Stores.

Aberdeen (Grampian). Excellent rock fishing for codling, saithe, mackerel, whiting, haddock and flatfish. Few boats. Tackleist: John Dickson & Son, 35 Belmont Street. Hotels: Caledonian, Imperial, Royal.

Stonehaven (Grampian). Rock fishing for haddock, saithe, lythe, flounder and mackerel very good. Cod, haddock, ling, etc, from boats; available from Mrs E Cargill, 16 King Street. Bait may be dug or obtained from Mrs Cargill. Annual festival. Tackleists: Davids, Market Square. Numerous hotels. Further data from Mrs Cargill.

Dundee (Tayside). Fishing from rocks, pier and boats at Broughty Ferry, Easthaven and Carnoustie for mackerel, saithe, lythe and flatfish. Boats: Mr Mirrey, 44 Holyrood Street, Carnoustie. Tackleist: John Gow & Sons, 12 Union Street. Club: Dundee and Dist Sea AA.

Dunbar (Lothian). Excellent rock, pier and boat fishing. Saithe (pollack), cod (up to 10 lb), codling, dabs, plaice, flounders, eels and, at times, small whiting, gurnard and mackerel can be caught.

FISHING CLUBS & ASSOCIATIONS IN SCOTLAND

INCLUDED in this list of fishing clubs and associations in Scotland are those organisations which are in England, but which have water on the Tweed and its tributaries or on the Border Esk. Further information can usually be had from the secretaries, and a courtesy which is appreciated is the inclusion of a stamped addressed envelope with postal inquiries.

NATIONAL BODIES

Anglers' Co-operative Association. Malcom W Thomson, 21 Heriot Row, Edinburgh EH3 6EN.

Dept of Agriculture and Fisheries, Scotland, Chesser House, Gorgie Road, Edinburgh EH11 3AW.

Forestry Commission. East (Scotland) Conservancy, 6 Queen's Gate, Aberdeen AB9 2NQ.

Halibut Club of Great Britain. Ted Simons, Caithness Tourist Association, 1 Francis Street, Wick. Tel: Wick 2596.

International Fly-Fishing Association. Alastair S Nicoll, PO Box 84, 51 Meadowside, Dundee, DD1 9PQ. Tel 0382 21081.

Scottish Anglers' Association. Duncan J McGregor, 10 Corrennig Drive, Edinburgh EH10 6EQ. Tel 031 447 1174.

Scottish Federation of Sea Anglers. H A Sharp, 11 Rutland Street, Edinburgh EH1 2AE.

Scottish National Angling Clubs' Association. Alastair S Nicoll, PO Box 84, 51 Meadowside, Dundee DD1 9PQ. Tel 0382 21081.

Scottish Record Fish Committee. Saltwater: Mrs Joyce C West, 10 Pearce Grove, Edinburgh EH12 8SP. Tel 031 339 7304. Aims as British Record Fish Committee.

Scottish Record Fish Committee. Freshwater: Colin T Carruthers, 26 Campsie Dene Road, Blarnfield, Glasgow G63 98N.

Scottish Salmon Angling Federation. W & J Burness, WS, 12 Hope Street, Edinburgh EH2 4DD. Tel 031 226 4241.

Scottish Tourist Board. 23 Ravelston Terrace, Edinburgh EH4 3EU. Tel 031–332 2433. Publishes "Scotland for Sea Angling".

Abercorn Angling Club. D Marshall, 10 Glendee Road, Renfrew, Gryffe. Tickets.

Aberdeen and District Angling Association. Messrs. Clark & Wallace, Solicitors, 14 Albyn Place, Aberdeen. Dee, Don and loch. Tickets.

Aberfeldy Angling Club. D Campbell, The Square, Aberfeldy, Perthshire. Tay. Tickets.

Aberfoyle Angling Protection Association. E A Howell, Tigh na Cruinn, Aberfoyle, Perthshire. Lochs. Tickets.

Abernethy Angling Improvement Association. John McInnes, "Balnafoich", Boat of Garten. Spey. Tickets.

Airdrie and District Angling Club. George Lennie, 11b Royal Terrace, George Street, Airdrie, Lanarkshire. Trout reservoirs. Tickets.

Allan Water Angling Improvement Association. P Nicholls, 5 Lister Court, Bridge of Allan, Stirling, Scotland (Central). Allan. Tickets.

Alness Angling Club. D A Ross, 19 Hill Street, Coulhill, Alness, Easter Ross. Alness River. Members only.

Annan and District Anglers' Club. J Trodden, 63 High Street, Annan, Dumfries. Annan, lochs, reservoir.

Arbroath Angling Club. J Gibb, 95 Sydney Street, Arbroath, Angus.

Ardrossan and District Sea Angling Club. D Arnott, 6 Winton Buildings, Ardrossan, Ayrshire.

Ardrossan Eglinton Angling Club. W Withnall, 22 Hunter Avenue, Ardrossan, Ayrshire. Trout reservoirs.

Arran Angling Association. M Aird, Lavencorrach, Isle of Arran. Tickets.

Arran Sea Angling Association. Mrs M S McLean, Torlin Villa, Kilmory, Isle of Arran.

Assynt Angling Club. S McClelland, Baddidarroch, Lochinver, Sutherland. Numerous lochs; tickets.

Auchinleck Angling Association. John McColm, 21 Milne Avenue, Auchinleck, Ayrshire. Ayr and Lugar. Tickets.

Avon Angling Club. H D Burns, Meadowside, Stonehouse, Lanarkshire. Avon.

Ayr Angling Club. J H McClement, 149 Whitletts Road, Ayr.

Badenoch Angling Association. The Secretary, Badenoch AA, Kingussie, Scotland (Highland). Spey. Tickets.

Banff and Macduff Angling Association. R Pederson, 3 Simpson Place, Macduff, Banffshire. Deveron. Tickets.

Barr Angling. P Tierney, Borulea Hotel, Barr, Ayrshire. Stinchar. Tickets.

Barra Angling Club. Desmond J Dunn, Seaview, Castlebay, Isle of Barra. Lochs; tickets.

Barrhead Angling Club. G Haydock, 20 Graham Street, Barrhead, Renfrewshire.

Beauly Angling Society. J MacKenzie, Viewfield Avenue, Beauly, Invernessshire.

Berwick and District Angling Association. J. Moodie, 12 Hillcrest, East Ord, Berwick-on-Tweed, Northumberland. Whiteadder. Tickets.

Blackridge and District Angling Club. Allan Neil, 9 Murdostoun Crescent, Harthill, Lanarkshire. Lochs. Tickets.

Blairgowrie, Rattray and District Angling Association. W P Lamont, Hope Cottage, James Street, Blairgowrie, Perthshire. Ericht. Tickets.

Brechin Angling Club. W Brooks, 20 Nursery Lane, Brechin, Tayside. Lochs. Tickets.

Bridge of Weir Loch Angling Club. G Scott, 10 Park Road, Bridge of Weir, Renfrewshire. No tickets.

Bridge of Weir River Angling Club. J Milne, 8 Beech Avenue, Bridge of Weir, Renfrewshire. Gryffe. Tickets.

Broughty Angling Club. D A Adams, 8 Bridge Lane, Barnhill, Dundee, Angus.

Buckie Angling Association. W Reid, 5 High Street, Buckie, Banffshire.

Bute Angling Association. J McVey, "Ardlerag" Academy Road, Rothesay, Bute.

Caithness Sea Angling Association. J Campbell, 29 Castlegreen Road, Thurso, Caithness.

Caledonian St Andrew Angling Club. A P Philip (match secretary), Caledonian Club, Princes Street, Edinburgh.

Campsie Angling Club. W McKie, 36 Holyknowe Crescent, Lennoxtown, near Glasgow. Glazert and burns. Tickets.

Carrick Angling Association. T L Wilson, 1 Church Square, Girvan, Ayrshire.

Carsphairn Angling Club. J A Hunter, The Knowe, Carsphairn, Castle Douglas, Galloway.

Castle Angling Club. E W Griffiths, 35 William Street, Johnstone, Renfrewshire. Black Cart. Tickets.

Castle Douglas and District Angling Association. E J Woodley, Torwood, Oakwell Road, Castle Douglas, Galloway. Urr. Tickets.

Catrine Angling Club. R M Miller, 35 Sloan Street, Catrine, Ayrshire.

Chatton Angling Association. A Jarvis, New Road, Chatton Alnwick, Northumberland, Till. Members only.

Coatbridge Angling Club. James Thom, 24 Drumpellier Avenue, Coatbridge, Lanarkshire.

Cockburn Angling Club. J S Stirling, WS, 27 Buckstone Terrace, Edinburgh.

Coldstream & District Angling Association. E M Patterson, 27 Leet Street, Coldstream. Tweed, Leet. Tickets.

Commissioners of Royal Four Towns Fishings. W Graham, Glenelg, Hightae, Lockerbie, Dumfries, Annan. Tickets.

Crianlarich Angling Association. R Leleux, 58 Benbecula, St Leonards, East Kilbride.

Crieff Angling Club. G Smith, Leesthorpe, Barrell Square, Crieff, Perthshire. Earn. Tickets.

Cumbrae Angling Club. I Hamilton, CA, 11 Carrick Crescent, Giffnock, Glasgow.

Cumnock and District Angling Association. D Stevenson, 57 Avisyard Avenue, Craigens, Cumnoch, Ayrshire. Lugar. Tickets.

Cupar Angling Club. R L Duncan, "Hame", 3 Hill Street, Cupar, Fife.

Cupar, St Andrews and District Sea Angling Club. P Hannigan, Brighton Place, South Union Street, Cupar, Fife.

Dalbeattie Angling Association. G D Bomphray, 7 Urr Road, Dalbeattie DG5 4DH.

Dalmellington Angling Club. J Coughtree, 40 Ness Glen Road, Dalmellington, Strathclyde.

Dairy Angling Association. James Shaw, "Craigie Lea", Dalry, Kirkcudbrightshire.

Dalry Garnock Angling Club. J S Martin, 146 St Margaret's Avenue, Dalry, Ayrshire. Garnock. Tickets.

Dalrymple Angling Club. W A Crosbie, 30 Barbieston Road, Dalrymple. Ayrshire.

Devon Angling Association. D M Beveridge, 5 Dirleton Gardens, Alloa, Clackmannanshire, Devon. Tickets.

Dingwall and District Angling Club. R G Donaldson, 8 Henderson Crescent, Conon Bridge, Ross and Cromarty. Conon and loch. Tickets.

Dornoch and District Angling Association. W A MacDonald, Castle Street, Dornoch, Sutherland. Sea trout and brown trout. Tickets.

Dreghorn Angling Club. Dr D D Muir, 6 Pladda Avenue, Broomlands, Irvine, Strathclyde. Irvine and Annick. Tickets.

Drongan Youth Group Angling Club. M Harvey, 19 Lane Crescent, Drongan. River Coyle; permits.

Drumgrange and Keirs Angling Club. Samuel Taylor, 27 Reicawr Avenue, Dalmellington, Ayrshire. Doon. Members only.

Dumfries and Galloway Angling Association. D G Conchie, Curriestanes Lane, Dalbeattie Road, Dumfries. Nith. Cairn. Tickets.

Dundee Angling Club. A S Nicoll, PO Box 84, 51 Meadowside, Dundee DD1 9PQ.

Dundee and District Sea Angling Club. D P Wilson, 118 Ellengowan Drive.

Dundee West End Angling Club. J Greig Sibbald, 8 Hillcrest Road, Dundee, Angus.

Dunfermline Angling Club. N G Smith, 34 Queen Anne Street, Dunfermline, Fife.

Dunfermline Artisan Angling Club. W Beveridge, 59 Maitland Street, Dunfermline, Fife. Trout reservoirs. Tickets.

Dunoon and District Angling Club. J Neilson, West Cottage, Strone, By Dunoon, Argyll.

Earlston Angling Association. W W Lothian, The Bungalow, Westfield Street, Earlston, Berwickshire. Tweed. Tickets.

East Lothian Angling Association. J. Crombie, 10 St Lawrence, Haddington, East Lothian.

Eckford Angling Association. R B Anderson, WS, Royal Bank Buildings, Jedburgh, Roxburghshire. Teviot, Loch. Tickets.

Eden Angling Association. J Fyffe, 67 Braehead, Cupar, Fife. Eden. Tickets.

Edinburgh Amateur Angling Club. C Turcan, CA, 64 Queen Street, Edinburgh.

Edinburgh Saturday Angling Club. Michael McKinnell, 16 Almondbank Terrace, Edinburgh EH11 1SS. Loch Leven, Linlithgow Loch, Lake of Menteith. Members only.

Edinburgh Walton Angling Club. Malcolm W Thompson, 21 Heriot Row, Edinburgh EH3 6EN.

Elgin Angling Association. D. Mackay, 49 Bailies Drive, New Elgin, Elgin, Morayshire. Lossie. Tickets from tackleists.

Ellem Fishing Club. Jas D Lyon, Murray Street, Duns, Berwickshire.

Esk and Liddle Fisheries Association. c/o Stevenson and Johnstone's Office, Langholm, Dumfriesshire, Border Esk and Liddle. Weekly and season tickets.

Fochabers Angling Association. John Cruickshank, Hursleigh, Fochabers, Morayshire.

Forestburn Fishing Club. J Gardner, 6 Watt Avenue, Armadale, West Lothian.

Forfar Canmore Angling Club. E Mann, 44 Sheriff Park Gardens, Forfar, Angus. Dean Water. Tickets.

Forfar East End Angling Club. J Grewar, 25 John Street, Forfar, Angus.

Forres Angling Association. W Cuthbert, 11 Fleurs Crescent, Forres, Morayshire. Findhorn. Tickets.

Fort William Angling Association. A E Reece, 29 Upper Achintore, Fort William, Invernesshire. Nevis. Tickets.

Fortrose and Rosemarkie Angling Club. Mrs P M Wilson, 5 Ness House, Ness Road, Fortrose, Ross.

Fyvie Angling Association. G A Joss, Bank House, Fyvie, Aberdeenshire.

Gairloch Angling Association. F Kelsey, Whindley, Achtercairn Gairloch.

Gairloch Sea Angling Club. I Cox, 23 South Erradale Gairloch.

Gala Angling Association. G L Watson, Plumtree Place, Galashiels, Selkirkshire. Tweed. Gala Water. Tickets.

Galston Angling Club. J Nisbet, 26 Orchard Street, Galston, Ayrshire, Irvine. Tickets.

Garpin Angling Club. A Mackay, 6 Lady-land Road, Maybole, Ayrshire. Girvan. Tickets.

Gatehouse and Kirkcudbright Angling Association. Mr Lamont, Royal Bank of Scotland, Kirkcudbright, Dumfries and Galloway.

Glasgow Academical Angling Club. J B Elder, Abbotsford, Loch Road, Miln-gavie, nr Glasgow G62 8BB.

Glenburn Angling Club. W Melvin, 53 Underwood Road, Paisley. Glenburn Reservoir.

Glen Garry Fishing Club. Capt E F Grey, Garry Gaulach, Invergarry, Inverness-shire. Loch Garry. Tickets.

Golspie Angling Club. John M Baddon, Fairburn, Golspie. Salmon and trout fishing. Permits.

Greenlaw Angling Association. A Lamb, Waterford, Wester Row, Greenlaw, Berwickshire. Blackadder. Tickets.

Greenock and District Angling Club. B Peterson, 22 Murdieston Street, Greenock PA15 4DS. Loch Thom. Tickets.

Gretna Angling Association. W G Graham, 126 Currock Park Avenue, Carlisle, Cumberland. Kirtle and Sark. Tickets.

Harris Angling Club. Hon Sec, Harris Angling Club, Isle of Harris.

Hawick Angling Club. R Johnston, Kelvin, Raeson Park, Hawick, Roxburghshire. 100m of rivers. Tickets.

Helensburgh Angling Club. A Nicol, "Hill-view", 36 Ardencaple Drive, Helens-burgh, Dunbartonshire. No tickets.

Hurlford Angling Club. J Miller, 25 Knowehead Road, Hurlford, Ayrshire. Irvine. Tickets.

Inverness Angling Club. J Fraser, 33 Hawthorn Drive, Inverness, Ness. Tickets.

Inverurie Angling Association. J E Duncan, 6 West High Street, Inverurie, Aber-deenshire.

Irvine and District Angling Club. R Gil-mour, 58 Muir Drive, Irvine, Ayrshire. Irvine. Tickets.

Irvine Angling Improvement Association. Wm H Caldow, 26 Drumleyhill Drive, Hurlford, Ayrshire.

Jedforest Angling Association. A Whitecross, 42 Howden Road, Jed-burgh, Roxburghshire. Teviot and Jed. Tickets.

Kelso Angling Association. C Hutchison, 53 Abbotseat, Kelso Roxburghshire. Tweed and Teviot. Tickets.

Kelvinside Academical Angling Club. F G Seligman, "Eastwood", Kilcreggan, Dunbartonshire.

Kilbirnie Angling Club. I Johnstone, 95 Dalry Road, Kilbirnie, Ayrshire. River, loch. Tickets.

Killin Breadalbane Angling Club. W Allan, Main Street, Killin, Perthshire.

Kilmarnock Angling Club. T Morrison, 39 Tinto Avenue, Kilmarnock, Ayrshire.

Kilmaurs Angling Club. J Watson, 7 Four Acres Drive, Kilmaurs, Ayrshire. Annick and Glaisart. Tickets.

Kilsyth Fish Protection Association. S Gil-lies, 24 Kingston Flats, Kilsyth, Stirling-shire. Garrel Burn, reservoirs. Tickets.

Kilwinning Eglinton Angling Club. M Tudhope, 15 Viaduct Circle, Kilwinning, Ayrshire. Garnock. Tickets.

Kincordie Fly-Fishing Club. J Miller, 15 Bright Street, Lochee, Dundee.

Kinross-shire Fishing Club. H Gardiner, 7 Sorley's Brae, Dollar, Clackmannan-shire.

Kintyre Fish Protection and Angling Club. John M B Anderson, 101 Ralston Road, Campbeltown, Argyll. Lochs. Tickets.

Kirriemuir Angling Club. H F Burness, 13 Clova Road, Kirriemuir, Angus.

Kyle of Sutherland Angling Association. R L Henderson, East End, Bonar Bridge. Tickets for Kyle.

Kyles of Bute Angling Club. A Morrison, Menteith, Kames, Tighnabruaich, Argyll.

Ladykirk and Norham Angling Improve-ment Association. R G Wharton, 8 St Cuthberts Square, Norham-on-Tweed, Northumberland. Tweed. Tickets.

Lairg Angling Club. J M Ross, Post Office House, Lairg, Sutherland.

Lamington and District Angling Improve-ment Association. P D McAndrew, Old Station House, Symington, Biggar, Lanarkshire. Clyde. Tickets.

Lanark and District Angling Club M A Murrie, 11 Castlebank Gardens, Lanark, Lanarkshire. Clyde. Tickets.

Larbert and Stenhousemuir Angling Club. A McArthur, Lynwood, Bellsdyke Road, North Broomage, Larbert, Stir-lingshire. Loch Coulter. Tickets.

Largs Angling Club. J D Dobie, 116 Alex-ander Avenue, Largs, Ayrshire.

Lauderdale Angling Association. D M Milligan, 29 Hillside Terrace, Selkirk. Lauder, Berwickshire. Leader Water. Tickets.

Laurencekirk and District Angling Association. A Fyfe, 113 High Street, Laurencekirk, Kincardineshire.

Lerwick and Bressay Sea Angling Club. E Lockwood, 26 Russell Crescent, Lerwick, Shetland.

Leith Fly-Fishing Association. W K Moncur, Royal Bank of Scotland, Bernard Street, Leith, Edinburgh EH6 6SN.

Loanhead and District Angling Club. John Thompson, 19 McKinlay Terrace, Loanhead, Midlothian.

Loch Achonachie Angling Club. D MacRitchie, Scarasdal, Park Road, Strathpeffer, Ross-shire. Upper Conon, Upper Blackwater, Loch, Achonachie and Meig. Tickets.

Loch Brora Angling Club. Rob Wilson (Rods and Guns) Brora, Sutherland.

Loch Finlas Fishing Club. W A McMillan, 27 Miller Road, Ayr KA7 2 BJ.

Lochgilphead and District Angling Club. D McDougal, 23 High Bank Park, Lochgilphead, Argyll. Lochs. Tickets.

Loch Leven Fisheries. Sir David Montgomery, Kinross Estates Office, Kinross. Tickets for Loch Leven.

Loch Lomond Angling Improvement Association. Messrs Harvey and Lumsden, 86 St Vincent Street, Glasgow G2 5UD. Loch Lomond, Rivers Leven, Fruin, Endrick, Gareloch. Waiting list.

Lochryan Sea Angling Club. J Patterson, 1 Main Street, Cairnryan, Stranraer, Wigtown.

Lossiemouth Angling Association. T B Clark, Dunconusg, Stotfield, Lossiemouth, Moray. Lossie (tidal). Tickets.

Mauchline "Ballochmyle" Angling Club. Robert Anderson, 85 Mary Morrison Drive, Mauchline, Ayrshire. Ayr. Tickets.

Maybole Angling Club. James Harper, 54 Kirkoswald Road, Maybole, Ayrshire. Girvan. No Tickets.

Melrose and District Angling Association. J Broomfield, "Ravensbourne", Douglas Road, Melrose, Roxburghshire. Tweed. Tickets.

Midland Counties Anglers Protection Association. J Neilly, 2 Cornish Street, Coatbridge, Lanarks. Balvaig. Tickets.

Midlothian Angling Association. S H G Glennon, 32 Glendevon Road, Edinburgh.

Mid-Nithsdale Angling Association. R W Coltart, Thornhill, Dumfries. Nith. Tickets.

Montrose Angling Club. G S Taylor, Braes, Russell Street, Montrose, Angus.

Muirkirk Angling Association. W Cooke, 3 Stoneyhill Avenue, Muirkirk, Ayrshire. Ayr. Tickets.

Nairn Angling Association. Mrs W R Mackay, 36 Mill Road, Nairn. Nairn. Tickets.

Ness Glen Fishing Club. J Semple, 160 Merrick Drive, Dalmellington, Ayrshire.

New Abbey Angling Association. A C Johnstone, Post Office, New Abbey, Dumfriesshire. Trout Stream. Tickets.

New Cummock Anglers' Association. Allan Lockhart, 79 Dalhanna Drive, New Cummock, Ayrshire. Nith. Tickets.

New Galloway Angling Association. J Freeman, Garplefoot, Dalry, Kirkcudbrightshire. Dee. Tickets.

Newburgh Angling Club. A F Buchan, Ythanbank, Knockhall Road, Newburgh, Ellon, Aberdeen AB4 0BL.

Newmilns and Greenholm Angling Club. H Smith, 3 Loudoun Road West, Newmilns, Ayrshire. Irvine. Tickets.

Newton Stewart Angling Association. R W McDowall, 9 Victoria Street, Newton Stewart, Wigtownshire. Cree. Tickets.

North Berwick Angling Club. George B Woodburn, 29 Craigleith Avenue, North Berwick, East Lothian. Trout Lake. Members only.

North Uist Angling Club. David Cockburn, Dunrossil Place, Lochmaddy, North Uist.

Oban Sea Angling Club. E Finyland, Great Western Hotel, Oban.

Ochiltree Angling Association. John Brown, 38 Brown Crescent, Ochiltree, Ayrshire. Lugar. Tickets.

Orkney Islands Sea Angling Association. A J B Scholes, 32 Dundas Crescent, Kirkwall, Orkney.

Orkney Trout Fishing Association. R Windwick, 36 Quoybanks Crescent, Kirkwall, Orkney. Tickets.

Paisley and District Angling Club. E Semple, 7 Maree Road, Foxbar, Paisley. No water.

Peeblesshire Trout Fishing Association. D G Fyfe, 39 High Street, Peebles, Peeblesshire. Tweed and Lyne Water. Tickets.

Peeblesshire Salmon Fishing Association. D G Fyfe, 39 High Street, Peebles, Peeblesshire. Tweed. Tickets.

Penwapple Angling Club. W R Jardine-Downie, 1 Church Square, Girvan, Ayrshire. Loch. Tickets.

Perth and District Anglers' Association. R M Black, 1 Schoonieburn Hill, Friarton, Perth.

Perth Anglers' Club. R R Thom, 10 Blackfriars Street, Perth.

Phoenix Angling Club. D A Biggart, CA, 307 West George Street, Glasgow G2 4LB.

Pitlochry Angling Club. R Harriman, Sunnyknowe, Nursing Home Brae, Pitlochry, Perthshire. Tummel. Tickets.

Port Glasgow Angling Club. J Tucker, 39 Marloch Avenue, Port Glasgow. Lower Loch Gryffe, Harelaw, Mill Dams, Knocknair. Tickets.

Portree Angling Association. Hon Sec. Portree, Isle of Skye. River Staffa and lochs. Tickets.

Prestwick Angling Club. A Sim (solicitor), National Bank Buildings, 41 Main Street, Prestwick, Ayrshire. Reservoir. Tickets.

Prestwick Sea Angling Club. W R Phillips, 48 Underwood, Kilwinning, Ayrshire.

Rannoch Angling Club. J Brown, The Garage, The Square, Kinloch Rannoch, Perthshire, PH16 5PQ.

Renfrewshire Angling Improvement Association. H Young, 41 Glentyan Avenue, Kilbarchan, Renfrewshire.

River Lochy Association. General Sir William Morgan, 5 Wellington Square, London SW3. Fishing on Lochy.

Rowbank Angling Club. J E Corson, CA, Ashtrees House, 9 Orr Square, Paisley, Renfrewshire. Reservoirs.

Roybridge Angling Club. J MacDonald, Blar-a-cha, Spean Bridge. Water on Roy.

St Andrew's Angling Club. P F Malcolm, 54 St Nicholas Street. St Andrews, Fife. Reservoir. Tickets.

St Boswells and Newtown and District Angling Association. R Black, Kilgraden, St Boswells, Roxburghshire. Tweed. Tickets.

St Fillans' and Loch Earn Angling Association. J McPherson, Rannoch, 4 Earnview, St Fillans, Perthshire. Loch and River Earn. Tickets.

St Mary's Angling Club. J Miller, 6 Greenbank Loan, Edinburgh 9. Loch. Tickets.

St Mirin Angling Club. W Provan, 1D Calside Court, Paisley, Renfrewshire.

St Winnoch Angling Club. J Eadie, 19 Glenpark Road, Lochwinnoch, Renfrewshire. Castle Semple Loch. River Calder. Tickets.

Saltcoats Sea Angling Association. S Dean, 20 Lindsay Avenue, Saltcoats, Ayrshire.

Scourie Angling Club. Hector Mackay, 5 Park Terrace, Scourie, Sutherland.

Selkirk and District Angling Association. A Murray, 40 Raeburn Meadow, Selkirk, Yarrow and Ettrick. Tickets.

Shetland Anglers' Association. Andrew Miller, 3 Gladstone Terrace, Lerwick, Shetland. Lochs. Tickets.

Shetland Association of Sea Anglers. M S Mullay, Market Cross, Lerwick, Shetland.

Slammanan Angling and Protective Association. W Collins, 6 Queens Drive, California, Stirlingshire. No Tickets; waiting list for membership.

Sorn Angling Club. John Quinn, 11 Firpark, Sorn, Ayrshire. Ayr. Tickets.

South Uist Angling Club. R T Sutton, 13 Liniclate, Benbecula, South Uist. Lochs. Tickets.

Southwick Angling Association. J Thomson, Mainsmill, Southwick, Dumfries. Southwick Water. Tickets.

Soval Angling Association. E Young, 1 Goathill Crescent, Stornoway. Isle of Lewis.

Stewarton Angling Club. D M Mechen, 15 Rigg Street, Stewarton, Ayrshire. Annick. Tickets.

Stonehaven and District Angling Association. Hon Sec, 19 East Glebe, Stonehaven AB3 2HW. Cowie, Carron. Tickets.

Stonehaven Sea Angling Association. J B Robertson, Solicitor and Town Clerk, Cameron Street, Stonehaven.

Stornoway Angling Association. Robt G Morrison, 37 Keith Street, Stornoway, Isle of Lewis.

Stornoway Sea Angling Association. Roderick Macleod, 11 Battery Park Road, Stornoway, Isle of Lewis.

Straiton Angling Association. R P Rae, The Cottages, Straiton, Ayrshire, Girvan. Limited tickets.

Stranraer and District Angling Association. John A Cairney, 8 Oakland Avenue, Stranraer, Wigtownshire. River and lochs. Tickets.

Strathgryfe Angling Association. F Sinclair, Dunedin, Port Glasgow Road, Kilmacolm, Renfrewshire. Gryfe. Tickets.

Strathmore Angling Improvement Association. Mrs Dewar, Airlie Cottage, Victoria Place, Monikie, Angus.

Strathpeffer Angling Club. W Brown, 1 Park Terrace, Strathpeffer, Ross.

Strathspey Angling Improvement Association. G G Mortimer, 81 High Street, Grantown-on-Spey, Moray. Spey. Tickets.

Thistle Angling Club. John Robertson, Public Library, Stirling.

Thurso Angling Association. J Robertson, of A A MacDonald, 23 Sinclair Street, Thurso, Caithness, Thurso. Tickets for visitors only.

Tongue and District Angling Association. c/o Ben Loyal Hotel, Tongue, by Lairg, Sutherland. Trout fishing. Tickets.

Townhill Angling Club. J Lightfoot, 39 Whitelaw Road, Dunfermline, Fife. Reservoir; trout; visitors may accompany members.

Turriff Angling Association. Ian Masson Sports Ltd, Main Street, Turriff, Aberdeenshire. Deveron. Tickets.

Ullapool Angling Club. E G Woodfield, 5 Seaforth Road, Ullapool, Ross and Cromarty. Ullapool River. Tickets.

Ullapool and Loch Broom Sea Angling Club. C F R Browne, 3 Castle Terrace, Ullapool IV26 2XD, will answer inquiries.

United Clyde Angling Protective Association Ltd. R C Sharp, 20 Cunningham Street, Motherwell. Clyde and tributaries, and Springfield Reservoir. Tickets.

Unst Anglers' Association. Hon Sec, Beltersound, Unst, Shetland.

Upper Annandale Angling Association. J Black, 1 Rosehill, Grange Road, Moffat, Dumfriesshire. Annan. Tickets.

Upper Nithsdale Angling Club. W Forsyth, Town Clerk's Chambers, Sanquhar, Dumfriesshire. Nith. Tickets.

Walton Angling Club. White Cart. Members only.

Waterside Angling Improvement Association. P Daly, 56 Burns Road, Harestones, Kirkintilloch, Dunbartonshire. Luggie Water. St only.

Waverley Angling Club. A J Dickson, 10 Kingsknowe Avenue, Edinburgh.

Whiteadder Angling Association. J Boyd, St Leonards, Polwarth, Greenlaw, Berwickshire, Whiteadder. Tickets.

Wick Angling Association. D Bruce, "The Sheiling", Newton Road, Wick, Caithness. Wick River. Tickets.

Wooler and Doddington Angling Association. G H Wilkinson, 3 Whitsun View, Wooler, Northumberland. Till. Tickets.

Check before you go

While every effort has been made to ensure that the information given in "Where to Fish' is correct, the position is continually changing and anglers are urged, in their own interests, to make preliminary inquiries before travelling to selected venues. This is especially important with reference to prices quoted. Inevitably, the rate of inflation is affecting stability in this quarter. Anglers' attention is also drawn to the fact that the hotels mentioned under the various fishing stations do not necessarily have water of their own. Any amendments or further data for inclusion in subsequent editions, and any criticism, will be welcome. All correspondence to the Editor.

FISHING IN NORTHERN IRELAND

Boards of Conservators, Close Seasons, etc.

FOR game fisher and coarse fisher alike, Northern Ireland is still largely undiscovered country. There is a wealth of lakes, large and small; miles of quiet unpolluted river plentifully stocked with large, healthy fish anything but well-educated to anglers and their methods. By the standards of most other parts of Britain, all of it is underfished. In recent years, coarse fishermen have begun to find out what Northern Ireland has to offer: there is as much for the game fisherman, much of it at prices so low that it can almost be described as "free". The visitor as yet unfamiliar with the country is recommended to concentrate on the waters owned and managed by the Department of Agriculture, possible the largest single fishery proprietor in the country. They include some of the very best. Where reference is made in the following text to accommodation, some of it is described as "rec" (ie "recommended"). This does not imply that "Where to Fish" has carried out an independent sampling or accepts responsibility for what is named. The addresses have been taken from the N.I. Tourist Board list of approved accommodation, which, in the case of the larger towns, may include a number of other addresses as much to be recommended. Limitations of space deny us the inclusion of all.

Statutory Bodies. The Dept of Agriculture (Fisheries Division, Hut 5, Castle Grounds, Stormont, Belfast) is the ultimate authority for fisheries in Northern Ireland.

In addition to the department, and working in co-operation with it, there are two Conservancy Authorities, The Foyle Fisheries Commission; and The Fisheries Conservation Board for Northern Ireland. They operate in separate areas.

The Foyle Fisheries Commission (8 Victoria Road, Londonderry, Tel: 42100) acts as conservator and issues rod licences in the Foyle area: i.e. the North-Western parts of the country drained by the Foyle/Mourne/Camowen river systems and the rivers Faughan and Roe. The Foyle Fisheries Commission is controlled jointly by the Governments of Northern Ireland and The Republic of Ireland, including in the total area the former Neville District in the Republic and the former Londonderry District in N.I.

The Fisheries Conservancy Board for Northern Ireland (21 Church Street, Portadown, Co Armagh, Tel: Portadown 32276 and 34666). This board acts as conservator and issues licences for the remainder of the country.

The Northern Ireland Tourist Board (River House, 48 High Street, Belfast BT1 2DS, Tel: 0232 31221) is also involved in angling, concerning itself with development and promotion. It issues literature on travel and accommodation; also angling guides.

Under the provisions of The Fisheries Act (N.I.) 1966, **The Fisheries Conservancy Board** and **The Foyle Fisheries Commission** co-operate with the **Dept of Agriculture** in the development and improvement of fisheries. As a result, there has been in recent years a dramatic improvement in the quantity and quality of angling, game and coarse, available to visitors. The department's Drainage Division is also actively engaged in the improvement of fisheries in watercourses under its control. Works include the construction of fishery weirs, groynes and deflectors; restoration of gravel, landscaping of altered watercourses and comprehensive schemes of tree-planting.

Rod Licences. With the following exceptions, anglers are required to take out a rod licence. 1. Anglers under 16 years of age fishing exclusively for coarse fish are not required to take out a licence in the Conservancy Board area. 2. Rod licences do not have to be taken out in the Foyle area by *any* angler fishing exclusively for coarse fish. Rod licences are issued by The Foyle Fisheries Commission and The Fisheries Conservancy Board in their respective areas. The holder of a licence in one area *may obtain on payment an endorsement to cover the other area.* (Charge included in the details below).

A Game Fishing Rod Licence in The Fisheries Conservancy Board area is valid for both game and coarse fishing, *but a coarse fishing rod licence is valid for coarse fishing only on designated coarse fishing waters.* A list of these is obtainable from the Board. Licences may be obtained directly from the Authorities, or from tackle dealers.

Charges. Foyle Fisheries Commission. S, MT, NT; s £5, ft £2.50 s (juv) £2.50. FF; no licence required.
Endorsement to Fisheries Conservancy Board annual game-fish licence £3.50.
Fisheries Conservancy Board. S, MT, NT; s £7.75, ft £5.25, FF, s £3, ft £2. Endorsement to Foyle Fisheries Commission annual game-fish licence £6.25.

Seasons. There are no statutory close seasons for coarse fish in Northern Ireland, nor for rainbow trout in designated rainbow trout waters in the **Conservancy Board** area. (List of such waters from Board and displayed by licence-sellers.)
For salmon, sea trout and brown trout, the OPEN seasons are: **Foyle area;** rivers: April 1 to Oct 20: lakes: March 1 to Oct 20. **FCB area: Lough Melvin:** Feb 1 to Sept 30. **Lough Erne system and Bush:** March 1 to Sept 30. **Other waters,** in general, March 1 to Oct 31, but late openings and early closings introduced on some stocked trout lakes.

Dept of Agriculture permits; *separate from and in addition to licences.* For Dept of Agriculture fisheries, of which there are more than 60 throughout the country. Charges. (All exclusive of VAT.) St (game) £13.60. St (game) juv £2. Ft (game) £5. Dt (game) £1.80. St (game, one water only) £8.60. St (coarse) £3. NB: "Ft" = 15-days. "Juv" = under 16 yrs of age. **R Bush,** *Special Stretch*, for holders of Dept's season or 15-day permit, March 1 to June 30: £6. July 1 to Sept 30: £13. For other members of the public, March 1 to June 30: £9. July 1 to Sept 30: £16. **R Bush,** *Restricted Stretch,* for holders of Dept's season or 15-day permit, March 1 to June 30: £2.40. July 1 to Sept 30: £4.80. For other members of the public, March 1 to June 30: £3.60. July 1 to Sept 30: £7.20. **R Shimna,** for holders of the Dept's season or 15-day permit (game) March 1 to July 31: 60p. pd Aug 1 to Oct 31: £4.20. Other members of the public, March 1 to July 31: £1.20 pd Aug 1 to Oct 31: £7.20.

FISHING STATIONS IN NORTHERN IRELAND

A S in other sections, principal catchment areas are dealt with in alphabetical order and details of close seasons, licences, etc. will be found on preceding page. Anglers wanting further details of accommodation, etc, should write to the Northern Ireland Tourist Board, River House, 48 High Street, Belfast, BT1 2DS, or 11 Berkeley Street, London (01-493 0601).

BANN (Lower)

(For close seasons, licences, see p 354 and 355)

A mainly slugglish river running approx 30m from where it leaves Lough Neagh to where it enters the sea below Coleraine. Good coarse fish population; sea trout fishing in the tideway. Salmon stretches in private hands and not usually available to visitors.

Coleraine (Co Derry). River tidal below Cutts. Sea trout permits from Coleraine AA. Good coarse fishing above tidal stretches. Hotels: Lodge; Bohill Auto Inn; Gorteen.

Kilrea (Co Derry). Pike and perch in local canals and loughs. Permits for **R Agivey** (small brown trout, late salmon and dolaghan) from Hon Irish Society, 8 Shipquay St, Londonderry.

Portglenone (Co Antrim). **Claudy River** joins Bann below town. Brown trout, late salmon and dolaghan. Permits from Clady & Dis AC. Rec accommodation: Bannside Farmhouse, 268 Gortgole Road.

Toomebridge (Co Antrim). Here, the Lower Bann leaves L Neagh. Lough Neagh, with an area of 153 sq miles, is the largest sheet of inland water in the British Isles. It supports an immense commercial eel fishery, but apart from that, its potential is as yet largely untapped. The bottom-feeding habits of the Lough Neagh trout and the exposed conditions on this enormous stretch of water have so far discouraged anglers from trying to exploit it. A principal problem is the absence of sheltered bays.

BANN (Upper)

Flows west and north from its source in the Mourne Mountains to enter Lough Neagh near the middle of its southern shore at a point north of Portadown.

Portadown (Co Armagh). For several miles above and below the town the river is sluggish, offering only coarse fishing. Rec accommodation Rockeden Guest House, Watson Street; Viewpoint Lodge, Markethill Road.

Hilltown (Co Down). From here for 20m downstream the river offers good trout fishing. Gilford AC, Banbridge AC, and Rathfriland & Dist AC all have water. Good trout fishing also in **Cusher,** for first three miles from confluence. Dept of Ag have four good trout lakes, totalling more than 350 acres in the area. Banbridge AC has 76 acre **Corbet Lake** (brown trout) dt £2.50. Dt £1.25 for other waters. **Lough Shark** (pike, perch and bream) free to licence-holders. Tackleist: J Coburn, 32 Scarva Street, Banbridge; J Edgar, 5 Market Street, Portadown. Hotel: Downshire Arms Inn; The Country Club Inn, (Craigavon); Ashmount Boarding House, (Rathfriland).

BLACKWATER

The largest of the rivers flowing into L Neagh, rising in S Tyrone to enter the lough at its SW corner. Coarse fish and trout.

Blackwatertown (Co Armagh). From here to its mouth, the river is mainly a coarse fishery.

Benburb (Co Armagh). Trout for 2½m downstream. Armagh & Dist AC leases or owns stretch on river, and seven

lakes. Dt for river and **Shaw's Lake** (brown and rainbow trout) £2, from tackleist: W R Johnson, 71 English St, Armagh. Rec accommodation: Salmon Leap View, Carrickaness Mills.
Clogher-Augher-Aughacloy. Trout fishing down to Caledon. Permits from Aughnacloy AC, Clogher/Augher AC, Augher Dist & Upper Blackwater AC and landowners. Permission from landowners for tributaries. **Callan, Oona** and **Torrent.** Dept of Ag has six trout lakes in the area totalling approx 250 acres of fishing. Rec accommodation: Hillview, 52 Favour Royal Road, Aughacloy.

SMALLER RIVERS EMPTYING INTO LOUGH NEAGH

MAINE: Flows 25m from source in Garryford Bogs to enter lough south of Randalstown, Co Antrim. With tribs **Kellswater, Braid** and **Clogh** provides good fishing for salmon, trout and dolaghan. Permits from Randalstown AC, Gracehill, Galform & Dist AC and Whitewell AC. Also from some landowners. Dept of Ag has two trout reservoirs in the area. Killylane and Dungonnell. Tackleist: J Matthews, 72 Ballymoney Street, Ballymena; who issues dt (50p–£1) for various club-waters in the area. Hotels: Adair Arms; Leighinmore House and Tullyglass House, Ballymena.
SIXMILEWATER: Flows 15m from Ballyclare to enter lough at Antrim, at its NE corner. A heavily-fished but highly productive trout water. Antrim & Dist AC issues permits for water below town; landowners for upper reaches. Hotel: Halls, High Street.

CRUMLIN AND GLENAVY: small rivers which flow west through these villages to enter lough. Trout fishing near their mouths. Centre: Crumlin. Rec accommodation: Hillvale, 11 Largy Road; Ashmore Farm, Fourscore, 31 Garlandstown Road.
BALLINDERRY: Flows east for approx 30m, through Cookstown, to enter lough about midway along W shore. Good fishing for brown trout and dolaghan for 20m up from the mouth. Permission from Cookstown AC and landowners. Hotel: Glenavon House, Cookstown.
MOYOLA: Flows east and south for 20m from its source in S Derry to enter lough at NW corner. Some brown trout in lower reaches and a reasonably good run of salmon from July. Permission from landowners. Centre: Castledawson. Rec accommodation: Moyola Lodge Guest House.

BUSH

(For close seasons, licences, see p 354 and 355)

The Bush flows 30m west and north through Bushmills, Co Antrim, to enter the sea near Portballintrae. The fishing rights of the entire catchment (except the stretch from the sea to Bushmills) have been acquired by the Dept of Agriculture primarily as an experimental river for studies into the biology and management of salmon. Within the terms of this programme, salmon angling is maintained at the highest possible level. Trout in the Bush and its tributaries are small but plentiful: there is a modest run of spring salmon and a grilse run for which the river is best-known which begins in June or July, according to flow.

For angling management, the river is divided into three sections: the *Special Stretch* about 200 yds downstream of the Project Centre at Bushmills; the *Restricted Stretch* upstream (approx 400 yds of water) and the *Unrestricted Stretch*, the remaining 24m of fishing water. Special daily permits, bookable in advance, are required for the Special and Restricted stretches, as shown under "Licences, permits and close seasons." The Dervock tributary, flowing through the village of that name, offers 2m of good trout fishing. Centre: Bushmills. Rec accommodation: Montalto Guest House; Cliff Cottage, 194 Causeway Road and six other farm and country houses. *For details of permit-charges, see p 355.*

LOUGH ERNE (Upper and Lower)

(For close seasons, licences, see p 354 and 355)

Upper and Lower Lough Erne, with the R Erne and tributaries feeding the loughs, comprise 37,800 acres of mixed game and coarse fishing owned by the Dept of Agriculture. The flow is in a NW direction, through the beautiful and largely unspoilt Fermanagh countryside, via Belleek, to where the R Erne reaches the sea at Ballyshannon. Infinitely varied fishing in the lakes, with innumerable secluded bays, inlets and small islands. Rich, unpolluted waters teeming with fish-life, the Erne system is truly an angler's paradise. Centres: Belleek; Kesh; Enniskillen; Bellanaleck; Lisnaskea; Newtown Butler.

BELLEEK (Co Fermanagh). River heavily populated with large bream and roach, pike of record-breaking proportions. A good centre for fishing Lower Lough. Hotel: Carlton *(advt p 359)*.

LOWER LOUGH ERNE. The trout fishing areas, in which the fish may run very large, are in the north and west of the lake. South and east of a dividing-line, the lake may be fished on coarse fishing licence and permit only.

TRIBUTARIES FEEDING LOWER LOUGH: The **Ballinamallard River** flows south through the village to enter the lake near St Angelo Airport. Coarse and game fishing by Dept of Ag permit and permission of landowners. **Colebrook** and **Tempo** enter lake from the West. Coarse fish in lower reaches; trout in upper. Permission from landowners.

UPPER LOUGH ERNE. Principally coarse fish. Centres: Lisnaskea; Bellanaleck; Newtown Butler; Enniskillen. Tackleist: Lakeland Tackle. Hotels: Killyhevlin; Manor House; Railway; all Enniskillen, and many guest houses etc. Lakeland at Bellanaleck *(advt p 380)*; and Ortine, Lisnaskea.

TRIBUTARIES FEEDING UPPER LOUGH ERNE: Swalinbar River flows north from Co Cavan to enter the lough midway on the S side. Coarse fish in lower reaches, trout in upper. Permission from landowners. The **Arney** flows from **Upper and Lower Loughs McNean** (large trout and exceptional pike fishing) to enter Upper L Erne near Bellanaleck. Dept of Ag mixed fishery from Drumane to Arney Old Bridge, Then good mixed fishing all the way to **Lough McNean.** Also ten Dept trout lakes of various sizes in the area. (5 acres to 100 acres).

FOYLE

(For close seasons, licences, see p 354 and 355)

The Foyle system is half in Northern Ireland, half in the Republic. It is formed by the **Derg** (draining **Lough Derg**) and the **Strule,** constituting the **Mourne,** which unites with the **Finn** at Strabane to become the **Foyle proper,** which enters the sea at Londonderry. That part of the system in Northern Ireland, including the **Faughan** and **Roe,** is the largest salmon and trout fishery in the country. It drains the north and west slopes of the Sperrin Mountains and most of Co Tyrone.

Londonderry. River tidal here, with fishing for salmon in tidal pools from July. Also a run of sea trout. Permits from Foyle Commission. Tackleist: Fitzpatrick Sports & Tackle, 145 Spencer Road, Waterside. Hotels: Everglades, Broomhill House.

Strabane. Here **Mourne** and **Strule** unite to form Foyle. Salmon and sea trout. Permits from Foyle Commission. Dept of Ag has five lakes in the area. Tacklist: R Cunningham, 10 Bridge Street. Rec accommodation: Glebe House, Bready; Glentimon Lodge, Sion Mills.

Tributaries of the Foyle

MOURNE: Excellent fishing in the 10m between Strabane and Newtownstewart, but largely private and unavailable to visitors. At Sion Mills, Dept of Ag has stretch and some farmers give permission. Brown trout; salmon and sea trout

from June/July. At Newtownstewart, the **Owenkillow** and **Glenelly** enter, offering 30m of ideal game fishing waters noted for their sea trout. Permission from Omagh AA and landowners. Some stretches of **Owenkillow** available on lease. Hotels: New Country Inn, Newtownstewart; Royal Arms; Silver Birch; Knock-Na-Moe; Omagh.

STRULE: Very good trout fishing from Omagh to Newtownstewart. Dept of Ag water at Victoria Bridge, otherwise permission from Omagh AA. More good fishing upstream of Omagh, to Camowen, but fish smaller. Salmon in season. **Owenragh, Quiggery/Fintona** and **Drumragh** enter near Omagh. More good trout fishing by leave of Omagh AA and landowners. Hotels: see above, under **Mourne**.

FAIRYWATER: Flows E from Drumquin (trout) to enter **Strule** below Omagh. Remarkably good roach fishing in lower reaches. Small brown trout and salmon in season in **Burndennett.** Permission for this and Fairywater from landowners.

DERG: flows E from Donegal for 50m to enter **Mourne** N of Newtownstewart. Good trout water for 15m to above Casteldery, Co Tyrone. Permission from Castlederg AA, Mournebeg & Derg AA.

FAUGHAN and ROE

The Faughan flows N for 20m to enter the Foyle area E of Londonderry city; the Roe flows the same distance in the same general direction to enter the Foyle Estuary N of Limavady, Co Londonderry. Salmon, sea trout and brown trout in Faughan; principally sea trout in Roe, but also salmon from July.

FAUGHAN: Good fishing for 15m from Londonderry up to Clady on ticket issued by Londonderry & Dist AA.

ROE: Good fishing for 15m from Limavady to Dungiven. Permission Roe AA. Dept of Ag has short stretch at O'Cahan's Rock, S of town. Tackleist: F J Mullen, 31 Main St, Limavady, who displays map of all local fishings and issues permits. Rec accommodation: "Knudsen", 71 Killane Road; "Shalimar", Ballykelly; and others, Limavady; Mount Prospect, 59 Magheramore Road, Dungiven.

GLENS OF ANTRIM RIVERS

(For close seasons, licences, see p 354 and 355)

GLENARM: Short privately-owned spate river. Salmon and sea trout. No permits.
GLENARIFF: Small sea trout river which flows into Red Bay at Glenariff. Permission from Glens AC. Guest House: Glenariff Inn, Waterfoot.
DUNN: enters sea at Cushendun. Fair run of late salmon and sea trout. Permission from Glens AC.
MARGEY/CAREY/GLENSHESK: a system of small rivers entering the sea at Ballycastle. Sea trout and salmon. Dept of Ag waters. Hotels. Antrim Arms, Rathlin Arms, Ballycastle; Bay Hotel, Cushendun. Tackleist: R Bell, 40 Ann St, Ballycastle.

LAGAN

(For close seasons, licences, see p 354 and 355)

A productive river which flows into the **Belfast Lough.** Trout fishing upstream from Magheralin, Co Down, for 12m. Permission from Iveagh AC and Dromore AC. Twelve Dept of Agriculture brown and/or rainbow trout lakes, totalling more than 700 acres, in the Lagan Valley area. Near to Belfast, these waters are fished more heavily than most in N Ireland. Abundant coarse fishing on canals and loughs. Tackleist: Lisburn Sports, 9 Smithfield Square, Lisburn.

LOUGH MELVIN

(For close seasons, licences, see p 354 and 355)

A 5,000 acre natural lake, approximately one fifth of which lies in Northern Ireland, (Co Fermanagh). A good spring run of salmon starts in February and a grilse run in June, but the lake is famous chiefly for the variety of its native brown trout. In addition to fish of orthodox appearance, there are dark "sonaghan" caught over the deeper water and the yellow-bellied "gillaroo", found in the shallows near the shore. Regarded as the Dept of Agriculture's best all-round fishery. Garrison is the centre for fishing the lough and **Lough McNean,** Upper and Lower, also in the vicinity. (Pike, large trout, general coarse fishing.) Rec accommodation: Lake House, Garrison; "Gormnish", Knockarevan. Small trout in L **Lattone** pronounced "Latoon") may be caught from the roadside between Belcoo and Garrison.

NEWRY RIVER

(For close seasons, licences, see p 354 and 355)

A small system flowing into the head of **Carlingford Lough** at **Newry, Co Down.** 3m of fair brown trout water above Carnbane Industrial Estate. Permission from Newry & Dist AC and landowners. Club also issues dt (£2) for **Guinan Lake,** stocked with brown and rainbow trout. Good coarse fishing in **Newry Ship Canal,** free to licence-holders. Hotel: Ardmore. Two Dept of Agriculture trout lakes in area: Brickland and Glassdrumman. Tackleist: J C Smith, 5 Kildare Street, Newry.

QUOILE

(For close seasons, licences, see p 354 and 355)

Flows into top of **Strangford Lough** at **Downpatrick.** Coarse fish and some trout in lower reaches; fair trout waters between Annacloy Bridge and Kilmore. Permits from landowners, Dept of Agriculture. Downpatrick & Dist AA, have good trout lakes in the area, but tickets for members' friends only. Guest House: Denvir's, 14/16 English Street.

SHIMNA

(For close seasons, licences, see p 354 and 355)

Small attractive river with deep rocky pools flowing from E slope of Mournes to enter sea at **Newcaslte, Co Down.** Sea trout and salmon from July. Dept of Agriculture fishery in forest areas, Shimna AC in lower reaches. Hotels: Slieve Donard; Enniskeen. Tackleist: J Mackie, Main Street, Newcaslte.

WHITEWATER

(For close seasons, licences, see p 354 and 355)

Small attractive sea trout water flowing into sea W of Kilkeel, Co Down,. 3m of good fishing. Permission; landowners. Hotel: Kilmorey Arms.

BELFAST, not mentioned specifically in connection with any river system, is a good centre for much of the fishing in the east of Northern Ireland. It is plentifully supplied with hotels and tackle shops. Tackleists: J Braddell, 9 North Street; K Rankin, 131 Royal Avenue; Rod & Wheel, 25 Gresham Street. Hotels: Regency Hotel (NI) Ltd; Camera Guest House; Somerton Guest House; Forest Park House; East-Sheen; Salisbury Court; Erne Court and many others.

SEA FISHING STATIONS IN NORTHERN IRELAND

THE popularity of sea fishing in N Ireland has grown immensely in recent years, leading to the discovery of new and exciting possibilities. 300 miles of unpolluted coastline offers fishing for a variety of species from rock and beach alike. Sheltered inlets of which Strangford and Belfast Loughs are the largest and best known, offer protection to the boat angler when the open sea may be unfishable due to adverse weather. Twenty-four species of sea fish are caught regularly, including blue shark, skate, tope, cod, bass and flatfish. The Tourist Board, well aware of anglers' needs (boats, bait, etc) spares no effort to assist visitors in finding both sport and comfortable quarters.

Portrush (Antrim) and **Portstewart** (Derry). Near mouths of Lough Foyle and River Bann. Rock, pier and beach fishing for pollack, mackerel, garfish, coalfish, flounder, plaice, sea trout and bass. Good bass fishing from Castlerock Strand. Plenty of boats and bait. Tackleists: Joe Mullen, 74 Main Street; J Minahan, 35 Bath Street, both Portrush. Hotels: Northern Counties; Royal; Skerry-Bhan; Lismara; all Portrush (and many more). Carrig-na-Cule; Golf House; Strand; etc, Portstewart.

Glenarm (Antrim). Pier, rock and boat fishing for pollack, mackerel, plaice, flounders and codling. Plenty of bait.

Larne (Antrim). Belfast 25m. Pollack, mackerel, whiting, cod, coalfish, etc, with jigging for herring off The Maidens, some miles off shore. Plenty of boats. Trout fishing in Town Reservoir. East Antrim AA has salmon and trout fishing; inquire hon sec. Club: Larne & Dist SAC. Hon Sec B Renshaw, 22 Elisabeth Ave. Hotels: Kings Arms; Highways; Laharna.

Whitehead and Carrickfergus (Antrim). Opposite Bangor at entrance to Belfast Lough (Belfast 16m). Pollack, mackerel, coalfish, garfish, cod, whiting, sea trout from rocks, beach and boats. Good trout July onwards (depending on spates); mostly free. **Castlewellan Lough;** brown and rainbow trout, boats. Dept of Ag water; permits from forest office. Marks for cod are Black Head and Gobbins. Tackleist: Cambridge & Co, High Street, Carrickfergus.

Bangor (Down). Bangor is on Belfast Lough, 12m from capital. Haddock, whiting, pollack, cod, coalfish and, after June, mackerel; fresh bait (Cockles, mussels, herring and mackerel) plentiful; lugworm can be dug. Some local boatmen now offer charter facilities as well as scheduled trips for holiday anglers. Visitors should contact Bangor Sea AC, which will take them out for trip of roughly six hours if space available. Other clubs with boats: RNA, Mountbatten House, and BETS Angling Section, Queen's Parade. Many hotels. Club: Bangor SAC, Hon Sec J Bradley, 27 Rosemary Drive.

Donaghadee (Down). Belfast 18m. Fishing from pier or rocks for pollack, codling and mackerel. Motor boats available for deep-water fishing about 3m offshore, where some large cod have been caught. Boats: Simpsons and others usual charge, £4 per day. Rag and lugworm and mussels are good baits. Numerous hotels. Club: Donaghadee SAC, Hon Sec W Greer, 29 Ravenscroft Avenue, Belfast. Tel Belfast 657816.

POLLUTION

Anglers are united in deploring pollution. To combat it, urgent action may be called for at any time from any one of us. If numbers of fish are found dead, dying or seriously distressed, take samples of both fish and water and contact immediately the office of the appropriate statutory body in whose area the incident occurs. For areas see p 354 and 355.

FISHING CLUBS & ASSOCIATIONS IN NORTHERN IRELAND

THE following is an alphabetical list of angling clubs and associations in N. Ireland. Particulars of the waters held by many will be found by reference to the index, in the section headed "Fishing Stations in N. Ireland", and information about the others, which may not have their own water, could be had from the secretaries. A courtesy appreciated by secretaries is the inclusion of a stamped addressed envelope for reply.

Antrim and District Angling Club. T Wilson, 125 Raceview, Muckamore, Co Antrim.

Armagh and District Angling Club. R Priestley, 12 Main Street, Bessbrook, Newry.

Augher District and Upper Blackwater Angling Club. J A Russell, Old Manse, Clogher.

Aughnacloy Angling Club. G Hamilton (chairman), Creaton House, Ballygawley, Co Tyrone.

Ballycastle and District Anglers' Club. Mrs Alice Ferguson, Kern House, Armoy, Ballymoney, Co Antrim.

Banbridge Angling Club. P Downey, 15 Hillview Terrace, Banbridge, Co Down.

Bangor Anglers' Association. B Rutherford, 3 Bayview Road, Bangor, Co Down.

Bangor Sea Angling Club. J Bradley, 27 Rosemary Drive, Bangor, Co Down.

Belfast Anglers' Association. R C Woods, Dhu Fin, Hawthorn Gardens, Belfast BT4 2H7.

Belfast Reservoir Angling Club. M Eardley, 38 Eblana Street, Belfast.

Belfast Waltonians Angling Society. W Bird, 60 Fernwood Street, Ormeau Road, Belfast BT15 3AN.

Belleek and District Angling Association. P J Farren, HM Customs, Belleek, Co Fermanagh.

Bessbrook and District Angling Club. B Priestley, Main Street, Bessbrook, Co Armagh.

Bushmills and District Angling Club. G Quinn, 14 Heronshaw, Bushmills.

Carrickfergus and District (Sea) Angling Club. R Craig, 56 Craigowen Road, Carrickfergus, Co Antrim.

Castlecaldwell and District Anglers' Club. B Faughan, Leggs, Enniskillen, Co Fermanagh.

Castlederg Angling Association. S P Mannion, Mount Bernard, Castlederg, Co Tyrone.

Clady and District Angling Club. Permits from McErlean's Bar, Clady, and "The Wild Duck", Main Street, Port Glenone.

Clogher/Augher Angling Club. Matt Ferguson, Augher, Co Tyrone.

Coleraine Anglers' Association. W J Walker, 23 Boulevard, Coleraine, Co Derry.

Crossmaglen and District Angling Club. Michael O'Brien, Newry Road, Crossmaglen, Co Down.

Donaghadee Sea Angling Club. W Greer, 29 Ravenscroft Avenue, Belfast.

Downpatrick and District Angling Association. R A Hall, 6 Castlehill Drive, Belfast.

Dromore Angling Club. R Russell, 49 Ravenscroft Avenue, Belfast.

Dundonald Angling Club. G Legge, Moatview Park, Dundonald, Co Down.

Dungannon and District Angling Club. J Arthur, Glenadush, Dungannon, Co Tyrone.

East Antrim Angling Association. A V Gardiner, 22 Bengore Gardens, Craigyhill, Larne, Co Antrim.

Fairhead Fishing Club. E C Redmond, Atlantic Avenue, Ballycastle, Co Antrim.

Fermanagh Anglers' Association. I Brown, 12 Drumday Road, Enniskillen, Co Fermanagh.

Fermanagh Fishery Federation. R E Bracken, Lisblake, Florencecourt, Co Fermanagh.

Finn Angling Club. H Curran, Glebe, Sion Mills, Co Tyrone.

Gilford Angling Club. J Thompson, 24 Ann Street, Gilford, Co Down.

Glebe Angling Associations. Edward Neeson, 6 School Terrace, Glebe, Sion Mills, Co Tyrone.

Glens Angling Club. J G Elliott, 384 Merville Garden Village, Newtownabbey, Co Antrim.

Gracehill, Galgorm and District Angling Club. Permits from T McCord's Shop, Bridgend, Galgorm.

Iveagh Angling Club. I Reilly, 125 Enniskeen, Craigavon. Permits from M Harrison, 12 Donard Gardens, Lurgan.

Kells and Connor Angling Club. T Bell, 32 Candiere Avenue, Connor, Kells, Ballymena, Co Antrim.

Kilrea and District Angling Club. J Templeton, Main Street, Garvagh, Co Londonderry.

Lisburn and District Anglers' Club. N Kennedy, 99 Tisowen Drive, Knockmore, Lisburn, Co Antrim.

Londonderry and District Anglers' Association. J H Wallace, 86 Spencer Road, Waterside, Londonderry.

Maine Angling Club. E McCready, 15 Inchkeith Road, Ballykeel, Ballymena.

Mournbeg and Derg Anglers' Association. J Davie, Main Street, Castlederg, Co Tyrone.

Moy Angling Club. D Towney, The Square, Moy, Co Tyrone.

Newcastle and Ballynahinch Anglers' Association. R C Masaroon, 44 Devon Parade, Belfast BT4 1LT.

Newry and District Angling Club. O McGaully, 5 Mountainview Terrace, Newry. Permits from J C Smith, Kildare Street, Newry.

North West Angling Federation. Dr B Deeney, The Bowling Green, Strabane.

Omagh Anglers' Association. P Rodgers, New Bungalow, Dromore Road, Omagh, Co Tyrone.

Pickwick Angling Club. R Vint, 21 Beechgrove Park Belfast, 6.

Randalstown Angling Club. W Spiers, 9 Neilsbrook, Randalstown.

Rathfriland and District Angling Association. S S Erskine, "Rosemount", Newry Road, Rathfriland, Newry, Co Down. Permits from D Crory, Main Street, or W R Trimble, Downpatrick Street, Rathfriland.

Roe Angling Association. S Maxwell, 51 Scroggy Road, Limavady, Co Derry.

Shimna Angling Club. J A Mackie, 125 Main Street, Newcastle, Co Down. Permits from T A Mackie, 125 Main Street, Newcastle, Co Down.

South Derry Anglers' Association. J Swann, Castledawson Road, Magherafelt, Co Derry.

Strabane Angling Association. Eric Wilson, Provincial Bank, Main Street, Strabane, Co Tyrone.

Ulster Coarse Fishing Federation. H Kearns, Scots House, Clones, Co Cavan.

Upperlands Angling Club. W J Cochrane, Boyne Row, Upperlands, Co Derry.

Warrenport and Rostrevor District Angling Club. J F Carroll, 93 Rosmara Park, Warrenpoint, Newry, Co Down.

Warrenpoint and Rostrevor Sea AC. H J Rice, 13 Clonallon Gardens, Warrenpoint, Newry, Co Down.

Whiterock Angling Club. B Donnelly, 18 St James's Road, Belfast.

Whitewell Angling Club. J Hoyles, 71 Station Road, Whiteabbey, Co Antrim.

Woodvale Angling Club. R Baillie, 43 Disraeli Road, Belfast.

FISHING IN THE IRISH REPUBLIC

THE Irish Republic, still relatively free from pollutive industry, is world famous for the quality of its fisheries. Salmon, sea trout, brown trout, pike and other coarse fish are to be found there at their best. The seas around Ireland contain very good quantities of many varieties of fish which provide excellent sport for visiting and native sea anglers.

Since the previous edition of Where to Fish was published, there has been a radical reorganisation of fisheries administration in which the Inland Fisheries Trust has ceased to exist, replaced by a Central Fisheries Board *(advt p 368)* and the seventeen Boards of Conservators previously in being replaced by seven Regional Fisheries Boards answering to the Central Board. IFT staff, people invaluably experienced, have been appropriately re-deployed. The function of each Regional Board is to conserve, protect and develop every aspect of the inland fisheries (salmon, trout, coarse fish, eels), including sea angling, within the Board's fisheries region. Each fisheries region consists of one or more of the former seventeen fishery districts and for legal reasons licences to fish for salmon (including sea trout) continue to relate to the fishery district named on each licence. Salmon and sea trout may not be fished except under licence issued by the relevant Regional Fisheries Board for the fishery district named on the licence. A salmon fishing licence to cover all seventeen fishery districts may be purchased from any Regional Fisheries Board. The cost of rod licences for salmon and sea trout is as follows:

Annual licence valid in all seventeen fishery districts, £10.
Annual licence valid for one named fishery district, £5.
Seven-day licence (all fishery districts), £3.
Late-season licence valid 1 July onwards (all fishery districts), £7.
Late-season licence valid 1 July onwards valid for one named fishery distict only, £3.

The modified close seasons now in force for salmon, sea trout and brown trout differ not only as between regions, but also within regions, in a formulation too complex for reproduction here in detail. The general pattern is as before, in that seasons for migratory fish tend to open early and close early, while that for brown trout opens early in many places (Feb 15) and does not close until a date in October. There are, however, important exceptions and anglers proposing to visit the Republic, especially early or late in the year, should make careful enquiries with the appropriate Regional Board before making firm plans, whether the intention be to fish for salmon, migratory or brown trout.

No licence is required for brown trout, coarse fish or sea fish angling.

The is no annual close season for angling for coarse fish or for sea fish.

Overall responsibility for the country's fisheries rests with the Department of Fisheries and Forestry, Agriculture House, Kildare Street, Dublin 2.

The Central Fisheries Board consists of the Chairman of the seven Regional Boards and from four to six members nominated by the Minister for Fisheries and Forestry. The functions of the Central Board are prescribed in the Fisheries Act 1980 and include such things as co-ordination and, where necessary, direction of the regional boards in the performance of their functions; management of any fishery, hatchery or fish farm possessed by the Central Board; preparation of an inland fisheries development programme, etc. Amongst other things the fisheries owned and operated by the former Inland Fisheries Trust are now controlled by the Central Fisheries Board. **Inquiries about fishing those waters (location, fees etc) should be addressed to The Chief Executive Officer, Central Fisheries Board, Weir Lodge, Earl's Island, Galway.**

The Department of Fisheries and Forestry owns and operates an important commercial and rod salmon fishery on the River Corrib at Galway, Co Galway. Inquiries to the Manager, The Fishery, Nun's Island, Galway, Co Galway.

The Electricity Supply Board also holds extensive fishing rights: principal salmon waters are the River Mulcair and the Shannon at Parteen, above Limerick, and at Castleconnell, Co Limerick. The Board preserves and develops the fisheries under it's control. Inquires to the Secretary, Electricity Supply Board, Fisheries Division, Lower Fitzwilliam Street, Dublin 2.

Inquiries about accommodation and general tourist angling information (e.g. leaflets, brochures about local angling resources and amenities throughout the country) should be addressed to **Bord Failte, (The Irish Tourist Board), Baggot Street Bridge, Dublin 2 or The Irish Tourist Board, 150 New Bond Street, London.**

THE REGIONAL BOARDS

The Eastern Regional Fisheries Board. Consists of the fishery districts of Dundalk, Drogheda, Dublin and Wexford, and covers all lakes and river systems entering the sea including coastal waters between Clogherhead, Co Louth and Kiln Bay, Co Wexford. Inquiries to the Board's Regional Fisheries Manager, 58 Dame Street, Dublin 2.

The Southern Regional Fisheries Board. Consists of the fishery districts of Waterford and Lismore and covers all lakes and river systems entering the sea, including coastal waters, between Kiln Bay, Co Wexford and Ballycotton Pier, Co Cork. Inquiries to the Board's Regional Fisheries Manager, 12 Gladstone St, Clonmel, Co Tipperary.

The South Western Regional Fisheries Board. Consists of the fishery districts of Cork and Kerry and covers all lakes and river systems entering the sea, including coastal waters, between Ballycotton Pier, Co Cork and Kerry Head, Co Kerry. Inquiries to the Board's Regional Fisheries Manager, Gurteenroe, Macroom, Co Cork.

The Shannon Regional Fisheries Board. Consists of the Limerick fishery district and covers all lakes and rivers entering the sea, including coastal waters, between Kerry Head, Co Kerry and Hag's Head, Co Clare. Inquiries to the Board's Regional Fisheries Manager, Thomond Weir, Limerick, Co Limerick.

The Western Regional Fisheries Board. Consists of Galway, Connemara and Ballinakill fishery districts and covers all lakes and rivers entering the sea, including coastal waters, between Hag's Head, Co Clare and Pigeon Point, near Westport, Co Mayo. Inquiries to The Board's Regional Fisheries Manager, The Weir Lodge, Earl's Island, Galway.

The North Western Regional Fisheries Board. Consists of Sligo, Ballina and Bangor fishery districts and covers all lakes and rivers entering the sea, including coastal waters, between Pigeon Point, near Westport, Co Mayo, and Carrickgarve, Co Sligo. Inquiries to the Board's Regional Fisheries Manager, Ardnaree House, Abbey St, Ballina, Co Mayo.

The Northern Regional Fisheries Board. Consists of Ballyshannon and Letterkenny fishery districts and covers all lakes and rivers entering the sea, including coastal waters, between Carrickgarve, Co Sligo and Malin Head, Co Donegal. Inquiries to the Board's Regional Fisheries Manager, College St, Ballyshannon, Co Donegal.

FISHING STATIONS IN THE IRISH REPUBLIC

DETAILS of close seasons and licences, etc, for Irish rivers and loughs, listed alphabetically here, will be found in pages 365–6. Anglers wanting further details of accommodation should write to Bord Failte (Irish Tourist Board), Baggot Street Bridge, Dublin, 2.

ANNAGH and ANNAGEERAGH

(For close seasons, licences, etc, see The Shannon Regional Fisheries Board, pp 365–6)

Best centre for these streams is **Milltown-Malbay (Clare).** Fishing free; brown trout plentiful, odd salmon and many sea trout in autumn. Near source of Annageeragh is Doolough; brown trout to ½ lb; boat available.

AWBEG

(For close seasons, licences, etc, see The Southern Regional Fisheries Board, pp 365–6)

A very good trout stream, especially for dry fly. Castletownroche AC issues visitors tickets for lower reaches.

BANDON

(For close seasons, licences, etc, see The South Western Regional Fisheries Board, pp 365–6)

From above Bandon Town to Desert Bridge, **Enniskeane** (about 6m), river controlled by River Bandon Salmon and Trout AA, except one small fishery on north bank; wt and dt for salmon and trout. A portion of river between **Bandon** and **Innishannon** also rented by association. (Hotels: Munster Arms, Bandon; and Innishannon; salmon, white and brown trout fishing). **Brinny** and **Argideen** in this district are white trout rivers. Tickets issued by association and obtainable (with salmon licences) from tackleists in Bandon: F Begley, South Main Street, and Mr Lee, Bridge House. Hon sec will be pleased to advise visiting anglers. The 4m stretch of river to about 1m above **Ballineen Bridge** is controlled by Ballineen and Enniskeane AA. This fishery is let on same terms (salmon and brown trout). A further stretch of 2m, known as Manch (property of District Justice Henry Conner of Manch House), provides best salmon angling in district. Above **Manch Bridge** is Dunmanway Salmon and Trout AA water. St £5 (S) £2 (t). River fishable for about 8m. Trouting also on **Caha River,** which joins Bandon 3m north of **Dunmanway.** 4½m SW, **Drinagh Lake.** Trout mt £2. Guests staying local hotels and guest houses for periods not exceeding one month may fish association waters for salmon and trout (salmon £5, trout £1). **River Argideen,** flowing into Courtmacsherry Harbour, has salmon and sea trout. Permit from J E Spiller, tackleist, 39/41 Pearse Street, Clonakilty, who also issues permits for Bandon, including the tidal water, and for **Shepperton Lakes,** (brown trout). Hotels: Emmet, Inchydoney, O'Donovans.

BARROW (including Suir and Nore)

(For close seasons, licences, etc, see The Southern Regional Fisheries Board, pp 365–6)

Rises well up in the centre of Ireland on the eastern slopes of the Shannon watershed and flows over 120m southerly to the sea at **Waterford** Harbour, entering by a long estuary. Salmon and trout. Salmon fishing fair and many stretches free. Good brown trout river suitable for dry fly. From Waterford. **Belle Lake** (pike, tench, rudd) and **Knockaderry Reservoir** (trout) may be fished. **Mahon River** (15m) holds sea trout and salmon, and mackerel, bass and pollack abound along coast. Dunmore Deep Sea AC, Co Waterford, welcomes visitors. Tackleist: Sports Shop, Quay, Waterford. Other fishing stations: **Graiguenamanagh** (Kilkenny), **Borris** (Carlow), **Carlow.** Hotels: Royal, Crofton. Salmon

Spinning on the Suir. *Photograph: Bord Failte.*

fishing free to licence-holders in this area. Trout fishing on **Rivers Lerr, Greese, Douglas** and **Burren,** which fish well wet or dry, controlled by Barrow AC and restocked yearly (membership £2 from local tackleists). Good coarse fishing in Barrow; perch, rudd, bream, pike, tench; free. Club. Carlow AA. Annual membership £2. **Athy.** Several tributaries, including **Bauteogue** and **Boherbaun,** within easy reach. There is some good free dry-fly water. About **Portarlington,** Portarlington-Monasterevan Dist AA have 10m water; visitors welcomed.

SUIR

(For close seasons, licences, etc, see The Southern Regional Fisheries Board, pp 365–6)

Runs into same estuary as Nore and Barrow, and is much better salmon river. Noted also for its trout fishing. Record salmon for Ireland, 57 lb, was caught in Suir, in 1874. Best months for spring salmon, which are usually heavy, are Feb to April. Usually good run in May. Grilse from June on, with occasional runs of small salmon to end of season. Principal stations on river are following: **Clonmel.** Hotels: Hearn's, Ormonde, Larkins. Clonmel and Dist AC controls good deal of water on river. Clonmel Salmon AA also has water; apply hon sec. **Nier** and **Tar** trout streams are within easy reach, but **Clogheen** and **Ardfinnan** are best for latter; contact hon secs, Clonmel and Clogheen AA respectively for further information. Mountain loughs can also be reached from this centre. **Cahir.** Cahir and Dist AA controls 6m of salmon fishing above town and 1m below. Association also has 3m of tributary **Aherlow;** trout. Hotels: Cahir House, Galtee and Kilcoran Lodge; 8m salmon and trout water. Licences from D Kavanagh, West Gate, Clonmel. Salmon and brown trout flies from E Heavey, Cahir Park, and R J Watkins, Castle Street. **Cashel.** Cashel, Tipperary and Golden AA issues visitors' permits; some spring salmon; grilse July and Aug; trout good (av ½ lb); pike up to 25 lb in upper reaches. Mar, April and May best months usually for trout. Salmon mid-Mar to June; grilse, July/Aug. Hotels: Zetland Hotel (3½m of private sea trout and salmon fishing and on several lakes *(advt p 373)*. Longfield House (1m of own fishing; many other waters). Royal, Tipperary. **Carrick-on-Suir.** Start of tidal water. Carrick-on-Suir AA has developed fishing in vicinity; £1 week. Upriver there is good trout fishing and occasional sea trout; mostly free. About 4m to south mountain loughs, largest of which are **Coumshingaun** and **Crotty's,** provide very good fishing as also does **Clodiagh River,** which springs from loughs and is close to road for part of way. Angler in search of good salmon and trout fishing would be advised to seek it anywhere from Carrick to Cashel. Most of river preserved for salmon, but some owners give permission to fish for trout. **Thurles** is good centre for upper river. Hayes Hotel can arrange fishing by the day or week. Club: Thurles, Holycross and Ballycamas AA. Wt £15, dt £3. Fly only. At **Templemore** is Templemore AA water; visitors' dt for Suir (trout only, av ½ lb).

NORE

Lies between Barrow and Suir, and runs into same estuary. Salmon fishing now mainly preserved. Spring fish are heavy; big grilse run from June onwards. Trout fishing good (regularly restocked), fish average ½–¾ lb. River holds large pike and perch. Tributaries also have been restocked and sport excellent. Fishing stations: **Thomastown** (Kilkenny), **Kilkenny** (Kilkenny). Thomastown AA has excellent salmon and trout stretch of Nore and issues temporary cards to visitors. Kilkenny AA has some excellent salmon and trout fishing on 12m of Nore and **Dinan** and issues permits to visitors. Wt (S) £6 (T) £3, dt (S) £3 (T) £1. Other stretches free. **King's River;** good brown trout. Hotels: Carmel, Club House, Imperial, Metropole, Newpark and Rose Hill. **Abbeyleix** (Leix). Guest houses with fishing: Mrs S Pratt, Dealgrove; Mrs H M Seale, The Glebe, Attanagh, Portlaoise. Fishing much deteriorated due to pollution and drainage works. Abbeyleix Club now disbanded. **Mountrath** (Leix). Nore; brown trout, pike, perch. **Coppal-Bawn River;** brown trout. Hotels: The Arch Bar, Hibernian, de Vesci Arms.

BLACKWATER

(For close seasons, licences, etc, see The Southern Regional Fisheries Board, pp 365–6)

Perhaps most famous salmon river in Southern Ireland. Rises west of Killarney Mountains and flows eastwards about 70m until it reaches town of Cappoquin, where it becomes tidal and turns sharply south, entering sea by estuary 15m long at Youghal Bay. Salmon (best stretches mainly between Mallow and Lismore), sea trout, brown trout, but large quantities of dace, bream, perch and pike in some parts. Best fishing strictly preserved. Big runs of spring salmon from Feb to April; grilse June to Sept; and often good run of autumn salmon during Aug and Sept. Sea trout in Blackwater and Bride, June onwards.

Youghal (Cork). On Blackwater estuary. **Turig River** enters estuary here; for fishing apply to hon sec, Turig AC. Other club: Youghal Sea AC. At **Killeagh** (6m) Glenbower Trout AC has river and lough; trout, sea trout; fly, bait; Cappoquin AC issues permits for trout and coarse fishing on Lismore Estate waters. Coarse fishing free to visitors. **Ballyduff** (4m Lismore) is popular centre. Best months for salmon: Feb, Mar, April and Sept. Sea trout June, Sept. Inquire Cappoquin AC (Tel: Cappoquin 22). **Fermoy** (Cork). Salmon, sea trout, trout; also dace and rudd. Well-known Careysville Fishery, owned by Duke of Devonshire, is here; lettings sometimes made. 20m of excellent salmon, (record results) sea trout, brown trout and coarse fishing on Lower Blackwater Fishery between Ballyhooley Bridge above Fermoy and Lismore. Also 2m of very good sea and brown trout fishing (few salmon) on **River Bride** at Tallow Bridge. Wt and dt £30–£60 and £6–£10 for Blackwater and Bride from Lower Blackwater Fishery Office, Station House, Ballyduff, or Blackwater Lodge Fishing and Sporting Centre (riverside lodges or hotel accommodation controlled by Blackwater Fishery Ltd) *(advt p 365)*. Tickets also from Tourist Office, Fermoy, and some local hotels: Clubs: Fermoy and Dist Trout AA; Fermoy Salmon AA. Hotels: Royal, Grand, both Fermoy; Blue Dragon, Kilworth; Royal, Mitchelstown. Guests at Toby Jug, **Cappoquin,** may enjoy good sport with salmon, trout and coarse fish *(advt p 367)*. Cappoquin AC issues permits for salmon fishing on Blackwater and Bride; and arranges accommodation; inquire hon sec for details. **Araglin** holds brown trout; good dry fly. **Funshion** runs in near Careysville on north bank; trout, dace, rudd. Another tributary, the **Bride,** holds salmon and sea trout as well as brown trout; also dace, rudd. All these tributaries can be fished on nominal payment to local angling associations. Kilworth Trout AA is for Araglin and Funshion, and Mallow Trout AA for the Bride. Mitchelstown and Kildorrey Trout AA has upper reaches of Funshion. **Mallow** (Cork). Salmon (preserved); trout and coarse fishing good (roach and dace are main species); fishing mostly free. Clubs: Mallow Trout AA; Mallow Coarse AA; Ballyhooly Trout AA; permits for trout fishing. Licences from Liam Ward (tackleists), Main Street. Hotels: Hibernian (salmon fishing for guests); Central (salmon fishing), Longueville House; Georgian mansion with 3m of fishing both banks, and very good salmon stretch lower down *(advt p 371)*. Isle of Skye, **Kanturk;** 1½m of Blackwater (salmon, sea trout, coarse fish). At **Castletownroche,** Castletownroche AC has good trout fishing; apply hon sec.

Coarse fishing on the Blackwater. *Photograph: Bord Failte.*

BOYNE

(For close seasons, licences, etc, see The Eastern Regional Fisheries Board, pp 365–6)

Rises near Edenderry and flows for about 70m, entering the sea near Drogheda north of Dublin. Very good early salmon river, although fresh-run fish are now caught throughout season in deep pools of Lower Boyne Fishery. Spring fish run large, a few over 30 lb being killed every year, but salmon fishing adversely affected by drainage operations. Sea trout only in lower part, running mainly up a tributary, the **Mattock,** fishable only after heavy spates. Main river preserved, though good number of beats are let.

Drogheda (Louth). Drogheda and District AC has game and coarse fishing on Boyne and Nanny. St for salmon, sea trout and brown trout. Lower parts of Boyne and Mattock preserved. Brown trout in two reservoirs; st from Drogheda Corporation. Hotels: Central, White Horse, Boyne Valley, Rosnaree, Cooper Hill House (Julianstown). **Navan** (Meath). Kilbride AA has salmon and trout fishing on 5m; dt issued £3 and 50p. Hotels: Central and Russell Arms. **Slane** (Meath). Fishing good, but preserved. Hotel: Conyngham Arms. **Trim** (Meath). Good trout in main river and tributaries. Trim, Athboy and Dist AA preserves and restocks **Athboy River** and some stretches on Boyne itself; st £4, dt £1. Deel and Boyne AA has trout and salmon water on tributary **Deel.** Hotels: Central, Railway (both Trim); Greville Arms (Mullingar). Longwood Anglers also have salmon and trout fishing on Boyne. **Kells** (Meath). Good trout fishing on **River Blackwater;** dry fly. Mayfly fishing good. 15m preserved and restocked by Kells AA; wt and dt; Trout up to 7 lb may be had in the river, also large pike and salmon, 1½m of free fishing from source. Hotel: Headford Arms. **Virginia** (Cavan). On headwaters. **Lough Ramour** gives good trout fishing and excellent fishing for bream, rudd, perch and pike; boats available, two tributaries. Ten lakes and four rivers within 5m; trout and coarse fish. Hotels: The Park, Virginia. (Salmon and trout fishing on **Blackwater;** trout in loughs and three small rivers; coarse fishing on **Lough Ramour).**

CORRIB SYSTEM

(For close seasons, licences, etc, see The Western Regional Fisheries Board, pp 365–6)

River Corrib drains **Lough Corrib** and runs 5½m to Galway Bay passing virtually through the city of Galway. Salmon, trout. Salmon fishing very good. For particulars as to present conditions and rods apply Fishery Office, Galway. Best fishing for springers early in season; grilse, May–June. Charges: £20 per rod per day; rods let by the day, the week and the month at the same rate. Fishing station: **Galway.** Hotels: Great Southern, Atlanta, Skeffington Arms. Tackle and salmon licences from Naughton's, Shop Street, **Kilcolgan River** (10m E) part tidal, salmon and sea trout. Free downstream of old bridge; preserved elsewhere, good free fishing higher up.

LOUGH CORRIB

This, the largest sheet of water in Republic (41,617 acres, 68 sq m), is dotted with islands, around which are shallows which make for good fishing. Specially noted for large brown trout. Trout fishing opens on Feb 15 and is mainly by trolling until April. Wet fly good in April and early May, but lough best known for dapping with mayfly (beginning last week in May) and daddy-longlegs (mid-July to end of season). Good dry-fly fishing on summer evenings. Salmon taken mainly by trolling, and in June on wet fly in many of bays. Also big pike and other coarse fish in Corrib, so that angling of some kind is available all year. Fishing free, but salmon licence required. Many hotels issue licences. Boats and boatmen at **Portacarron, Oughterard, Baurisheen, Derrymoyle, Glan Shore, Cong, Greenfield, Doorus, Carrick, Salthouse, Carey's** and **Inishmacatreer.**

Oughterard (Galway). Currarevagh House (boats; one on top lake of Screeb fishery); dt £5. Oughterard House (free fishing on Corrib; private water within 12m; salmon and sea trout) *(advt p 376);* Corrib, Angler's and Egan's Lake. Also new motel: Connemara Gateway (Reservations: Tel: 01-567 3444) and Ross Lake Hotel, Rosscahill (boats and

boatmen). **Owenriff River** flows through Oughterard; good in high water late summer. Tackleist: W Keogh.
Headford (Galway). Convenient for the east side of Lough Corrib. **Black River** (limestone stream) provides excellent if somewhat difficult dry fly water. Affected by drainage work. Best near village of **Shrule**. Accommodation at Angler's Rest Hotel *(advt p. 376)* and guest houses.
Greenfield (Galway). First-class centre for eastern bank. Ower House Hotel stands on lough shore and is very popular with anglers; boats and boatmen available. £17.50 per day. **Lough Hackett** (large pike, perch) is 9m away.
Maam Cross (Galway). Hotels: Peacock's, Maam Cross *(see also Ballynahinch–Mid-West Coastal Streams)*.
Cong (Mayo). Good for Lough Mask also. Hotels: Ashford Castle *(see also Ballynahinch)* which provides boats and ghillies £17.50 per day. Ryan's Corrib Guest House. Tackleist: S Ryan.

LOUGH MASK

Limestone lake of 20,496 acres connected by underground channel with Lough Corrib holding large brown trout, pike, eels, perch and a few char. Trout to 15 lb are taken by trolling and on dap (5–6 lb not uncommon). Mayfly, May and June. Daddy-longlegs and grasshopper, late June to Sept; wet fly, Mar–April and July–Sept. **Ballinrobe, Cong, Clonbur** and **Tourmakeady** are good centres. At Cong is Cong AA; at Ballinrobe is Ballinrobe and Dist AA and at Tourmakeady is Tourmakeady AC. All are open to visitor-membership at modest charges. Tackleists: Mr Ryan, Cong; John Finlay, Main Street, Ballinrobe; Mr O'Toole, Tourmakeady. Boats for hire at Cushlough Pier, Bay of Islands Park, Rosshill Park, Caher Pier. Good accommodation at Tourmakeady Lodge, recently converted into guest house and which caters especially for fishermen. Also Mask Lodge and Mask Villa on lake shore. River fishing on **Finney** and canal joining Mask and Corrib. At Tourmakeady are some good spate rivers, and mountain lake fishing can be had in **Dirk Lakes;** brown trout. Connected to Mask are **Loughs Carra** (4,003 acres, limestone, brown trout run large; boats at Flannery's Pier and Henneghan's Pier) and **Nafooey** (good coarse fish). Good trout, perch, pike in three tributaries of Mask: Robe, Finney, Bulkaun.

CLARE–GALWAY

Flows into Lough Corrib, near Galway, and was considered one of best spawning streams for Galway River fish. Recovering from drainage work. Best season: Spring salmon, mid-April to mid-May; grilse, third week June to third week July; brown trout, April to June. Holds large trout and suitable for dry fly. Fishing station: **Galway,** for lower reaches; *(for hotels, see Corrib)*. 25m W of Galway on coast road is new Carraroe Hotel; sea and lake fishing. **Tuam** (Galway). For upper waters. Some free fishing. Club: Tuam and Dist Trout AA. A private club (Corofin Association) has salmon and dry-fly trout water on river; particulars from hon sec. **Castlegrove Lake;** pike, perch, bream, rudd.

SPIDDAL

Short river 12m W of Galway. Salmon, sea trout. Fishing formerly owned and let by Lord Killanin now unavailable. Remainder of bank is property of Mrs McDonagh, Villa, Galway. Headquarters are property of Irish Land Commission (to let by season with shooting); some free fishing. Inquire Herbert Buckley, Spiddal House, **Spiddal. Boliska Lough** (sea trout, some salmon) is free.

NORTH DONEGAL STREAMS

(For close seasons, licences, etc, see The Northern Regional Fisheries Board, pp 365–6)
Donegal is mostly salmon and sea trout country. Its waters are generally acid; rocky or stony streams and small lakes in which the brown trout run small—though there are one or two fisheries where they may be taken up to 2 lb and more.

LENNON (or LEANNAN)

Rises in **Lough Gartan** and flows through south end of **Lough Fern** into sea on west coast of **Lough Swilly.** Salmon, trout. From **Lough Fern** to town of **Ramelton,** Co Donegal, provides 4 to 5m of good salmon water. Permission may be obtained from various landowners. St and dt for local club water from P Cullen, Kilmacrennan. Salmon run from January (given mild weather) to June, followed by grilse and sea trout to season's end. Lower portion of river at Ramelton owned by Ramelton Fishery Ltd (rods very limited). Free brown trout fishing on various loughs. **Lough Fern,** midway between towns of **Milford and Kilmacrennan,** usually provides excellent free salmon fishing during April and May (by boat only). Boats usually obtainable at Milford and Kilmacrennan Hotels or at McFadden's at Lough Fern. Kilmacrennan and **Churchill** are for Upper Lennon. Loughs Gartan, Akibbon and Nacally (trout) may be fished from here, some free, some by ticket. Trout fishing in Lennon equally good on both upper and lower reaches. Best season: April to July. At **Letterkenny** local association has salmon, sea trout and brown trout fishing on rivers and lakes, trout average ½ lb; st and dt from hon sec and local tackleists (see below). **River Swilly** provides good salmon and trout fishing and is free. Hotels: Angler's Haven and Fern Arms (Kilmacrennan); McClafferty's and Wilkin's (Churchill); McFadden's (Lough Fern), McCready's Arm (Milford). Licences from hotels and H P Whorisky, The Bridge, Ramelton. Tackle and permits. Ed Barr (information), M Speers, both Upper Main Street, Letterkenny; Wm Gardiner, Milford; Bernard Harte, Lifford; Doherty's (Churchill); Doherty's Leannon Stores and Gorman's Stores (Kilmacrennan).

LACKAGH

Excellent salmon, sea trout and brown trout fishing in **Lackagh River, Owencarrow** and **Glen Lough.** Free fishing on **Lough Fern** (10m) and **Doe Estuary** (4m). Glen Lough is early and Owencarrow late. In former, fishing is best in April, May and June, and in latter in July and Aug. Glen Lough is 4m from hotel. Owencarrow is 8m distant by road, but can be reached by boat up lough. Numerous other lakes and streams in neighbourhood. Hotel: Rosapenna.

CRANA

Crana enters tidal water of **Buncrana** on Lough Swilly. Salmon and sea trout few until May; good fishing June onwards. Season: Mar 1 to Oct 12. (MT) Sept 7 (S). Buncrana AA; mt £15, wt £5, dt £2 for salmon and sea trout; brown trout (plentiful, but small). Other waters: **Mill River;** brown trout to ½ lb numerous; free. **Lough Inch** (6m); good sea trout; free. **Dunree River** (6m); free; brown trout, occasional salmon and sea trout. **Clonmany River** (5m); free salmon and sea trout fishing; fair sport in good water; best June onwards. Further information, and flies, from hon sec, Buncrana AA.

WEST DONEGAL STREAMS

(For close seasons, licences, etc, see The Northern Regional Fisheries Board, pp 365–6)

GWEEBARRA

Drains Lough Barra and flows south-west about 7m to Doochary Bridge, where it becomes tidal and flows thence through long estuary between high hills a further 6m to the Atlantic. Salmon, sea trout. Best season: Spring salmon, Feb–May; grilse and sea trout, end of June to Sept. Fishing belongs to riparian owners, leave obtainable. Salmon and sea trout run into Lough Barra and other tributaries. Fishing station: **Doochary** (Donegal). Doochary AA restocks. Bridge here marks end of tidal water; several trout lakes in vicinity. **Rosses Fishery** at **Dungloe** offers magnificent facilities to the visitor. Rivers and 130 + lakes; all stocked with brown trout av ½ lb (to 4 lb). All lakes on **Dungloe** and **Derrydruel** systems have sea trout. Derrydruel and **Crolly** salmon and sea trout from late May onwards. 5 lakes stocked rainbows to 4 lbs. Visitors st £5, wt £2, dt £1. Boats ticket-holders £2 per day. Permits from hon sec, C Bonars, Tackleists, or Beedy's Bar. Salmon permits from above £10 state, £5 local. Rainbows fly only.

OWENEA AND OWENTOCKER

Short rivers running into head of Loughrosmore Bay near Ardara, Co Donegal. Salmon, sea trout. Lower beat of Owenea leased by Ardara AA; remaining beats (about 5m in all, both banks) leased by Glenties AA. Ardara AA also has Owentocker Fishery 14m, both banks. St £10, wt £5 and dt £1 available from John McGill, Ardara, and Patrick O'Donnell, Glenties. When in condition Owenea is one of best in country for salmon; many pools. River restocked annually from hatchery at Glenties. Free fishing for brown trout in 22 lakes. Boats on several. Salmon: best months April–June. Grilse and sea trout: June, July–Sept. Free salmon and sea trout fishing on **Rivers Brackey** and **Duog.** Many lakes also free. Fishing stations: **Ardara** and **Glenties,** both Donegal. Tackleists: John McGill, Main Street, Ardara (licences), Joseph McDevitt and Co-op Stores, both Glenties. Licences also from P O'Donnell, Glenties. Hotels: Highland and Kelvon House (Glenties), Nesbitt Arms and Woodhill Guest House (Ardara). Other hotels (seaside) at Maas and at Narin; Portnoo and Rosbeg.

CLADY AND GWEEDORE

Clady drains **Lough Nacung** and runs to sea in about 5m. Formerly good salmon river, but fishing affected by hydro-electric works. Commercial salmon fishing now prohibited to conserve stocks. Small run of sea trout, good brown trout. Best seasons: salmon, April–May; grilse, June–July; sea trout, Sept. Gweedore is good salmon and sea trout water, Mar to Sept. Electricity Supply Board now controls Clady, Gweedore Estuary, **Lough Nacung, Dunlewy Lough,** and part of **Lough Anure.** Salmon fishing on Clady only; st £8.80, wt £2.75, dt £1.10 VAT incl; trout fishing free; permits from Fisheries Manager, ESB, Lower Fitzwilliam Street, Dublin 2, M Gallapher, Chemist, Bunbeg and C Bonner, Bridgend, Dungloe.

ESKE AND INVER

Eske River provides free fishing for salmon (July–Aug) and good sea trout. It drains **Lough Eske,** 3m from **Donegal Town,** which holds brown trout of above average size for this area. Permits for guests, and occasionally for non-residents. Ardnamona Guest House, Lough Eske. Inver Fishery embraces **Eany Water** and tributaries and drains into Inver Bay. 7m west of Donegal Town. Salmon, sea trout, small brown trout. Pike, perch and bream lakes in the vicinity. St £5 and dt £1 from C Doherty, Tackleist, Main Street, Donegal Town. **Bradley** and **Tubber Loughs** (10m) hold good trout, especially Bradley. Other good loughs: **Lough A'Capall** and **Lough Suibhne.** Much free lake fishing in area for troat and coarse fish.

GLEN AND OWENEE

These rivers in the Carrick district of south-west Donegal are well stocked with salmon and sea trout. Guests at Slieve Liag Hotel, **Carrick,** can fish them, and good lake and rock fishing available.

For other Donegal centres see p 360 and 394 (Lough Melvin)

CO. DUBLIN and CO. MEATH (streams)

BRAY (DARGLE) RIVER. Dublin District. Association has boats for trout fishing (members only) on **Vartry Reservoirs at Roundwood** (11m from Bray; see Vartry). Bank permits can be obtained from Dublin Corporation, 28 Castle Street, Dublin, or from the Superintendent, Vartry Lodge, Roundwood. Dt £1. Boat £2. Associate members' st or visitors' dt can be had for Dargle at **Bray.** Salmon, sea trout, small brown trout, salmon licences from Owens Sports Shop, Bray.

BROADMEADOW RIVER. Dublin District. Trout; rights held by Swords AC in lower reaches of river which enter tidal water at **Swords;** Limited membership. Drainage scheme has affected sport.

DELVIN RIVER. In Drogheda District. Fair brown trout stream entering sea at **Gormanstown;** Holds few sea trout. Gormanstown and Dist AA has water. River being stocked and developed with co-operation of landowners and members. **Balbriggan** is convenient centre. (Hotel: Grand.)

DODDER. Dublin District. **Dublin;** brown trout (av 8 oz), with some sea trout fishing in tidal portion. Dodder AC annual sub £2 controls all fishing; free to visitors; fly; best months: March/April (brown trout); Aug/Sept sea trout. Fishing on Dublin Corporation's **Bohernabreena Reservoirs** (8m from Dublin); dt from Waterworks Office, Castle Street, and club members.

GLENCREE RIVER. In Dublin District. **Enniskerry** is a centre; small brown trout. Mostly free.

NANNY RIVER. In Drogheda District. River enters sea at **Laytown,** Co Meath. Fair brown trout fishing; some sea trout in lower reaches. Drogheda and Dist AC has water and issues permits at small charge.

TOLKA RIVER. In Dublin District. A once-excellent trout stream dying of pollution in the lower reaches; eutrophication and urban development in the higher. Fishing for the remaining fish free.

ERNE

(For close seasons, licences, etc, see The Northern Regional Fisheries Board, pp 365–6)

A large hydro-electric scheme has turned the River Erne into two large dams. Trout permits (free) from Electricity Supply Board, Lower Fitzwilliam Street, Dublin 2 or Generating Station, Ballyshannon. **Lough Melvin** is best fished from **Bundoran;** boats; free fishing; gilaroos and brown trout that rise freely to fly. Sea trout fishing in estuary from June to Sept. Coarse fishing excellent; bream, rudd and perch abundant and roach multiplying following their introduction in recent years. Hotel: Hamilton. **Lough Erne** is in Northern Ireland; noted for pike and perch. **Enniskillen** is a centre. Trolling usual method to catch trout, but mayfly season is best. Tackleists in Ballyshannon: J Gormley, Main Street (Ballyshannon AA); Rogan's; Timothy's. Hotels in Bundoran: Central, Palace, Atlantic, Imperial, Hamilton (for Bundrowes River; see Bundrowes and Lough Melvin), Maghera. Hotel in Ballyshannon, Millstone. **Dunduff River** is 3½m from Bundoran; dt available; good salmon late June–July. There is some sea fishing out from Bundoran.

Lough Oughter, fed by the Erne, is maze of lakes; holds large trout (av 2½–3 lb, mayfly best but wet fly improving) and a wealth of coarse fish; bream, rudd, pike and roach. Tench in Killmooney Lake. Fishing free. Fishing stations: **Cavan** (two hotels on lake shore), **Swellan Lake** (¼m); coarse fish (**tench, rudd, perch, pike).** Lavey Strand Lake (5m SE). 37 acres; brown trout. Lough Oughter fed by **Annalee** (3m); good coarse fishing (bream, rudd, perch, pike) from **Butlersbridge** (3½m) to the **Erne;** good trout fishing upstream; has rise of mayfly and is suitable for dry-fly fishing; free. **Annagh Lake, Butlersbridge,** 100-acre water; trout averaging 1lb and more; boats. **Lough Gowna**

accessible from Cavan, which is also good station for Lough Oughter, Erne and Annalee. Further details from Cavan District Tourist Association. **Belturbet** (Cavan). Salmon and trout in Erne (Aug to Sept), fly fishing upstream and excellent coarse fishing downstream. Numerous lakes. **Annagh Lake,** fishing well on trout; six boats. Hotel: Seven Horse Shoes, many guest houses. **Annalee** gives good trout fishing; has rise of mayfly and is suitable for dry-fly fishing. Free. **Cootehill** (Cavan). Good trout fishing with wet and dry fly on Annalee and Dromore rivers; 16 lakes provide trout and coarse fishing. Club: Cootehill AA. Hotel: White Horse. **Barnagrove Lake** (4½m) holds good trout. Numerous lakes hold large pike, perch, rudd, bream; fishing free. **Lough Sillan** (8m) holds big trout (to 6lb and over); free; fishable from entire shore. On the **Finn,** a sluggish tributary of Upper Lough Erne, is **Clones.** Within 5m of town are six lakes; pike, perch, rudd, bream. River Finn good for bream, and tench recently introduced; all free fishing; boats. Club: Clones and Dist AA. Hotels: Creighton, Hibernian, Lennard Arms and others, and private house accommodation. In **Monaghan** districts are tributaries of the Blackwater *(see Lough Neagh),* brown trout; Monaghan AA has water; wt. Many free loughs. Emylough provides very good trout fishing (up to 5lb); fly only; two boats. Excellent coarse fishing in area.

FANE (including Glyde and Dee)

(For close seasons, licences, etc, see The Eastern Regional Fisheries Board, pp 365–6)

Flows from Castleblayney, Co Monaghan, to enter sea at Blackrock, 3m south of Dundalk. Salmon, sea trout, trout; late river; good dry-fly water. Dundalk Salmon AA has about 20m of rivers; salmon, sea trout up to 5½lb; particulars from hon sec. Fishing station: **Dundalk** (Louth); Dundalk Brown Trout Assn stock heavily and issue permits for over 20m of **Fane.** Permits from hon sec. Good points at **Blackstaff, Inniskeen, Culloville.** Excellent late salmon and sea trout water on **Blackwater** at **Castledown.** Tackleists: J O'Meara, Earl St, Dundalk. Hotels: Imperial, Williams', Lorne, Fairways, Derryhale. **Castleblayney** (Monaghan). Castleblayney Trout AA hon sec and tackleist: Mrs J Livingstone, Main Street. Hotels: Hope Arms, Central Park View. Several Loughs near: **Lough Muckno,** large pike, good trout and perch; many boats. **Lough Eagish** (5m) holds pike and perch. **Lough Ross** (3m) holds large pike and good trout. Many small loughs around Castleblayney hold pike, perch, rudd and carp. **Ballybay** (about 7m W) is good coarse fishing centre: **Dromore River and loughs;** details from hon sec, Ballybay AA.

River Laune and the mountains of Killarney. *Photograph: J. A. Cash.*

GLYDE

Drains Ballyhoe and Rahans Lakes in Co Monaghan and runs roughly parallel to and south of River **Fane**. Salmon, sea trout, brown trout, with pike, some bream and perch near lakes. Has now recovered from drainage work. Salmon best in spring, depending on spates June onwards. Brown trout (small) in fast water; larger fish (up to 2lb) in deep water, but slow risers (little fast water on river). Heavily stocked by Dee and Glyde FDA, which owns extensive rights on both rivers. Water well fished in spring, mostly free, except for Bellingham Castle estate, one stretch at **Tallanstown** and two stretches downstream from **Castlebellingham** (Dee and Glyde FDA). Hotels: Ardee Castlebellingham, Dunleer. Also guest house at Castlebellingham.

DEE

Rises in Co Meath and joins sister River Glyde ⅓m from common mouth. Salmon, sea trout, brown trout, some pike. Now recovered from drainage operations, but has become dependent on spates for salmon; best in spring (Mar–June; Sept good if spates). Well stocked with brown trout by Dee and Glyde FDA (see Dee); heavily fished; trout average less than ½lb. Sea trout (early July onwards) only from Willistown Head Weir (1½m upstream from mouth) to Cappoge Bridge (main Dublin-Belfast road). Mostly free. Fishing stations: **Ardee, Aclare, Castlebellingham, Dunleer.** Hotels: Aclare, Ardee, Dunleer.

FEALE

(For close seasons, licences, etc, see The Shannon Regional Fisheries Board, pp 365–6)

Rises on north-west slopes of Blackwater watershed and runs into Atlantic near extreme end of Shannon estuary on south shore. Salmon, sea trout, brown trout (small). Best seasons: Salmon, Mar to May; sea trout, mid-June on. Fishing stations: **Abbeyfeale** (Limerick). Best centre for Feale. Waders essential. Brosna AA has 6m upstream; good salmon sea and brown trout. Fishes best from June onwards. Trout permit from Les Flanagan, Seconglass, Mount Collins, Abbeyfeale. Hotel: Leen's. Several guest houses. Tackleists: Harnett's, Main Street; Rocke's, Bridge Street; O'Connell's, Church Street. Club: Abbeyfeale Salmon AA, which has water. **Listowel** (Kerry). River has improved out of all recognition. Freshwater nets now taken off. North Kerry AA has 7m; excellent salmon, sea trout and brown trout; wt and dt. Tralee AA has 2m, both banks; dt issued. Fly fishing for salmon quite good from mid-Aug. Salmon licences from P Horgan, 41 Charles Street. Other tackleists: A Crowley, Main Street; Joseph Guerin, Convent Street. Hotels: North County, Stack's, Central, Listowel Arms, Mountrivers. **Tralee** AA has water; salmon, sea trout; wt and dt; keeper on duty. Tackle: W Benner, Bridge Street.

ILEN

(For close seasons, licences, etc, see The Southern Regional Fisheries Board, pp 365–6)

Swift river rising on watershed of Bantry district and flowing into sea through long estuary, at head of which is fishing station: **Skibbereen** (Cork). Salmon, sea trout. Small spring run of salmon as rule, followed by big run of grilse. Sea trout fishing very good in summer and autumn. Night fishing usually provides best of sport. R Ilen AA have fishing on river. Wt £10, dt £3. Several trout loughs nearby. Two good hotels: West Cork, Eldon; also Ilenside Guest House. Tackleist: Fallon's Sports Shop, 20 and 51 North Street. At **Glandore**, 8m E, **Roury River** provides fair sport with salmon and sea trout, and numerous lakes and small rivers hold brown trout. Excellent sea fishing. Kilfinnan Castle Hotel provides boats for shark fishing and tackle may be hired.

LAUNE and MAINE (including Killarney Lakes)

(For close seasons, licences, etc, see The South Western Regional Fisheries Board, pp 365–6)

NEWPORT HOUSE

Newport
Co. Mayo

Telex: 33740
Telephone: 098/41222

GEORGIAN ESTATE IN THIRTY ACRES BY RIVER AND QUAY
OWN FARM AND GARDENS

Rest and recreation, comfort and elegance, good food and wine.

Touring centre for Achill and Scenic West.

Own fishing on Newport River and Lough Beltra West. Arrangements for Loughs Furnace and Feagh and Beltra East. Cabin cruisers on Clew Bay.

Shooting over 30,000 acres. Holiday sports and golf.

Twenty bedrooms, twenty bathrooms. Grade "A", R.I.A.C., A.A.***

LAUNE

Drains **Killarney Lakes** and flows N and W to Dingle Bay on Atlantic, about 14m. Tralee & Dist AA issues wt £15 and dt £3 for 2m (both banks) of Feale at Trieneragh. Salmon and sea trout. Best months March–May and Sept. Apply Hennebery's Sports Centre, Ashe Street. Dt from Office of Public Works for 4m of Laune, salmon, sea trout, brown trout. Fishing stations: **Killorglin** (Kerry) for lower reaches; tidal. Club: Killorglin AA. Hotels: Laune, Taylors. **Baufort** (Kerry) for upper reaches. Near here is the **Black Valley** with several brown trout lakes. Farm accommodation. At **Glenbeigh** are Glenbeigh and Towers Hotels: salmon, sea trout and brown trout fishing for guests on the lower **Caragh**, Laune, **Blackwater, Feale, Flesk, Behy** and ten lakes, including **Caragh Lake.** For 5m down from Lough Lein (see Killarney Lakes) Laune is State fishery. Good for sea trout and brown trout; good mid-April to Oct for salmon. Coolgown Guest House, Beaufort, adjoins fishery. *(See Caragh)*.

MAINE

Maine and tributary, **Brown Flesk,** hold salmon, sea trout and brown trout. Salmon fishing fair; sea and brown trout fishing often good. River is late. Best months: Salmon, April to June; sea trout, Aug to Sept. About 15m of free fishing. Anglers can have accommodation at **Castleisland,** on headwaters, and at **Tralee,** 11m distant. At Tralee is Tralee and Dist AA; see Feale.

KILLARNEY LAKES

Consist of three lakes: **Upper Lake, Muckross Lake** (middle), **Lough Lein** (lower), last being much the largest, connected with sea by Laune. Salmon and trout fishing good; free. Best season for salmon: Lough Lein, Feb to July; Muckross and Upper, Jan 17 to April or May. Both lakes: Aug to end of season. Mayfly hatch in June. **Flesk** feeds Lough Lein;

inquire Lough Lein AA, which also has 7m on Flesk (restocked annually); st and dt for salmon and trout; £5 and £2: £1.50 and 50p. Spinning best for salmon. Many small mountain lakes; free trout fishing. **Kilbrean Lake** is well stocked with brown trout, fishing by permit only. Fishing stations: **Killarney.** Hotels: Dunloe Castle and Hotel Europe (both issue salmon and trout permits and arrange deep sea excursions; Hotel Europe has gillie available) Castlerosse convenient for lakes and River Laune. Licences and tackle from The Handy Stores, Main Street. Guests at Lake Hotel, Killarney, can exchange fishing with Butler Arms *(see Waterville).*

LEE

(For close seasons, licences, etc, see The South Western Regional Fisheries Board, pp 365–6)

Draining **Gougane Barra Lake** and flowing 53m to Cork Harbour, Lee was formerly notable early salmon river (Feb to May) but fishing spoilt by hydroelectric schemes; salmon sport restricted to lower 6m. **Cork** (Cork). Permits for trout fishing on **Lee Reservoirs** (dt 28p, boat £5.50) from Electricity Supply Board, Lower Fitzwilliam Street, Dublin 2. Fishing free to local club members. Tackleist: T W Murray & Co, 87 Patrick Street, who will be pleased to give information. Numerous hotels. *(See Coachford).* **Coachford** (Cork). About half-way between two hydro-electric dams on Lee; trout and coarse fish in reservoirs; fishing improved; spinning best. Coachford Trout AA and Cork Trout AA members fish free; boat or bank; visitors may join or obtain dt from Electricity Supply Board. Free, but difficult, trout fishing on other smaller streams; banks bushed, but wider streams well stocked with trout by Cork club. **Macroom** (Cork). Convenient for Upper Lee and three other rivers **Sullane, Laney** and **Feorish;** brown trout, free. Also reservoirs; trout and coarse fish. Tackleist: B Baker, South Square. Club: Macroom Trout AA. Hotel: Castle. The **South Bridge, Dripsey** and **Shournagh,** all tributaries of the Lee, are good brown trout streams. Fishing mostly free. Hotels: Victoria and Castle.

LIFFEY

(For close seasons, licences, etc, see The Eastern Regional Fisheries Board, pp 365–6)

Winding river rising only some 13m in direct line south-west of **Dublin,** but with course of over 80m before entering sea. Salmon, brown trout and few sea trout in tidal reaches. Spring fishing January to May; grilse mid-July on. Mayfly hatch end of May. Best salmon fishing preserved, but association water on some lower reaches. Dublin and Dist Salmon AA has various stretches; permits from J W Elvery and Co, 19 Suffolk Street; Rory's, 17a Temple Bar, Fleet Street, and Moorkens Ltd, 11 Upper Abbey Street. Hon sec of Dublin Coarse Fish AC (address in club list) will help visiting coarse fishermen. High reaches about **Kilbride** controlled for 7m by Kilbride AA; dt 50p from Hon sec or Downshire House Hotel, Blessington. Mr Redmond, Cloughlea House. Kilbride AA also has 5m on **Blackwater** (Boyne) at Navan. Upper reaches of Liffey at **Ballyward, Poulaphouca Lake** (ESB trout restocking at rate of 100,000 per year). **Leixlip Reservoir** and 10½m at **Straffan, Ballymore Eustace, Clane** and **Celbridge** are controlled by Dublin Trout AA; brown trout and perch; dt 25p, st £2; also 2m of **King's River** above Poulaphouca; dt and st from D K Ring, Bawnard, Wilson Road, Mt Merrion; and from J Miley, Main Street, Blessington. Middle reaches, **Kilcullen** to below Millicent Bridge, controlled by North Kildare AA; salmon, brown trout, pike, perch; st £4, wt £1, dt 50p, from hon sec, or Moorkens, 11 Abbey Street and Roy Harkins, 17a Temple Bar, Fleet Street, both Dublin. Dublin Corporation control fishing on **Roundwood Reservoirs** (20m) and on **Bohernabreena Reservoirs** (8m); (fly only); bank fishing, st and dt. Dublin Trout AA fish Bohernabreena. **Grand Canal,** which runs alongside Liffey for some distance, holds brown trout, bream, rudd, perch and pike. Stretches about **Sallins** provide sport in pleasant surroundings. Fishing club at **Prosperous;** inquire hon sec.

MID-WEST COASTAL STREAMS

(For close seasons, licences, etc, see The Western Regional Fisheries Board, pp 365–6)

A local angler fishing at Ballynahinch, with the "Twelve Bens" forming the back drop. *Photograph: Bord Failte.*

BALLYNAHINCH

Salmon, sea trout. Rights on this famous fishery and associated waters held as follows: **Ballynahinch River, Lower Ballynahinch Lake** and **Snabeg** belong to Ballynahinch Castle Hotel, **Ballinafad,** Co Galway. Dt for salmon: £20. Priority given to hotel guests. **Glendalough** is private, together with **Lough Lehanagh,** and parts of **Owentoey** and **Bealnacarra Rivers. Upper Ballynahinch Lake** is private, together with part of river. **Loughs Inagh** and **Derryclare** are let; inquire of Ashford Castle Hotel, **Cong,** Co Mayo. **Loughs Cappahoosh, Derryneen, Shanakeela, Locodheas, Oorid** and **Owentoey River** are owned by Mr T Lyons, Tullaboy House, **Maam Cross,** Connemara, who lets with or without accommodation; salmon, trout and sea trout. A little south lie a number of loughs which can be fished from **Carna** (Galway), including **Skannive** and **Glenaun.** Zetland Hotel, **Cashel Bay** *(advt 373),* has rights on Upper Ballynahinch water, and tributaries **Athry, Emlough** and **East Lakes** (boats). Season on Ballynahinch is from mid-June to Oct 12. A few springers run from mid-Mar onwards; grilse, summer salmon and sea trout mid-June and July; sea trout, grilse, salmon Sept–Oct *(see Owengowla).*

OWENGOWLA

This river, with its chain of lakes, forms **Gowla Fishery,** one of best sea trout fisheries in Ireland; also contains salmon. The fishery is owned by the Zetland Hotel, Cashel Bay, Connemara. Four beats on the river and five boats (ten rods) on the lakes. The hotel also owns the **Athry lakes** on the **Upper Ballynahinch** system with three boats (six rods); salmon and sea trout. No spinning. Boats and gillies available for all waters. Full details from the hotel (Tel Cashel 8) or Scafco Ltd, Jamestown Road, Finglas, Dublin 11. Tel: 342211. Hotel Telex 28853: Scafco Telex: 31388. *(advt p 373)*

SCREEBE

Screebe Fishery owned by Screebe Estates Ltd, Screebe, Co Galway is a vast undertaking including 21 lakes and its own hatchery. 20 new boats have recently been added to the operation. Two head lakes, **Shindilla** and **Ardery,** reserved for guests at Currarevagh Guest House, **Oughterard,** Co Galway and Peacock's Hotel, Maam Cross, respectively. Screebe House has first-class salmon and sea trout fishing; own hatchery. Formerly a guest house, Screebe House is now available to rent; accommodation for 15 people. For details apply Manager, Screebe Estates Ltd, Camus, Co Galway.

CASHLA (COSTELLOE)

At head of next large bay to east, Cashla Bay, lies Cashla River and lakes, an exceptionally good sea trout fishery, the **Costelloe and Fermoyle Fisheries:** *(advt p 369).* Salmon, sea trout. Best months for Costelloe: salmon, June to Oct; sea trout, June to Oct, best Aug; fly only. Costelloe Cottage may be rented with fishing. Inquire of Manager, Bridge Cottage, Costelloe, Co Galway (Tel Galway 72196). Mt (2 rods) £700, wt (2 rods) £200; dt (2 rods) £20. Boat on lake, with ghillie, £35. Licences from Fishery Office, Costelloe Lodge. Nearest hotels: Carraroe (3m), Oughterard (17m). Guest house in Costelloe village. On the north-west shore of Ballyconneely Bay, near **Roundstone** (Galway), lies **Doohulla Fishery** which consists of short river and several lakes, chief of which are **Lough Maumeen** and **Lough Emlaghkeeragh,** both readily accessible. Sea trout, brown trout and occasional salmon. Proprietor: N D Tinne, Emloughmore, Ballyconneely. Local application to The Fishery Restaurant, Ballyconneely. Dt £5; bank only £2. Hotel accommodation at **Roundstone** (6m) or **Clifden** (9m), Clifden House Hotel arranges salmon fishing on **Owenglen River,** and trout fishing on Clifden Trout Anglers lakes and other salmon and trout fishing farther afield. Also cruiser for deep sea angling. Owenglen now good for salmon following erection of fish pass. Tackleists: Gerald Stanley & Son and H Sullivan, both Clifden. Clifden Trout AA fish numerous loughs; boats on some. Clifden AA are developing salmon and sea trout fishery; wt £5, dt £2, boat £3 extra, fishery opens after first June flood; 100,000 rainbow trout stocked into local lakes. Mt £2. Inquiries of G P Stanley. Clifden hotels include Clifden Bay, Lavelles, Rock Glen, Alcock & Brown, Celtic, Atlantic Coast, Clifden House, Abbey Glen. Several good guest houses.

CARROWNISKY

(For close seasons, licences, etc, see The Western Regional Fisheries Board, pp 365–6)

Rises in Sheefry Hills and flows 6m to sea beyond **Louisburgh** (Co Mayo). Louisburgh and Dist AC has water on river; salmon, sea trout (June to Oct). Tackle, tickets and licences from hon sec, Bridge Street. Salmon and trout in Altair Lake. Good shore fishing for bass, pollack, etc; boats available at Roonagh and Old Head. **Bunowen River:** salmon, sea trout; preserved by Marquess of Sligo. Five beats available, inquiries to Estate Office, Westport, Tel 127. Season: May–Sept. Hotels: Old Head *(for fishing on Delphi Fisheries, see Erriff)* Clew Bay and Durkans. For sea fishing Bay View Hotel, Clare Island, recommended; boats available.

ERRIFF

Good salmon and sea trout river lying short distance north of Ballynahinch country and flowing westwards from Corrib watershed to sea at head of Killary Harbour. **Erriff Fisheries, Leenane,** offer eight 2-rod beats each approx 2m in length on river, and two boats on Tawnyarm Lough. Spinning permitted on five of the beats. 340 salmon, largest 36 lbs, caught in 1980 and 700 sea trout 1½–3 lbs. Wt for river £45–£55; dt £9 and £10. Boat on lough for 2 rods, engine and petrol incl £18. River season April–Sept, on lough, July 1–Sept 30. Enquiries to C Harper, Erriff Fishery Office, Ansleagh, Leenane, Co Galway. Enquiries respecting Delphi Fishery, (**Bundorrogha River** and **Finlough, Dhulough and Glencullin Lough and Bunowen River**) to Estate Office, Westport, Tel 127.

GLENAMOY

Strictly preserved by Lord Digby (lower) and Irish Land Commission (upper), which lets fishing. Further information from owners. Principal tributary is **Muingnabo.** Salmon, sea trout.

BURRISHOOLE SYSTEM

Boat fishing for salmon and sea trout on **Lough Feeagh** and **Furnace** with short tidal stretch of river. Fishery owned and administered by Salmon Research Trust of Ireland. Fishing season effectively mid-June to end September but salmon closed earlier in 1979 and 1980 by Government order. Boats available with or without boatmen, package holidays arranged by request incorporating local accommodation of varying grades. Rates (1981) from £22–£36 per day for two rods (without/with boatman) or £110/180 per week (6 days). Full details from SRTI, Newport, Co Mayo. Tel (098) 41107. Beats arranged on **Lough Beltra** by Newport House Hotel which also rents boats on Lough Furnace and Feagh for guests. Other hotels: Abbeyville Guest House, Burrishoole, and Anglers', **Newport** *(see also Newport River).*

OWENMORE

Owenmore, 20m long and principally spate river from Bellacorick Bridge, rises near Ballycastle and flows into Blacksod Bay. Principal tributary is **Oweniny** (Crossmolian AA). River divided among number of owners. Good for spring salmon from April 1, given really high water; good grilse and sea trout from mid-June to end of Sept, if water is right. Upper and middle reaches owned by syndicate. Information from Dr I R Moore, 20 Temple Gardens, Dublin 6, and Terence Chadwick, Lissenhall, Swords. Lodges and fishings let by the fortnight when syndicate-members are not fishing. Enquiries respecting **Carrowmore Lough,** Bangor Erris, salmon, sea trout and brown trout, to Seamus Henry, Bangor Erris PO Ballina. Accommodation at Altnabrocky Lodge, **Bellacorick,** Ballina, Co Mayo, and at Glenmore Lodge, **Bangor Erris,** Co Mayo. For lower reaches inquire of Mr W J Sweeney, Bridge House, Achill, Westport.

OWENDUFF AND OWENGARVE

Owenduff good for salmon from end of Mar. Grilse and sea trout, mid-June to end of Sept. Provides excellent all-round fishing when water right. Upper reaches managed by F Chambers, Rock House, Ballycroy, Westport; 4½m both banks and entire stretch of **Bellareeny River** (sea trout) wt for 4 rods, £110. Dt (one rod) £11. Middle reaches: (1) Owned by Craigie Bros, Finglass, Co Dublin (no lettings). (2) Top beat, Rock House; lower beat, Lagduff Lodge. All privately held, but occasional lettings by lodges named. Lower down, a small beat is owned by Mr Justice Barra O'Briain of Enniskerry, Co Wiclow. Good accommodation, Shranamanragh Lodge, let with fishing and shooting by the month. Good for salmon (April/May), grilse and sea trout (July onwards).
Owengarve is a spate river. Grilse and sea trout, early June to early Oct. Most of river controlled by Newport AC, which has mutual agreement with Dr J Healey (Rosturk Castle, **Rosturk,** Westport, Co Mayo) whereby whole river can be fished. Daily, weekly and monthly rods available from club hon sec, £1.50, £4 and £6.

NEWPORT

Drains **Lough Beltra** and runs into Clew Bay, at **Newport,** Co Mayo. River over 7m long and usually fished from banks. Good for salmon and very good for sea trout. There are about 20 pools, some for both day and night fishing. Lower reaches are fly only, but spinning permitted above main weir. River known for length of season April to end Sept. Some 15m of fishing held by Newport House, 4m on **Skerdagh,** a tributary. Beltra is good early lake for salmon, and from late June very good for sea trout also. Fishing stations: **Newport** (Mayo) Hotel: Newport House (fishing on Newport River and five loughs; cabin cruisers on Clew Bay; *advt p 383).* St £125, mt £50, wt £20, dt £5 from hotel. Other hotel:

Anglers'. Various small trout loughs around Newport. Club: Newport AC, which issues permits for salmon and sea trout fishing (June to Sept) on small spate river near **Mulrany.** Hotel: Moynish House *(see also Sea Fishing Stations).* **Castlebar** (Mayo) is central also for **Loughs Conn** and **Cullen** (Good for salmon and very good for brown trout (1 lb to 7 lb); free; and for **Loughs Mask** and **Carra** (very good brown trout; good wet fly; best months, April–June, Aug, Sept; free; inquire hon sec, Lough Carra Trout AA for boats etc). Extensive lake system to south-west now reduced by drainage works to a single lake, but good trout can still be taken on **Islandreavy/Bilberry Lough.** Book with Austin Gibbons, Cloggernagh, Islandeady. Good coarse fishing in **Castlebar** area. Club: Castlebar and Dist Trout AA. Lough Conn AA, **Crossmolina,** Co Mayo, has been implementing an ambitious scheme for developing sport on lough; inquire of hon sec. Tackleists: O'Connor's; Quinn's; Hanley's. Hotels: Travellers' Friend, Imperial, Breaffy House.

Achill Island, off Mayo coast, has become famous in recent years for its sea fishing, including shark, large conger, pollack and ling; porbeagles of over 300 lb taken *(see Sea Fishing section).* **Keem Bay** is a favourite locality. There is some fishing in small lakes on the island for brown trout and also in Keel Lake for sea trout. Club: Achill Sporting Club. Hotel: Amethyst, Keel.

MOY

(For close seasons, licences, etc, see The North Western Regional Fisheries Board, pp 365–6)

Drains **Loughs Conn** and **Cullen** with numerous smaller loughs and joins Atlantic at Killala Bay through long estuary, at head of which stands Ballina. Salmon, sea trout. Very good salmon river and noted for grilse. Season: Spring fish, February to May; grilse, July onwards; good autumn run, Sept and Oct, sea trout in estuary (best July and Aug). Sea trout permits (free) from Manager, Moy Fishery, Ballina. Hotel: Mount Falcon Castle *(advt p 388)* also bookings for famous Ridge Pool on Moy. Hotels: Moy, Imperial, Hurst, Belleek Castle, Central and Downhill, the latter having its own cruiser for Moy Estuary and Killala Bay. At **Foxford** the Pontoon Bridge Hotel offers free salmon and trout fishing to guests on 4m of water, including famous salmon pool at Pontoon Bridge. Boats and ghillies available. Loughs Conn and Cullen are nearby. Other hotels: Hely's, Foxford, Anglers' Rest, Dolphin and Hughes' Guest House, Crossmolina, for Lough Conn. East Mayo AA has 6m of river near **Swinford;** tickets £3 day. Spring salmon best from mid-Mar, grilse June onwards. Hotel: O'Connors, numerous guest houses. **Palmerstown River,** 6m from Ballina, good for sea trout July to Oct, if there is a spate; free fishing, except for portion by Palmerstown Bridge leased by Ballina Dist AA; dt 75p from waterkeeper. **Loughs Conn** and **Cullen** provide good free fishing for salmon, trout and pike; trout fishing much improved since coarse fish clearance started by Inland Fisheries Trust. Record Irish pike (53 lb) caught in Lough Conn. Trout up to 5 lb. Boats at Gortnorabbey. Crossmolina (car park and caravan site); Cloghans, Gilbroo Bay and Phuilawokouse Bay. Boats also available on L Cullen but fishing not so good as Conn. **Lough Talt,** 10m east of Ballina, is good brown trout lake; free; boats available. **Crossmolina** is good centre for district. Club: Crossmolina AA.

SHANNON

(For close seasons, licences, etc, see The Shannon Regional Fisheries Board, pp 365–6)

Largest river in British Isles, 160m long with catchment area covering greater part of central Ireland. Enters Atlantic on west coast through long estuary. A typical limestone river, rich in weed and fish food, of slow current for most part, and though some of its sources rise in peat, acidity counteracted by limestone reaches. Many of the adverse effects of the Hydro-electric scheme introduced 45 years ago now overcome by re-stocking and other forms of fishery management. With exception of famous Castleconnell Fisheries, Shannon mostly sluggish. In few stretches, however, reasonably good salmon and grilse fishing can be obtained. Trout fishing poor except during mayfly rise, when excellent sport can be enjoyed, free of charge, in **Loughs Derg** and **Ree** at **Athlone;** trout grow large. River has a well-deserved reputation for its coarse fishing. Excellent pike, perch, bream and rudd at many centres. Coarse fishing can also be had in Derg and Ree. **Lough Allen,** northernmost lake of Shannon, specially good for pike.

Limerick (Limerick). On tidal Shannon. Good spring salmon fishing at **Parteen** (1m); and **Plassey** (2m); st £5; boat £7 from ESB. Six m above city is **Mulcair River,** a tributary of the Shannon; excellent fly water; best months June, July and Sept; st £23; wt £10; dt £3.50; st for brown trout, £2.20, all from Fisheries Office, ESB, 27 Lower Fitzwilliam Street, Dublin 2.

Castleconnell (Limerick). Principal centre for salmon angling on Shannon and within 3m of Mulcair River. Traditional big fish water; catches improved recently, despite salmon disease. Fishing on six Castleconnell beats controlled by Fisheries Manager, Electricity Supply Board, 27 Lower Fitzwilliam Street, Dublin, who will book beats and provide information. (Dt charges range from £3.30 to £12.10 VAT incl) available from Head Warden, M Murtaph, 10 Briens Bridge. Advance booking advisable. Best months for salmon and grilse, May, June, July and Sept. Trout fishing free. Coarse fishing in area good, especially for bream. Hotels: Lakeside, Killaloe; Cruises and Ardhu House, Limerick (8m).

Killaloe (Clare). At outlet from Lough Derg, good centre for trout and coarse fishing on lake. Trout angling can be very good in May and autumn; fish average 3 to 4 lb. Boats available.

Dromineer (Tipperary). Best centre for middle sections of **Lough Derg.** Large trout taken spinning or trolling; also good centre for dry fly and dapping; trout up to 10 lb caught. Mayfly starts about first week in May. Coarse fishing very good; large pike and perch. Boats and ghillies available; fishing free on lake, but small annual fee payable to Ormond AA for fishing on **Nenagh River,** which flows in at Dromineer. Salmon and trout, with coarse fishing, lower down. Salmon fishing free to licence holders. Hotels: Sail Inn, Dromineer; Ormond, O'Mearas, Carmel and Central in Nenagh. Tourist centre in Pearse Street, Nenagh, will give details of further accommodation.

Portumna (Galway). At north (inlet). end of **Lough Derg.** Hotel: Clonwyn (see Dromineer for fish, etc). Some good dapping bays within reach. Good centre for pike and perch in autumn. Towards Galway (19m from Portumna) is **Loughrea;** trout, pike and perch. Fishing open to members of Loughrea AA, which has improved and restocked water; trout average 2 lb, pike over 30 lb; best months (trout), April, May, June; good evening rise mid-Aug, mid-Sept; fly only for trout; pike fishing by arrangement, July–Aug; boats available. Accommodation at Lake Villa House. Further information from hon sec. Hotels at Loughrea: Central, Railway.

Banagher (Offaly). Hotel: Shannon. Salmon and trout, May to July. Coarse fishing good; boats obtainable. **Brosna** improving as salmon river, after trouble with drainage and peat pollution; permits £8.25 season from local office of ESB. Good fly fishing for brown trout (wet and dry) in tributaries **Clodiagh** and **Big Silver.** Good dry fly trout water and coarse fishing. **Tullamore** (Offaly) is good centre. Club: Tullamore and Dist AA. **Little Brosna,** which comes in some miles lower down, can best be fished from **Birr** (Offaly) Club: Birr and Dist AA. For salmon fishing, permit needed from Electricity Supply Board. Little Brosna gives good trout fishing throughout season, but especially good during mayfly (June–July); dry fly good. **Cam-Cor** river also at Birr, gives fine sport with large Shannon trout (end of June to end Sept) on large wet flies and spinner; another fishery, improved

by IFT management is 25-acre **Pallas Lake;** brown and rainbow trout; wet fly in spring and large dry patterns useful in Aug and Sept; fly only; bank only. Hotels: Dooley's, Egan's, County Arms.
Athlone (Westmeath and Roscommon). Athlone AA has water within 20m radius (visitors can fish for 50p); restocked with trout. Some salmon. Shannon and **Lough Ree** abound with trout (good rise to mayfly, late May to late June), pike, roach, and bream; bank or boat. Tench plentiful on Lough Ree. **Lough Garnafailagh,** which has produced remarkable catches of tench and bream, may be fished from here. Hotels: Royal, Prince of Wales, Hodson's Bay, Shamrock, Lodge and several smaller places. Tackleists: Browne's, Custome Place; Foy's, Hogan's, Church Street.
Lanesborough (Longford). Best station for upper Lough Ree. Hotels: Anchor; Lough Ree Arms. Other Shannon centres: **Rooskey** (coarse fish; accommodation at Killianker House); **Carrick-on-Shannon** (trout, coarse fish). Hotels: County (run by anglers). Bush, Cartown House, Brogans. **Clondara:** good trout water below Termonbarry Weir; also coarse fish; free. **Elphin:** coarse fish, trout. Graffa House has good accommodation.

Principal Tributaries of the Shannon

DEEL. Enters estuary near Askeaton some miles below Limerick. Fishing stations: **Rathkeale** (Limerick), and **Askeaton** (Limerick). Salmon (best Feb to May), white trout (on summer floods) and brown trout (good mid-Mar to Sept). Parts of river preserved by Mrs R Hunt, Inchirourke, Askeaton, and Altaville Estate. Hotels at Rathkeale: Central, Madigan's. Deel AA issues st for 15m water at Rathkeale. Nearest tackleists at Limerick.
MAIGUE. Enters estuary between mouth of Deel and Limerick. Salmon, trout, mostly preserved. Major drainage-work in progress, fishing at week-ends only. Fishing station: **Adare** (Limerick). Hotel: Dunraven Arms (1¼m fishing free to guests). Above Adare road bridge to Croom preserved. Some free tidal water below town. **Croom** (Limerick), Maigue AA. Issue wt £5 and dt £1.50. Further information from hon sec. Preserved water below town, free above to Bruree and beyond, wet and dry-fly water. **Bruree** (Limerick). Hotel: Murphy's. Tributaries **Camogue, Loobagh** and **Morningstar** mostly free and very good for trout. Centres: **Kilmallock,** where hon sec of angling association will help. **Kilfinane** (inquire hon sec. Development Assn, re cottages to let).
FERGUS. Limestone stream with gin-clear water, trout fishing good; few salmon in spring. Fishing free. Fishing station. **Ennis** (Clare). Good centre for fishing principal waters of Co Clare, including several coarse fish lakes and rivers (tench, pike, perch, rudd). Good brown trout fishing in Fergus and lakes it drains: **Loughs Inchiquin, Dromore, Atedaun,** and numerous smaller loughs. Inchiquin holds good stock of trout averaging 1/1¼ lb; in Dromore fish run larger; big duck fly hatch in Mar–April. On coast between **Doonbeg** and **Liscannor** are several rivers with fair runs of sea trout. Part of **Quin** at **Dromoland** and fishery in Falls Hotel grounds at **Ennistymon** preserved; latter free to hotel guests. Aberdeen Arms Hotel at **Lahinch** caters for anglers. Tackleist in Ennis: M Tierney, Church Street. Accommodation: Auburn Lodge, Old Ground, Queen's, West Country Inn. **Corofin** (Clare; Ennis 8m). Numerous lakes very good for trout, others for perch, rudd and tench, and all for pike. Accommodation at a number of family guest houses. **Lakes Inchiquin, Atedaun** and **Ballycullinan** and River Fergus close by; boats. Excellent bream and pike fishing in **Tulla** area; fishing free in about 40 lakes within 10m radius (Ennis 10m). Inquire hon sec, Tulla Coarse AA.
SUCK. Joins Shannon at **Shannon Bridge** between Banagheer and Athlone. Holds large brown trout in parts. Pike, bream, rudd and perch fishing very good. Fishing stations: **Ballinasloe** (Galway and Roscommon). Suck and tributaries, including Lough O'Flynn, controlled by CFB. Hotels: Hayden's, Holloway's, O'Carroll's. **Bunowen** and **Shiven** good early season waters. **Lough Acalla,** 8m from Ballinasloe; rainbow trout up to 7 lb, good for wet fly in June (CFB). **Castlerea** (Roscommon), station for upper reaches, which hold good trout. Hotels: McCormack's; O'Reilly's. **Lough O'Flynn** now excellent trout fishery thanks to IFT improvement work. Trout and coarse fish in **Lough Glinn. Roscommon** also good centre for Suck (3m; unlimited coarse fishing) and **Lough Ree** (5m). **Strokestown,** to north, is centre for fine coarse fishing on streams and loughs. River good for trout in mayfly season. Irish record rudd (3 lb 1 oz) caught in nearby **Kilglass Lake.** Hotels:

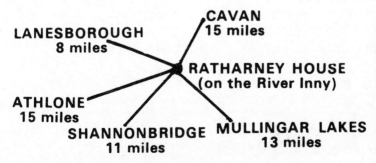

Greally's Royal, Central. Roscommon Gun and Rod Club have **River Hind;** trout; dry-fly water.
INNY. A slow-flowing river densely populated with roach, large bream and large tench. Trout between **Abbeyshrule** and **Shrule Bridge.** Fishing stations: **Ballymahon, Multyfarnham, Ballinalach, Granard Castlepollard, Mullingar.** Innay AA Control much fishing. **Mullingar** a good centre for the famous limestone lakes **Ennell, Owel** and **Derravaragh,** of large acreage and offering fly fishing of the highest order as trout rise freely to the succession of chironomids, ephemera and sedges which hatch almost continuously from April to the end of September. Average size of trout large: eg. 3 lbs 4 ozs on L Ennell in 1980. All developed by the IFT, now succeeded by the new Central Fisheries Board. Smaller private lakes, e.g. **Lough Lane** and **Lough Shelvior,** privately managed for trout and coarse fishing. St £3 from J O'Malley, tackleist, 33 Dominick Street, Mullingar, covers much water; information given on others. Hotels in Mullingar: Greville Arms, Broders. Hotels in Castlepollard: Pollard Arms, Brogan's, Kearney's. Near **Ballyjamesduff** lies **Lough Sheelin** st £5, dt £1 plus boat-charges. Sheelin Shamrock Hotel, on lakeside, and guest-houses, can provide boats and services. **Lough Kinale** (CFB; pike, perch, rudd, tench, some trout). **Cornagrow Lake** and **Bracklough** also afford good coarse fishing (pike, perch, rudd, tench). **Lough Gowna** (trout and coarse, including bream) is accessible from Granard. Hotels: Greville Arms, Macken's Guest House. Park Hotel, **Virginia,** is convenient for **Lough Ramor** (trout, coarse fish); also **River Blackwater** and other loughs. **BOYLE.** Connects **Lough Gara** and **Key.** Trout (good). Fishing station: **Boyle** (Roscommon). River, 6m long affected by drainage scheme; restocked by Boyle Trout Pres Assn. Hon sec, N R Johnston (tackleist), will give further information. Lough Key (coarse fish, trout). **Lough Arrow;** trout fishing improved by IFT (av 2¼ lb). Lough Key abounds in coarse fish and trout; free. Hotel Rock House *(advt p 392).*

SLANEY

(For close seasons, licences, etc, see The Eastern Regional Fisheries Board, pp 365–6)

Rises in corner between Barrow and Liffey watersheds and flows south 73m to Wexford Harbour. During most of course has rocky beds, rapids alternating with deep pools. Good salmon river, especially in Tullow-Bunclody reaches (Mar, April, May best; no autumn run) but of little account for brown trout save in upper reaches and in some tributaries. Good sea trout lower down and in tributaries **Urrin** and **Boro.** Best sea trout fishing around Enniscorthy. Most salmon fishing private, but certain parts let from season to season and no permission needed to fish for salmon or sea trout from Enniscorthy Bridge to Ferrycarrig (Feb 26 to Sept 15). Fishing station: **Wexford Lough.** Garman AC has made efforts to restock. **Owenduff;** good white trout fishing in June, July and Aug. **Sow River** near **Castlebridge** good for brown trout and sea trout; permits from angling club. Fishing for brown trout on **Wexford Reservoir,** st £2. Sea fishing (including sea trout, bass and mullet) in estuary. Tackleist: Bridges of Selskar, North Main Street. Hotels: Talbot, White's, County. **Enniscorthy.** Sea trout good; brown trout poor; free fishing downstream of bridge. Tackleists: Nolan, 3 Wafer Street, and C L Cullen, 14 Templeshannon. Hotels: Portsmouth Arms, Slaney Valley. **Tullow** (Carlow), Slaney; dt for trout fishing (fly only)

John Barr: it's smootherr by farr.

Tucked into a quiet glen near Dufftown on Speyside is the village and distillery of Mortlach.

For over one hundred and fifty years this small, traditional distillery in the heart of whisky country, has produced the soft, mellow malt whisky which forms part of the John Barr blend.

There are approximately forty carefully chosen single whiskies in John Barr. The result is an exceptionally smooth scotch which you might prefer to other blends.

GEORGE COWIE & SON LIMITED
MORTLACH.
DUFFTOWN, SCOTLAND.
DISTILLERS SINCE 1854.

from Tullow Salmon and Trout AA. Hotel: Slaney. At **Bunclody** (Wexford), Bunclody Trout AC has fishing for visitors. Tackleist (licences): Mrs Nolan, Irish Street, The Square.

SLIGO and LOUGH GILL

(including the Bonet, Ballysodare, Lough Arrow, Bundrowes and Lough Melvin)

(For close seasons, licences, etc, see The Eastern Regional Fisheries Board, pp 365-6)

Garavogue River connects Lough Gill with sea, which it enters in Sligo Bay to south of Donegal Bay and Erne. Salmon, trout, coarse fish. Fishing station: **Sligo** (Sligo). Hotels: Great Southern, Imperial, Grand, Kelley's, Clarence, Silver Swan, Jury's. **Lough Gill,** 2m away, holds salmon (spring), trout (av 2 lb, mayfly only) and pike, perch and bream. Fishing free except on preserved parts under control of Sligo AA. Permits from hon treasurer, E Armstrong, 68 Riverside and tackle shops. Lough Gill not a good fly water; trolling best for trout and salmon. Permits also cover fishing on south shore of Sligo portion of **Glencar Lake,** 7m; salmon (grilse), sea and brown trout; boat available. **Lough Colga,** 4m; brown trout; free; boat available to Sligo AA members. Tackleists in Sligo: F Nelson & Son Ltd; Barton Smith. Hotels: Innisfree, Sligo Park, Silver Swan and others.

BONET

Feeds Lough Gill. Salmon, trout. Best for salmon in summer. Fishing station: **Dromahaire** (Leitrim). Abbey Hotel has free, all-round fishing for guests. Manorhamilton AA also preserve some water; inquire hon sec.

BALLYSODARE

Formed by junction of three rivers, **Unshin** or **Arrow, Owenmore***, and **Owenbeg,** near Collooney. Unshin drains Lough Arrow and district lying south of Lough Gill. Near mouth of river, at Ballysodare Falls, is earliest salmon ladder erected in Ireland (1852). Salmon, trout, very few sea trout. About 2½m of salmon water let as complete fishery (usually in advance of season) by Lt-Commander Edward F P Cooper, Markree Castle, Collooney (not normally let for less than two weeks): wt £200, incl furnished lodge. Dt at times from Collooney and Dist AA. Best season, May to July. Fishing dependent on sufficient rain. Leave for sea and brown trout sometimes obtainable. Good dry fly. River contains sizeable pike; permission from riparian owners. Fishing station: **Collooney** (Sligo). **Lough Bo** fished from here (trout).

LOUGH ARROW

Lough Arrow is a rich limestone water of 3,123 acres on the border of Sligo and Roscommon. It is about 5m long and varies in width from ½m to 1½m. Unshin or Arrow River drains the lake into Ballysodare Bay. Arrow River joins Owenmore from Templehouse Lake near Collooney and the combined rivers form what is known locally as **Ballysodare River.** This is a well-known 2m salmon stretch. The lough is almost entirely spring-fed and has a place of honour among Ireland's best known mayfly lakes. Nowhere else is the hatch of fly so prolific or the rise to exciting. Three and four-pounders are common. Trout rise to mayfly from late May to mid-June and sport is varied at this time by wet-fly and dry-fly fishing with green drake and the spent gnat. This is followed soon after (mid-July to mid-Aug) by a late evening rise to big sedge called the murrough, which may give the lucky angler as much fun as mayfly. The marked improvement in fishing at Lough Arrow can be attributed to the removal of coarse fish from these waters by the Inland Fisheries Trust and regular stocking with trout. Boats and ghillies may be hired at all times and at many centres on lake shore. At **Ballinary** (Arrow Cottage) large fleet of boats available and nearby at **Ballindoon** is Rock House *(advt p 392),* a modernised and re-equipped hotel on the lakeside run by an angler of considerable experience, willing to

---

* *Not to be confused with Owenmore River, Co Mayo.*

help others. Boats arranged. **Feorish,** good trout stream nearby. Boats and accommodation also at **Ballinafad, Castlebaldwin, Heapstown Cross** and at **Boyle** and **Ballymote.** The last-named is in centre of Sligo's coarse fishing district. It caters for anglers to **Templehouse Lake** and **Cloonacleigha Lake** (good pike fishing, boats) and **Owenmore River.** Ballymote is also centre for **Lough na Leibe,** Ireland's first rainbow trout lake, and **Feenagh Lake,** where 2 lb trout will often appear among limit of six which CFB prescribes. Excellent hotel, guest house and private accommodation. Inquiries to Hon Sec, Tourist Assn, Ballymote, Co Sligo, **Lough Bo,** near Lough Arrow, provides good shore fishing for brown trout.

BUNDROWES AND LOUGH MELVIN

(For close seasons, licences, etc, see The Northern Regional Fisheries Board, pp 365–6)

About 4m south of Erne, Bundrowes River carries water of Lough Melvin to sea in Donegal Bay. **Bundoran** (Donegal) is 1½m from Bundrowes River and 3m from west end of Lough Melvin. Hotels: Great Southern, Central, Hamilton (6½m of salmon, sea trout and gillaroo trout fishing; boats and boatmen available). Permits for salmon and trout fishing from garage in main street. Sport with brown trout very good at times. River opens Jan 1 for salmon, Feb 15 for trout. Club: Bundoran AA, hon sec of which will be pleased to give information.

Part of Lough Melvin is in Northern Ireland and is served by village of **Garrison.** Hotels: Lakeside, Melvin; lake is free fishing except for two bays for which hotels issue permits. Other hotel: Casey's Lake. Lake has excellent run of early spring salmon and holds perch, brown trout (av ¾ lb), sonaghan (av ¾ lb), gillaroo (to 3½ lb), lake trout (to 9 lb), sea trout and a few char. Boats and boatmen from boat station at **Kinlough.**

SOUTH-WEST COASTAL STREAMS

(For close seasons, licences, etc, see The South Western Regional Fisheries Board, pp 365–6)

WATERVILLE (or Currane) and INNY

Waterville River, short river joining **Lough Currane** and sea in Co Kerry. Popular with visitors. Salmon, sea trout, brown trout. All migratory fish running to Lough Currane go through this river, which also has spring run of large sea trout. There is a commercial fishery, traps of which are lifted on July 15. Lough Currane (excellent trout and salmon fishing) free to licence-holders. Boats available. Inny River is late salmon river with sea trout; best season for salmon May to Oct. Fishing station: **Waterville.** Butler Arms has preserved fishing on four loughs (Derriana, Cloonaughlin, Coppal and Namona) plus six beats on the R Inny. Lakes: dt £5 to guests, £10 to others: river, dt £2 to guests, £3 to others. Lake Hotel has rights on Waterville River (Butler's Pool) and Inny and **Cummeragh Rivers,** and on Loughs Derriana, **Cummeragh, Nahiska,** Namona and Cloonaughlin; salmon, sea trout, brown trout. Season, Jan 17 to Oct 13. (Salmon: Sept 7). Boats and boatmen available at both hotels for freshwater and sea fishing. Bay View Hotel has similar extensive fishing rights and facilities. Dt issued at hotels. Guests at Bulter Arms can interchange meals and fishing with Lake Hotel, Killarney.

KENMARE BAY RIVERS

Several small salmon rivers empty into this bay, which provides excellent sea fishing (large skate, tope, etc). Best season, May to August. Fishing station: **Ardtully.** Kenmare Salmon AA own part of **Roughty.** Permits from T O'Shea, Kenmare: dt and wt, few spring salmon (March/April); good grilse runs (June to Aug); fly, spinning, prawning and worming permitted; fish average 9 lb. **Sheen** runs in on south shore and is preserved by owner. **Finnihy,** on north shore, is free fishing for brown trout, grilse and some sea trout in floods. **Kilgarvan** SA fish 10m of Roughty and **Slaheny** (salmon, sea trout, some brown trout); particularly good after spates. Mt and wt £5; dt £1. Visitors welcome. These rivers are all close to **Kenmare** (Kerry). Hotels: Great Southern, Lansdowne Arms, Central,

Kenmare Bay (sea fishing especially catered for); Riverdale House; and guest houses. **Cloonee,** on the south shore, drains four lakes; permits to fish some from Estate Office, Kenmare also for **Lough Inchiquin** and **Glenmore River and Lake,** for salmon and sea trout. Best months April, May, June and September. **Cloonee Lakes,** 8m south, provide excellent brown trout fishing with occasional salmon: boats and boatmen, accommodation, etc; apply to Lake Hotel, Lake House, Kenmare. **Loughs Uragh** and **Barfinnihy** and Finnihy River are fished by Kenmare AA; hon sec willing to help visitors. For fishermen with taste for mountain climbing there are at least 40 lakes holding brown trout on plateau of Caha Mountains, all easily fished from Kenmare. **Kerry Blackwater** drains **Lough Brin** and is preserved, but permission can be obtained from Estate Office, Kenmare. Blackwater is excellent salmon river, at its best in July and August, and also holds good stock of sea trout from June onwards. Ceimeen or **Glass Lakes** are easily fished from Kenmare; brown trout. **Sneem River,** farther west is preserved by owner. Further information from hon sec, Kenmare Salmon AA.

CARAGH

River runs through **Caragh Lake** to sea at Dingle Bay. Salmon, sea trout, trout (small). Salmon best Feb–April and Sept–Oct; sea trout best Sept–Oct. Bass and mullet in estuary. Fishing stations: **Glenbeigh** (Kerry) for lower water, where rights reserved for guests at Towers *(advt p 367)* and Glenbeigh Hotels. Guests can also fish 6m of **Laune** (single bank only), 8½m of **Feale,** 3m of **Flesk,** and **Behy** River and loughs **Caragh** and **Currane** (Waterville). **Glencar** (Kerry) for upper river. Hotel: Glencar, which has 7m of upper river (both banks) reserved for guests only; salmon; best months, Feb to end of June; grilse June onwards; sea trout. The hotel has also **Loughs Cloon, Acoose, Rea and Drombrain,** and Rivers **Meelagh, Brida, Owbeg, Owenroe** and **Small Caragh;** salmon, brown trout. Many smaller rivers and lakes holding brown trout. Gillies and boats available; wt £56, dt £9, also tackle and licences at hotel *(advt below).*

The tailer in use on the Blackwater. A much under employed item of landing equipment. *Photograph: S. J. Newman.*

BANTRY BAY RIVERS

Rivers within easy reach of **Bantry** are **Ilen** (see Ilen), **Dunnamark** (private), **Owvane** (3½m; spate stream, fair salmon run in March; sea trout late May; mostly free; Ballyhahill AA welcomes visiting anglers), **Snave** (5m; similar to Owvane), **Glengariff** (11m; spate river; salmon and sea trout only fair but good early run of latter; Glengariff AA has water). Brown trout fishing in rivers poor, but good sport sometimes had on loughs: **Bofinna** (3m; fish average 6 oz and reach 1 lb; best March, April, May). **Farnamanagh** (17m; free; fish average 9 or 10 oz; late evening usually best; fancy flies). Loughs **Avaul** (Upper and Little); tickets from keeper; trout to 2 lb; boat on upper lake from keeper). Numerous other lakes hold trout of 4 oz to 1 lb. **Reenydonagan L** (between Bantry and Ballylickey) 6 acre tidal lake stocked with brown trout averaging 1½ lb (two boats). Boats for sea fishing can be hired; inquire Bantry Bay Sea AA.

VARTRY

(For close seasons, licences, etc, see The Eastern Regional Fisheries Board, pp 365–6)

Small river which can be reached from Dublin (25m) drains **Roundwood Reservoir** and flows into sea near Wicklow. Sea trout in lower reaches, brown trout (small). Reservoir can be fished; dt £1, boat £2 from Dublin Waterworks Office, Castle Street, Dublin, or from the Superintendent, Vartry Lodge, Roundwood. Fishing station: **Rathnew** (Wicklow). Hotel: Hunter's.

SEA FISHING STATIONS IN THE IRISH REPUBLIC

As elsewhere, the sea fishing in the Irish Republic has been growing in popularity. The inshore potential of these waters is now widely appreciated. Bass are much sought after along the south and west coasts, and pollack are abundant off the rocks. Deep-sea boats land specimen skate, conger, halibut, turbot and so on. Fishing facilities are improving all the time. Space will not permit more than a few centres to be listed, but club secretaries and local tackleists will be pleased to give further information and to help visitors.

Rosslare (Wexford). Fishing from shore and pier, but mainly from boats up to 50 ft. Latter can reach Tuskar Rock, famous offshore mark; smaller craft, 18–20 ft, fish Splaugh Rock, excellent bass mark. Apart from bass, main species are flatfish and tope. Many bass taken on spinner from boats. Several boatmen. Tackleist: Bolands Garage, Rosslare Harbour, John Murphy and also Bridges, both N Main Street, Wexford. Club: Rosslare Harbour SAC, which holds competitions.

Kilmore quay (Wexford). Bass from shore; boat and pier. St Patrick's Bridge, reef of rocks to east of harbour, is good boat mark. Excellent pollack, bass and tope around Saltee Islands. Surf fishing for bass and tope at Ballyteigne Bay. Mullet and flatfish abound. Lugworm from harbour. Trawlers and lobster boats available for parties and bookable in advance. Other boats from Fethard. Club: Kilmore Quay SAC. Tackleists in Rosslare, Wexford and Kilmore Quay.

Dungarvan (Waterford). Harbour popular venue for mullet; also good bass and flounders. Pier at Helvick provides good sport with congers, and mullet taken in Helvick Harbour. Bass now spasmodic. Blue shark plentiful. Also pollack off Black Rock, flatfish and dogfish bottom fishing. Boats from Harbour. Crab and lugworm on foreshore. Boats from Bowmans (Fishing Tackle Dept) Tel 05841395 and Casey (Fishing Tackle) Tel 05841738. £7–£8 per person per day. Rods for hire.

Youghal (Cork). Fishing in Youghal Harbour; shore; pier mainly for bass (April–Oct), pollack (July–Sept), mackerel (July–Aug), codling (May–Sept), and sea trout (June–Aug). Youghal Bay: bass (April–Oct), pollack (May–Nov), mackerel (May–Nov), and sea trout (June–Aug). Deep-sea fishing, except bass and sea trout as for Bay plus skate (April–Oct), blue shark (June–Oct), conger (May–Nov), ling (May–Nov), and some other species same period. Tackleists: various shops and on deep-sea boats. Charter-boat for 8 anglers. £70. Hotels: Hilltop Hotel and Walter Raleigh. Guesthouses: various. General inquiries to Capt M Vastenhout, Stonebridge Cottage.

Ballycotton (Cork). One of the best-known of Irish sea fishing centres; large catches of prime fish and excellent facilities. Skate, blue shark, tope, porbeagle, cod, ling, pollack. coalfish, bass, conger are among species taken. Fishing from shore, pier, rocks or boat; best shore fishing at Ballymona; big bass. Good mullet in harbour. Several boatmen but early booking advised. Tackleist: J A Connolly, Corner Shop (hon sec Ballycotton Sea AC), who will be pleased to give local information. Monthly competitions May to Oct. Principal hotels: Bay View, Congress.

Kinsale (Cork). Best-known centre on the south coast for deep-sea fishing, esepcially for shark. Famous marks at Ling Rocks, Pango Reef, off the Old Heads, and the wreck of the "Lusitania". Blue shark, skate, ling, conger, dogfish, rays, pollack, coalfish, red bream and wrasse. Well-equipped boats and experienced skippers. Charges: (deep-sea) £13 pd, (harbour and estuary of Bandon River) self-drive boats at £4 per hour. Two comprehensively organised angling centres; Trident and Kinsale. Club: Kinsale Sea AC; monthly competitions and annual festival. Irish Shark Club; occasional competition and annual festival (addresses in club list). Other hotels: Actons, Perryville House, Blue Haven. Many guest-houses, in and out of town.

Rosscarbery (Cork). Noted for surf fishing for bass; three fine beaches. Bass and mullet also taken in small harbour, and from mouth of estuary. Lugworm and ragworm in estuary, sandeel from beach. Boats for inshore fishing. Club: Rosscarbery SAC.

Baltimore (Cork). Shark (very good, July–Oct), skate, conger, tope, ling, cod, pollack and mackerel from boats; pollack, bass and mackerel from shore. Best June–Oct. Deep-sea angling boats from Baltimore Deep Sea AC. Boats with outboards from R Kennedy. Club: Baltimore DSAC. Tackleists: Fuller & Co.

Castletownbere (Cork). Good sheltered fishing in Berehaven and offshore at marks in Bantry Bay. Shark, pollack, ling, conger, ray, skate, pouting, huss, bream, wrasse, spurdog, gurnard, flounder, plaice, grey mullet, whiting and mackerel. Tackleist and tourist agent: C Moriarty, The Square. Club: Castletownbere SAC. Hotels: Cametrignane and Beara Bay.

Caherciveen (Kerry). For **Valentia Island**. Catches include conger (up to 72 lb), turbot (to 26 lb), halibut (to 152 lb), skate (to 218 lb), red bream (to 9 lb), bass (to 16 lb). Also large gurnard, mackerel, garfish, tope and blue shark. Boat fishing most popular, but good sport also from shore. International Deep Sea Festival at Caherciveen in Aug. Club: Valentia Harbour Sea AC. Information from Tourist Office, Caherciveen and Atlantic Holidays (Caherciveen 107); Kerry Boats Ltd (Caherciveen 122); Rod & Reel Ltd (Caherciveen 120).

Dingle Peninsula (Kerry). Provides some of best surf fishing for bass in British Isles; good centres are **Smerwick, Cloghane** and **Castlegregory**. Offshore fishing also very good; large pollack, coalfish, sea bream, conger and ling caught off rocky ground. Big skate, tope, turbot and halibut also taken. Late autumn, winter and early spring best for bass. Club: Dingle SAC.

Clifden (Co Galway). First-class boat and shore angling in sheltered conditions. Blue shark, tope, coalfish, pollack, skate, ray, ling, cod, turbot, brill and plaice. Good marks include: Slyne Head; Barrister wreck off Inishark; Inishbofin, Inishturk and Fosteries Shoals. Other good bays are Mannin, Ballinakill, Killary, Roundstone, Cleggan and Bunowen. Tackleists: E Sullivan, Main Street, and P Stanley, Market Street. Boats from F. Mannion, J O'Grady, G Jeffries, all Market Street, and J Ryan,

Main Street. Sea trout and brown trout fishing available *(see freshwater section)*. Club: Clifden Sea AC. Hotels: Clifden Bay, Alcock and Brown, Abbeyglen, Clifden House, Atlantic Coast and Celtic. Boats available at Bunowen and Roundstone.

Westport (Mayo). Good boat and shore fishing. Local clubs run nine of forty-eight sea angling competitions in the area each year. Fish caught include: the record monkfish (69 lb), skate (up to 167½ lb), tope and conger (to 40 lb and more), cod, codling, pollack, flounders, plaice, gurnard, coalfish, bass, wrasse, turbot, dogfish, white skate (146 lb), and blue shark (up to 206 lb) and porbeagle shark and tunny. Dr O'Donnell Browne's 365 lb porbeagle was taken here. Good marks include Tower in Inner Bay, off Lighthouse, Pigeon Point, Cloghormack Buoy, Sheltered sport in Clew Bay. Tackleists: Hewetson's, Dyar's Bridge Street; Clarke's, The Octagon; Mulloy's & Gibbons, Shop Street. Club: Westport Sea AC and Westport Boat Club.

Achill Island (Mayo). Excellent boat fishing; pollack, conger, ling, tope, flatfish, etc; fish run large. Noted area for blue shark; July–Oct best; also thresher and porbeagle. Tunny also reported in area. Pollack fishing off rock produces specimens in 15 lb class. Flatfish from Tullaghan Bay on north side of island. Boats from McHugh, Bullsmouth; Bradley and Jim O'Gorman, both Dooagh. Tackleist: Sweeny and Son, Achill Sound. Hon sec, Achill Tourist Development Ltd and Achill Sea AC, will supply further details. Hotel: Beach House (boats and tackle for hire).

Newport (Mayo). One of Eire's finest sea fishing centres. Large mackerel, tope, skate, conger, dogfish, monkfish, whiting, coalfish, pollack, gurnard and sea trout may be taken in Clew Bay. Boats (motor, sailing and rowing), tackle and information from P McIntyre, Acres. Hotel: Abbey Ville, Newport House.

Belmullet (Mayo). Rapidly rising in popularity as sea-fishing centre. Sheltered water, Turbot, bream and pollack especially good. Belmullet Sea AC developing facilities; inquire hon sec. Deep-sea cruisers available. Annual festival.

Moville (Donegal). Foyle Sea AC arranges Lough Foyle Festival of Sea Angling. Tope, conger, skate, pollack, cod, gurnard, plaice, ling and others. Plenty of boats (20 ft–30 ft) and bait. At **Rosapenna** (Downings) is excellent boat fishing for tope. For deep-sea bookings apply Mrs C O'Donnell, "The Fleets Inn", Downings (Tel: 21). Other information from Donegal Deep Sea Angling Ltd, 1 Mount Southwell, Letterkenny. Tackleists: Co-operative Stores. Many hotels.

FISHING CLUBS ETC. IN THE IRISH REPUBLIC

THE following is an alphabetical list of angling clubs and associations in the Irish Republic. Particulars of the waters held by many will be found, by reference to the index, in the section headed "Fishing Stations in the Irish Republic", and information about the others, which may not have their own water, could be had from the secretaries, whose addresses are given. A stamped/addressed envelope should be enclosed with inquiries.

NATIONAL BODIES

Anglers' Information Service Bord Failte (Irish Tourist Board). Baggot Street Bridge, Dublin 2. Telephone: Dublin 65871.

Clean Waters Association. P J Cassidy, 11 Westmoreland Street, Dublin 2.

Irish Federation of Sea Anglers. Capt G Moorkens, Endsleigh, Templeogue Road, Terenure, Dublin 6.

Department of Fisheries and Forestry, Agriculture House, Kildare Street, Dublin 2. (Tel: 789011).

Irish Shark Club. Thadaei K Dempsey, The Glen, Kinsale, Co Cork.

Irish Specimen Fish Committee. D Brennan, Balnagowan, Mohbi Boreen, Glasnevin, Dublin 9.

National Salmon Anglers' Federation of Ireland. P J Concannon, 23 St Assam's Avenue, Raheny, Dublin (Tel 335888).

Trout Anglers' Federation of Ireland. P J Byrne, 33 College Street, Newbridge, Co Kildare.

Abbeyfeale Salmon Anglers' Association. J Fitzgibbon, The Square, Abbeyfeale, Co Kerry.

Achill Sea Angling Club. Pat Walsh, Curraun, Achill, Co Mayo.

Achill Sporting Club. David Quinn, Achill Sporting Club, Keel, Achill Island, Co Mayo.

Araglien Anglers' Association. John B Murphy, "Harp and Shamrock", Kiskeam, Co Cork.

Ardara Anglers' Association. J McGill, Ardara, Co Donegal.

Ardfinnan Angling Association. Matthew O'Sullivan, Ardfinnan, Clonmel, Co Tipperary.

Argideen Anglers' Asscociation. Mrs Claire O'Reagan, Hill Terrace, Bandon, Co Cork.

Askeaton Angling Association. M McCarthy, 13 St Francis Avenue, Askeaton, Co Limerick.

Athlone Anglers' Association. Jack Brennan, 1 Wolfe Tone Terrace, Athlone, Co Westmeath.

Atlantic Sea Angling Club. C Gannon, The Bungalow, Glenties, Co Donegal.

Athy Angling Association. P S Mulhall, Athy Sports, 20 Emily Square, Athy, Co Kildare.

Ballaghaderreen Angling Association. J. McGoldrick, St Mary's Terrace, Ballaghaderreen, Co Roscommon.

Ballina Trout Anglers' Association. Sean O'Connell, 5 Humbert Street, Ballina, Co Mayo.

Ballinasloe Anglers' Association. Mattie Cunningham, c/o Gibbons, Society Street, Ballinasloe, Co Galway.

Ballinrobe and District Anglers' Association. R Ansbro, 59 New Street, Ballinrobe, Co Mayo.

Ballybay and District Angling Association. P. Murname, Main Street, Ballybar, Co Monagham.

Ballybofey and Stranolar Angling Association. Jas Harkin, Finn View Terrace, Ballybofey, Lifford, Co Donegal.

Ballycotton Sea Anglers' Club. Mrs Sheila Egan, Ballycotton SAC, Main Street Ballycotton, Co Cork (Tel 646786).

Ballyduff Trout Fly Angling Association. J Tobin, Ballyduff, Co Waterford.

Ballyhahill Angling Association. Patrick, J Walsh, Ballyhahill, co Limerick.

Ballymote and District Angling Association. Michael Rogers, O'Connell Street, Ballymote, Co Sligo.

Ballyshannon and District Trout Anglers' Association. P McGettigan, Main Street, Condon, Ballyshannon, Co Donegal.

Baltimore Deep Sea Angling Club. Mr Heffer, Stone House, Baltimore, Co Cork.

Bandon River Angling Association. G P Baines, Riversdale, Bandon, Co Cork.

Bandon River Salmon and Trout Anglers' Association. D Cahill, Casement Road, Bandon, Co Cork.

Bantry Angling Association. D J Ducker, Beach, Bantry, Co Cork.

Barrow Angling Club. Brendan Nolan, 38 Burrin Street, Carlow.

Belmullet Sea Angling Club. Sean Gannon, American Street, Belmullet, Co Mayo.

Belturbet Angling Club. Sean McGovern, The Lawn, Belturbet, Co Cavan.

Birr and District Anglers' Association. Fred Ryan, 16 Moorpark Street, Birr, Co Offaly.

Boyle Trout Preservation Association. N R Johnston, Main Street, Boyle, Co Roscommon.

Brittas Fishing Club. Desmond Clarke, 22 Palmerston Park, Dublin 6.

Buncrana Anglers' Association. Major S Spragg, Fahan, Co Donegal.

Bundoran and District Angelers' Association. B MacCafaid, Ardan Muire, Bundoran, Co Donegal.

Cahir and District Anglers' Association. Denis McGrath, NT, Old Church Street, Cahir, Co Tipperary.

Cahirciveen Angling Association. P Donnelly, Valentia Road, Cahirciveen, Co Kerry.

Cappoquin Angling Club. J L Landers, (asst sec), Tivoli Terrace, Cappoquin, Co Waterford.

Carlow Angling Association. B Nolan, 38 Burrin Street, Carlow.

Carlow Salmon Angling Association. N Sheehan, Upper Burrin, Carlow.

Carrick-on-Shannon Angling Club. E Gray, Cartown House, Carrick-on-Shannon, Co Leitrim.

Carrick-on-Suir and District Anglers' Association. P J O'Sullivan, Park View, Carrick-on-Suir, Co Donegal.

Cashel Tipperary and Golden Anglers' Association. John Evans, Main Street, Tipperary, Co Tipperary.

Castlebar and District Trout Anglers' Association. T Coucill, Humbert Inn, Main Street, Castlebar, Co Mayo.

Castlebar Salmon Anglers' Club. Gerard A McCormack, Saleen, Castlebar, Co Mayo.

Castleblayney Trout Anglers' Federation. B Geoghegan, Castleblayney, Co Monaghan.

Castlebridge Anglers' Association. W Shortle, Castlebridge, Co Wexford.

Castletown Trout Anglers' Club. D Twomey, Castletownbere, Co Cork.

Castletownbere Sea Angling Club. Dr C H Phillips, Mill Cove, Waterfall, Nr Castletownbere, Bantry, Co Cork.

Castletownbere Trout Anglers Club. Dr C H Phillips, Mill Cove, Waterfall, Nr Castletownbere, Bantry, Co Cork.

Castletownroche Angling Club. J A Batterbury, Main Street, Castletownroche, Co Cork.

Cavan Angling Club. Sean Young, Main Street, Cavan, Co Cavan.

Clifden Anglers' Association. Hugh Griffin, Clifden, Connemara.

Clifden Sea Angling Club. F Connolly, Derryclare Guest House, Clifden, Co Galway.

Clogheen and District Anglers' Association. M G Gleeson, Cascade View, Clogheen, Co Tipperary.

Clonakilty Angling Association. David Spiller, 39 Pearse Street, Clonakilty, Co Cork.

Clonbur Trout Angling Association. P H O'Malley, Clonbur, Co Mayo.

Clones and District Anglers' Association. P F Goodwin, Fermanagh Street, Clones, Co Monaghan.

Clonmel and District Salmon and Trout Anglers' Association. Permits: J Kavanagh, Westgate, Clonmel, Co Tipperary.

Cloone Angling Association. Owen Mitchell, Keeldra, Cloone, Co Leitrim.

Coachford Trout Anglers' Association. E Hayes, Nadrid, Coachford, Co Cork.

Cobh Sea Angling Club. E W Cullinane, 1 O'Donovan Place, Cobh, Co Cork.

Coleraine Angling Association. Eugene Hayes, Nadrid, Coachford, Co Cork.

Collooney and District Angling Association. G B McKenzie, The Rapids, Ballysodare, Co Sligo.

Cong Angling Association. I V Stenson, Cong, Co Mayo.

Cootehill Anglers' Club. M McCluskey, NT, Bridge Street, Cootehill, Co Cavan.

Cork and District Trout Anglers' Club. Paul Mellamphy, 49 Ballyhooly Road, Cork.

Cork Salmon Anglers' Association. W Cronin, Lisieux, Cross Douglas Road, Cork.

Cork Sea Angling Club. D Looney, 37 Mumount Circle, Montenotte, Cork.

Cork Trout Anglers' Association. Joe Cahill, 87 Patrick Street, Cork.

Corofin Salmon Anglers' Association. H F McCullagh, Eyre Square, Galway, Co Galway.

Co Longford Angling Association. Peter Malone, 121 Sefton Park, Longford.

Co Wicklow Anglers' Association. T Hore, 2 Milton Terrace, Seapoint Road, Bray, Co Wicklow.

Co Wicklow (Salmon) Angling Association. H U Valentine, Shankhill, Ravenscur, Co Dublin.

Crosshaven Sea Anglers' Club. A Scully, Four Winds, Myrtleville, Co Cork.

Crossmolina Anglers' Club. Frank Corduff, Ballina Street, Co Mayo.

Culdaff Angling Association. B. Doherty, Donagh Stores, Carndonagh, Co Donegal.

Cullane and District Anglers' Association. J O'Brien, Tulla, Co Clare.

Dee and Glyde Angling Association. A O'Callaghan, Castlebellingham, Co Louth.

Deel and Boyne Angling Association. E E Wright, Hyde Park, Killucan, Co Westmeath.

Deel Anglers' Association. Brian Sparling, The Garage, Croagh, Rathkeale, Co Limerick.

Deele Angling Association. P Hoey, Raphoe Road, Convoy, Lifford, Co Donegal.

Derravaragh Anglers' Association. Sean Rielly, Rathganny, Multyfarnham, Co Westmeath.

Dingle Anglers' Association. M E Burke, Solicitor, Green Street, Dingle, Co Kerry.

Dingle Sea Angling Club. Leo Brosnan, 13 Marian Park, Dingle, Co Kerry.

Dodder Angling Club. R O'Hanlon, 82 Braemore Road, Dublin 14.

Donegal Anglers' Association. Sean McBrearty, Drumcliffe, Donegal.

Drogheda and District Anglers' Club. Thos Doherty, 107 Avenue 1, Yellow Batter, Drogheda, Co Louth.

Drogheda Sea Angling Club. R Ryan, 24 William Street, Drogheda, Co Louth.

Drumshanbo AC and Tourist Development Assn. Joseph Mooney, Drumshanbo, Co Leitrim.

Dublin and District Salmon Anglers' Association. S Canavan, 10 St Patrick's Park, Clondalkin, Co Dublin.

Dublin City Sea Anglers. P Gratten, 20 Deanstown Avenue, Finglas W, Dublin 11.

Dublin Coarse Fish Angling Club. Bernard Hanson, 47 Eaton Square, Terenure, Dublin 6.

Dublin Trout Anglers' Association. Major Patrick McDonagh, 151 Foxfield Park, Dublin 5.

Dundalk and District Salmon Anglers' Association. James J Donegan, Rock Manor, Dunleer, Co Louth.

Dundalk and District Trout Anglers' Club. J T Quinn, 19 St Patrick's Terrace, Dundalk, Co Louth.

Dungarvan and District AA. Jas Kiely, 1 Shandon Street, Dungarvan, Co Waterford.

Dungarvan Sea Angling Club. (Phone 058 41395).

Dun Laoghaire Sea Anglers' Association. K Bolster, 136 Beaumont Road, Beaumont, Dublin 9.

Dunmanway Salmon and Trout Anglers' Association. Sean Lomasney, East Green, Dunmanway, Co Cork.

Dunmore East Sea Angling Club. John Walsh, "Morion", Morymont, Ferrybank, Waterford, Co Kerry.

East Mayo Anglers' Association. E Kennedy, The Modern House, Swinford, Co Mayo.

Ennis and District Anglers' Association. D P Nonan, The Square, Ennis, Co Clare.

Feale Salmon and Trout Anglers' Association. Patrick Mann, Church Street, Abbeyfeale, Co Limerick.

Fealebridge and Brosna Angling Association. J O'Connor, NT, Knockbrack NS, Knocknagoshel, Co Kerry.

Fermoy and District Trout Anglers' Association. P J O'Reilly, Church Place, Fermoy, Co Cork.

Fermoy Salmon Anglers' Association. Patric, Phelan, 1 Chapel Square, Fermoy, Co Cork.

Finn Valley Anglers' Association. P J Coll, Castlefinn, Co Donegal.

Foxford Salmon Anglers' Association. Peter Tolan, Maryville, Foxford, Co Mayo.

Foyle Sea Angling Club. T Mehan, Malin Road, Moville, Co Donegal.

Galway and Corrib Anglers' Association. Thomas J Browne, Rockport, 9 Maunsell's Road, Galway, Co Galway.

Galway Bay Sea Angling Club. Mrs K Conroy, "Porres", Dublin Road, Renmore, Co Galway.

Galway Deep-Sea Fishing Association. S O'Ciardubain, 13 Pearse Avenue, Mervue, Galway, Co Galway.

Garda Angling Club. B Prendergast, Garda Club, 9–10 Harrington Street, Dublin 8.

Glanmire and District Anglers' Association. J O'Sullivan, Lotamore Cottage, Glanmire, Co Cork.

Glenbower Trout Anglers' Club. M Lee, Main Street, Killeagh, Co Cork.

Glengariff Anglers' Association. A P Tisdall, Firlands, Glengariff, Co Cork.

Glengariff Sea Angling Club. John Power, Reemeen, Glengariff, Co Cork.

Glenties Anglers' Association. C McDyer, Glenties, Co Donegal.

Gort and District Anglers' Association. Colman Keane, Gort, Co Galway.

Gweedore Angling Association. William Alcorn, Bunbeg, Letterkenny, Co Donegal.

Headford and Corrib AA. Kevin Duffy, Headford, Co Galway.

Ilen River Anglers' Association. M O'Keefe, Gortnacloy, Skibbereen, Co Cork.

Inny Anglers' Association. James Nally, Greenview, Multyfarnham, Co Westmeath.

Kells Anglers' Association. W Fitzgerald, Church Street, Kells, Co Meath.

Kenmare Bay Deep-Sea Anglers. Club. M J O'Connor, 12 Main Street, Kenmare, Co Kerry.

Kenmare Salmon Anglers' Association. Tony O'Shea, Henry Street, Kenmare, Co Kerry.

Kilbride Anglers' Club. J J Johnston, 54 Avondale Park, Raheny, Dublin 5.

Kilgarvan Anglers' Association. M O'Donovan, Killafadda Cottage, Kilgarvan, Co Kerry.

Kilkenny Anglers' Association. P A Troy, College Road, Kilkenny, Co Kilkenny.

Killala and Dist Sea Angling Association. Mrs B Maughan, Barrack Street, Killala, Co Mayo.

Killybegs Sea Angling Club. B O'Callaghan, St Catherine's Road, Killybegs, Co Donegal.

Kilmallock and Disrict Angling Club. Denis O'Keepfe, Glenfield, Kilmallock, Co Limerick.

Kilmore Quay Sea Angling Club. E J Doyle, Kilmore Quay, Co Wexford.

Kilworth and Dist Angling Club. Dan Roche, 11 McDermot Place, Fermoy, Co Cork.

Kinsale Sea Anglers' Club. D Enright, Villa Pio, Monkstown, Co Cork.

Laune Anglers' Association. G W Gallagher, "Doirin", Ballyvelly, Tralee, Co Kerry.

Letterkenny and District Anglers' Association. P McLoone, 114 Ard O'Donnell, Letterkenny, Co Donegal.

Limerick and District Anglers' Association. P J Power, 139 Lynwood Park, Limerick, Co Limerick.

Longwood Anglers' Association. M F Bird, Riverview, Longwood, Co Meath.

Lough Arrow Fish Preservation Association. C J Doyle, NT, Corrigeenroe, Ballinafad via Boyle, Co Roscommon.

Lough Carra Trout Anglers' Association. Sean Murphy, Moorehall, Ballyglass, Claremorris, Co Mayo.

Lough Conn Angling Association. J Marrinan, Erris Street, Crossmolina, Co Mayo.

Lough Derg Anglers' Association. Hon Sec, Portumna, Co Galway.

Lough Ennel Preservation Association. Supt John Doddy, Garda Siochana, Mullingar, Co Westmeath.

Lough Garman (Sea and River) Angling Club. W J Guilfoyle, 12 Casa Rio, Wexford, Co Wexford.

Lough Lein Anglers' Association, P Curan, St Anthony's Place, Killarney, Co Kerry.

Lough Mask Angling Preservation Society. T Molloy, Tourmakeady, Co Mayo.

Lough Owel Trout Preservation Association. L W Murray, Mount Murray, Bunbrosna, Mullingar, Co Westmeath.

Loughrea Anglers' Association. John F Quinn, Caheronaun, Loughrea, Co Galway.

Lough Sheelin Trout Protection Association. R A Kilroy, Moydristan, Kilnaleck, Co Cavan.

Louisburgh and Dist AA. J J Chilbin, Bridge Street, Louisburgh, Co Mayo.

Macroom Trout Anglers' Association. B Baker, South Square, Macroom, Co Cork.

Maigue Anglers' Association. E P Costello, Ballycarney, Co Limerick.

Mallow Trout Anglers' Association. Tom Purcell, "Avondhu", Town View, Mallow, Co Cork.

Manorhamilton and District Anglers' Association. P L Coyle, Hazelville, Manorhamilton, Co Leitrim.

Mohill Angling Association. M Cox, Hill Street, Mohill, Co Leitrim.

Moy Angling Association. P Tolan, Foxford, Co Mayo.

Muckross Fisheries Trust. T Hennebery, The Manor House, Tralee, Co Kerry.

Newport Angling Club. Martin Maguire, Castlebar Road, Newport, Co Mayo.

Newport Sea Angling Club. Tony Burns, Mullrany Road, Newport, Co Mayo.

North Clare Anglers' Association. Kevin Duffy, Ennestymon, Co Clare.

North Kerry Salmon Anglers' Association. L P O'Farrell, 75 Church Street, Listowel, Co Kerry.

North Kildare Trout and Salmon Anglers' Association. Patrick Byrne, 21 College Park, Newbridge, Co Kildare.

Old Head Sea Angling Club. J. Donovan, 19 Richmond, Black Rock Road, Cork.

Oughterard Angling Association. Joseph Lydon, Oughterard, Co Galway.

Pontoon and Foxford Angling Association. M P Howley, Gurteen, Foxford, Co Mayo.

Prosperous Fishing Club. E O'Farrell, Prosperous, Naas, Co Kildare.

Roscommon Gun and Rod Club. John F Neilan, Abbey Street, Roscommon, Co Roscommon.

Rosscarbery Sea Angling Club. Kenneth Casey, Tanyard Hill, Rosscarbery, Co Cork.

Roscrea and District Angling Association. M O'Connell, Abbey Street, Roscrea, Co Tipperary.

Rosses Fishery Anglers' Association. John Doherty, Dungloe, Co Donegal.

Rosslare Sea Angling Club. J F O'Brien, Villa Nova, Rosslare Harbour, Co Wexford.

Sligo Anglers' Association. J McCarney, Annalen, Cornageeha, Sligo, Co Sligo.

Strokestown Angling Club. George Gearty, Bridge Street, Strokestown, Co Roscommon.

Swords Angling Club. R Shortt, Church Road, Swords, Co Dublin.

Tallow Anglers' Association. John Forde, Main Street, Tallow, Co Waterford.

Templemore Anglers' Association. Michael Devanney, 11 Park Road, Templemore, Co Tipperary.

Thurles, Holycross and Ballycamas AA. Muiris O Cleirigh, Turtulla, Thurles, Co Tipperary.

Tralee Anglers' Association. T Hennebery, The Manor House, Tralee, Co Kerry.

Tramore/Waterford Sea Angling Club. J Cashin, 21 Rockshire Road, Ferrybank, Waterford, Co Waterford.

Trim, Athboy and District Anglers' Association. P McManus, Manorland, Trim, Co Meath.

Tulla and District Coarse Angling Association. Brian A Culloo, Tulla, Co Clare.

Tullow Salmon and Trout Anglers' Association. P Lennon, c/o Slaney Hotel, Tullow, Co Carlow.

Upper Blackwater Angling Association. T Moynihan, Ballydesmond, Mallow, Co Cork.

Valentia Harbour Sea Angling Club. Michael Quinlan, Cahirciveen, Co Kerry.

Virginia and District Angling Association. M MacNamee, Virginia, Co Cavan.

Waterford Trout Anglers' Association. Post vacant, inquire local tackleists.

West Clare Angling Association. F Meaney, Francis Street, Kilrush, Co Clare.

Westport and District Anglers' Club. M Berry, James Street, Westport, Co Mayo.

Westport Sea Angling Club. Vincent Coakley, Quay Road, Westport, Co Mayo.

Westport Boat Club. M Brooker, Westport.

Wexford and Dist Sea Angling Club. L Meyler, "Garryowen", Rosslare Strand, Co Wexford.

Youghal Sea Anglers' Club. M Clancy, 13 Strand Street, Youghal, Co Cork.

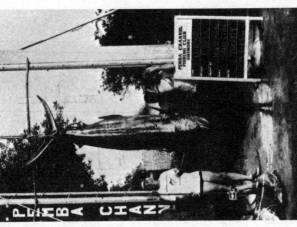

FISHING ABROAD

THE primary purpose of this section is to give the angler contemplating visiting, or even, in the case of Commonwealth countries, emigrating to, one of the countries listed a brief description of the fishing to be had. It is neither necessary nor practicable to enter into such detail as in the British sections, but the addresses of various authorities from whom further information can be obtained are given, together with that of the appropriate London tourist or Government information office, at the end of each description.

CENTRAL AFRICA

ZAMBIA. Most rivers and lakes carry good stocks of fish, giving very reasonable sport. But the angler must be prepared to travel long distances over rough roads, carrying his own camp equipment and finally making his camp beside the river he intends to fish. There are very few hotels off the main roads, and fewer still in fishing areas, though the Tourist Board is conducting a successful drive for more hotels and rest houses. In spite of this, for parties who appreciate camping holidays in the bush, some delightful trips can be planned, particularly in August and September, when there is little fear of rain and the nights are warm enough to make camping pleasant. Most of the rivers are either heavily wooded right down to the water or are swamp-edged, so the addition of a boat and outboard motor to the camp equipment is a sound policy. On the other hand, canoes and paddlers can be hired, and the latter are usually good guides to the best fishing grounds. Youths are also very helpful as camp attendants, and little trouble is normally experienced in hiring one or two to take care of the heavy work of the camp. The visiting fisherman must remember that the hippopotamus and crocodile are found in nearly all Zambian waters. Wading in rivers can be a dangerous pastime, and hippos, especially with calves, should be given a wide berth.

Indigenous species. These include tiger-fish, which probably provide the best sport, and goliath tiger fish, a separate species running up to 80 lb or more; fish of the Nile perch variety and their close relatives, giant perch (top weight around 200 lb); giant vundu (sampa), large- and small-mouthed bream, catfish, barbels, local pike, yellow belly (cichlid), lake salmon, kupi and labeo.

The great Zambezi and its large tributary, the Kafue, are outstanding among the rivers. A good centre for the Zambezi is Livingstone, though there is a small, comfortable hotel at Mongu, in Western Province. The tiger fishing is splendid and there is excellent sport with bream (cichlids), vundu (common downstream of Victoria Falls) and barbel.

Lake Tanganyika is another anglers' mecca and a good centre is Kasaba Bay, where there are three small lodges. A launch service is operated by the Zambia Travel and Touring Co Ltd. The lake holds giant perch, tiger fish, yellow belly and vundu among a wide variety of sporting fish.

Apart from Nile perch and sampa, which call for heavy tackle, most of the fish mentioned can be handled with a spinning rod. Steel traces are necessary for tiger-fish, kupi and pike. A light bait-casting rod will usually cover other species. Fishing is free as a rule and can take place all the year round, but most rivers are in spate during the rainy season from December to April.

Exotic species. Zambia is unlikely to prove to be a land in which trout will thrive, owing both to the high temperature range and the lack of suitable highlands, but an exception may be provided by the picturesque Nyika Plateau, north of Chipata on the Malawi border, where an experimental stocking with rainbow trout in the headwaters of the Shire River is being carried out.

Other information can be obtained from the several fishing clubs scattered throughout the territory. For general data inquire of Zambia Veterinary & Tsetse Control Dept, Box RW 60, Ridgeway, Lusaka, or the Zambian National Tourist Board, Zimco House, 129/139 Finsbury Pavement, London EC2A 1NA.

MALAWI. Excellent sport with rainbow trout may be enjoyed in the bracing climate of the Zomba, Mlanje and Nyika Plateaux as a result of consistent restocking of rivers and streams by the Government. Lake Malawi holds over 200 species, including varieties of catfish, perch and carp. Most of these are found in the Shire River above the Livingstone Falls, but below the falls the main species are related to those found in the Zambezi. They include the famous tiger fish. Further information may be obtained from the Ndirande Angling Society, PO Box 102, Blantyre, Malawi.

EAST AFRICA

ETHIOPIA. With large areas of the country only recently opened to tourists, Ethiopia's many rivers and lakes abound with fish, forming a veritable fisherman's paradise.

The best time of the year to visit Ethiopia is during the dry season, which is from late October to the beginning of February. Virtually no rain falls during this period and the sky is usually cloudless. During the period February to mid-April, some rain falls, but not in such quantities as to disrupt sport. Most of the areas which offer good fishing are accessible by road or by air. Cars (with or without chauffeurs) can be hired at Addis Ababa, and Ethiopian Airlines have a good domestic network. Tackle should be brought from one's own country as there are no facilities for hire or purchase.

Indigenous species: Ethiopia has three of Africa's most sought-after fish—the tiger-fish, Nile perch and giant catfish. The tigerfish is probably the most sporting, giving a good account of itself on reasonably light spinning tackle, like that commonly used for pike. The crushing power of the tigerfish's jaws is immense, though, and metal spoons are preferable to plastic or wooden lures. Tigerfish also have extremely sharp teeth, so a wire trace should be used and great care exercised when unhooking the catch. Tigerfish average 2–6 lbs, although much larger specimens are known to exist and can weigh more than 50 lbs. The Nile perch, which can reach a top weight of nearly 300 lbs, can be caught by live- or dead-baiting (a ledgered tigerfish is best) or by spinning. A particularly deadly method is to work a medium or large-size plug at mid-water. Tackle should be fairly heavy and line breaking strength should not be less than 18 lbs, in view of the size of the fish and the hazards of underwater snags. Catfish can also be caught by bait-fishing and sometimes will also take a lure. For both these species a wire trace should also be used, attached to the line by a large swivel. Catfish can make tremendous runs, so make sure that there is plenty of line on the reel.

The best place to try for these species is Lake Chamo in the southern part of the country, and the angler is based at the town of Arba Minch, where there are comfortable hotels. Fishing can be done from boats (although this should be arranged in advance on arrival at Addis Ababa) or from jettys. The Baro River near Gambela is another good source of these fish and the fisherman can stay at the pleasant Ras Hotel. In both areas, the fisherman should remember that he shares the water with hippopotamuses and crocodiles, and wading and swimming is therefore highly inadvisable.

Lake Chamo also contains tilapia, barbus and smaller species of catfish for those who prefer less exerting sport. Light tackle should be used (5 lbs breaking strength is quite suitable) and a strip of meat or worm is a very good bait. These fish are also found at Lake Awassa in the Ethiopian Rift Valley, and at Lake Tana in the north, where they can grow to specimen size—barbus weighing in excess of 20 lbs are not uncommon and even tilapia can reach weights of over 6 lbs.

Imported species: Both brown and rainbow trout have been introduced into the rivers of the Bale Mountains National Park and these have flourished with the high altitude and climate. The trout grow to quite respectable sizes and fish over 8 lbs are caught quite regularly. The Shiya River holds the largest trout but these are more difficult to catch; whereas the Dinka and the Ueb have an abundance of smaller fish which almost seem to give themselves up to the angler. Spinning with small blade spinners is the most effective method with the occasional fish falling to the fly. The local children can be recruited as guides and ghillies and their willingness to be of service for a small fee holds much to the pleasures of fishing.

There are plans to introduce black bass into some of the lakes but at the time of writing there has been no definite results.

Sea-fishing: Sea fishing in the Red Sea is possible for barracuda, tuna, shark and other tropical species. The centres are Massawa and the Dahlak Islands off the coast. Boats can be hired but one should bring one's own tackle.

KENYA. Kenya is well-developed for the sporting tourist and offers a variety of fishing off the coast, in its rivers and in the lakes of the Great Rift Valley. Licence fees are modest; accommodation of some variety is established at or near virtually all main centres. The coast. Black, blue and striped marlin; broadbill swordfish, sailfish, yellow fin tuna, wahoo, barracuda, cobia, dorado, mako shark. 36 out of 79 All-Africa records are held at the time of going to press by Kenya anglers. Centres at Mombasa, Shimoni (for the famous Pemba Channel fishing) Kilifi, Watamu, Lamu and Malindi, the latter the largest. Accommodation at club premises or hotels. Charter boats. Good fishing almost all the year round, peaking Oct–April: at its least attractive May–June. The mountain rivers. Stocked early in the century with brown trout, later with rainbows. Camps with rondavel accommodation at Thiba, Thego, Kimakia, Koiwa. Rest house at Kaibabich; lodges at Ngobit and Kiandorogo. A dozen or more specially recommended hotels and clubs. Camp accommodation may be primitive; nothing should be taken for granted. There are limits on size, method and bags, but wholesale poaching is an ever-present problem despite sincere governmental efforts to curb it. The lakes. Naivasha is famous for black bass, but the angler in pursuit of them should forget any preconceptions he might have. Smallish coppery-tinted bar-spoons are the most successful lure and the bigger fish are found not so much in the shallows as in pockets of deeper water inshore, where they shelter in the papyrus. In Lake Turkana (formerly Rudolph) the principal quarry are Nile perch and tiger fish, the former growing to more than 250 lb. Also in Turkana, the rare and beautiful golden perch, which may weigh 150 lb. Lake Baringo, well off the beaten track, is noted for its tilapia fishing; also for its wildlife-watching potential, but that is a bonus attaching to much of the Kenya fishing. Sport-fishing is now developing in Lake Victoria and the Sasuma Dam. Accommodation at all centres, but the extreme variety of types calls for detailed investigation in advance. Kenya Tourist Office: 13 New Burlington Street, London W1X 1FF. Tel 839 4477/8 and 930 3837.

TANZANIA. Tanzania can provide some of the finest big-game fishing in the world, and delightful sport with trout in mountain streams and lakes.

Big-game fishing: From October to March there is first-class sport with sailfish, shark, tunny, marlin, wahoo, horse mackerel and dolphin, particularly off Dar es Salaam, around Latham Island and Mafia Island, and also in the Pemba Channel off Tanga. Mafia offers some of the finest sport in the world in quantity, variety and excitement, and here particularly, and in addition to those already mentioned, can be found king fish, barracuda, red snapper and rock cod. There is a lodge on Mafia Island, but less services than there used to be in the way of boats and boatmen. Tackle available at club. Flights to Mafia Island from the mainland (about 40 minutes run) are operated daily in each direction, and the club has its own airstrip which can be reached by air charter services from anywhere in East Africa.

Lake fishing: Lake Tanganyika provides the best sport fishing where, from Kigoma, it is possible to obtain Nile perch, tiger fish and tilapia, which provide excellent sport.

Trout fishing: At Moshi and Arusha trout fishing can be undertaken on the slopes of Mount Kilimanjaro and Mount Meru from confortable hotels in the area. The Kilimanjaro Fishing Club controls all the trout streams in that area (PO Box 10, Moshi). In the Southern Highlands the Mbeya Trout Association, PO Box 104, Mbeya, maintains fishing camps on rivers in the Mporotos mountain range. At Morogoro the Uluguru Fly Fishing Association, PO Box 98, Morogoro, should be contacted to obtain accommodation at their fishing camp at Bunduki. The best season is November to January, though this. particularly in the mountain areas, may be affected by rains so that access is difficult or rivers in spate; otherwise June, July and August are good. Visitors are recommended to take all requirements in the way of fishing tackle with them.

Licence fees: Daily Shs 10; weekly Shs 30; half-year Shs 50; full year Shs 75.

Further information (licences etc) may be obtained from the Tanzania Tourist Corporation, PO Box 2485, Dar es Salaam, and PO box 694, Arusha (For Mt Meru fishing), or from Tanzania High Commission, Tourism Division, 43 Hertford Street, London W1.

SOUTH AFRICA

CAPE PROVINCE. Since the establishment of large-mouthed and small-mouthed black bass, the inland fisheries of the Cape area have been greatly extended; but this development has not been at the expense of the rainbow trout fisheries, which are as flourishing as ever. A few rivers hold brown trout, and brook trout were also introduced to upland waters some time ago. All the inland waters fall under the laws of the Cape Provincial Administration. In proclaimed trout rivers no fishing may be done at all except with the artificial fly and during the open season for trout, which extends from the beginning of September to the end of May. Trout licences are required, but the charges are extremely moderate (R2 per year). In addition, however, the permission of riparian owners will be needed and sometimes a fee is payable.

Most of the rivers in the Western Cape are within a day's motoring range of Cape Town on tarred roads, and some of the best waters are on State Forest Reserves, to which anglers have access on permit. This area has a winter rainfall, and the best months are September, October and November, late April and early May. Steenbras Reservoir holds a rare hybrid known as "tiger trout" which is a cross between brown trout and the American eastern brook trout. Along with Wemmershoek Reservoir (rainbow trout) Steenbras can be fished for a small charge on tickets obtainable from the Secretary, Cape Piscatorial Society, Westminster House, 122 Longmarket Street, 8001 Cape Town; Tel 43-6723. (This Society should also be approached for general information regarding inland fishing in the Cape Western Province.)

The Olifants River in the Citrusdal and Clanwilliam districts provides excellent fishing for small-mouthed bass and the indigenous yellowfish, *Barbus capensis*. The latter takes artificial lures, is very game and runs as large as 20 lb. Further afield, the mountainous areas of East Griqualand, adjoining the Transkei, have rivers which provide boundless opportunities for the trout fisherman.

Sea Fishing along the Cape Province's coastline is very good indeed, with hundreds of species to be caught. The big-game potential is only beginning to be realised, and remarkable catches of bluefin and longfin tuna have been taken. Skiboat fishing is an interesting and highly successful technique for taking many varieties of off-shore fish. Every type of tackle is available and accommodation is plentiful and comfortable. Among the many sea-angling clubs in the Cape Province (some of which are affiliated to the South African Anglers' Union, PO Box 3676, 2000 Johannesburg) are the Cape Boat and Skiboat Club, PO Box 4191, 8000 Cape Town, the Rock and Surf Angling Association, 28 Silverlea, 7800 Wynberg, and the SA Light Tackle Boat Anglers' Association, 70 Diaz Road, Parsons Hill, 6000 Port Elizabeth. The Address of the Game Fish Association of South Africa is PO Box 424, 9460 Welkom.

NATAL. The streams originating in the Natal Drakensberg mountains, which rise to 11,000 ft, form several river systems before emptying into the Indian Ocean. Although the sources are in general too torrential to support fish life in any quantity, below the torrent source each river enters a series of pools and rapids suitable for trout and other fish. Moreover, the construction of numerous dams in the Natal Midlands has been the means of providing many extra fishable waters.

Only waters at an altitude of about 4,000 ft and more have, in general, been stocked with trout. Below this level most rivers are too warm and silt-laden for the species to thrive. Black bass have been established in a number of these waters. however, and the indigenous "scaly" (yellowfish), catfish, and eels provide additional angling. Dams in the midland areas have been stocked successfully with black bass and tilapia. The State dams administered by the Natal Parks, Game and Fish Preservation Board (Albert Falls, Midmar, Wagendrift, Spioenkop and Chelmsford) not only provide abundant angling for many types of fish, including black bass, carp, scaly, tilapia, catfish and eel, but also provide a wide range of other recreational facilities and comfortable accommodation.

Rainbow and brown trout are the most important sporting fish of the province. The open season for trout streams is from September 1 to May 15, but dams are open throughout the year. The best fishing is usually obtained at the beginning and end of the season. From November to February the heavy summer rains and thunderstorms are apt to discolour the lower waters and render fly fishing difficult. It is almost always feasible.

however, to obtain fishing on the headwaters or on artificial lakes and dams. The average size of Natal trout runs from about ½ lb to 2 lb, but on the larger waters, especially dams, much heavier fish can be expected and each season a few trout of about 5 lb are taken. The Natal record for a rainbow trout is 5.13 kg (11 lb 10 oz) caught at Bulwer in May 1976.

There are three fly fishing clubs in Natal: The Underberg-Himeville Trout Fishing Club, PO Box 7, 4590 Underberg; the Natal Fly Fishers' Club, PO Box 1535, 3201 Pietermaritzburg, and the Natal Midlands Fly Fishing Club, 32 Brewitt Road, 3310 Estcourt. Each of these has control over some private waters (rivers and dams) in different areas, so visiting anglers should refer to all three clubs for information and advice.

Public waters and the Provincial nature reserves (where accommodation is available close to fishing areas) are controlled by the Natal Parks, Game and Fish Preservation Board; all queries regarding licences, accommodation etc should be directed to the Secretary, PO Box 662, 3200 Pietermaritzburg, who will supply full information to visitors and handle reservations. Natal Parks Board rangers are stationed at the more important public fishing areas to assist visitors and enforce regulations for the protection of trout, black bass and indigenous fish.

Sea Fishing. The majority of salt water anglers fish in the surf, casting their baits and lures from sandy beaches or from rocky promontories. Estuaries offer sport, while he open sea attracts those who have access to suitable craft. A wide variety of fish may be caught in the surf, ranging from sharks to small members of the bream family. Tackle varies accordingly, but a light fibre-glass rod of about 10 ft together with a fixed-spool reel gives a chance of catching many of the inshore species.

In June and July the annual migration of "sardines" may attract game fish such as king mackerel into the surf and sport is likely to be fast and furious. The best estuarine fishing is at Lake St Lucia, a nature reserve controlled by the Natal Parks Board; large numbers of grunter and kob enter the estuary leading to the main lake in spring and autumn. Deep sea angling takes place from ski-boats (small, speedy, flat-bottomed craft) as well as from the larger types of vessel. Advice on the organisation of deep sea trips will be provided by the Natal Parks Board (PO Box 662, 3200, Pietermaritzburg). Tackle for every branch of angling is obtainable. Innumerable hotels, holiday cottages, holiday flats and rest camps provide accommodation for visitors to the Natal or Zululand coastal resorts. Enquiries should be directed to the Durban Publicity Association, PO Box 1044, 4000, Durban.

Other useful addresses: Secretary, Natal Coast Anglers' Union, 77 Waller Crescent, Roseglen, 4091, Durban; Durban Ski-boat Club, PO Box 2570, 4000, Durban.

TRANSVAAL. Rainbow trout can be caught in a number of fine mountain streams in the Eastern Transvaal at altitudes varying from 4,000 to 6,000 ft. Magoebaskloof, Sabie, Pilgrim's Rest, Lydenburg, Machadodorp, Belfast, Dullstroom and Waterbal Boven are the principal trout fishing centres. Some waters contain only fish over 3 lb in weight. There is no closed season for trout fishing although fishing conditions are at their best in October and April. The rule is fly only, with dry and wet flies being used. Size limits and bag limits vary according to the area fished. Most waters are privately owned and, except where angling clubs have fishing rights, the permission of the riparian owner must be obtained.

Good bass fishing is to be found in a large number of public, club and private waters. Large-mouth and small-mouth bass are widely distributed but some of the best waters are in the White River area of the Eastern Transvaal: dams in that region, such as Longmere, Klipkoppies, Witklip, Stanford and Dagama have produced excellent fishing in recent times. Tiger fish may be caught in the Komati River at Komatipoort and in the Limpopo. Minimum takeable size, 12 in, daily bag limit, 6. Tiger fish are best caught in September and October.

Yellowfish abound in the waters of the Transvaal. There are four species, all belonging the genus *Barbus*. In the Vaal River they grow to 30 lb in weight and can be caught on mealiemeal dough, earthworms, grasshoppers or crabs. The two species of the east-flowing rivers grow to 15 lb and take crab, earthworms, mealiemeal dough and spinners.

Tilapia, commonly known as "kurper", is a very popular fish. There are two species, both being restricted to warmer waters. They can be caught, on earthworms, mealiemeal dough (a paste bait) and spinners, with a light trout rod. They average about 1¼ lb, but specimens of 4½ lb are commonly caught. The best waters for this species are the

Hartebeestpoort, Rust der Winter, Roodeplaat, Loskop and Njelele dams, also those in the White River area—although they may be caught in almost any lowveld water.

Not just the Transvaal, but the whole of the Republic of South Africa is a carp angler's paradise, with the fish attaining exceptional weights in very short periods due to the nature of South Africa's waters. The record caught on rod and line is 48 lb 10 oz, although much larger specimens have been caught but not recorded, and the heaviest known fish was a monster of 83¼ lb which was trapped in an irrigation furrow near Bon Accord Dam north of Pretoria. Carp are found throughout South Africa in many public and private dams. No bag or size limits apply to these fish.

The Transvaal's fisheries are administered by the Department of Nature Conservation of the Provincial Administration, Pretoria. The Provincial Fisheries Institute, Private Bag 1088, 1120 Lydenburg, is the scientific headquarters, and information about fishing in the Transvaal may be obtained from the Senior Fisheries Officer at that address, or from the Rand Piscatorial Assn, PO Box 2813, 2000, Johannesburg.

General Information: Licences relative to the particular province can be obtained from Receivers of Revenue, magistrates' offices and reputable tackle stores throughout the Republic.

For further information contact the South African Tourist Corporation, 13 Regent Street, London SW1Y 4LR, Tel: 01-839-7462.

FISHING IN AUSTRALASIA; INDIA; SRI LANKA AND MALAYSIA

AUSTRALIA

As a result of acclimatisation and planned research in Australia, many of the lakes and rivers in the State of Tasmania, New South Wales, Western Australia and Victoria are well stocked with trout, which sometimes reach a large size. The island State of Tasmania is world-famous as a trout fishing centre, and continues to attract anglers from all parts of the Commonwealth each year.

Many rivers are still subject to flooding despite hydro schemes and thus imposes a standstill on angling, so that the tendency is to reduce close seasons. The angler is strongly advised to check on river levels before going to fish. Before water temperatures have warmed up will be found to be the best times—midsummer is generally worst for trout fishing.

Freshwater Murray cod, perch and blackfish are found in good numbers in Australia. The Murray River, which forms the boundary of the eastern States of Victoria and New South Wales, and its many tributaries provide good sport for thousands of anglers, including trout in the upper reaches, Murray cod may weigh up to 150 lb; another Murray River fish, the callop or golden perch, grows to over 50 lb. Macquairie perch (to 11 lb) and silver perch or grunter (to 6 lb) are also taken. Another perch, or Australian bass, is taken in coastal streams and estuaries.

Australia was said by the late Zane Grey, noted big game authority, to possess the finest big game fishing grounds in the world. Centre of interest for sportsmen is Montague Island, off the coast of New South Wales, where there are marlin, tuna, shark and other big fish. The island is 14m from Bermagui, a safe harbour that can be used in all weathers. The tropical waters of the Great Barrier Reef, which extends for about a thousand miles along the east coast of Queensland, form Australia's most fascinating grounds; there are many unusual varieties of fish. There is good beach and rock fishing almost everywhere.

The principal fishing organisation is the Game Fishing Association of Australia, Birkenhead Point, Drummoyne, NSW 2047.

NEW SOUTH WALES. The streams near Sydney are mostly too small to support a large trout population, but good sport may be had in parts of the Blue Mountains area. Easily best from the fishing point of view, however, is the Snowy Mountains area. Very large reservoirs constructed as parts of the hydro-electric scheme in the Southern Alps are now ranked equal to any in the world for brown and rainbow trout. The scenic beauty of the streams and these lakes is outstanding. Lake Eucumbene is the largest of the dams and in recent years has become the mecca of Australian trout anglers, but there are many other fine fisheries. Good accommodation and camping sites are available and many fine fishing waters are reached easily over good roads.

Apart from these new waters, one of the most renowned centres is Cooma, which has produced many of the heavier fish caught in the state. The Murrumbidgee and its tributaries near Kiandra are well worth fishing at the right time.

Atlantic salmon have been introduced into the Burrinjuck Dam, and if they become a self-supporting stock will be tried in other cold water storages.

With the exception of a number of small spawning creeks, which have extended close seasons, and the larger impoundments, which are open all the year round, the trout streams are open to fishing from the beginning of October to the end of May. Other inland waters are open the whole year. The most popular times for trout fishing are in the cooler months of the open season; that is October, November, March, April and May.

It is now necessary for anglers fishing for any species of fish, including trout, to hold an inland angling licence ($6 pa, $3 for 21 days). Licences and information are available from the State Fisheries, 211 Kent Street, Sydney, and from local agents. All fees collected are required to be used for the improvement and protection of the inland fisheries. There are many attractive native species inhabiting the freshwater streams. Murray cod being

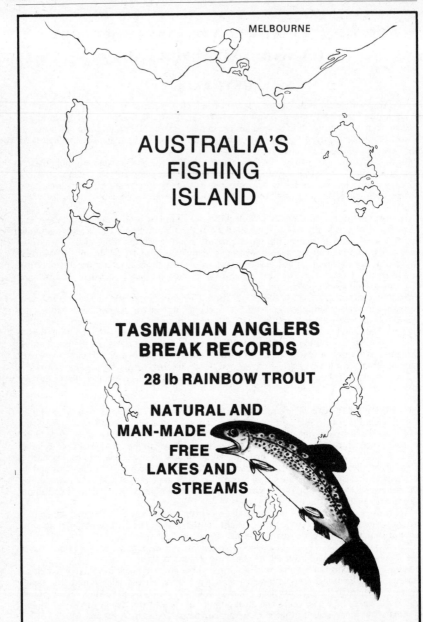

perhaps the most popular, and the taking of fish up to 50 lb is not uncommon; these fish do, in fact, run much larger.

The State is noted for its attractive coastal lagoons and estuary fisheries. At many excellent resorts bream, flathead, whiting, blackfish, etc, give good sport, while big game fish like tuna, marlin and shark abound in waters off the coast. The NSW Game Fishing Association, Birkenhead Point, Drummoyne, NSW 2047, will give further information. Tourist information can be had from the NSW Government Travel Centre, 16 Spring Street, Sydney. The London office of the New South Wales Government is at 66 Strand (01-839 6651).

QUEENSLAND. There are no trout fishing centres, no licence fees and no close season. Golden perch or "yellow-belly" are found in the freshwater rivers of the south-west and as far north as the upper river of the Dawson. Murray cod are also caught in the south-western rivers, and freshwater perch or grunters (several species) are found in most inland streams. Barramundi are taken from all the inland rivers of eastern Queensland north of and including the Dawson River. Nile perch have been introduced into a number of waters.

Off the coast are the Greater Barrier coral reefs (1,230 miles long), which abound in fish life. Big game fish are plentiful along the whole coastline, and the following species are commonly caught: Marlin, spearfish, sailfish, tuna, bonito, Spanish mackerel, sharks (white pointer, mako, tiger, whalers, etc), amberjacks, emperor, trevallies, etc. Recently Cairns has assumed world significance as a big-game resort, as several large marlin, including one over 1,000 lb, have been landed. The mainland coast provides excellent estuary, beach and rock fishing for bream, whiting, flathead, tailor, trevally, giant perch, grunter, jew fish and so on.

Further information can be had from the Director, Queensland Fishery Service, 77–86 George Street, Brisbane, Queensland, Australia or Queensland Game Fishing Assn, Penthouse 04, 182 Dornoch Terrace, Highgate Hill, Brisbane, Queensland and tourist information from the Queensland Government Tourist Bureau, Adelaide Street, Brisbane. The Queensland Government's Office in London is at 392/3 Strand (01-836 3224).

SOUTH AUSTRALIA. South Australia has very few freshwater streams if the River Murray is excluded. Relatively little trout fishing is available except in some streams near Adelaide and in farm dams. There is no closed season on trout fishing but there is a legal minimum length of 28 cm.

The River Murray, which flows through the State to the sea supports both commercial and recreational fisheries for native freshwater species, callop, Murray cod, silver perch and catfish and a freshwater crayfish. Introduced golden carp, common carp, English perch and tench are also caught in considerable numbers. Murray cod may not be taken during September, October and November whereas all other fish may be taken through the year.

Very enjoyable and profitable sea fishing can be had along most of the coast of South Australia with rod and line or hand line. Amateur anglers do not require licences; neither do game fishermen who go after the huge white death shark. The largest specimen so far caught on game tackle weighed 2,536 lb.

Tourist information can be had from the South Australian Government Tourist Bureau, 18 King William Street, Adelaide, and further information on fishery matters from the Director, Department of Agriculture and Fisheries, 25 Grenfell Street, Adelaide and the Secretary, South Australian Fly Fishers Association Inc. (Mr J Moreland Mitchell), 42 Tusmore Avenue, Tusmore, 5065.

TASMANIA. Tasmania, not without justification, describes itself as Australia's "Fishermens' Mecca". A multitude of lakes and rivers are generously stocked with the native black fish and with introduced brown, rainbow and brook trout, species which have achieved growth-rates on the island second to none. The size-bracket in which the angler expects his captures to fall spans 2–10 lb, with even larger trout an ever-present possibility. Most of the waters are within motoring distance or of air-services from Hobart and Launceston. Mobile campers are widely employed. Guides are available, and can arrange, where necessary, flies, lures, boats and camp services.

Great Lake (situated in the central plateau of the island at an altitude of 3,372 ft, 83 miles from Hobart, the capital, and about the same distance from Launceston, second largest city in the island, situated in the north), Lake King William, Lake St Clair (a natural lake), Lake Echo, Little Pine Lagoon, Bronte Lagoon, Brady's Marsh, Lake Binney, Tungatina Lagoon, Dee Lagoon, Arthurs Lake, Lake Rowallan and Lake Pedder (all new waters created by Hydro-electric schemes). Other popular fishing waters are Lake Leake and Tooms Lake on the east coast, Lakes Sorell and Crescent in the central midlands, and Lake Dulverton on the main highway between Hobart and Launceston. The northern part of the island is more richly endowed with trout streams than the south, having the South Esk, North Esk, Piper, Macquarie and Brumby. The north-west has the Rubicon, Mersey, Forth, Leven, Blyth, Cam and Inglis. In the south are the Derwent, Franklin, Huon and Esperence.

Angling licences are available from most sports stores, general stores, police stations or the Inland Fisheries Commission. The principal angling associations are the Southern Tasmanian Licensed Anglers Association, the Northern Tasmanian Fisheries Association, the North-Western Fisheries Association and the Tasmanian Game Fishing Assn, 86 Murray St, Hobart. Tourist information can be had from the Tasmanian Government Tourist Bureau, Elisabeth Street, Hobart *(advt p 414)*, and the address of the hon sec, Inland Fisheries Commission, is 127 Davey Street, Hobart.

VICTORIA. The Yarra River, which enters the sea at Melbourne, the capital, is well stocked with brown trout, and rainbow trout are caught at Lake Eildon, 90m from Melbourne. In the Goulburn River at Eildon both browns and rainbows are plentiful and specimens up to 14 lb have been landed. These fish take spinners, and can also be landed on long-tailed flies which imitate the small smelt on which they feed. Other trout fisheries in the Lake Eildon district are the Howqua, Delatite, Jamieson, Big Rivers and Jerusalem Creek, together with a number of tributary streams of this system. These waters all hold both rainbow and brown trout. Good centres in North-Eastern Victoria for waters holding both brown and rainbow trout are Omeo, Swift's Creek, Benambra, Tallangatta, Eskdale, Corryong, Towonga. Lakes Bullen Merri and Purrumbete can be fished from Camperdown. Both these waters carry very large rainbow trout and Purrumbete also holds quinnat salmon. In the Horsham district, Murray cod, rainbow and brown trout are to be taken in a number of streams and lakes. Good rainbow and brown trout fishing can also be had in a number of steams around Wangaratta and Whitfield, and other trout fisheries are Lakes Konongwootong, at Coleraine, and Wendouree, at Ballarat. Trout fishing in the Murray River is virtually restricted to only a fraction of the river's length above and below Hume Weir, but Murray cod (80–100 lb) and three varieties of perch (to 10 lb) are among other fish to be caught. Little fishing is available in the Snowy River. Good fishing can be had in the Kiewa. In recent years a number of western lakes have been successfully stocked with rainbow trout. With surveys showing many rivers overstocked with trout, new regulations have been introduced—no close season, no bag limits etc—in an attempt to produce fewer and bigger fish. All anglers must possess an Inland Angling Licence ($2) obtainable from the Fisheries and Wildlife Department, 605 Flinders Street, Melbourne.

Numerous species and varieties of sea fish can be caught in the bays and estuaries of the State within easy reach of the capital, Melbourne. They include snappers, flatheads, whiting, bream, bass and luderick. The snapper appears from September to April and has been taken up to 25 lb. Another bay fish is the pike, which resembles the river pike in some respects. The pike superficially resembles another bay fish, the barracouta, caught in large numbers by both amateur and commercial anglers.

The principal and governing piscatorial body is the Piscatorial Council of Victoria. Tourist information (including a booklet *Fishing in Victoria*) can be had from the Victorian Government Tourist Bureau, 272 Collins Street, Melbourne. The address of the Victorian Government Office in London is Victoria House, Melbourne Place, Strand (01-836 2656).

WESTERN AUSTRALIA. Recent years have seen a wide expansion in trout fishing and propagation in Western Australia. Many streams in the south west of the State are now well stocked with brown and rainbow trout, bred at the Pemberton hatcheries, and many excellent catches have been recorded. In one recent season, for instance, the trout caught, weighed between 1 lb and 6 lb 5 oz, with the majority turning the scales at between 2 lb and 3 lb. The best centre for all five areas have daily road services from Perth. The trout season runs from September 1 to April 30. An inland fishermen's licence is required (fee $5.00) available from the Department of Fisheries and Wildlife, Perth, or district office at principal centres. Legal minimum size for trout is 30 cm; no fish caught must be sold.

Principal centres for ocean fishing are: Exmouth, Shark Bay, Carnarvon, Kalbarri, Geraldton, Fremantle, Perth, Rottnest Island, Rockingham, Mandurah, Bunbury, Busselton, Augusta, Albany and Esperance. Various types of accommodation are available and boats may be hired or chartered at most centres. The fish to be caught include: black and silver bream, kingfish, whiting, tailor, flathead, sea herring, skipjacks, garfish, Australian "salmon", flounder, mullet, mackerel, leather-jackets, snapper, jewfish and groper. Marlin and other gamefish are taken in northern waters and centres for game fishermen are being developed. Prawns and lobsters may be taken in many areas. An amateur Fisherman's Licence must be held to take these species (fee $5.00).

The Department of Fisheries and Wildlife is located at 108 Adelaide Terrace, Perth and President of the Amateur Anglers Association is L. Birchall, 144 Alice Street, Doubleview, Perth. The address of the Western Australian Government Tourist Bureau is: 772 Hay Street, Perth. The address of the Western Australian Government Office in London is: 115 Strand, London WC2R 0AJ (01-240 2881).

NEW ZEALAND

(Notes compiled by George Aitken)

Fishing in New Zealand can be compared in some ways to Caesar's Gaul, in that it divides into three parts—Trout, Salmon and Big Game angling.

Trout, both brown and rainbow, were introduced about 100 years ago and have long been fully distributed in both islands. Rainbow predominate in the North Island, and Browns in the South, but many waters have a mixture of the two in varying proportions.

The main areas in the North are centred on Lake Taupo and the Rotorua district with its group of important lakes. The rivers flowing into and out of these lakes are also noted fisheries, particularly late in the season when the main runs commence. The Tongariro, Waitahanui, Tauranga-Taupo and others flow into Lake Taupo, while in the Rotorua area there are the Kaituna, Ohau Channel, and Ngongotaha to name a few.

The South Island has thousands of miles of rivers and streams, and numerous lakes of all sizes. It was once calculated, at the turn of the century, that there are 17,000 miles of river fishing in New Zealand, and of course it is all open to the public, subject only to right of access and to reasonable accessibility.

Good trout fishing is widely available, and large trout can still be caught within an hour's drive of the main cities, but obviously many of the best waters are more remote and some are seldom fished, although helicopter or floatplane services are readily available out of the towns of Queenstown, Wanaka and Te Anau to reach places like Lakes Alabaster and McKerrow, or the Pyke and Hollyford rivers for example.

The main, and also the lesser, rivers of Southland and Otago provinces offer excellent dry fly and nymph fishing for brown trout, and fish of from 12 to 15 pounds are caught each season, but a good average would be from 3 to 4 pounds. Guide services are again widely available, although obviously concentrated somewhat in the more popular areas. An Angling Guides Association was formed some time ago, all professional guides are licensed, and are fully equipped with 4-wheel drive vehicles and boats as necessary for their local areas.

In general, the open season is from Oct 1 to the end of April.

Salmon, the Pacific Quinnat or King Salmon, introduced to the main Canterbury rivers, is found in about ten of them, from the Clarence to the Clutha. The main ones would be the Rakaia, Rangitata, Waimakariri and Ashburton. The fishing is mainly heavy spinning, with spoons most favoured as lures, in the lower rivers, estuaries and even in the surf at the mouths. A certain amount of fly fishing, using very large lures or flies, is done upriver, notably in the Rakaia Gorge area. In all the salmon rivers the fish are mostly in the 12 to 20 pound class, but larger are quite frequent.

Big Game Fishing, made famous by Zane Grey, continues its excellent tradition. The main bases for this are at Russell, Paihia and Whangerei in the Bay of Islands, and also out from Tauranga to the Mayor Island area. There are ample charter boats, with professional Skippers and hands, based in these places, catering for parties of up to four anglers. The tackle, bait and so on are all provided in the charter. Sailfish, marlin and shark are caught at no great distance from the shore.

Big Game angling is mainly from January to the end of April, with the period from mid-February on offering fine sport.

Licences are needed for trout and salmon fishing. These cover the whole country, with the most minor exceptions, and for a Visitor cost NZ$4 a month, and are available from the Government Tourist Offices in main cities. It is interesting to note that it is illegal to sell, or offer for sale, either trout or salmon, but your hotel would cook yours for you obviously.

Further Information and advice on any aspects of angling in New Zealand can be obtained by writing to the Tourist Office, New Zealand House, Haymarket, London, SW1Y 4TQ. Telephone 01-930 8422.

INDIA

One of the big attractions for the fisherman in India—in more sense than one—is the mighty mahseer. This renowned sporting quarry is found in the upper reaches of the large rivers where the water is cold and the river-bed strewn with boulders and pebbles. It lies in pools above or below the rapids and preys on small fish.

The mahseer can be taken on a spoon, but strong tackle is essential. It not only runs large—the biggest caught on rod and line weighed 119 lb (Cauvery River, South India, 1919)—but is a splendid fighter. The sport has, in fact, been compared most favourably with salmon fishing.

Mahseer abound in the upper reaches of the Brahmaputra and its many tributaries in Assam, and the beautiful Titsa river valley in North Bengal is good just before and after the rainy season (June to September). Large fish may also be taken in the Bombay area—in the Rivers Kalu, Bhima and Mula. One of the best centres in the Punjab is Tajewala, on the River Jamuna. A catch of 80 lb of mahseer a few years ago is recorded in the visitors' book at the Rest House there.

The River Jhelum in Kashmir also holds mahseer—fish of more than 90 lb have been taken—but the fishing is not now so good as it was some years ago. Kashmir is renowned for sport with brown and rainbow trout, which have thrived since they were introduced at the turn of the century. The many streams in the area are regularly stocked from two large hatcheries and are divided into "beats" of about two miles. Great variety is available, the rivers ranging from foaming torrents, when spinning is permitted, to gentle streams suitable for dry fly. There are "fly only" beats. The most suitable flies are those usually included in every angler's selection, but in Kashmir they are usually dressed on hook sizes between No 9 and No 5 (old sizes). The season lasts from March 15 to October 15; charges range from approx £50 per season to a shilling or two for a day ticket. The first month of the season is also the rainy season, and fishing is a little uncertain. There is also good trout fishing in the Kulu valley, where the season starts a few days earlier—on March 10.

India's rivers contain numerous other species. The Jamuna at Okhla, in Delhi, for instance, holds no fewer than eight varieties, including heavy catfish, the silund—a predator running up to 50 lb, which can be taken on a spinner—and a humpbacked fish called the cheetul or moh, which will be seen constantly rising to the surface and turning over broadside. There is also plenty of huge carp in the slow-flowing rivers and the lakes and tanks. The sea fishing can be excellent, too, but is dependent upon seasonal migrations and the weather. A considerable body of angling literature has now been published by the Bombay Natural History Society, 114 Apollo Street.

While the tourist-angler should not expect to find luxurious cabins on his expeditions, numerous camping-sites and comfortable rest-houses have been provided, often in the most beautiful surroundings; sometimes the call of the tiger and the trumpeting of wild elephants may be heard.

So far as tackle is concerned, the trout or mahseer fisherman will be specially well catered for at Srinagar, capital of Kashmir, where he may hire first-class gear, but rates are rising due to restricted imports, and it is preferable to take one's own equipment.

Further information from the India Government Tourist Office, 21 New Bond Street, London (01-493 0769).

SRI LANKA (CEYLON)

Nuwara Eliya is the best centre for trout fishing. As it is above the 6,000 ft level, the climate is temperate. Good hotel accommodation is available. The fishing is, with few exceptions, restricted to fly only and most common patterns of wet fly are successful. Dry fly is rarely used, there being little natural fly. There is no statutory close season, though the club imposes one in parts following restocking. Size limits vary from 8 in to 15 in.

The main waters are: Nuwara Eliya stream (flows through the golf course and park); Ambawela stream (8m from Nuwara Eliya; jungle and grassland); Bulu Ella stream (2½m jungle); Portswood Dam (4m; tea estate); Agra Oya and Gorge Valley rivers (10–15m; tea estates), and the magnificently spectacular Horton Plains stream (30m; jungle and grassland, Nature reserve). Motor transport can be hired. On any of these waters it is possible to maintain an average of 1 lb and several fish over 3 lb are caught.

Trout fishing is now controlled by the Nuwara Eliya District Fishing Club. Stocking has so far been carried out in Portswood Dam and the Horton Plains. It is proposed to stock in the current year 1980/81 Agra Oya and Gorge Valley. For licences application should be made to the Honorary Secretary, Nuwara Eliya District Fishing Club, Court Lodge Estate, Kandapola. Visitors are advised to bring their tackle as fly tackle is scarce in Sri Lanka.

The two main varieties of indigenous sporting fish in Sri Lanka are the mahseer and the walaya (freshwater shark), found in the jungle rivers of the Low Country, particularly the Mahaweli, the upper reaches of the Kelani and the Amban Ganga. Ceylon mahseer, though small compared with those in some Indian rivers, provide good sport, but fishing for them can be somewhat difficult. Fishing for indigenous sporting fish in Sri Lanka is free.

With a shoreline of 1,140 miles and a continental shelf of 10,000 square miles, the seas around Ceylon have an unlimited fishing potential hardly exploited. There are no fewer than 856 species listed from the marine, brackish and fresh waters of Ceylon, encompassing most of the game fish of the world.

The outfalls of 103 major river basins and hundreds of other estuaries, lagoons and coastal lakes all round the island are the most popular spots frequented by local surf casters as well as bait fishermen. Many varieties of game fish of the Carangid family, locally called paraw and known elsewhere as trevally, horse mackerel, etc, are taken. These swift and powerful carnivorous fish attain a length of 5 ft and a weight of 150 lb. The schooling habits of the caranx, their keen eyesight and some built-in sensory mechanism make them congregate in estuaries immediately after monsoons and rains.

Next in popularity among surf-casters come the barracuda and Spanish mackerel. Both these species of voracious predatory fish attain lengths of 6 ft as do other species known locally as "giant perch", "threadfins" and "tassel fish" which frequent the estuaries.

Trolling over the continental shelf yields catches of tuna ranging from the 2–3 ft skipjack to the 6 ft yellowfin and bluefin, the acrobatic dolphin, swordfish and marlin which attain a size to provide a challenge to the best big game fishermen of any country. The broadbill swordfish found in deeper waters reach a length of 15 ft and a weight of well over 1,000 lb. Though reaching only 10 ft and 250 lb, the sailfish compensate for their smaller size by their remarkable agility.

The monsoons regulate the fishing in Sri Lanka Seas. The western and southern coasts are favoured during the North-East monsoon (from October to April) and the east coast during the South-West monsoon (from May to September).

Good hotels and rest-houses (local inns) are available in the fishing areas and information on fishing will gladly be given by the Secretary, Ceylon Sea Anglers Club, 311 Galle Road, Colombo 3. Boats may be hired from professional fishermen.

Further information from Ceylon Tourist Board, 52 High Holborn, London WC1V 6RL (01-242 9111).

MALAYSIA

Some good sport is available in the jungle-covered highlands where fast-flowing, clean streams will delight the eye. These are well stocked with cyprinids or members of the carp family, which include the well-known mahseer of India, known locally as kelah. This group of which the most common species are kelah (up to 20 lb), sebarau (up to 12 lb), and kejor or tengas (up to 8 lb), are sporting fish which fight well when hooked. Kelah and tengas are good to eat. They are best when curried and provide a good change of diet in the jungle when living on operational 24-hour pack rations.

All these fish will take an artificial bait; the most popular being a 1 in or 1½ in silver or silver/copper spoon. A normal salmon spinning outfit is ideal. For those who prefer it, a fixed-spool reel can be used provided it will hold sufficient line. Owing to the crushing power of the jaws of the kelah, extra strong treble or large single hooks should be used and some people recommended the use of a 2 ft wire trace.

Malaysia's National Park, on the borders of Kelantan, Trengganu and Pahang, provides the best fishing, and a visit to the HQ at Kuala Tahan is well worth the journey. It may be reached by Royal Malaysian Air Force Pioneer aircraft to a landing-strip at Kuala Tahan, but the more normal method is to go by rail to Tembeling and thence by "perahu". These long, narrow, locally-built boats are fitted with 40 hp outboard motors and can do the journey up the Sungei Tembeling in three to four hours depending on the condition of the river. One may also travel in a Dowty turbocraft from Jerantut ferry. The supervisor at Kuala Tahan makes all arrangements. At Kuala Tahan there is a VIP bungalow and a rest-house providing full board. A number of visitors' lodges and halting bungalows have been built throughout the park so the fishermen can stay near the river they are fishing.

From Kuala Tahan all onward movement is by smaller boats with lower-powered engines to negotiate the shallower rivers, such as the Tahan itself. There are many large pools well stocked with fish in the lower reaches and above the Lata Berkoh barrier many pools and rapids, all excellent fishing water. Malay and Aborigine boatmen are happy to act as guides and are delightful companions.

It is easier and pleasanter to cast from the bank, but this will necessitate some wading where the bank is steep and overhung by the jungle. The water is pleasantly warm and waders would be far too hot to wear. Those with a good sense of balance can try fishing from a slowly paddled peradu, but as this is only a shell at the most 2 ft wide, it is liable to be something of a circus act.

Most reliable times to fish are the months February/March and July/August, because in other months fishing will be spasmodic owing to the heavy rainfall. Spates and floodwater so colour the rivers that fishing is a waste of time.

Apart from the fishing there is always the chance of seeing the wild animals of Malaysia at the many salt licks. There are usually monkeys, iguanas, snakes and flying foxes to be seen, as well as many varieties of birds such as hornbill eagle and kingfishers.

Intending visitors should write well before the date of their visit, giving as much information as possible on their special interests to the Chief Game Warden, PO Box 611, Kuala Lumpur, Malaysia, so as to enable the Game Dept to plan their itineraries.

FISHING IN NORTH AMERICA
CANADA

On the Atlantic side of the Dominion there are plenty of salmon rivers in Quebec and New Brunswick, and a good deal of fishing is available to the non-resident who takes out the appropriate provincial licence. There is a great deal of splendid trout fishing in many of the inland lakes and rivers, while in the Great Lakes region there are big muskellunge, and fine black bass fishing in various waters. The land-locked salmon is found in Quebec, both in the tributaries and discharge of Lac St John, and in some lakes in Nova Scotia, such as Grand Lake and Beaver Bank Lake. The "trout" of this side of Canada are char *(Salvelinus fontinalis)*, while some of them are migratory and become "sea trout". In the lakes are "grey trout", some of which reach a great size. There are also char *(Salvelinus namaycush)* in the Arctic.

On the other side of Canada, British Columbia offers splendid opportunities of sport with Pacific salmon, steelhead and rainbow trout. Fishing for Pacific salmon has until recently been considered of necessity a matter for tidal waters. The Campbell River, Vancouver Island, has been the most favourite resort, and there quinnat (now known locally as tyee) up to 70 lb have been caught on the troll. At Prince Rupert a 93 lb quinnat was caught on a spoon in 1929 by Mr O P Smith, a professional fisherman. An 82 lb tyee was caught in August, 1951, at Rivers Inlet. The cohoe has been caught on fly, also in tidal waters. Of late years it has become clear that quinnat will take in fresh water in certain conditions. To the far north there are evident possibilities of sport in Alaska.

So far as tackle is concerned, the trend is towards lighter outfits. Brook trout, for instance, are almost universally taken on a nine-foot, five-ounce fly rod, and many anglers use the same rod for steelhead or Kamloops trout, although this is probably foolhardy. Tackle should always be carefully geared to the area and quarry, and on-the-spot advice is desirable.

Much work is done by the Federal and Provincial hatcheries, and waters in various parts of Canada are supplied with fry of species suitable to their needs, chiefly salmonidae, but also bass and other kinds of the best big-game fishing so far discovered anywhere.

Note: The Canadian Government Office of Tourism publishes some useful guides to fishing in Canada, and copies may be obtained from their London Office at Canada House, Trafalgar Square, London SW1.

ALBERTA. Alberta is fortunate in having more than 4,000 miles of good fishing streams and more than 500 lakes. Fisheries management is the basis of the sportfishery capabilities and as such scientific data collected by the field staff plays the major role in determining fishing seasons and catch limits. Recent changes in regulations include a reduction in the daily catch and possession limits for trout in the province's streams and rivers. These and other regulations protect cold water species; however, warm water species are also carefully managed and in this regard seven lakes have been set aside as trophy lakes with specific reduced catch limits.

Closely allied to the management of native fish is the production of fish by hatchery. Last year, 5.3 million trout were produced and stocked in over 200 lakes and ponds throughout the province. These fish are occasionally stocked in lakes to bolster present breeding populations, however they are usually stocked in lakes which do not contain native fish and which are readily accessible to the public.

There are 15 species of sportfish in Alberta of which there are 9 cold water and 6 warm water sportfish. The cold water sportfish include brook, brown, cut-throat, golden, rainbow, and lake trout, Dolly Varden, arctic grayling and Rocky Mountain whitefish. These fish are generally found throughout the lakes and streams in the foothill and mountain areas in the south west of the province.

The warm water sportfish include lake whitefish, walleye, perch, pike, goldeye, and lake sturgeon. These fish are generally found in rivers and lakes throughout the south east and northern areas of the province. The major exception to this distribution is the sturgeon which is restricted to the south east corner of the province.

Further information may be obtained by writing to the Fisheries Administrative Assistant, Alberta Fish and Wildlife Division, 8th Floor, South Tower, Petroleum Plaza, 9915-108 Street, Edmonton, Alberta, T5K 2C9.

BRITISH COLUMBIA. The game fish of British Columbia comprise two species of salmon, the spring (or quinnat, locally known as tyee) and the cohoe, which may be taken with the fly, but are more easily caught by trolling; all varieties of Pacific Coast trout, particularly, the steelhead, the rainbow, and the cut-throat; Arctic grayling; two varieties of char, of which the commoner is the Dolly Varden; and the Eastern brook trout which has been introduced. The province has a coastline of 7,000 miles and is drained by innumerable rivers and freshwater lakes.

Some of the most important fishing areas are Kootenay District, Okanagan District (including Beaver, Bear, Dee, Ideal, Mabel, Sugar, South and Woods Lakes), Kamloops District (including Adams, East Barriere, Murtle, Shuswarp and Nicola Lakes), Cariboo District (including Quesnel, Horsefly and Canim Lakes, and Fraser and Thompson Rivers), and Princeton District (including Copper-Five-mile, One-mile, Otter Wolf and Sumners Creeks, and Pasayten, Similkameen and Tulameen Rivers). Most of the lakes and rivers are easily accessible, especially by car, and yield excellent fishing. Lodges, cabins and boats are available on many waters.

Vancouver Island offers excellent cut-throat and steelhead trout fishing. The important waters are Cowichan, Cameron, Sproat Lakes, Alberni and Qualicum Districts and the Campbell River area. Steelhead trout are in Sproat, Somass, Ash and Stamp Rivers, to name but a few. Quinnat (or spring) salmon and cohoe are found in good quantities in all of the main streams, bays and tributaries of the mainland draining into the Pacific Ocean. On Vancouver Island there is splendid salmon fishing to be had at Brentwood Bay, Saanich Arm, Cowichan Bay, Comox Bay, Port Alberni, Beecher Bay, Victoria, Vancouver and Campbell Bay and river. Campbell River is famous on account of the large quinnat caught there.

Further information (including details of licence charges and open seasons) can be had from the Fish and Wildlife Branch, Department of Recreation and Conservation, Parliament Buildings, Victoria, BC. For travel information, write to Tourism British Columbia, 1117 Wharf Street, Victoria BC V8W 2Z2.

MANITOBA. Manitoba is at the centre of a country more than 4,500 miles wide, from St John's, Newfoundland on the east to Victoria, British Columbia on the west.

The province is enormous by British standards, covering 250,000 square miles and measuring 735 air miles from north to south. Lake Winnipeg, 40 miles north of the capital city of Winnipeg, is the largest inland body of water in North America, apart from the Great Lakes. The northern three-fifths of the province is laced with innumerable streams and rivers, and someone claims to have counted 100,000 lakes, although many are too small to even appear on a map.

As the trout waters in the wilderness areas of this province become better known, they are acquiring the reputation of providing some of the finest trout fishing in North America. In particular, God's River in north-eastern Manitoba is famous for trophy-sized brook and lake trout, northern pike and walleye. The Limestone and Weir rivers, tributaries of the Nelson River in the vicinity of Gillam on the Hudson Bay Railway, are other famous brook trout waters. Lake trout *(Cristivomer namaycush)* are widely distributed fom the south-eastern area of the province through to the northern boundaries in the deep, cold-water lakes of the Pre-cambrian shield. Specimens over 40 lb are taken each year.

The Arctic char *(Salvelinus alpinus)* is common along the north-western coast of Hudson Bay and its tributary streams, which include the North Knife, Seal, Little Seal and Caribou rivers. The Arctic grayling *(Thymallus arcticus)*, with its spectacular beauty, is the delight of those fly-fishermen who are able to travel to the Churchill area or the fly-in areas in the far North.

Other fish. In the smaller lakes and streams in the southern part of the province, and in the southern portion of Lake Winnipeg, walleye, northern pike and yellow perch are plentiful. In Lake Winnipeg and the tributary Red River, freshwater drum are taken in large numbers at certain seasons. Winnipeg River is the locale for large walleye and great northern pike, together with an abundance of small-mouth black bass, which provide excellent sport.

Further information (including details of licence charges and open seasons) can be had from George Nelson, Sport Fishing, 1495 St James Street, Winnipeg, Manitoba R3H 0W9, or Travel Manitoba, Room 107, Legislative Building, Winnipeg.

NEW BRUNSWICK. Atlantic salmon in the Restigouche, Upsalquitch, Kedgwick, Patapedia, Jacquet, Nepisiquit, Tabusintac, North-West Miramichi, South-West Miramichi, Little South-West Miramichi, Sevogle, Renous, Dungarvon, Cains, Rocky Brook, Clearwater Brook, St John River, Nashwaak, Tobique, Serpentine and Salmon rivers. Parts of some of these streams are leased, some are Crown reserve waters and some are privately owned, but there are open stretches on all except the Kedgwick, Patapedia, Rocky Brook, Clearwater and Serpentine, and non-residents who take out the appropriate provincial licence can fish a good deal of water.

In addition to salmon fishing, there is good trout fishing in most of the lakes and streams of New Brunswick. Small-mouth bass and landlocked salmon are caught in some waters in the south-west of the province and a few striped bass in the St John River.

Non-resident licences must be obtained from a Forest Service Office in the province. These must be carried by the holder at all times, but do not convey right of fishing on Crown-reserve waters or any private fishery without the consent of the lessee or owner. Holders of non-resident licences must be accompanied by an authorised guide when fishing for Atlantic salmon or in waters fished mainly for salmon, except when wading or fishing from the shores, when a party of three may be accompanied by the same guide. There is now a strictly enforced tagging-programme in operation.

Further information, including details of licences and open seasons, can be had from the Department of Natural Resources, Fish and Wildlife Branch, PO Box 6000, Fredericton, and New Brunswick Dept of Tourism, PO Box 12345, Fredericton.

NEWFOUNDLAND. Newfoundland has probably some of the best game-fishing in North America. Almost a quarter of the island's area is water, and its many fine salmon rivers, some of them practically unfished, flow through unspoiled forest and hill country. Several kinds of trout—speckled, sea-run speckled, brown, rainbow and lake (char)—can be caught in the rivers and lakes, and tuna (tunny) fishing holds great possibilities off the coasts.

Salmon fishing is fly only, and the season is June 20 to August 31. The trout seasons are: rainbow trout, June 1 to November 30; sea-trout, May 15 to September 15; other trout, January 15 to September 25. Daily bag limits; sea trout: 24 (8 in certain waters); rainbow and other, 24. Bag limit for salmon: 2 per day, maximum of 4 in possession.

Some of the best salmon rivers are: Baie d' Est, Bay du Nord, and Counne; Bay du Nord, Fortune Bay; Fishels, Gander; Grand Codroy, North and South Branch; Grey; Harry's; Little Codroy; Long Harbour; Lower Humber; Portland; River of Ponds; Robinson's; Serpentine; South-west and Bottom Brooks; Upper Humber; Western Brook; White Bear. Further details, including licence charges and the names and addresses of "operators" and guides can be had from the Newfoundland Tourist Development Office (address below).

The best tuna fishing areas are probably in Conception Bay. Commercial fishermen have harpooned fish up to 12 ft in length and 1,200 lb in weight.

Further information can be had from the Department of Development, Tourist Services Division, PO Box 2016, St Johns A1C 5R8.

NOVA SCOTIA (including Cape Breton Island). Atlantic salmon in St Mary's, LaHave, Medway, Stewiacke, Moser, Musquodoboit, Gold, North, Petite Riviere and Maccan rivers; some 30 addition rivers have substantial runs of salmon but water levels and conditions are a major factor in the annual take. There are 11 rivers scheduled and posted for fly fishing only, but it should be noted Atlantic salmon may only be taken by fly; brook trout are common in streams and lakes, many of which are accessible from woods roads known as roads to resources; sea trout (brook and brown) in most tidal streams in the Northern and Eastern part of the province; 65 salt water charter boats are available for ground and tuna fishing in all areas except the upper reaches of the Bay of Fundy.

For further information please contact the Director of Wildlife Conservation, PO Box 516, Kentville, Nova Scotia and the Department of Tourism, PO Box 456, Halifax, Nova Scotia. The Department of Tourism publishes Fish Nova Scotia Fresh Water and Fish Nova Scotia Salt Water.

ONTARIO. Brook trout are widely distributed in eastern Canada. In Ontario this excellent game-fish occurs from the Great Lakes northward to streams entering Hudson Bay and James Bay. Included in the eastern part of this area west of the Quebec boundary are Algonquin Park, tributaries of the Upper Ottawa River, North Bay, Timagami-Metachewan, the Porcupine, Matheson-Abitibi and Cochrane areas, the Moosonee and the Goose country.

The western and northern area includes waters draining into Lake Superior west of Sault Ste Marie to Nipigon Bay, Nipigon River (where the world record brook trout was caught, 14½ lb), Nipigon Forest Reserve, the Lakehead District and the Lake St Joseph and the Albany wilderness. The numerous tributary waters of the Albany River offer some of the finest trout fishing to be found in Ontario.

In southern Ontario, west of the eastern area, the brook trout waters include the Muskoka lakes, the Haliburton and Hastings highlands and the Magnetawan area. Farther south and west, trout are available in some streams tributary to Lakes Huron, Erie, Ontario, Simcoe and Georgian Bay. Lying between the eastern and western areas of northern Ontario there are numerous brook trout waters, among which are the Sudbury, Manitoulin, Sault, Michipicoten, Mississaga, Biscotasing-Gogama, Chapleau, Missinabi-White River-Franz, Elsas, Oba, Hornepayne, Hearst, Kapuskasing, Nakina and Albany River areas.

The range of black bass fishing, small-mouth and large-mouth, in Ontario extends from the Ottawa and St Lawrence rivers and Lake Ontario and Lake Erie to the Timagami Forest Reserve and the north channel of Georgian Bay. Included in this range are the following areas: Long Point Bay (Lake Erie), Rideau lakes, Haliburton Lake District, Trent Valley, Kawartha lakes, Muskoka lakes, Algonquin Park, Lake Nipissing, the French and Pickerel rivers, and the Georgian Bay District areas. In the north-west section of Ontario bass are found in the Black Sturgeon lakes section of the Nipigon country and in the Lake of the Woods area.

The muskellunge range in Ontario includes the Ottawa and St Lawrence rivers, Lake Ontario, Lake Erie, Lake St Clair and Lake Huron, Trent Valley and Kaiwartha lakes, Lake Nipissing, French and Pickerel rivers and tributary waters. The best fishing is to be had in what is known as the Lake of the Woods district in the north-western section of the province, an extensive area some 150m wide east to west, and 160m from the international boundary north. This district has hundreds of lakes, very few of which have been fished, and large muskies are taken here every year by light spinning. Lake trout, pike-perch (walleye) and Gt Northern pike are fairly plentiful throughout the province. Rainbow and brown trout (not native to the province) have been stocked in limited areas. Splake, a cross between lake trout (char) and brook trout, have recently been introduced into some waters.

There are nearly 500 fish and game associations in the province, many of which are federated with the Ontario Federation of Anglers and Hunters (Executive Director, Box 1269, Campbellford, Ontario, K0L 1L0). Further information (including licence charges) can be had from the Ministry of Natural Resources, Parliament Buildings, Toronto, Ontario, M7A 1W3, and the Ministry of Industry and Tourism, 900 Bay Street, Toronto, Ontario, M7A 2E1.

PRINCE EDWARD ISLAND. This island, which lies in the Gulf of St Lawrence off the north coast of Nova Scotia, has an enviable reputation for its speckled trout fishing. The streams and rivers are spring fed, and the whole province may be considered a natural hatchery for trout and salmon. The salmon fishing, however, is not first class, and the best runs do not begin until towards the end of the season. Both non-migratory and migratory trout are to be caught. Fishing for rainbow trout can be had in Glenfinnan, and Keefe's lakes. Noted trout streams are the Fortune, Morell and Dunk rivers, and large freshwater dams also afford good sport. Mackerel fishing is becoming popular (late July to September) in coastal waters.

The Prince Edward Island Wildlife Federation and the Fly Fishing Federation are the bodies involved in the province, and further information may be obtained from the Prince Edward Island Visitor Services Division, PO Box 940, and Dept of Community Affairs, Fish and Wildlife Unit, PO Box 2000, both Charlottetown, PEI. Post codes C1A 7M5 and C1A 7N8.

QUEBEC. While a good deal of fishing in the province is preserved by clubs, there is such a vast and well-watered area between the Labrador and New Brunswick boundaries on the east and the Ontario boundary on the west that a great deal of fishing is available to the travelling angler. West of Montreal the more important game fish are the bass, the muskellunge, and the brook trout. To the north and east of that city the brook trout and the grey trout are the angler's chief interests; while to the south, bass and, in Lake Memphramagog, fully acclimatised Atlantic salmon form the attractions. Below Quebec all the rivers and lakes on the south side of the river harbour the brook trout, and most of the rivers have a run of sea trout, while numerous salmon rivers exist, but under club management. Good fishing for striped bass may be had in the St Lawrence River below Quebec City during August and September. There is fishing also for cod, halibut, tuna and mackerel.

From Lake St John eastwards, several rivers hold the ouananiche (small land-locked salmon) in their upper waters, together with brook trout. The Laurentides Park of 3,000-odd square miles affords a fishing ground open to the public by arrangement with the Leisure, Hunting and Fishing Ministry at the Quebec address shown below. The numerous salmon rivers of this eastern area are on lease, many of them from the Government. All these north-shore rivers are well stocked with sea trout, especially in the tidal waters. The north of the province remains largely unexplored. There is no shortage of "outfitters" (the Quebec term for "guide"—and perhaps a little more) whose services are obligatory N of the 52nd parallel.

Rivers which are under Government control are the Romaine, St John, Little Caseapedia and the Matane. Further information about these and other rivers, and licence charges, can be had from the Dept of Tourism, Fish and Game, 150 St Cyrille Boulevade East, Quebec G1R 4Y3, Quebec. Other sources of detailed information are the booklets of the Canadian Pacific Railway, Montreal; the Canadian National Railway, Montreal; and the Consolidated Paper Company, Montreal.

For further information write to Dept of Tourism, Fish and Game, Parliament Buildings, Quebec.

SASKATCHEWAN. Rainbow and brook trout (not native to the province) are to be obtained in some waters which have been stocked. Lake trout are plentiful in the northern areas of the province. Pike-perch and northern pike are plentiful throughout the province.

Further information (including details of licence charges, limits, accommodation and road-map) can be had from the Extension Services Branch, Dept of Tourism and Renewable Resources, 3211 Albert Street, Regina, Saskatchewan 54S 5W6.

THE UNITED STATES OF AMERICA

The United States of America covers an enormous area of land and water space, offering everything between the near-Arctic conditions met in winter near the 49th parallel and the semi-tropical climate of Florida, Luisiana and Arizona, providing almost every conceivable environmental opportunity for freshwater or saltwater fish-species to exploit to their full advantage. This creates a great swathe of corresponding angling opportunities on such a scale that holidays spent fishing and camping in the backwoods have long been a commonplace of the American way of life as holidays on the coast—and, more recently, on the shores of the Mediterranean—have been of the British.

Such a demand compels a supply: and there is nowhere in the world where so sophisticated a blend of modern comfort and primitive atmosphere can be found at the waterside, made, as it were, to measure. And signs reading "Keep out: fishing private" are not readily to be found in America. Apart from small lakes on private land immediately adjacent to private homes, the water and its inhabitants are the property of the community, managed expertly for the good of all by the community's public agencies. Fishing may not literally be "free", but it is available to all with a few dollars to invest in recreation. The US population is four times Britain's; but the space available for it is ten times greater.

Because of the way in which, traditionally, exchange-rates and living costs have related, the USA has never in the past figured as a place where the adventurous British angler was likely to take a fishing holiday. All that, though, has now changed and it makes just as

Arizona, USA. A once arid valley in an arid state, now dammed to provide good fishing. *Photograph: Lonsdale Educational.*

much sense, financially and otherwise, for an Englishmen to holiday in **Tennessee,** fishing for large-mouth bass, or in **Minnesota** in search of *Esox masquinongy*, as for a Texan to come to Scotland to catch a Spey salmon. Going out from the **Florida Keys** in pursuit of marlin, sailfish or tarpon has for many years been a branch of the sport attracting a trickle of wealthy Britishers, but fishing American freshwaters has been a practice confined to angling writers and such, out to broaden their professional education.

Since it is the state geographically nearest to Britain, let us begin our review of the northern tier of states and their fishing with **Maine,** whose beaches offer the classical opportunity to contact the greatest of all saltwater sporting fish to be angled for feasibly from the shore anywhere, the striped bass. Though scarcer now than in years gone by, unfortunately, there are still specimens to be taken by the persistent specialist surf-caster. Offshore, there are cod and pollack, and bluefin tuna, some of these registering on the beam-scale weights of more than 500 lb.

Inland, there is a multitude of wilderness lakes and streams offering sport with small-mouth bass, brown and rainbow trout and the unique native of Eastern North America, the brook trout, actually a fine handsome member of the char family. Atlantic salmon which ran Maine's rivers by the ten thousand a hundred years ago suffered near-extermination, but are now being nursed back by conservation technology.

Moving west to the **Great Lakes,** thoughts turn to another char, the "lake trout", a fish which grows to great size in deep and cold water throughout this latitude and in Canada. One fishes for them in hopes of a 40-pounder. An attempt to pass over without comment the damage done to some waters, the Great Lakes included, by the consequences of unthinking industrialisation would be dishonest, but remedy is now the order of the day. None has been more spectacular in its success than the stocking of **Lake Michigan** with coho salmon from the Pacific shore. Here, a new and tremendously exciting sport-fishery has been created, as it were, out of nothing, based on a food-supply left uncropped by lake trout no longer present in sufficient numbers to preserve a natural balance. Most see that as a net gain. The coho gives better sport than the "Mackinaw", as it is sometimes named farther north.

On to a state where water-area challenges land-space: Minnesota, as the North American Indian dialect-name implies, and the cream of the fishing for great northern pike (our pike), walleyes (resembling our zander) and the greatest lantern-jaw of them all, *Esox masquinongy*, the muskellunge or "muskie". While these predators are distributed throughout the region, Minnesota is the heartland. Muskies there may grow to 80 lb weight and leap like trout when hooked.

Passing through a varied landscape, some of it watered by trout streams, we arrive eventually among the foothills of **the Rockies,** where the brilliantly-coloured dolly varden and cutthroat trout (the former another char, to be pedantic) and representatives of the five sub-species of the so-called "golden" trout join the ranks awaiting the angler's thinning, not to mention the sea-going rainbow trout, the steelhead. It was in the Rocky Mountain watershed that the rainbow, sedentary and sea-going, was first encountered and employed to provide the broodstock for the eventual artificial populating of the entire temperate world with this enormously successful species.

Over the mountains: the ocean: and the feeding grounds of the Pacific salmons, five species, of which two, the king or "Tyee" and the coho, are of sporting significance.

Going back East and starting again farther south, we traverse a band of warmer states, less favorable to the cold-water salmonids, but affording an ideal environment for pickerel (another pike-species) and for the small-mouth and large-mouth bass, the fish on which the romance of North American angling is largely founded. These big athletic cousins of the European perch (called there, incidentally, the "yellow perch") hit surface flies and lures with astonishing ferocity, fight like tigers when hooked and lie habitually in the shade and cover of the water-plant zone where only the most expert of tackle-handlers can present the offering and cope with the ensuing seizure without disaster. As the cooler uplands are again reached, the typical population of the upland waters is met again, and the pattern replicates.

Repeat the journey starting in **Georgia,** and one covers territory with a yet warmer climate, swamplands, and then an area of low rainfall. Traditionally, what fishing there was did not enjoy sporting prestige. The image was one of a poor coloured man employing crude tackle to harvest cheap protein; a typical quarry, the Mississippi catfish. One is

Fish-America★★★★★★★★

Moosehead Lake, Maine

Log Cabin accommodation. 6 species of trout, plus salmon, chain pickerel, black bass etc. Lakeside, river bank, or boat fishing; fly trolling or general. Season 1st May to 30th Sept. Wilderness area which also offers whitewater boating and canoe trips.

This is where it's at . . .

Lonsdale's America★★★★★★★★

Where the fisherman fishes!

Send for full details to: Lonsdale's America Ltd.
The Rowans, Nether Tabley, Knutsford, Cheshire. Tel. 056-581-2094

Fish-America★★★★★★★★

Lake Powell, Utah

Large man-made lake 186 miles long. Trout, Bass – striped and largemouth, sunfish, black crappie, carp, catfish, walleye, etc. Trolling, general and livebait fishing. Houseboat or motel accommodation. Spectacular scenery. No close season.

south of that section of the lowland region where water-temperature falls low enough to permit salmonids to spawn successfully in natural waters.

But the water-demand of growing population growing also in affluence has necessitated the construction of chains of dams in the drier states; vast new sheets of deep water offering environments novel in their setting, with a variety of temperature regimes encouraging the successful introduction of some of the great sporting species found naturally to the north and west. Even **Arizona**—the "dry country" itself—now provides fine fishing for sport, and offers it in hot sunshine, a combination of pleasures not frequently encountered by the proverbially frozen-fingered angler acquiring lumbago from his water-logged nether end.

We have discussed none but the prime sporting species. They, however, are not the last word. US waters are inhabited also by others; carp, blue-gill sunfish, crappies and what-have-you, fish present in higher population densities and easier to catch, fish whose presence has traditionally ensured that the less expert members of the specialist angler's family on holiday may take their share of the pleasures and the triumphs. The travel business has now started international operations in this field and British anglers can expect a rapid growth in attractive opportunities *(see advt on facing page)*.

FISHING IN EUROPE

AUSTRIA

Austria is understandably popular with anglers from all over the world, with its abundance of streams and lakes, providing first-class sport with brown and rainbow trout, grayling, char, and coarse fish such as pike and pike-perch, huck, sheat-fish and carp. Some of the main centres tend to be overfished, so a car is immensely valuable; many mountain streams of indescribable beauty are easily reached by road. Much of the sport is on the lower reaches of these mountain rivers, but the more venturesome can often find better fishing on the high alpine streams and lakes. Grayling are highly regarded, often more so than trout, the Traun being one of the best grayling rivers in Europe. Some good centres for trout and grayling are Kitzbühel and Lermoos (Tyrol) and Gnesau and Gmünd (Carinthia).

To keep the sport at a high level, the authorities maintain strict conservation measures and a specially close watch is kept on pollution and abstraction. Generally speaking the rule is fly only for trout, grayling and char. Spinning is usually only permitted for larger fish such as lake trout, pike, huck, pike-perch, sheatfish and so on, and natural bait only for coarse fisheries. Many waters are controlled by the two principal fishing associations, the Austrian Fishing Association (ÖFG) and the Association of Austrian Workers' Fishing Clubs (VÖAFV). The former issues annual permits for several trout preserves as well as daily ones costing from 30 to 250 Austrian Schillings. Temporary permission and information can be obtained from the association's office. The same applies to the VÖAFV. There is a provincial fishing association in Upper Austria which issues licences *(see below for addresses)*.

Wherever he fishes, the visitor usually needs two permits, a general licence issued by the State and costing from about 20 to 240 Austrian schillings, according to the district—or a temporary fishing permit from the local owner costing from 45 to 120 schillings for 2–4 weeks—and a private permit from the local owner which usually amounts to 50–150 schillings a day, but may be as much as 600.

More information and a booklet entitled *Fishing in Austria* can be had from the Austrian National Tourist Office, 30 St George Street, London W1R 9FA (01-629 0461) or 19 Mosley Arcade, Piccadilly Plaza, Manchester 1 (061-236 2909). Addresses of the main angling association are Österreichische Fischereigesellschaft, A-1010 Wien 1, Elisabethstrasse 22. Verband der Österreichischen Arbeiter-Fischerei-Vereine, A-1080, Wien VIII, Lenaugasse, 14, Landesfische-reiverein (Provincial Fishing Assn), Postfach 185, A4021, Linz.

BELGIUM

Although Belgium has never made a name for itself as a visiting fisherman's country, it has, in fact, in its many canals and rivers, most of the fish which British fishermen know, with sea fishing along its 40 miles of coast.

In general terms the freshwater fishing water can be divided thus: the Scheldt basin, with the rivers Scheldt, Lys, Rupel, Dyle, Demer, Dendre and Nèthe holding bream, roach, perch, pike, burbot, smelt, shad and eels; the Meuse basin, with the rivers Meuse, Semois, Lesse, Sambre, Ourthe, Amblève, Warche and Vesdre holding trout, grayling, chub, barbel, perch, roach, bream, pike, carp, tench and eels; and the streams between the Sambre and the Meuse, holding trout, grayling, chub, perch, pike, roach, bream, carp, tench and eels. Many waters of the lowlands and near industrial centres suffer from pollution and over-fishing.

All Belgian waters fall into one of three categories; closed water, not subject to fishing laws; public, or navigable, water belonging to the State; preserved, or non-navigable water belonging to the landowners. Waters in the last two groups are subject to the fishing laws, and anyone fishing in them must possess a current licence. The cost varies from 30 francs to 500 francs, according to the type of fishing, number of rods used and the number of days' fishing to be done in a week. Trout fishermen should note, for example, that they will need a 500-franc licence to enter the water, in addition to any other permit necessary.

Licences may be obtained at post offices. The close seasons are: Coarse fish, from the Monday following the fourth Sunday of March until the second Sunday of June, with certain exceptions; trout, October 1 to fourth Sunday of March. Fly fishing falls off sharply on the Ardennes streams after June.

For visiting trout fishers the greatest attraction probably lies in the streams of the Ardennes, where many hotels have private fishing and there is a good deal of association water. These are mostly mixed fisheries on the lines of the Hampshire Avon in England, with trout and grayling predominating in the upper reaches and being increasingly joined by coarse fish on moving downstream. The best fishing will usually be found in the least accessible places. Standard British fly patterns will take fish on the Ardennes streams but the local flies should be tried where possible.

Sea fishing along the sandy, shelving coast is largely for dabs and plaice (Oct–June), flounders (all year), and sole (May–Oct), with piers and breakwaters providing sport with conger (all year), cod (Sept–Mar), and whiting (Oct–Jan). Turbot are occasionally taken (May–Sept) and rays, shad and garfish are also caught (Sept–Oct). Zeebrugge, Ostend, Niewpoort, Blankenbergh, and Knokke-Heist are good centres.

Belgian fishing legislation is extremely complex and anglers are strongly advised to consult the local tourist centres. For example, Namur province publishes a special angling brochure in French. Further detailed information (in English) from the Belgian National Tourist Office, 66 Haymarket, London (01-930 9618) and, in Belgium itself, from the secretary of the Confédération des Sociétés de Pecheurs à la ligne, 1 Place Jean Jacobs, Brussels.

DENMARK

Fishing in Denmark is plentiful, varied and easy to come by. A few of the rivers hold salmon, and many of them sea trout, brown trout and grayling, as well as coarse fish, which are found also in many lakes.

In many places visitors can fish by purchasing tickets from the local fishing association; in some places the hotels have water. The association tickets are invariably cheap and available through local tourist bureaux.

The principal rivers are all in Jutland. They are the Skjern, the Store, Varde, Ribe and Karup. All are game-fish waters, but of them the best salmon fishing is probably to be had on the Skjern and the best sea trout fishing on the Karup. The water is generally good for fly fishing, and the flies used are much the same as those used in this country. Spinning is much practised. Added variety is given by the sea trout fishing which can be had from the rocks and from boats off both the mainland and the various Baltic islands, by ordinary seafishing for cod, coalfish, flatfish, tope, mackerel, garfish, whiting, ling and pollack. Salmon and sea trout fishing in fresh water is best from mid-July to the end of October.

The coarse fishing potential is considerable and relatively unexplored. Many lakes are hardly ever fished and could hold some surprises, notably for the carp fisherman.

Further information about both fishing and accommodation can be had from the Danish Tourist Board, Sceptre House, 169–173 Regent Street, London, W1R 8PY (01-734 2637/-8).

FINLAND

Finland can offer the angler no fewer than 62,000 lakes and rivers, and some 3,000 miles of sea-shore and archipelago. In the north and centre of the country he can catch very big fish on very big, remote waters; conditions which, in Europe at any rate, are becoming increasingly harder to find. The long days of midsummer give plenty of fishing time—the best sport in fact is often enjoyed in the brief twilight which elsewhere is called "night".

Salmon, sea trout, brown trout and brook trout all run well above the European average, and the size of grayling, too, is often remarkable; four-pounders are not rare. There are also arctic char *(Salvelinus alpinus)* which in the right conditions will take a fly.

The cream of the sport is to be found in Lapland, though there are individual waters farther south which can match them in quality. Some of the best game fishing in Europe is to be found in the region north of Lake Inari. The lake itself holds taimen; lake trout up to 20 lb and more, best fished for duting their migratory runs up the tributaries in late summer.

The salmon fishing, however, is not what it was. Hydro-electric schemes have ruined the runs in many famous waterways. Only two good salmon rivers are said to remain—the Ii and the Torne, which Finland shares with Sweden.

There are problems, too, for the fly fisherman. Many rivers are so wide, deep and fast-flowing that comfortable fishing from the bank is out of the question; it is often impossible to reach the salmon and sea trout lies, in fact. Hence on great rivers like the Teno and Näätämö which flow along the frontier with Norway, the fishing is mainly from a boat with an outboard motor from which large flies are cast by short but stout rods over enormous pools and streams—a technique known as "harling". Reels carrying 250 yards of line of up to 1 mm thick and over 40 lb breaking strain are employed.

These rivers, incidentally, are subject to special rules, involving the purchase of a permit from both countries in those parts through which the common national frontier passes. They are heavily poached. The spring fishing is usually best.

Another problem is transport—many of the best waters are "off the beaten track" and although there are excellent air services between the main centres, after that the angler is on his own and must be prepared for a good deal of foot-slogging and camping. A car, with a fibreglass boat strapped to the roof, is a valid alternative where the roads are not too bad.

Although the north has special attractions for the angler, there is no need to travel so far for good sport. There is excellent trout fishing, for instance, on the Lemmenjoki River, near Inari, which abounds with fish up to 4 lb.

Some very good coarse fishing is to be found in the south, notably for pike and perch and pike-perch—not, as many believe, a hybrid, but a separate species. Opportunities for the fly fisherman in the south have been extended in recent years by the stocking of ponds with rainbow, brown and brook trout.

Fishing regulations are strict and strictly enforced—there are game wardens even in remote districts. A licence is required. Then a period permit must be bought. They can be bought at state tourist hotels, foresters' offices and camping grounds.

Close seasons: salmon and trout, Sept 10–Nov 16; pike-perch, June; grayling, April and May.

One important accessory for the angler is some form of repellant to ward off mosquito attacks, which can often be unbearable—some Finnish fishermen wear head-nets.

Further information may be had from a useful booklet called *Sports Fishing in Finland* published by the National Board of Forestry and available free from tourist offices. These offices will also help in other ways, or the Finland Travel Bureau, Kaivokatu 10A, Helsinki 10 can be approached.

FRANCE

Excellent sport with trout and some salmon fishing are available at reasonable cost in this country. French waterways are divided into the navigable public rivers, where fishing rights are owned by the State, and private rivers, where they belong to the riparian owner, fishing association or local authority. Even on the public rivers, however, anglers must belong to an angling and fish-breeding association and pay a tax based on the method of fishing adopted. Most rivers of this type provide coarse fishing only. Trout and salmon rights will nearly always be privately held, but the visitor should have little difficulty in obtaining a permit. Information should be sought from the local club or tackle dealer. Close seasons vary a great deal according to the locality, especially for salmon, and it is best to make local inquiries. A rough guide, however, would be: salmon, Oct 1 to Jan 10; trout and char, from last Tuesday in Sept to third Friday in Feb; coarse fish, from Tuesday following April 15 to Friday following June 15.

Perhaps the best salmon fishing in France is to be found on a small number of fast-flowing streams in the Western Pyrenees. The noted Gave d'Oloron is in this area. Oloron, Sauveterre and Navarrenx are good centres for this river. The Gave d'Aspe, which joins it at Oloron, and its tributary, the Lourdios, have provided good sport in recent years. They may be fished from Lurbe. At Peyrehorade the Gave d'Oloron is joined by the Gave de Pau, on which sport has also been improving, and Pau itself makes a fine place to stay. Salmon also run up the Gaves d'Ossau and de Nive.

Because of melting snow, the season begins later here than elsewhere in France, but it extends later, too. For the Oloron area the best months are from June to the end of August.

Brittany, too, provides some opportunities for the salmon fisherman, though the fish are on the small side, especially on the River Aulne, which flows into the sea near Brest. Try the Châteaulin area until April and Chateauneuf-du-Faou later on. Châteaulinn is also a good centre for the Ell'le and from Landerneau and Landivisiau the Ellorn may be fished. Other productive streams are the Blavet, Laita and Odet, which flow into the Atlantic; the Trieux and its tributary the Leff, with Guingamp a suitable venue.

Flowing northwards through picturesque countryside to feed the Loire, the Allier offers the best opportunities for salmon fishermen in Auvergne. This is a region comparatively unknown to British anglers. The place to make for is Brioude, on the upper reaches of the river. The Bajace dam, where salmon congregate before taking the leap, is half a mile away. Vichy, Pont-du-Chateau, Veyre and Issoire are other centres. The upper reaches of the Loire itself can provide good sport. Roanne is a suitable place to stay.

Some of the Normandy rivers have good runs of fish, but the best of the fishing is hard to come by, being largely in the hands of syndicates. The visitor may find opportunities, however, on the Orme and Vire, the Sée, the Sienne and the Sélune. Pontfarcy, Quetteville, Avranches and Ducey are suggested centres.

France is a splendid country for the trout fisherman, with an abundance of well-stocked streams flowing through glorious scenery. He way find solitude and beauty not very far from Paris—in fact, on the upper reaches of the Seine and its tributary, the Ource. A little farther south lies Avallon, from which the Cure and its tributaries may be fished.

But the visitor will find the Pyrenees very hard to beat for trout. The Gave d'Ossau is one of the best of the many first-class streams in this area, offering particularly fine sport at the Fabrège dam. From Lurbe the Gave d'Aspe and its tributary, the Lourdios, may be fished, and excellent sport is available on the Gave d'Oloron above Pont-de-Dognen, the Nive above Itxassou, and the Gave de Pau upstream of Pont-de-Lescar.

In the fascinating and comparatively unexplored regions of Creuse, Haute-Vienne, Corrèze and Lot, are innumerable streams with torrential upper reaches holding fine trout. Downstream they become less tumultuous and wider until, in the Dordogne, they harbour a variety of coarse fish. Figeac is a good centre for the trout. Farther east lies the wild, mountainous region of Lozère, where grand and beautiful rivers like the Lot and its tributary, the Colagne, may be fished. The Bés and Truyére should also be tried.

Wherever one turns in France, it seems, there are trout to be caught. In the Savoy Alps are innumerable streams of quality, like the Isère and Doron, near Albertville, and the Sierroz, Tillet and Chéron near Chatelard-en-Bauges, the Arvan and Arc, near Saint-Jean-de-Maurienne. Auvergne and the Dauphiny Alps are ideal for the explorer with a fly rod. Grenoble commands a number of valleys through which flow some noted trout streams.

Normandy has some trout fisheries of high repute, like the Risle, Eure, Charenton and Andelles, but they are strictly preserved for the most part. Fishing on the streams of Brittany is more easily obtainable. Quimper is an excellent centre for the large fish of the Odet and its tributaries. Trout abound throughout Finistère, notably in the Aulne tributaries.

The lake fisherman is also well catered for in France, with some splendid opportunities in the Pyrenees, especially near Luz-Saint-Sauveur, and in the Alps. Lakes Leman, Annecy and, farther south, Lauvitel and Besson are good for trout.

One cautionary note for the fly fisherman—many French rivers are so torrential and boulder-strewn that they cannot be fished with fly. It is as well to check, with a club or tackle dealer in the area to avoid disappointment. Best months of the fly are generally May, June and Sept in the north and before April and in Sept in the south. British patterns do well in the north, but are not so good in the south.

Further details from the French Tourist Office, 178 Piccadilly, London W1V 0AL, who issure 47-page booklet with lists of local contacts. By post, 50p.

GERMANY

Bavaria and the Black Forest offer the best prospects for the trout fisherman. Although pollution and over-fishing are producing a decline in sport, Bavarian waters like the Wiesent, Pegnitz, Loisach, Isar, Ammer, Saalach and Salzach, to name only a few, still offer fishing of high quality amid beautiful surroundings. Brown and rainbow trout, as well as grayling, are widely distributed.

For anglers who like to fly-fish for trout and char from a boat, the Hintersee at Berchtesgaden is highly recommended—the char in particular are good, reaching weights of 6 lb and more.

In the Black Forest, streams like the Kinzig, Murg, Obere Wolf, Nagold and Bernbach provide good sport with trout and grayling. The best waters are usually fly-only.

The Harz mountain area, south-east of Hanover, is also well worth exploring—the Radau, fished from Bad Harzburg, is good. Trout are found, too, in some of the streams and lakes of the Rhine valley, especially in the Eifel district, and in some parts of North Rhine-Westphalia and Lower Saxony.

Elsewhere there is good coarse fishing. In Baden-Wuerttemberg (apart from the Black Forest), carp, bream, tench, whitebait, roach, barbel, pike, eels and trout can be had in the Neckar Valley, the Hohenloe district, the Swabian Forest area and elsewhere, including trout, pike and barbel fishing in the Danube. Other coarse-fishing areas are the Rhineland-Palatinate (Moselle, Ahr, Lahn), and most of Lower Saxony.

The Angler will need a licence from the Landratsamt (rural district council) or from the local police (up to DM 20) and a permit from the owner or lessee of the fishing. Many Hotels and clubs also have fishing rights. The principal seasons are as follows: river trout, Mar 1–Oct 10; lake trout, Jan 1–Sept 30; river char, Jan 10–Oct 10; lake char, Jan 1–Oct 31; pike, May 1–Dec 31; pike-perch, July 1–Mar 31; huck, May 1 to last day of Feb. (The seasons vary slightly in the different Federal states.)

Intending visitors are advised to obtain a copy of *Deutscher Angelsportfuehrer* (Fishing in Germany) published by Graefe & Unzer-Verlag, Isabellastrasse 32, 8, Muenchen 13 in two volumes covering Southern Germany and Northern and Western Germany. This has English introductions.

Further information about fishing can be had from the German Anglers' Association (VDSF), D-200 Hamburg 11, Venusberg 36 and the Verband Deutscher Sportfischer, Bahnhofstrasse 37, D6050, Offenbach/Main, and general tourist information (including some on fishing) from the German National Tourist Office, 61 Conduit Street, London (01-734 2600).

ICELAND

Much of the salmon fishing in Iceland is now controlled by the Salmon Fishing Society (Stangaveidifelagid), from whom permits may be obtained through the Iceland Tourist Information Bureau in London (address below). It is as well to inquire about fishing as early as possible, for the best rivers are booked well in advance of the opening of the season. Most of the rivers are well out in the country where hotels are scarce and facilities for the fisherman are limited, but many have adequately furnished fishing huts which are let with the river. Arrangements can be made for accommodation at the nearest farm.

The average weight of the Icelandic salmon is about 10 lb, though fish up to 30 lb are not infrequent and fish up to 40 lb have been landed. There are over fifty rivers frequented by salmon in Iceland, and about half of them are regarded as first-class. The annual catch of salmon is estimated at about 30,000. In the south the rod-fishing season starts at the beginning of June and in other districts about the middle of June. The season lasts for about three months. Trout fishing last from April to Oct 1.

The great lake at Thingvellir is well stocked with trout, char, and two small fish known to the Icelanders as *murta* and *depla*. The latter two fish have not yet been clearly classified, but some experts think they are char at an early stage of development. The lake, which is called Thingvallavatn, is 30 miles from Reykjavik, and there is a hotel there. Near to the "northern capital" of Iceland, Akureyri, is Lake Myvatn, which is also stocked with trout and char. There are two hotels. Lakes in the interior provide excellent fishing for trout and char, but camping is necessary and transport facilities meagre.

Daily air services are operated by Icelandair and Loftleider, Companies now merged. Travel within Iceland is mostly by air and bus services. Further tourist information may be obtained from the Iceland Tourist Information Bureau, 73 Grosvenor Street, London (01-493 7661), or from their Scottish Office, 11 Royal Exchange Square, Glasgow G13 BD.

ITALY

Fishing can be had in many parts of Italy, in rivers, mountain torrents and lakes, for trout, pike, perch, carp and several local varieties. Generally speaking, the trout fishing is in waters above the 1,800 ft contour, the close season being Oct 15 to Jan 15. Sport is often good though pollution has caused a sharp decline on many of the lowland lakes. Everywhere it is necessary to obtain a licence from the local police *(prefettura)*, the charge varying from 4,500 to 1,300 lire. Tourists may obtain a special licence, valid for one month. The Bolzano and Trentino districts of the Dolomites are good. Sea fishing is first class. Deep-sea sport with tuna, albacore and swordfish has become increasingly popular, and so has underwater fishing. Further information can be had from the Italian State Tourist Department in London, 201 Regent Street (01-439 2311), from the Federazione Italiana Pesca Sportiva, Viale Tiziano 70, Roma, or from the provincial tourist boards (their addresses may be obtained from the Tourist Dept in London).

LUXEMBOURG

Most of the rivers of Luxembourg are mixed fisheries holding trout and coarse fish, including pike, barbel, chub and tench. Much of the water is private, although visitors can obtain sport on various hotel lengths or on private water with the owner's permission. There is a fine reservoir at the head of the Sûre, heavily stocked with chub and carrying a good head of pike, some of them very large.

A licence is required in order to fish in the interior rivers of the Grand Duchy as well as in the Upper Sûre Lake. This is delivered by the District Commissioners in Luxembourg, Diekirch and Grevenmacher. In order to obtain a licence you will need a recent photo and a receipt from the Administration de l'Enregistrement that the tax due has been paid. Written permission from private land owners must be obtained also.

No permit is required for bait or fly fishing from the banks of the frontier rivers, the Moselle and Sûre, from Schengen to Wallendorf-Pont.

As fishing regulations are very strict it is advised that visitors contact the National Tourist Office before making arrangements.

Tackle can be purchased, and local information gained, from Maison Zeus-Brucher, 62 rue d'Anvers, Luxembourg Ville, GD Luxembourg. Further tourist information, including details of hotels with fishing, can be had from the Luxembourg National Tourist Office, 36/37 Piccadilly, London (01-434 2800).

NORWAY

Norway has acquired a world-wide reputation for its salmon and sea trout, which can be fished for in a superb setting of mountains and fjords, spectacular waterfalls and peaceful valleys. Beats on such renowned waters as the Tana, Alta, Laerdal, Driva and Surna, fetch very high prices and are in the hands of specialised agencies (inquire Hardy's of

London and Sporting Services International). Excellent sport at more modest charges may be had from the many hotels with private stretches, especially in the north. The salmon season is from late May to Sept 5 (best in June and July) and the best sea trout fishing is to be had in August, although the season extends into Sept, the actual date varying in different districts.

Floating line fishing is becoming more widely practised, but it is more usual on the big rivers to employ heavy, fast-sinking lines and large flies, from size 3/0 upwards. Streamers and bucktails are popular for salmon, and sea-trout are often fished dry fly or nymph—in the clear waters the fish can often be seen and cast to.

Less well known, and much less expensive, is fishing for brown trout and char, which can be very good indeed. Countless streams and lakes well stocked with trout lie within easy reach of Oslo, while anglers prepared to travel further afield will be amply rewarded. Trout of 25 pounds and over have been caught on the Drammen, near Vikersund, and the Rands, near Kistefoss, and Lake Mjösa, near Gjövik. Several fish of around this weight have fallen to fly.

Arctic char are mostly found in the deep and cold mountain lakes, where they can provide thrilling sport, though this is a difficult art. There are taxi flights to the lakes from the big towns. The brown trout season varies with altitude, the extremes being late May until mid-Sept. As several rivers have rather swift currents, strong tackle is recommended. Most fishing rights are owned privately, but there are vast areas of Crown land where good fishing may be enjoyed at no great cost. Any fisherman in Norway, in addition to the application fee, is required to take out a licence available from post offices. It covers the entire country for a year and costs Norwegian Kroner 25 (£2.20). Most hotels in the country have their own rivers and lakes for brown trout fishing, making no charge to guests.

Dry-fly fishing is very popular, especially in smaller lakes and tarns or slow rivers. Most suitable gear is a fly-rod of 9½ ft to 10½ ft, with a No 7 line, which may be used anywhere at any time. Best flies are those in douce colours, such as March Brown and Greenwell's Glory etc. For red char fishing, use stronger colours such as Red Cardinal, Butcher or Coachman, etc. The best all-round spinning lures are those with slow movements and in golden or red colours. For hooking, use Devon or Phantom lures, or artificial minnows. No gaff is required, but a large landing-net is desirable. Rubber boots or waders come in handy, practially everywhere. Boats are available almost everywhere.

Intending visitors are advised to write to the Norwegian Tourist Office, 20 Pall Mall, London, who provide information "Angling in Norway", £1.65 from Stanfords International Map Centre, 12 Long Acre, WC2, will be found helpful.

PORTUGAL

Salmon and trout are found mostly in the River Minho and its tributaries in the far north, but the lack of controls has diminished sport. Very good sea trout fishing may be enjoyed in the Minho estuary near Moledo and on the Lima near Viana do Castelo. The fish are usually taken on bait or spinner, but fly fishing should prove productive.

The close season for salmon and trout fishing is from Aug 1 to the last day of Feb. Licences for visitors are not as a rule required.

The sea fishing is excellent. This is for many of the fish known to British fishermen in home waters, but in the south it includes game species such as swordfish, marlin, tunny, bonito and amberjack, as well as blue and mako sharks. School tunny and meagre (the so-called salmon-bass) are also taken.

Many of the fish known to British fishermen reach heavier weights in Portuguese waters. Bass of around 20 lb are reported to be taken inshore from boats, for instance, and smaller fish of 10 lb–14 lb from the shore. Large shoals of mackerel up to 6 lb were found by a British team fishing off Peniche in 1956. Good shore fishing for bass can be had more or less everywhere. Other fish regularly caught include: mullet (to 5 lb), conger and dogfish, various types of bream, some running up to 25 lb; pollack, cod, turbot, rock gurnard, wrasse, John Dory, tope and several others. Meagre (salmon-bass) attain weights up to 200 lb, amberjack to 18 lb, and school tunny to 80 lb. The comparatively recent discovery of this vast potential has led to the rapid development of a number of small fishing ports. Boats and boatmen are available at most of them, and hotel accommodation is reported to be good. Most important of the new-found fishing centres is perhaps Sesimbra, south of Lisbon. Others are Praia da Rocha (for Portimao) and Faro in the south, Cascais (near Estoril), Peniche, Nazaré, and Ericeira (all to the north-west of Lisbon) and Sines (south of Sesimbra). Apart from the fishing, most of these places have good beaches and are good holiday and tourist centres. Boats are available at many places, including Albufeira, Lagos and Monte Gordo.

Visiting anglers will be made welcome at such clubs as the "Clube dos Amadores de Pesca de Portugal", Rua do Salitre 175R/CD, Lisbon (for all kinds of angling, especially big game fishing), "Clube Invicta de Pesca Desportiva" at Rua Santo Antonio, and the "Amadores de Pesca Reunidos", at Largo des Loios, both Oporto, where information on local fishing may be obtained and where all visitors will be treated as honorary members. In the Algarve, several hotels provide or can arrange sea fishing parties. They include the Hotels Praia, Algarve and de Baleeira. The best centres in this region are in the Sagres and Cabo Carroeiro areas where large mackerel are frequently taken. Details can be had from Portuguese Airways (TAP-AIR PORTUGAL), 19 Lower Regent Street, London who publish an information booklet *Guide to Fishing in Portugal*, or from the Portuguese National Tourist Office, 1/5 New Bond Street, London W1Y 0NP.

SPAIN

Spain is a well-endowed country, offering the most southerly fishing for Atlantic salmon in Europe; brown and rainbow trout, coarse fish including large carp and barbel, both in rivers, and shore fishing for sea bass, mackerel, mullet, conger and other species. Black bass, pike and Danube salmon are among comparatively recent introductions.

Twenty-six rivers draining the Cantabrian range and the Galician Coast are entered by salmon. The Deva-Cares, Navia, Sella, Narcea and Asón provide the best sport. Arrangements for licences and permits for visitors are not uniform and the British angler contemplating salmon fishing in Spain is advised to contact the Spanish National Tourist Office, 57/58 St James Street, London SW1A 1LD. Much the same is to be said of the trout fishing, applying equally to seasons and permitted methods. In some areas, trout grow impressively large. Spain has not yet become as notable for high-grade coarse fishing as it may at some future date, but few who have connected with large carp or barbel in a deep, fast-flowing Spanish river do not cherish ambitions to renew the experience.

The tourist office publishes an interesting full-colour booklet covering both fishing and shooting facilities in the country.

SWEDEN

Sweden cannot be compared with Norway for salmon, but there are splendid opportunities for sea trout, fish of well over 20 lb having been caught on the rod. The country is rich in brown trout waters and well supplied with char and grayling.

The game fisherman will be advised to go north for his sport, where swift and powerful waterways hold some really heavy trout and up which migratory fish run in fair numbers from mid-July onwards; rivers like the Torne älv, Kalix älv and Vindelälven, so far untouched by hydro-electric schemes which have marred sport in so many other Swedish waters.

For the fly fisherman, however, such awe-inspiring torrents present special difficulties. They are too wide, deep and fast-flowing to be fished effectively from the bank, except perhaps for sea trout which swim closer to the shore than salmon but which are not too plentiful in these northern parts. The most productive angling technique is harling— casting large flies into vast pools from a boat equipped with an outboard motor. Quite a few salmon are, however, taken on spinning lures, especially where rock ledges can be found to command the pools.

Many once-famous salmon rivers are hardly worth fishing nowadays, notably the Mörrum in Blekinge Province, where the National Board of Crown Forests and Lands (Domänverket) still issues permits for fishing over a 3m stretch. This used to be the best salmon river in the country, but the spring fishing is now chiefly for sea trout kelts and there are relatively few fresh-run fish later on. The Em, Atran and Örekil are other salmon streams which provide somewhat indifferent sport, though the Em is good for sea trout.

Farther north, in central Sweden, the position on the Dalälven is not much better, but the river still has a fair run of large fish from midsummer to late autumn; harling is again the most effective way of taking them.

If the present situation in regard to salmon fishing is far from favourable, the outlook is somewhat brighter, as the Swedes are engaged in a massive restocking programme with smolts which is already bringing results.

Most of the fishing for sea trout is with the dry fly, as the wet fly will rarely take fish by day. Hackled coch-y-bondhu patterns are commonly employed. Of course in the north "night" fishing is something of a misnomer as it never really gets dark.

There are some very big trout to be caught in the large rivers and lakes of the north—fish of 20 lb and more—and trout also run to a respectable size in the lowland streams. The grayling, too, are not to be despised. It will interest anglers to learn that they can be caught in the sea along the north Baltic coast, using small dry flies and keeping well out of sight as grayling in the sea tend to be shy.

Sport with arctic char is confined mainly to the deep cold lakes. It can be exciting at times, but nearly always difficult. Char are best taken on wet fly from the shallows where a stream enters a lake.

Many of the best fishing areas are away from roads and habitation, but the angler who takes a tent with him and is used to mountainous terrain has every chance of success.

There is no stream fishing in the Stockholm region but there is an increasing amount of sport with rainbow, brown and brook trout in artificially stocked lakes.

Pike, perch and carp abound in these lowland lakes and the City of Stockholm issues a card at a modest charge which is valid for several places in Lake Mälaren and in the archipelago.

For salmon and trout fishing, licence charges vary considerably: charges for trout fishing in stocked lakes and ponds are somewhat higher than for natural waters. No charge is made to fish for grayling in the sea.

Close seasons vary widely. For salmon and sea trout it usually runs from Sept 1 to Jan 1, though fishing is prohibited on some waters after Aug 15.

Further and more detailed information can be had from the year book published by Fiskefrämjandet (Association for the Promotion of Sport Fishing), Brunkebergstorg 11, Stockholm, which lists about 1,800 fishing waters. The association cannot, however, answer detailed inquiries from abroad. These should be directed to the Swedish National Tourist Office, 3 Cork Street, London W1X 1HA or to The Fishery Board, Fack, S-403 10, Göteborg 1.

SWITZERLAND

There is no shortage of water in Switzerland—20,000 miles of rivers and streams, and 520 square miles of lakes within a small area—and as most of these waters hold trout, the country is a fly-fisherman's dream.

Unfortunately, the dream is often of brief duration, as the streams at appreciable altitudes are in snow spate often until July. But in the lower valleys there is sport to be had from May to the end of the summer. Lake fishing consists mainly in trolling at great depth. Swiss waters may be classed as follows:

The Lakes. Most of the lakes contain trout and char, pike, perch and other coarse fish. The trout and char *(Ombre chevalier)* run to a great size, but they lie at such depths that fly fishing or trolling with a rod is practically useless. Most of the lakes in the central plain are now suffering to some degree from pollution, but they still provide sport. Best results are obtained by spinning with light tackle.

The Great Rivers. Both the Rhine and Rhône hold very big trout. Spinning with a 2¼ in silver Devon is the best method, though a small silver-bodied salmon fly will sometimes give good results. The Rhône, above the lake of Geneva, is fishable only till the middle of April. In summer months it is thick with snow water. Many Swiss rivers contain good stocks of coarse fish, including barbel, carp and pike.

Plain and Lower Valley Streams. Trout in these streams run from ¼ lb to 2½ lb or more. There is always a good hatch of fly, and the Mayfly is up on most of them from May to July. Wading is not as a rule necessary. Fine tackle is essential. Carry a couple of small silver Devons for thick water.

The Hill Torrents. Trout run four or five to the pound in the best of the hill torrents, rather smaller in the others. As the hatch of fly is usually poor, the upstream worm pays best. The coch-y-bondhu is sometimes useful, while in July and Aug the "daddy-longlegs" is deadly. Wading is usually an advantage. Watch for the spate that often occurs towards midday owing to melting snow.

It should be said that Switzerland, in common with most European countries, is experiencing a growth of angling pressures, but the authorities, concerned to ensure that sport remains at a high level, release at least 100 million fish, mostly trout, from hatcheries every year.

The close season for trout runs most commonly from Oct 1 to Mar 15, and for grayling from Mar 1 to April 30.

Fishing regulations vary. Generally speaking the angler will require a canton licence and may also need a permit for private waters. Further tourist information and a booklet giving the various permit charges can be had from the Swiss National Tourist Office, Swiss Centre, 1 New Coventry Street, London W1V 3HG (01-734 1921).

YUGOSLAVIA

Here is a country well worth exploring by the angler. The rivers are often difficult to reach, but offer sport of the highest quality. Even in the more accessible places, sport with trout (brook and rainbow) and grayling is often very good indeed.

Some streams are too torrential for the fly, but many rivers and lakes provide excellent fly fishing. Sport is carefully supervised. Each province, or people's republic, has its own federation of fishing societies which encourages fishing as a sport and protects and restocks the waters.

Mostly the rivers are clear and fast-flowing direct or indirect tributaries of the Danube. There are 25 species of game fish out of a total of 198 of all types in Yugoslav waters. Besides brook and rainbow trout there are large river char and marble trout. Among coarse fish, the pike-perch of the Danube basin is a big attraction. In the lakes trout run large and some lakes contain pike, carp and eels. Everywhere a fisherman must obtain a permit from the local federation, the cost varying from less than 20 to as much as 180 dinars a day (£1 = 40 dinar, tourist exchange rate).

In Croatia visitors staying in Dubrovnik can easily make one-day fishing expeditions, reaching the river after a drive of only thirty minutes. In Zagreb the Croatian Federation can provide expert guides, linguists as well as fishermen, and tackle. Bosnia and Herzogovina, however, probably form the most interesting fishing region, the best season for brook trout being May and June and from late Sept to the first frosts, while rainbows give best sport then onwards to Feb. The Drina river and tributaries form a splendid and extensive fishery, containing large huck, trout and grayling. Slovenia also affords good sport likely to appeal to British fishermen. There the season is May 1 to Sept 15.

Further detailed information can be had from Savez Udruzenja Sportskih ribolovaca, Jugoclavije, 11000 Beograd (Belgrade) Alekse Nenadovica 19, or through the Yugoslav National Tourist Office, 143 Regent Street, London W1R 8AE (01-734 5243).

SOME NOTABLE BRITISH AND IRISH FISH

U NTIL the British Record (Rod Caught) Fish Committee was set up in 1957, there was no recognised method of establishing a list of record fish. Such lists as did exist were based largely on data culled from books, the angling press and so on. Clearly, many of the claims were suspect, as the committee found when it examined the lists it had inherited and, as a result, discarded many so-called "records". Some species are still open for claims. Anglers catching a fish above the following weights are entitled go submit a claim: silver bream 1 lb, sea trout 15 lb.

Fishermen catching fish equal to or greater in weight than the established record should claim recognition of the fish through Peter Tombleson, Secretary, British Record (Rod-caught) Fish Committee, now under the aegis of the National Anglers' Council, 5 Cowgate, Peterborough, PE1 1LR (54084) and Peakirk, Peterborough (Glinton 428). A claim should be made as soon as possible after the capture of the fish, preferably by telegram or telephone, and a confirmatory letter should give full details of the catch (date, time, tackle, etc) and the names and addresses of two independent and reliable witnesses capable of identifying the fish, which should be retained for inspection, dead or alive, by the committee or its representative. Fish should not be weighed on spring balances, but on a steel-yard or scales which can be tested if necessary.

The committee is always pleased to receive similar details of any unusual catches. Only fish in the coastal waters of England (including the Channel Islands and the Isle of Man), Scotland, Wales and Northern Ireland are eligible. Fish caught in the Irish Republic should be reported to the Secretary, Irish Specimen Fish Committee, Balnagowan, Mobbi Boreen, Glasnevin, Dublin 9.

Fish marked * in the following lists are those recognised by the BRFC after very careful examination of all the relevant factors, as the official record for the species.

Irish records, that is, those recognised by the Irish Specimen Fish Committee—are indicated thus † in the following lists. **Note:** *The Irish keep separate records for rivers and lakes in respect of pike and brown trout.*

The other notable catches recorded here—ie those apart from the established records— are included for interest only and, because they have not been subjected to such rigorous scrutiny, should not be viewed as beyond question. Further data on any of these fish would be welcome.

Pressure on space has caused curtailment of the following lists, and regrettably many other notable fish have had to be left out.

FRESHWATER FISH

BARBEL *(Barbus barbus,* Linn)
16 lb 1 oz C H Cassey, while spinning for salmon in the Hampshire Avon at Ibsley on March 6, 1960. Fish was foulhooked and therefore disallowed as a record.
14 lb 6 oz T Wheeler, Thames at Molesey in 1888.
14 lb 6 oz H D Tryon, Hampshire Avon (Royalty Fishery), Sept, 1934.
14 lb 6 oz F W Wallis, Royalty Fishery, Sept 1937. The same angler had another of 14 lb 4 oz from the Royalty in Sept, 1933.
14 lb 4 oz R Jones, Thames at Radcot Bridge in 1909.
14 lb 2 oz A Jessop, Hampshire Avon, Dec, 1968.
14 lb E A Edwards, River Kennet, 1954.
14 lb Mr Simmons, Dorset Stour, Sept, 1930.
13 lb 14 oz C A Taylor, Hampshire Avon, Oct, 1934.
13 lb 14 oz P Mays, Troop Fishery, Dorset Stour, Oct, 1964.
13 lb 12 oz* J Day, Royalty Fishery, Oct, 1962.
13 lb 8 oz J Ginifer, Thames, Sept, 1968.
13 lb 2 oz J Harrigan, Royalty Fishery, Nov, 1965.
13 lb 2 oz E Upton, Royalty Fishery, Oct, 1970.

BLEAK (*Alburnus alburnus*, Linn)
5¼ oz Henry Stubbins, Nottingham, at Radcliffe-on-Trent, about 1890. Recorded by H Coxon in his *Coarse Fish Angling*, 1896.
4 oz 2 dm F Brown on Trent at Long Higgin, 1959.
3 oz 15 dm* D Pollard, Staythorpe Pond, nr Newark, Aug, 1971.
3 oz 8 dm N D Sizmur, Thames at Walton, Surrey, 1963.

BREAM (COMMON) (*Abramis brama*, Linn)
13 lb 8 oz* A R Heslop, private water, Staffs, 1977.
13 lb 8 oz E G Costin, Chiddingstone Castle Lake, in Oct, 1945.
13 lb R Wills, Duchess Lake, Bristol, Sept, 1949.
12 lb 15 oz F T Bench, Tring Reservoirs, Oct, 1945.
12 lb 14 oz G J Harper, Suffolk Stour, July, 1971.
12 lb 14 oz Caught by one of two brothers (Messrs Pugh), Tring Reservoirs, on July 28, 1933. They had two other bream, 12 lb and 10½ lb, on same day.
12 lb 12½ oz A J Fisher, July 30, 1931, Tring Reservoirs (thus beating an Irish fish of 11¾ lb, which had held the record for 49 years). Later that year Lord Rothschild reported a fish of 13 lb 10 oz found dying at Tring. Several other fish of 12 lb and over have been taken from Tring.
11 lb 12 oz W Gollins, Ellesmere (Salop), 1970.
11 lb 12 oz† A Pike, River Blackwater (Co Monaghan), 1882.

BREAM (SILVER) (*Blicca bjoernka*, Linn)
4 lb 8 oz C R Rhind from Tortworth Lake, Gloucestershire, in 1923.
4 lb 4 oz K Armstrong, lake at Rugeley, Staffs, Jan, 1970.
4 lb Two fish of this weight were caught by J Bowater from Yorkshire Derwent in July, 1933.
4 lb G Burwash from Thames at Egham in Feb, 1922.
4 lb J Bowater, Yorkshire Derwent, July, 1933.
3 lb 7½ oz A Engers from Plucks Gutter (Stour, Kent), July, 1949.

CARP (*Cyprinus carpio*, Linn)
56 lb 6 oz C Yates, Redmire Pool, Herefordshire, 16/6/80. (Still, as we go to press, a contender for the British record.)
44 lb* Richard Walker on Sept 13, 1952, Redmire Pool, Herefordshire. The best of many huge carp from Redmire. "Dick" Walker himself had another of 31 lb 4 oz in June, 1954.
42 lb R Clay, Billing Aquadrome, Sept, 1966.
40 lb 8 oz E G Price, Redmire Pool. Sept 27, 1959. King carp.
40 lb 0½ oz R Groombridge from a lake at Hemel Hempstead, July, 1956.
38 lb 8½ oz R Bowskill, Redmire Pool, Sept, 1966.
37 lb 8 oz J Sims, Wyver Pool at Belper, Derbys, July, 1968.
36 lb 4 oz W Quinlan, Redmire Pool, Oct, 1970.
35 lb J Hilton, Redmire Pool, Oct, 1967.
34 lb 8 oz J Ward, pond near Wokingham, Berkshire, July 28, 1959.
34 lb 4 oz W Beta, Electricity Cut, River Nene at Peterborough, June, 1965. Thought to be the "record" river carp. The Electricity Cut has produced several big carp—one of 33 lb 12 oz was taken by P Harvey in Jan, 1965.
34 lb P Chillingworth, Billing Aquadrome, June, 1970.
Fish of over 30 lb have also come from the Ashlea Pool, Gloucester (two), Waveney Valley Lakes and the Layer Pits, near Colchester. Biggest catch of carp is thought to have been taken by Bob Reynolds from Billing Aquadrome. In August 1957 he took carp of 26 lb 1 oz, 27 lb 9 oz, 27 lb 13 oz, and 28 lb 4 oz, making 109 lb 11 oz in all. The record Irish carp is a fish of 18 lb 12 oz taken by J Roberts from Abbey lake in 1958.

CARP (CRUCIAN) (*Carassius carassius*, Linn)
5 lb 10½ oz* G Halls, King's Lynn lake, June, 1976.
4 lb 15½ oz J Johnstone, Johnson's Lake, New Hythe, Kent, June, 1972.
4 lb 11 oz H C Hinson, Broadwater Lake, Godalming, 1938.

4 lb 10 oz M Benwell, Notts gravel pit, July, 1971.
4 lb 9½ oz B Cole, Kent lake, Sept, 1971.
4 lb 8 oz F J Axten, Bedfont Lake, July, 1964.
4 lb 8 oz B Burman, Shoebury Park Lake, Sept, 1971.
4 lb 7½ oz A Palfrey, South Ockendon pit, 1962.
4 lb 7½ oz F James, Leighton Buzzard pit, June, 1965.
4 lb 7¼ oz A Donison, Guildford lake, Aug, 1968.
4 lb 6½ oz G Bott, Godalming lake, March, 1966.

CHAR *(Salvelinus alpinus)*
1 lb 12 oz* M C Imperiale, Loch Insh, Inverness, May, 1974.
1 lb 11 oz B A Richardson, Lake Windermere, April 1973.
1 lb 9 oz A Stein, Lake Windermere, March, 1973.

CHUB *(Squalius cephalus,* Linn)
10 lb 8 oz Dr J A Cameron from the Annan in 1955.
8 lb 14 oz Caught out of season on the Wissey by J Roberts in May, 1960, while spinning for trout.
8 lb 12 oz J Lewis, River Mole, Oct, 1964.
8 lb 8 oz D Deeks from Sussex Rother, July, 1951.
8 lb 4 oz G F Smith from Avon at Christchurch, Dec, 1913.
8 lb C Harmell, Royalty Fishery, Aug, 1964.
7 lb 15 oz P Minton, Yorkshire Ouse, Oct, 1964.
7 lb 14½ oz Mrs H M Jones, from Stour at Canford (Dorset) in Sept, 1937.
7 lb 6 oz* W Warren, Hampshire Avon, 1957.

DACE *(Leuciscus leuciscus,* Linn)
1 lb 8¾ oz S Horsfield, Derbyshire, Derwent, Jan, 1947.
1 lb 8 oz 5 dm R W Humphrey, from tributary of Hampshire Avon, Sept, 1932.
1 lb 7¾ oz J S Upton, from the Penk, Dec, 1933.
1 lb 7½ oz F W Arnold, River Mole, Jan, 1934.
1 lb 7½ oz S Rolfe, Suffolk Stour, Feb, 1962.
1 lb 7 oz Abe Hibbard, near Sheffield, Feb, 1934.
1 lb 5 oz 2 dm S Wilson, Llynfi, July, 1966.
1 lb 5 oz R Walker, Cam, July, 1938.
1 lb 5 oz J Cartwright, Cynon, 1965.
1 lb 4½ oz* J L Gasson, Little Ouse, Thetford, Feb, 1960.
1 lb 2 oz† J T Henry, River Blackwater (Cappoquin), 1966.

EEL *(Anguilla anguilla,* Linn)
11 lb 2 oz* S Terry, Kingfisher Lake, Hants, 1978.
8 lb 10 oz A Dart, Hunstrete Lake, July, 1969.
8 lb 8 oz C Mitchell, Bitterwell Lake, in 1922. An eel of equal weight was taken from a trap on the Warwickshire Avon in Aug, 1960.
8 lb 4 oz J McFarlane, River Tees, 1964.
8 lb 4 oz J Taylor from pond at Arlesey, Bedfordshire, in July, 1958.
8 lb R Jones, Monmouthshire lake, May, 1968. Mr Jones had another from the same lake of 7 lb 8 oz.
7 lb 15 oz P Climo, Monmouthshire lake, May, 1969.
7 lb 13 oz M Hill, Arlesey Lake, Beds, Aug, 1970.
7 lb 5¼ oz B Young, Pluck Pond, Swansea, Aug, 1970.
7 lb 1 oz D Holwill, River Wallington, Fareham, Oct, 1968.
7 lb W F Simmons from Dorset Stour at Christchurch in 1931.
An interesting catch was made by R Smith (13) and W Busk (14) from Hollows Pond, Whipps Cross, London, in Sept, 1958, when an eel weighing 6 lb 8 oz took both boys' baits.

GOLDEN ORFE *(Leusiscus idus)*
4 lb 3 oz* B T Mills, R Test, Jan, 1976.

GRAYLING (*Thymallus thymallus,* Linn)
7 lb 2 oz From River Melgum by J Stewart, July, 1949. This fish is believed to be somewhat legendary and was eliminated as a record by the British Record Fish Committee in 1968.
4 lb 8 oz Dr T Sanctuary on the Wylye at Bemerton, in 1885. A fish of 4 lb 12 oz was netted from the Avon at Longford by G S Marryat and Dr Sanctuary in the same year and returned to the water.
4 lb 4 oz G Bryant on the Itchen.
4 lb Three a fraction over this weight caught by H J Mordaunt and M Headlam on the Test (Oakley Stream) at Mottisfont on Boxing Day, 1905.
4 lb E Chambers, Chess, near Chorley Wood, Jan, 1965. Mr Chambers had another of 3 lb 13 oz on the same outing, making a remarkable brace.
3 lb 14 oz E J Stanton, Driffield Canal, Sept, 1967.
3 lb 12 oz J Wigram on the Test near Stocksbridge, in 1873.
3 lb 12 oz J W Gieve from the Test in 1917.
2 lb 9¼ oz* D Hauxvell, R Teviot, Jan 12, 1980.

GUDGEON (*Gobio gobio,* Linn)
4¼ oz* M J Brown, pond at Ebbw Vale, Gwent, 1977.
4¼ oz Geo Cedric from the Thames at Datchet in Aug, 1933.
4¼ oz W R Bostock from Hogg's Pond, Shipley, near Derby, in Oct, 1935.
4¼ oz J D Lewin from the Soar in 1950.
4 oz 1 dm Caught at Sudbury by O S Hurkett, Mar, 1950.

PERCH (*Perca fluviatilis,* Linn)
5 lb 15 oz 6 dm P Clark, Suffolk Stour, 1949.
5 lb 14½ oz D Florey from Farlows Lake, Dec, 1953.
5 lb 12 oz E V Hodd from Diana Pond, Hampton Court, in Aug, 1957.
5 lb 8 oz† S Drum from Lough Erne, 1946.
5 lb 4¾ oz H Green from Stradsett Lake, Norfolk, on Nov 9, 1936.
5 lb 4 oz Caught ag Sandford Mill, Woodley, Berks, by Wm Leach in 1873.
5 lb 4 oz K Gardner from a lake in Norfolk, July, 1970. Other fish of over 5 lb were reported from lakes in Worcester and Suffolk, and a pit in Colchester.
4 lb 12 oz* S F Baker, Oulton Broad, 1962.

PIKE (*Esox lucius,* Linn)
53 lb Lough Conn in July, 1920, by John Garvin. This fish is entitled to rank as the premier pike landed in Great Britain and Ireland. Mr Garvin caught a 30-pounder on the same day. Bigger pike than this have been reported, including a fish of 72 lb from Loch Ken in 1774 and one of 60 lb found dying at Dowdeswell. One approaching the weight of Mr Garvin's fish 52 lb is said to have been recovered when Whittlesey Mere, Cambs, was drained in 1851.
48 lb Reported from Lough Corrib in 1905.
47 lb 11 oz T Morgan from Loch Lomond in July, 1945.
45 lb 8 oz Reported from Lough Conn, Ballina in 1917. In *The Fishing Gazette* of May 9, 1925, Bernard Brown, the captor, altered these details by giving the weight as 49 lb and the year as 1916.
42 lb 8 oz W Carney from Lough Mask, July, 1932.
42 lb† M Watkins, River Barrow (spoon), 1964. Irish river record.
41 lb 8 oz From Foxborough, Tulsk, Ireland, by P J Mannion in June, 1922.
41 lb Mr Cawley from Lough Conn in Mar, 1918.
40 lb 8 oz From Lough Arrow. This fish was sent to *The Fishing Gazette* in 1900, together with another of 35 lb. These fish were caught on "set lines".
40 lb E Oulton from Lough Ramor in Nov, 1950.
40 lb Lough Erne by John H Thompson in 1922. Hooked while the angler was playing another and smaller pike.
40 lb* P Hancock, Horsey Mere, Feb, 1967.
39 lb C Loveland, Knipton Reservoir, 1967.
38 lb 4 oz P Emmings, Cheshunt pit, Dec, 1969.

38 lb H Mumford Smith, Lough Conn, June 8, 1929.
38 lb H A Robinson on Lough Mask in 1905. Various fish from this weight up to 40 lb or more have been reported from Irish lakes, and there is little doubt that most of them have been authentic.
38 lb† P Earl. Lough Ree (minnow), 1967 (Irish lake record).
37 lb 8 oz C Warwick, Avon at Fordingbridge, Oct, 1944.

PIKEPERCH (Zander) *(Stizostedion lucioperca)*
17 lb 4 oz* D Litton, Gt Ouse Relief Channel, 1977.
15 lb 5 oz W G Chillingworth, Gt Ouse Relief Channel, February, 1971. This angler had another of 12 lb 13 oz from the relief Channel, Feb, 1971.
12 lb 12 oz Neville Fickling, Relief Channel, October, 1979. (This angler had another of 12 lb 6½ oz.) He had another of 12 lb 7½ oz from the same water the previous August.
12 lb 5 oz Dr R B Rickards, Relief Channel, Feb, 1970.

ROACH *(Rutilus rutilus,* Linn)
4 lb 1 oz* R G Jones, Gravel Pit, Notts, 1975.
3 lb 14 oz W Penny, Metropolitan Water Board's Lambeth Reservoir at Molesey, Sept 6, 1938 (l 18½ in, g 12⅝ in).
3 lb 14 oz A Brown, Oakham gravel pit near Stamford, Lincs, 1964.
3 lb 14 oz Caught out of season on fly by F I Hodgson while fishing for trout in a spring-fed Lancashire pond in May, 1960.
3 lb 10 oz W Cutting, Hornsea Mere, Yorkshire, in 1917. On the same day he had another 3-pounder.
3 lb 10 oz A Whittock from the Hampshire Avon, Jan, 1953.
3 lb 9¾ oz T G Player from the Thames at Sonning in June, 1949.
3 lb 9 oz J Osborn, River Thurne, July, 1962.
Staines Reservoir produced three roach, each weighing 3 lb 6 oz in the autumn of 1962 and 1964.

RUDD *(Scardinius erythrophthalmus,* Linn)
4 lb 8 oz* The Rev E C Alston on a mere near Thetford, July, 1933. He had another of 3 lb 15 oz during the month.
4 lb 4 oz Caught at Blackheath by J F Green, 1888.
3 lb 15 oz W Clews, Moor Lane Fisheries (Staines), 1957.
3 lb 13 oz A Oldfield from a mill pool in Cheshire, 1960.
3 lb 13 oz W Tucker, from the Thames at Chertsey, Jan, 1962.
3 lb 12 oz D A Fisher, pond at Stanmore, July, 1959.
3 lb 12 oz L Lindsay, Landbeach Lake, 1962.
3 lb 12 oz K Palfrey, Bridgwater and Taunton Canal, 1963.
3 lb 10½ oz E G Costin, Home Pond, Swanley, Oct, 1954.
3 lb 10 oz A Brogan, The Delph at Wisbech, July, 1935.
3 lb 10 oz Master D Denham, pit at Shepperton, July, 1954.
3 lb 1 oz† A E Biddlecombe, Kilglass Lake, on worm, 1963.

SALMON *(Salmo salar,* Linn)
69 lb 12 oz By the Earl of Home on Tweed about 1730. The "record" rod-caught salmon for the British Isles. This fish has been described as "somewhat legendary". In 1935, however, the Earl of Home sent a note giving evidence that the fish indeed existed.
67 lb On the Nith at Barjarg by Jock Wallace in 1812. Wallace, a well-known poacher is said to have played the fish from 8 am to 6 pm.
64 lb* On the Tay (Glendelvine water) by Miss G W Ballantine on Oct 7, 1922. Hooked in the Boat Pool at 6.15 pm and landed half a mile below at 8.5 pm. The fish took a spinning bait, a dace. The biggest salmon caught by a lady. Length 54 in, girth 28½ in. A cast of the fish was made and is at Glendelvine.
61 lb 8 oz On the Tay below Perth by T Stewart on the last day of the season, 1907, with a worm. It took an hour to land.
61 lb J Haggart on the Tay in 1870.

61 lb Mrs Morison on the Deveron on $1\frac{1}{4}$ in fly (the weight probably was more as the fish was not weighed till 24 hours after capture), Oct 21, 1924.

60 lb On the Eden by Lowther Bridger in 1888. Length 54 in, girth 27 in. Exhibited in the British Museum. It appears to be the biggest fish caught on fly in English rivers.

59 lb 8 oz On the Wye at Lower Winforton by Miss Doreen Dovey on Mar 12, 1923. This appears to be not only the record fish for the Wye, but also the biggest spring fish so far caught on a rod in Great Britain.

59 lb On the South Esk by J K Somerville in Oct, 1922. Length 53 in, girth 28 in.

58 lb Reported from the Shannon in 1872.

57 lb 8 oz On the Tweed (Floors water) in 1886 by Mr Pryor. This is usually accounted the biggest Tweed fish.

57 lb† From the Suir by M Maher in 1874. The record fish for Ireland.

57 lb On the Awe by Major A W Huntingdon on July 8, 1921. Length $52\frac{1}{2}$ in, girth $27\frac{1}{2}$ in.

56 lb From the Deveron on Oct 31, 1920, by Col A E Scott. This fish took a 1-in fly. Length 50 in, girth 29 in.

56 lb On the Dee, Ardoe Pool, by J Gordon in 1886.

56 lb From the Eden at Warwick Hall by G Mackenzie in 1892.

56 lb On the Awe (Pol Verie) on June 12, 1923, by H G Thornton. Took a 5/0 fly and fought from 1 pm till 3.30 pm.

SEA TROUT (*Salmo trutta*, Linn)

22 lb 8 oz S R Dwight, Dorset Frome, at 11 am, above the hatches at Bindon Mill, May 18, 1946.

21 lb The Rev A H Upcher, Bothie Pool on the Awe on June 30, 1908. The "record" Scottish sea trout.

21 lb Dorset Frome at Bindon in Mar, 1918, by R C Hardy, Corfe.

20 lb 2 oz T Williams, the Dovey, in June, 1935. The "record" Welsh sea trout.

20 lb J A Humphreys, the Dovey, in Aug, 1958, on fly.

TENCH (*Tinca tinca*, Linn)

10 lb 1 oz* L W Brown, Peterborough Brick Pit, Aug, 1975.

9 lb 1 oz J Salisbury, gravel pit at Hemingford Grey, Hunts, 1963.

9 lb G Young, Berkshire pond, Oct, 1964.

8 lb 14 oz K Baldock, Staplehurst pit, Aug, 1970.

8 lb 12 oz P Pilley, Middx lake, June, 1970.

8 lb 9 oz F Bailey, Lincolnshire drain, Aug, 1970.

8 lb 8 oz M Foode, Leicester Canal, Aug, 1950.

8 lb 6 oz K Morris, Cheshunt pit, Aug, 1964.

8 lb 6 oz J Brooksbank, Farningham pit, Dec, 1964.

8 lb 4 oz J Marshall, Grantham lake, 1961.

8 lb 4 oz R Hill, Bucks lake, Aug, 1970.

8 lb 2 oz A Lowe, Wraysbury pit (date unknown).

7 lb $13\frac{1}{4}$ oz† Raymond Webb, River Shannon, Lanesboro, 1971 (bread flake).

Tench of 11 lb and 9 lb 9 oz 12 dm were caught from a pit at Wraysbury, Middlesex, in July, 1959. The larger fish was returned to the water; the smaller was sent to the London Zoo where it subsequently died. An autopsy showed it to be diseased and to contain 1 lb 12 oz of fluid. The larger fish was probably also diseased and neither could be allowed as a new record. Garnafailagh Lough, Westmeath, has produced a remarkable series of big tench in recent years, many over 7 lb.

TROUT (BROWN) (*Salmo trutta*, Linn)

39 lb 8 oz On Loch Awe by W Muir in 1866. It was foul-hooked on a trout fly and took two and a half hours to land. It was set up, but the case was unfortunately lost in a fire.

30 lb 8 oz J W Pepper on spoon bait, Lough Derg, 1861. *The Irish Times* gave credence to this fish in 1903. The same angler claimed to have caught one of 24 lb from Lough Corrib about the same period.

29 lb On Loch Stenness in 1889 on a hand line. A "slob" or estuarine trout. A cast of this fish is in the Flyfishers' Club.

27 lb 8 oz Colonel Dobiggin on the Tay at Murthly in 1842; length 39½ in. Recorded by the late Duke of Rutland in his book on *The Trout*.

27 lb 4 oz Dr H H Almond, of Loretto, on the Inver about 1870. Said to have taken a small salmon fly. Probably a fish from Loch Assynt.

26 lb 2 oz† From Lough Ennel by W Meares on July 28, 1894, on a spoon bait. (Irish lake redord.)

22 lb From Loch Rannoch by F Twist in 1867.

21½ lb Lough Derg by James Lucas, keeper at Derry Castle. This fish was preserved. Date of capture uncertain. (There was also a case containing a brace of trout, 16 lb, 13 lb, caught at the same time by trolling.)

21 lb Loch Rannoch by Miss Kate Kirby in July, 1904. Probably the biggest trout ever caught by a lady.

20 lb† From the Shannon in February, 1957, by Major H Place on a trolled silver Devon. (Irish river record.)

19 lb 9¼ oz* J A F Jackson, Loch Quoich, Invernessshire, 1978.

19 lb 4½ oz From Lower Lough Erne, Co Fermanagh, NI, by T Chartres, April 6, 1974.

19 lb 2 oz F Smith from Lough Corrib on spoon, Aug, 1971.

18 lb 2 oz K J Grant, Loch Garry, Tomdoun, on a Black Pennel fly, in July, 1965.

Note: Lt Col G F McDonald, proprietor of Strathgarve Lodge Hotel, Garve, Ross-shire, has a trout of 26 lb in a glass case reported taken in Loch Garve on September 17, 1892, by Wm Ogilvy Dalgeish. Among notable Thames trout is a fish of 14 lb taken by A Pearson (Shepperton) on fly in August, 1962.

TROUT (RAINBOW) *(Salmo gairdnerii)*

19 lb 8 oz* A Pearson, Avington Fisheries, Hants, 1977.

19 lb 2 oz R W Hopkins, Avington Fisheries, Hants, April, 1977.

18 lb+ Richard Walker, Avington Fisheries, Hants, 1976.

18 lb A Pearson, Avington Fisheries, Hants, June, 1976

14 lb 4 oz J L Farmer, Avington Fisheries, Hants, July, 1975.

13 lb 2 oz Dr W J Drummond, Downton Tannery Stream (tributary of W Avon) Sept 28, 1974.

13 lb M H Lenthall, Exe Valley Fisheries, Dulverton, July 13, 1974.

12 lb 4 oz I L Johnstone (aged 14 yrs) Exe Valley Fisheries, July 5, 1974.

12 lb 4 oz* Miss A P D Berger, Exe Valley Fishery, Dulverton, May, 1974.

10 lb ¼ oz M Parker from a private lake in King's Lynn, July, 1970.

8 lb 14 oz Brian Jones, Packington Fisheries, May, 1970 (taken out of Trent RA season).

8 lb 10 oz C F Robinson, River Test at Stockbridge, Aug, 1970.

8 lb 8 oz From Blagdon in Sept, 1924, by Lieut-Colonel J Creagh Scott.

8 lb 7 oz† On Lough Eyes, Co Fermanagh, by Dr J P C Purdon on fly, in March, 1968. Irish record; Fish was just over 4 years of age.

TROUT (AMERICAN BROOK) *(Salvelinus fontinalis)*

5 lb 6 oz* A Pearson, Avington Fisheries, Hants, 1979.

WHITEFISHES

Group A *(Coregonus clupeoides)*
Local names—schelly (Haweswater, Ullswater), gwyniad (Lake Bala), powan (Loch Lomond, Loch Eck)

1 lb 10 oz* W Wainwright, Ullswater, 1976.

1 lb 7 oz J M Ryder, Loch Lomond, 1972.

1 lb 4 oz J R Williams, Lake Bala, 1965.

Group B *(Coregonus vandesius)*
Local name—vendace (Derwentwater, Bassenthwaite Lake, Loch Maben).

Group C *(Coregonus pollan)*
Local name—pollan (Loughs Erne, Ree, Derg and Neagh).
Entries in categories B and C awaited since reclassification.

SEA FISH

ANGLER (*Lophius piscatorius,* Linn)
82 lb 12 oz* K Ponsford .... Mevagissey .... April, 1977
74 lb 8 oz   J J McVicar .... Eddystone .... Aug, 1972
71 lb 8 oz† M Fitzgerald .... Cork (Cobh) ....July, 1964
68 lb 2 oz   H G Legerton .... Canvey Island 1967
62 lb 9½ oz G V Williams .... Dunlaoghaire Pier,
                                                     Dublin .... April, 1962

BASS (*Morone Labrax,* Linn)
18 lb 6 oz* R Slater .... off the Eddystone .... Aug, 1975
18 lb 2 oz   F C Borley .... Felixstowe Beach ....Nov, 1943
17 lb 8 oz   W G Byron (caught with a Gig-
             gan bait), 1 12¼ in, g 32½ in. .... Castlerock, Derry ......Oct 22, 1935
17 lb 4 oz   J Drysdale .... Kinsale .... Aug, 1943
16 lb 6 oz   T Browne .... Bangor ....July, 1935
16 lb†   Major Windham. Reported taken
             with a fly on a trout rod .... Waterville 1909
A fish of 18½ lb was reported caught in the Teifi estuary by a salmon fisher in 1956.

BREAM (BLACK) (*Spondyliosoma cantharus,* Gonelin)
6 lb 14¼ oz* J A Garlick .... from wreck off Devon
                                                      coast, ...1977
6 lb 7¾ oz   J L D Atkins .... E Blackstone Rocks,
                                                      Devon .... Aug, 1973
6 lb 5 oz   M Brown, jnr .... Menai Straits .... Oct, 1935
6 lb 1 oz   F W Richards .... Skerries Bank .... Sept, 1969
4 lb 14 oz   A Procter .... Looe .... Aug, 1953
4 lb 12½ oz H Pavey .... Littlehampton 1963

BREAM (RED) (*Pagellus centrodontus,* De La Roche)
9 lb 8¾ oz* B H Reynolds............................. off Mevagissey ....July, 1974
9 lb 6 oz†   P Maguire .... Valentia .... Aug, 1963
7 lb 8 oz   A F Bell .... Fowey ....July, 1925
6 lb 3 oz   Brig J A L Caunter .... Nine miles off Looe ......June, 1939
5 lb 12½ oz Brig J A L Caunter .... Looe 1954

BRILL (*Scopthalmus rhombus,* Linn)
16 lb*   A H Fisher .... Derby Haven, Isle of Man 1950
13 lb 10 oz J L Williams .... Brighton 1933

BULL HUSS (*Scyliorhinus stellaris*)
21 lb 3 oz* J Holmes .... Hat Rock, Looe 1955
21 lb   F C Hales .... Poole, Dorset .... Aug, 1936
21 lb   H Jupp .... Brighton .... Oct, 1953
20 lb   F Matthews .... Newhaven .... Sept, 1954
19 lb 12 oz† M Courage .... Bray 1969

CATFISH (*Anarhichas lupus*)
15 lb 12 oz* E Fisher .... off Filey, Yorks 1973
12 lb 12½ oz G M Taylor .... Stonehaven, Scotland 1978

COALFISH, or Saithe (*Gadus virens,* Linn)
33 lb 7 oz* L M Saunders .... Start Point, Devon 1980
30 lb 12 oz A F Harris .... S of Eddystone .... Feb, 1973
29 lb 2½ oz R Phillips .... SE of Eddystone ....Jan, 1973

27 lb 12½ oz	J J McVicar	Eddystone	Jan, 1972
26 lb 2 oz	T J Trust	Start Point, Devon	1971
24 lb 7oz†	J E Hornibrook	Kinsale	1967
23 lb 8 oz	Capt Hugo Millais	Land's End (Carnbase)	1921

COD (*Gadus callarias*, Linn)

53 lb*	G Martin	Start Point, Devon	June, 1972
46 lb 0½ oz	R Baird	Firth of Clyde	Feb, 1970
45 lb 14 oz	D D Dinnie	Gourock	Jan, 1970
44 lb 8 oz	Brandon Jones	Barry (Glam)	Mar, 1966
42 lb†	Ian L Stewart	Ballycotton	1921
34 lb	The late R Blair	Ballycotton	1916
33 lb 8 oz	John E Timmins	Kinsale	Sept, 1962

A cod of 140 lb landed at Hull Fish Dock in July, 1927, is worth adding to the record as a remarkable specimen, though it was not, of course, an angling trophy.

CONGER (*Conger conger*, Linn)

109 lb 6 oz*	R W Potter	SE of Eddystone	Sept, 1976
102 lb 8 oz	R B Thomson	off Mevagissey	June, 1974
95 lb 11 oz	W K Oaten	Berry Head, S Devon	July, 1973
92 lb 13 oz	P H Ascott	Torquay	June, 1970
85 lb	C E Chapman	Hythe (Hants)	June, 1970
84 lb	H A Kelly	Dungeness	July, 1933

On the same day this angler had four more congers, 70 lb, 33½ lb, 21½ lb, 15½ lb.

80 lb 8 oz	H J West	Brixham	July, 1966
74 lb	Mrs H Eathorne	Looe	1954
72 lb†	James Green	Valentia	June, 1914
66 lb	W H Pryce	Coverack	June, 1941
63 lb 3 oz	Miss B Klean	Hastings	1922

DAB (*Limanda limanda*, Linn)

2 lb 12¼ oz*	R Islip	Gairloch	Aug, 1975
2 lb 10¾ oz	A B Hare	Skerries Bank	April, 1968
2 lb 9½ oz	M L Watts	Morfa Beach, Port Talbot	July, 1936
2 lb 8½ oz	L White	Netley Pier, Southampton	Nov, 1937
2 lb 5½ oz	C Stone	Ryde, I o W	Dec, 1934
2 lb 4¼ oz	N Coleman	Hastings	Jan, 1951
2 lb 4 oz	P A Heale	Southsea	Dec, 1933
1 lb 12½ oz†	I V Kerr	Kinsale	1963

DOGFISH (LESSER SPOTTED), or Rough Hound (*Scyliorhinus caniculus*, Linn)

4 lb 8 oz	J Beattie	Ayr Pier	1969
4 lb 2 oz*	B J Solomon	Newquay	Oct, 1976
3 lb 15 oz†	unknown	S Ireland	1980
3 lb 12½ oz	A Gibson	Firth of Clyde	July, 1967

FLOUNDER (*Platichthys flesus*, Linn)

5 lb 11½ oz*	A G L Cobbledick	Fowey	1956
5 lb 5½ oz	D Clark	Littlesea	Mar, 1957
4 lb 13 oz	R Hitchman	Exmouth	1949
4 lb 5 oz	E F J Plumridge	Fowey Estuary	April, 1938
4 lb 3oz†	J L McMonagle	Killala Bay	1963

GARFISH (*Belone belone*, Linn)

3 lb 10¼ oz†	E G Bazzard	Kinsale	Sept, 1967
3 lb 8 oz	Hanson Horsey	Kinsale	Oct, 1969
2 lb 14 oz	K C Ettle	Kinsale	Aug, 1968

2 lb 14 oz	D O'Donovan	Kinsale	Aug, 1968
2 lb 13 oz 14 dm*	Stephen Claeskens	Newton Ferrers	Aug, 1971
2 lb 12 oz	K C Ettle	Kinsale	Aug, 1968
2 lb 12 oz	M L Walsh	Ballycotton	June, 1967
2 lb 11¾ oz	Dennis Collins	Kinsale	1966
2 lb 10½ oz	J O'Sullivan	Courtmacsherry, Co Cork	Aug, 1971
2 lb 10 oz	Mrs Sandra Parker	Kinale	Sept, 1969
2 lb 9 oz 2 dm	A W Bodfield	Dartmouth	1963
2 lb 9 oz	F T Goffin	Coverack	July, 1935

GURNARD, or Tub Fish, or Yellow Gurnard (*Trigela lucerna,* Linn)

11 lb 7¼ oz*	C W King	Wallasey	1952
10 lb 8 oz†	C Gammon	Belmullet	1970
10 lb 2¼ oz	E Sederholm	Belmullet	May, 1969
9½ lb	W Adams	Isle of Man	1907
8 lb 4 oz	D Flanagan	Achill Island	July, 1967

GURNARD (GREY) (*Eutrigla gurnardus*)

3 lb 1 oz†	B Walsh	Rosslare Bay	1967
2 lb 7 oz*	D Swinbanks	Caliach Point Isle of Mull	July, 1976
2 lb 2 oz	D H Taylor	Off Portrush, NI	July, 1973
1 lb 10 oz	D Cameron-McIntosh	Isle of Arran	1971
1 lb 6 oz	K R Manson	Bressay, Shetland	1971

GURNARD (RED) (*Aspitrigla cuculus*)

5 lb*	D B Critchley (captor nine years of age)	off Rhyl	July, 1973
4 lb 9½ oz	C Butler	off Anglesey	June, 1973
4 lb 4¾ oz	W R Shaw	Conway	June, 1973

HADDOCK (*Gadus aegifinus,* Linn)

13 lb 11¼ oz*	G Bones	off Falmouth	1978
12 lb 10 oz	Sub-Lieut K P White	Manacles, Falmouth Bay	Jan, 1975
10 lb 13½ oz†	F A E Bull	Kinsale, Co Cork	July, 1964
10 lb 12 oz	A H Hill	Looe	July, 1972
10 lb 0½ oz	David Hare	Valentia	1971
9 lb 14½ oz	J O'Gilvie	Valentia	Aug, 1969
9 lb 8¾ oz	L A Derby	Kinsale	June, 1965
9 lb 4½ oz	Mrs L Morley	Mevagissey	1969
9 lb 2¼ oz	Eric Smith	Kinsale	July, 1963

HAKE (*Merluccius merluccius,* Linn)

25 lb 5½ oz*†	H W Steele	Belfast Lough	1962
20 lb	Frank Vinnicombe	Falmouth	Aug, 1960
17½ lb	Mrs J T Ashby	Penzance	1911

HALIBUT (*Hippoglossus hippoglossus*)

234 lb*	C Booth	off Dunnet Head, Scotland	1979
212 lb 4 oz	J A Hewitt	off Dunnet Head	Aug, 1975
196 lb	J T Newman	off Dunnet Head, Caithness	April, 1974
161 lb 12 oz	W E Knight	Orkney	Aug, 1968
152¾ lb†	E C Henning	Valentia	1926

He also had two, 128¾ lb, 120½ lb on another day in 1926.

135 lb   J N Hearn .... Ballycotton 1912

A halibut weighing 500 lb was landed by a commercial fishing boat at Grimsby in October, 1957.

JOHN DORY (*Zeus Faber,* Linn)
11 lb 14 oz*	J Johnson	off Newhaven	1977
10 lb 12 oz	B L Perry	Porthallow, Cornwall	1963
8 lb 8 oz	J F Vallin	Mevagissey	1922
8 lb 4 oz	R Brown, Dreadnought SAS	Fowey	July, 1932

LING (*Molva molva,* Linn)
57 lb 2½ oz*	H Solomons	off Mevagissey	1975
50 lb 8 oz	B M Coppen	off Eddystone	Mar, 1974
46 lb 8 oz†	A J C Bull	Kinsale	July, 1965
46 lb	T D Walker	off Plymouth	Mar, 1974
45 lb	H C Nicholl	Penzance	1912

LUMPSUCKER (*Cyclopterus lumpus*)
14 lb 3 oz*	W J Burgess	Felixstowe Beach	1970

MACKEREL (*Scomber scombrus,* Linn)
5 lb 6½ oz*	S Beasley	Eddystone Lighthouse	1969
4 lb 11 oz	L A Seward	Flamborough Head	1963
4 lb 0½ oz	F/Lt P Porter	Peel, Isle of Man	June 9, 1952
3 lb 10 oz	A Cave	Peel, Isle of Man	Aug, 1953
3 lb 8 oz	W Adams		1906
3 lb 6 oz†	J O'Connell	Valentia	1969

A fish of 4½ lb was caught at Looe in June, 1935, by W C Butters on a handline.

MEGRIM (*Lepidohumbus wiffiagonis*)
3 lb 12½ oz*	Master P Christie	Gairloch	Aug, 1973

MONKFISH (*Squatina squatina,* Linn)
69 lb†	Monsieur Fuchs	Westport	July, 1958
66 lb*	C G Chalk	Shoreham	1965
62 lb	S Morris	Littlehampton	1919
62 lb	A E Beckett	Porthcawl	1960

A fish of 68 lb was reported from Beaulieu in August, 1953.

MULLET (GREY, THICKED-LIPPED) (*Chelon Labrosus*)
10 lb 1 oz*	P/O P C Libby	Portland	1952
8 lb 12 oz	W E Wallis	Portland	1921
8 lb 7 oz	F V Daunou ..,....	Margate	About 1903
6 lb 12¾ oz†	W H Connolly	Ballycotton Harbour	Aug, 1971

MULLET (RED) (*Mullus surmuletus*)
3 lb 10 oz*	J E Martel	Guernsey	Oct, 1967
2 lb 1 oz 3 dm	T F Cleal	Guernsey	Oct, 1967

OPAH (*Lampris guttatus*)
128 lb*	A R Blewitt	Mounts Bay, Penzance	1973

PLAICE (*Pleuronectes platessa,* Linn)
10 lb 3½ oz*	Master H Gardiner	Longa Sound	Oct, 1974
7 lb 15 oz	Ian Brodie	Salcombe	Oct, 1964
7 lb 13 oz 1 dm	W F Parker	Teignmouth	1961
7 lb 6 oz	D Brown	Dartmouth (Skerries)	June, 1963
7 lb 6 oz	J P Wright	Dartmouth	May, 1960
7 lb 5 oz 6 dm	C Riggs	Teign Estuary	1949
7 lb†	E Yemen	Portrush	1964

POLLACK, or Lythe (*Gadus pollachius,* Linn)
25 lb*   R J Hosking .... Eddystone 1972
23 lb 8 oz   G Bartholomew .... Newquay 1957
22 lb 8 oz   W Digby .... Looe 1955
21 lb   Capt Hugo Millais .... Land's End (Carnbase) 1921
    Capt Millais has had others of 17 lb and 18 lb at the same place.
20 lb 8 oz   Mrs Hugo Millais .... Land's End (Carnbase) 1921
    Mrs Millais also had a specimen of 19½ lb.
20 lb 8 oz   J H Layton .... Lochinver 1920
19 lb 3 oz†   J N Hearn .... Ballycotton 1904

POUTING (*Gadus luscus,* Linn)
5 lb 8 oz*   R S Armstrong .... Berry Head 1969
4 lb 10 oz   H B Dare .... Coverack .... Sept, 1935
4 lb 10 oz†   W G Pales .... Ballycotton 1937
4 lb 9 oz   E Burton .... Belfast Lough .... April, 1968

RAY (BLOND) (*Raia brachyura,* Lafont)
37 lb 12 oz*   H T Pout .... Salcombe .... Oct, 1973
36 lb 8 oz†   D Minchin .... Cork (Cobh) .... Sept, 1964
35 lb 9 oz   A J Pearce .... Portland .... May, 1970
34 lb 8 oz   T Hutchinson .... Cobh .... Sept, 1967

RAY (BOTTLE-NOSED) (*Raja alba*)
76 lb   R Bulpitt .... off The Needles, I o W 1970

RAY (CUCKOO) (*Raia naevus*)
5 lb 11 oz*   V Morrison .... off Causeway Coast, NI 1975
5 lb 6 oz†   K Derbyshire .... Causeway Coast,
                              Co Antrim .... Aug, 1971
5 lb 3 oz   P J Rankin .... off Causeway Coast, NI 1974
5 lb   N C McLean .... Lamlash Bay, Isle of
                              Arran .... June, 1968

RAY (EAGLE) (*Myliobatis aquila*)
52 lb 8 oz*   R J Smith .... off Nab Tower, I o W 1972

RAY (ELECTRIC) (*Torpedo nobiliana*)
96 lb 1 oz*   N J Cowley .... off Dodman Point,
                              Cornwall .... July 1975
47 lb 8 oz   R J F Pearce .... Long Quarry,
                              Torquay .... Aug, 1971

RAY (SMALL-EYED) (*Raia microcellata*)
16 lb 4 oz*   H T Pout .... Salcombe .... Sept, 1973
13 lb 11½ oz   H T Pout .... Bolt Tail, Devon 1971
13 lb 8 oz   Mrs P Whippy .... Pevensey Bay .... Aug, 1969
12 lb 1½ oz   A T Scoones .... Littlehampton .... July, 1969

RAY (SPOTTED) (*Raia montagui*)
16 lb 3 oz   E Lockwood .... Lerwick, Shetland 1970
14 lb 3 oz   W C Furnish .... St Anne's Head, Pembroke 1970
6 lb 14 oz*   H A Jamieson .... Causeway Coast, NI 1978

RAY (STING) (*Trigon pastinaca,* Linn)
61 lb 8 oz*   V W Roberts .... off Pwllheli 1979
59 lb   J M Buckley .... Clacton-on-Sea 1952
52 lb 8 oz   T E Stone .... Lymington River mouth 1938
52 lb   J Manser .... Brighton .... June, 1954
51 lb 8 oz   P J Hill .... Hastings .... Oct, 1956

RAY (THORNBACK) (*Raia clavata,* Linn)
57 lb	S G Lugger	Exmouth	July, 1951
38 lb*	J Patterson, Jnr	Rustington Beach	May, 1935
37 lb†	M J Fitzgerald	Kinsale	May, 1961

UNDULATE RAY (*Raja undulata*)
19 lb 7 oz*	L R LePage	Herm, CI	1970

ROCKLING (THREE-BEARDED) (*Onos tricirratus,* Block)
3 lb 2 oz*	N Docksey	Portland	Oct, 1976
2 lb 14¼ oz	S F Bealing	Poole Bay	Oct, 1972
2 lb 13 oz 2 dm	K Westaway	Portland Harbour	June, 1966

SCAD, or Horse Mackerel (*Trachurus trachurus,* Linn)
3 lb 5¼ oz*	M A Atkins	Torbay	1978
3 lb 4½ oz	D O Cooke	Mewstone, Plymouth	1971
3 lb 3 oz	J B Thorton	Deal	July, 1934

SHAD (ALLIS) (*Alosa Alosa*)
4 lb 12½ oz*	P B Gerrard	Chesil Beach, Dorset	1977
3 lb 4½ oz	B H Sloane	Princess Pier, Torquay	1964

SHAD (TWAITE) (*Alosa finta,* Cuvier)
3 lb 2 oz*	T Hayward	Deal	Nov, 1949
3 lb 2 oz*	S Jenkins	Torbay	1954

SHARK (BLUE) (*Carcharinus glaucus,* Linn)
218 lb*	N Sutcliffe	Looe	July, 1959
206 lb†	J L McGonagle	Achill	Oct, 1959
184 lb	T Robinson	Looe	1960
180 lb	H Widdett	Looe	1955
180 lb	F A Mitton	Looe	1960

SHARK (MAKO) (*Isurus oxyrhinchus,* Raf)
500 lb*	Mrs J M Yallop	Eddystone Light	1971
498 lb 8 oz	K Burgess	Looe	July, 1966
476 lb	W J Rogers	Falmouth	July, 1964
435 lb	S G Miller	Looe	June, 1964
428 lb 8 oz	J E Sefton	Looe	1961

It was not until 1956 that the mako shark was positively identified as a British species, and it is probable that some of the fish listed earlier as porbeagles were, in fact, makos.

SHARK (PORBEAGLE) (*Lamna cornubica,* Gonetin)
465 lb*	J Potier	off Padstow, Cornwall	July, 1976
430 lb	D Bougourd	South of Jersey	1969
367 lb	B D Phillipps	Jersey, CI	June, 1960
365 lb†	Dr O'Donnel Browne	Keem Bay, Co Mayo	1932
324 lb	T Paince	Nab Tower	Aug, 1968
311 lb	K C Wilson	Looe	1961
300 lb††	J Eathorne	Looe	1951

The identification of the mako shark in British waters has thrown some doubt on the authenticity of this list. Dr O'Donnel Browne's fish was certainly a porbeagle, but the one marked †† is now thought probably to have been a mako. Fish caught since 1956 are definitely porbeagles.

SHARK (THRESHER) (*Alopias vulpes,* Gonetin)
295 lb*	H J Aris	Dunose Head, I o W	1978
280 lb	H A Kelly	Dungeness	1933
149 lb	R Romilly Lunge	Christchurch	July, 1937

SKATE (COMMON) (*Raia batis,* Linn)
336 lb   Captor unknown .... Beer 1934
226 lb 8 oz*   R S Macpherson .... Shetland .... Aug, 1970
221 lb†   T Tucker .... Ballycotton 1913
218 lb 8 oz   E C Henning .... Valentia 1927
214 lb   J A E Olsson .... Scapa Flow ....July, 1968
211 lb   Dr C Ayton Marrett .... Ballycotton 1912
208 lb   Leonard F Hopkins .... Clare Island,
                                                         Co Mayo .... Aug, 1971
205 lb   A W Bowie .... Kinsale .... Aug, 1956

SMOOTHOUND (*Mustelus mustelus*)
28 lb*   A T Chilvers .... Heacham 1969

SMOOTHOUND (STARRY) (*Mustelus asterias*)
23 lb 2 oz*   D Carpenter .... Bradwell on Sea 1972

SOLE (*Solea solea,* Linn)
4 lb 8 oz*   H C L Pike .... Alderney, CI 1978
4 lb 3½ oz   R Wells.................................. Redcliffe Beach ....Mar, 1974
4 lb 1 oz 14 dm   R A Austin .... Guernsey ....Dec, 1967
4 lb   M Stinton .... Clevedon Pier .... Sept, 1943
3 lb 4 oz   S Hayman .... Weymouth ....Nov, 1956
3 lb 4 oz   J Justice .... Lyme Regis 1934

SOLE (LEMON) (*Microstumus Kitt*)
2 lb 3 oz*   D R Duke .... Douglas Isle of Man 1971

SPURDOG (*Squalus acanthias,* Linn)
21 lb 3½ oz*   P R Barnett .... off Porthleven 1977
20 lb 3 oz   J Newman .... Needles .... May, 1972
17 lb 1 oz   S Bates .... Deal 1971
16 lb 12½ oz   R Legg .... Chesil Beach 1964
16 lb 4 oz†   C McIvor .... Strangford Lough ....June, 1969
15 lb 12 oz   John Rowe .... Killala Bay, Sligo .... Aug, 1967
15 lb 5 oz   J S W Fisher .... Strangford Lough .... Oct, 1971
15 lb   W Hamilton .... Strangford Lough ....July, 1969
14 lb 6 oz   J C Nott .... Clare Island ....June, 1969
14 lb 1 oz   D R Angiolini .... Valentia .... Sept, 1968
14 lb   R Wickens .... Kinsale .... Oct, 1962

SUNFISH (*Mola Mola*)
108 lb*   T F Sisson .... Saundersfoot .... Aug, 1976
49 lb 4 oz   M G H Merry .... Cornwall .... Aug, 1976

TOPE (*Eugaleus galeus,* Linn)
74 lb 11 oz*   A B Harries .... Caldy Island ....July, 1964
73 lb 3 oz
 (female)   L Andrews .... Hayling Island 1949
65 lb   Lt-Col R I P Earle .... Studland 1956
64 lb 8 oz   J H Swan .... Camel Estuary, Padstow
                                                         July, 1963
62 lb 11 oz   A J Drew .... Herne Bay 1911
62 lb 8 oz
 (female)   R J Weston .... Eastbourne ....June, 1955
62 lb 2 oz
 (female)   A B Fitt .... Herne Bay ....June, 1951
62 lb (male)   D S Southcombe .... Weymouth 1946

61 lb 8 oz
(female)   G T Northover .... Herne Bay .... June, 1936
60 lb 12 oz†   C McIver .... Strangford Lough 1968

TORSK (*Brosme brosme*)
12 lb 1 oz*   D Pottinger .... Shetland 1968

TUNNY (*Thunnus thynnus*)
The fish given in the following list were all caught in the North Sea tunny fishing grounds off Scarborough and Whitby:

851 lb*	L Mitchell-Henry, 1933	764 lb	H W Holgate, 1934
812 lb	Colonel E T Peel, 1934	763 lb	G Baker, 1933
798 lb	H G Smith, 1934	762 lb	M W Holgate, 1935
798 lb	Colonel E T Peel, 1932	749 lb	S Cohen, 1949
785 lb	Major R T Laughton, 1947	747 lb	H E Weatherley, 1952

TURBOT (*Scopthalmus maximus,* Linn)
32 lb 8 oz†   Unknown .... S Ireland 1980
32 lb 3 oz*   D Dyer .... off Plymouth .... May, 1976
31 lb 4 oz   Paul Hutchings (11) .... Eddystone Light ....July, 1972
29 lb   G M W Garnsey .... The Manacles .... Aug, 1964
28 lb 0½ oz   T Tolchard .... Dartmouth 1961
27 lb 14 oz   F S Stenning .... Salcombe 1907
26 lb 8 oz   J F Eldridge .... Valentia 1915
25 lb 8 oz   Mat Kearney .... Cork Harbour .... Aug, 1971
25 lb 4 oz   R Tolchard (age 12) .... off Dartmouth ....June, 1958

WHITING (*Gadus merlangus,* Linn)
6 lb 4 oz*   S Dearman .... Bridport .... April, 1977
6 lb 3 oz 3 dm Mrs R Barrett .... Rame Head,
                                           Cornwall 1971
6 lb   E H Tame .... Shieldaig .... Mar, 1940
5 lb 2 oz   H C Nicoll .... Penzance 1912
5 lb 1 oz   H W Antenbring .... Shieldaig .... June, 1938

WRASSE (BALLAN) (*Labrus bergylta,* Ascanius)
12 lb 1 oz   F A Mitchell-Hedges .... Looe 1912
12 lb   F A Mitchell-Hedges .... Looe 1912
11 lb 8 oz   F A Mitchell-Hedges .... Looe 1912
10 lb 12 oz   F A Mitchell-Hedges .... Looe 1912
7 lb 13½ oz*   D R Gabe .... off Start Point, Devon 1978
7 lb 10 oz
15 dm   B K Lawrence .... Trevose Head, Cornwall 1970
7 lb 6 oz†   A J King .... Killybegs 1964

WRASSE (CUCKOO) (*labrus mixtus*)
2 lb 0½ oz*   A M Foley .... Plymouth ....Nov, 1973
1 lb 14¾ oz   R G Berry .... Sennen, Cornwall .... Sept, 1973
1 lb 12½ oz   L C Le Cras .... Guernsey .... Aug, 1972
1 lb 10 oz 8 dm B Perry .... Torquay .... Sept, 1971

WRECKFISH (*Polyprion americanus*)
7 lb 10 oz*   Cdr E St J Holt .... Looe, Cornwall 1974

THE SALMON AND TROUT ASSOCIATION

This association is the only body which exists solely to protect the interests of game fish, fisheries and fishermen in the United Kingdom *(advt p 22)*.

Secretary: Pat de Warrenne Waller, Fishmongers' Hall, London EC4R 9EL. 01-626 3531.

Field Secretary–England and Wales

Lt-Col J C Inglis, Hope Bowdler Hall, Church Stretton, Shropshire SY6 6DD. 069-42 2041.

Scottish Committee Secretary

J R Gardiner, Esq, W S Brodie, Cuthbertson and Watson, 7 Rothesay Terrace, Edinburgh EH3 7SD. 031-225 1444.

ENGLAND
North West Water Authority Region

North Cumbria and Border Esk
J Howard, Esq, (Branch Chairman), Corby Castle, Gt Corby, Carlisle, Cumbria. Tel No Wetheral (0228) 60246. Mrs A Stokstad (Branch Secretary), Hawthornes, Crosby Moor, Crosby-on-Eden, Carlisle, Cumbria. Tel No Crosby-on-Eden 676.

South Cumbria
J H Fell, Esq, (Branch Chairman), White Gates, Backbarrow, Ulverston, Cumbria, LA12 8PA. Tel No Newby Bridge 459.

West Cumbria
C H Wheeler, Esq, (Branch Chairman), 37 Towers Lane, Cockermouth, Cumbria. Tel No Cockermouth 822668. I Nicholson, Esq, (Branch Organiser), The Gun Shop, Jubilee Bridge, Lorton Street, Cockermouth, Cumbria. Tel No 0900-822058.

Lancashire
T A F Barnes, Esq, (Area Chairman and Branch Chairman for Lancashire), Woodplumpton House, Woodplumpton, Nr Preston, Lancs. Tel No Catforth 690392.
Dr F S Martin, (Area Secretary/Tresurer), Lambourne House, Lea Road, Lea, Preston, Lancs. Tel No Preston 726910.

Cheshire & Manchester
R G Oliver, Esq, (Branch Chairman), c/o David Bentley Ltd, Greengate, Salford, Manchester, M3 7NS. Tel No 061-834 8851.

Merseyside
S Newton, Esq, (Branch Chairman), 13 Mount Pleasant, Oxton, Birkenhead, Merseyside. Tel No 051-652 6242.

Northumbrian Water Authority Region

Northumbria
E S J Standen, Esq, (Regional Chairman), 6 Friar's Pardon, Hurworth-on-Tees, Darlington, Co Durham, DL2 2 DZ. Tel No Darlington 720538.
C H Noble, Esq, (Regional Organiser), 38 Westcliffe Court, Darlington, Co Durham. Tel No Darlington 487863.

Severn-Trent Water Authority Region

Shropshire
Captain R W Corbett, T D, (Area Chairman and Branch Organiser for Shropshire), Grove Farm House, Longnor, Nr Shrewsbury, Shropshire. Tel No Dorrington (0743 73) 370.
Major J B Oakley, (Vice-Chairman), Ashleigh, Bowbrook, Shrewsbury, Shropshire. Tel No Shrewsbury 4048.
I A Riegan, Esq, (Area Secretary), 10 Oaks Road, Church Stretton, Shropshire. Tel No Church Stretton 3104.

Telford
M W N Ward, Esq, (Branch Chairman), Holley House, Broseley, Shropshire. Tel No Telford 882253.
A R Wickson, Esq, (Branch Secretary), 12 Wyvern, Woodside, Telford, Shropshire. Tel No Telford 583180.

Hereford and Worcester
R W Darlington, Esq, (Branch Chairman), 1 Havelock Road, Leominster, Hereford. Tel No Leominster 2584.
P M Evans, Esq, (Branch Organiser), Staunton House, Staunton-on-Arrow, Pembridge, Hereford. Tel No 05447-313.

North Powys and Lake Vyrnwy
Lt-Colonel Sir John Baynes, Bt, (Branch Chairman), Lake Vyrnwy Hotel, Via Oswestry, Shropshire, SY10 0LY. Tel No Llanwddyn 244.

Nottinghamshire and Derbyshire
J Mills, Esq, (Branch Chairman), Millstones, 1 Rectory Gardens, Beckingham, Doncaster, South Yorkshire, DW10 4PP. Tel No Saundby 358.
L C Baker, Esq, (Branch Secretary), 40 Gervase Gardens, Clifton Village, Nottinghamshire. Tel No Nottingham 211666.
M A Baker, Esq, (Membership Secretary), 520, Burton Road, Littleover, Derbyshire. Tel No Derby 41340.

Staffordshire
D S Sault, Esq, (Branch Chairman), Hollyhurst Cottage, Woodhouses, Yoxall, Nr Burton-on-Trent, Staffordshire. Tel No Yoxall 472649.
L K M Masters, Esq, (Branch Secretary), 12 Winchester Drive, Newcastle, Staffordshire. Tel No Newcastle 613741.
T Byatt, Esq, (Branch Treasurer), Rivendell House, Rivendell Lane, Birchall, Leek, Staffordshire. Tel No Leek 371929.

West Midlands and Warwickshire
Lord Guernsey (Branch Chairman), Fishery Lodge, Broadwater, Maxstoke Lane, Meriden, Nr Coventry, West Midlands, CV7 7HR. Tel No Meriden 22754 (office) and Meriden 22573 (home).
J Blackburn, Esq, (Branch Secretary/Treasurer), 2 Glass House Lane, Kenilworth, Warwickshire. Tel No 0926 59705.

Leicestershire
P Buckland-Large, Esq, (Branch Chairman), Crudwell House, Holmfield Avenue, Stoneygate, Leicester. Tel No Leicester 707607.
Mr I Kilgour, (Branch Organiser), 121 Allington Drive, Birstall, Leicestershire. Tel No Leicester 673259.
J R Hardy, Esq, (Branch Treasurer), The Old Vicarage, Belton, Loughborough, Leicestershire, LE12 9XD.

Gloucestershire
D Gifford, Esq, (Branch Chairman) (See under **Wessex Water Authority Region**).
S Marsh-Smith, Esq, (Branch Secretary) (See under **Wessex Water Authority Region**).

Yorkshire Water Authority Region
Yorkshire Region (including North Humberside)
C T Waite, Esq, (Regional Chairman), Estate Office, Wensley, Leyburn, North Yorkshire, DL8 4HW. Tel No Leyburn 2314.
The Hon Hugh R Feilding, (Deputy Chairman), Home Farm, Bainton, Driffield, East Yorks, YO25 9NJ. Tel No Middleton-on-the-Wolds 216.
P Guest, Esq, (Regional Organiser), "Tanwood", Margaret Avenue, Bardsey, Leeds, Yorks, LS17 9AU. Tel No Collingham Bridge 2326.
J Mills, Esq, (Deputy Regional Organiser), Millstones, 1 Rectory Gardens, Beckingham, Doncaster, DN10 4PP, South Yorkshire, Tel No Saundby 358.
Colonel J D Ellerbeck, MC, TD, (Regional Treasurer), Manor House, Scruton, Northallerton, N Yorks, DL7 0RD. Tel No Kirkby Fleetham 270.
A M Gibson, Esq, (Regional Abstraction Officer), 7 Hollybush Green, Collingham Yorks. Tel No Collingham Bridge 2101.
N Ayling, Esq, (Regional Water Resources Officer), 35 Turker Lane, Northallerton, N Yorks, DL16 1QL. Tel No Northallerton 4261.
W N Bygate, Esq, MBE, TD, (Deputy Treasurer), 457 Otley Road, Adel, Leeds, LS16 6AJ. Tel No Leeds 673895.
R Kershaw, Esq, (Regional Publicity Officer), c/o Times Newspapers Ltd, 7 Mill Hill, Leeds 1.
J Land, Esq, (Assistant—Publicity Committee), Ivy Bank, 24 Etherley Lane, Bishop Auckland, Durham. Tel No Bishop Auckland 2237.
B Morland, Esq, (Branch Organiser), 3 Greengate View, Knaresborough, N Yorks, HG5 0NB.

East Yorkshire
The Hon Hugh R Feilding, (Branch Chairman) (See Region above).
The Hon Mrs Sheila Feilding, (Branch Organiser), Home Farm, Bainton, Driffield, YO25 9NJ, East Yorks. Tel No Middleton-on-the-Wolds 216.

Leeds & District
C P B Mackenzie-Philps, Esq, (Branch Chairman), Deer Springs, Stockeld, Wetherby, West Yorks, LS22 4AP. Tel No Wetherby 63646.
W N Bygate, Esq, MBE, TD, (Branch Organiser), 457 Otley Road, Adel, Leeds, LS16 6AJ. Tel No Leeds 673895.

Nidderdale
A C J Burningham, Esq, (Branch Chairman), 2 Strayside Court, Victoria Road, Harrogate, Yorks, HG2 0LJ. Tel No Harrogate 69567.
D M Ogden, Esq, (Branch Organiser), Crimple Farm, Harrogate, Yorks. Tel No Harrogate 884 197.

North East Yorkshire
E Horsfall Turner, Esq, (President), Beestone Cottage, Aislaby, Pickering, N Yorks. Tel No Pickering 72533.
Major R B Kirkup, TD, (Branch Chairman), 25 Station Road, Great Ayton, Middlesbrough, Cleveland, TS9 6BW. Tel No Great Ayton 2361.
J B Woodham, Esq, CBE, (Branch Organiser), "Lea Rig", 10 Manor Drive, Hilton-in-Cleveland, Yarm, Cleveland, TS15 9LE. Tel No 0642 590 889.

South Yorkshire
Lt Commander J McMillan, (Branch Chairman), 13 Edderthorpe Lane, Darfield, Barnsley, S Yorks, DN12 1PU. Tel No Barnsley 753158.
G R Stocks, Esq, (Branch Organiser), 6 School Walk, Old Edlington, Nr Doncaster, S Yorks, DN12 1PU. Tel No Rotherham 862497.
P Fawcett, Esq, (Branch Secretary), 51 Barnsley Road, Darfield, Nr Barnsley, South Yorks.

Swaledale
Colonel J D Ellerbeck, MC, TD, (Branch Chairman) (See Region above).
J M Burton, Esq, (Branch Organiser), 3 St Johns Crescent, Leeming Village, Northallerton, N Yorks. Tel No Bedale 2944.

Wensleydale
Lt-Col A M L Price, MBE, (Branch Chairman), Kelspring House, Aysgarth, Leyburn, N Yorks, DL8 3AJ. Tel No Aysgarth 366.
B Morland, Esq, (Branch Organiser), 3 Greengate View, Knaresborough, N Yorks, HG5 0NB.

Western Yorkshire
D P H Hield, Esq, (Branch Chairman), "Personal", Hield Brothers Ltd, Brigella Mills, Bradford, Yorkshire, BD5 0QA. Tel No Bradford 71181.
L Emberson, Esq, (Branch Organiser), 28 Springbank Avenue, Farsley, Pudsey, West Yorks, LS28 5LW.

Anglian Water Authority Region

Northamptonshire, North Buckinghamshire, Cambridgeshire, Bedfordshire and West Suffolk
R F Graves, Esq, (Branch Chairman), Mitchell Hill Farm, Cottenham, Cambridge, CB4 4PS.
M W Taylor, Esq, (Branch Secretary), 47 Thornton Close, Girton, Cambridge, CB3 0NF. Tel No Cambridge 76735.
G M Vickers, Esq, (Liaison Officer), 6a Kings Parade, Cambridge. Tel No Cambridge 76270.

Norfolk and East Suffolk
G S Allen, Esq, (Branch Chairman), East Hall Farm, Langham, Holt, Norfolk. Tel No Binham 276.
Lt Commander L D Temple-Richards, (Branch Organiser), Vale Farm, Stibbard, Fakenham, Norfolk. Tel No Gt Ryburgh 217.

Lincolnshire and South Humberside
Lt Colonel R E H Drury, DSO, MC, (Branch Chairman), The Old Rectory, Langton by Spilsby, Lincs. Tel No Spilsby 2332.
D A Baxter, Esq, (Branch Organiser), Banchory Lodge, North Thoresby, Lincs. DN36 59S.
Mrs G P D Hall, (Assistant Branch Organiser), Manby House, Manby, Louth, Lincolnshire, LN11 8UF. Tel No South Cockerington (0507-82) 777.

Essex
A F Lankshear, Esq, (Branch Chairman), Motts Green, High Easter, Chelmsford, Essex. Tel No Good Easter 454.
C Landells, Esq, (Branch Organiser), 29 Looe Gardens, Barkingside, Ilford, Essex. Tel No 01-551 0477.

Thames Water Authority Region

Oxfordshire, South Buckinghamshire & Hertfordshire
C Harrison-Baker, Esq, (Regional Chairman & Branch Organiser), Midhurst, 142 Links Way, Croxley Green, Rickmansworth Herts. Tel No Watford 44195.
A McDonald, Esq, (Secretary). 18 First Avenue, Amersham, Bucks.

Berkshire
M Metcalfe, Esq, (Branch Chairman), Walnut Tree Cottage, Sulham, Pangbourne, Berks. Tel No Pangbourne 2494.

J A G Coates, Esq, CBE, (Branch Organiser), "Moss Hill", Fishers Wood, Sunningdale, Ascot, Berks, Tel No Ascot 20386.

C Farnell, Esq, (Branch Secretary/Treasurer), White Gables, Gipsy Lane, Wokingham, Berkshire. Tel No Wokingham 780843.

London
Mrs B Part, (Branch Chairman), 24 Luttrell Avenue, London, SW15. Tel No 01-789 6133.

Surrey
M Elliot, Esq, (Branch Chairman), Derwent House, Chobham Road, Woking, Surrey. Tel No Woking 68258.

A W Bird, Esq, (Branch Secretary), 50 Brooklands Way, Redhill, Surrey. Tel No 01-222 1911.

Gloucestershire
D Gifford, Esq, (Branch Chairman) (See under **Wessex Water Authority Region**).

S Marsh-Smith, Esq, (Branch Secretary) (See under **Wessex Water Authority Region**).

Wiltshire
Dr H M Darlow, (Branch Chairman), "Cuckoo Pen", Porton, Salisbury, Wilts. Tel No Idmiston 610223.

N K S Bramer, Esq, (Branch Secretary), 32 Bedwin Street, Salisbury, Wilts. Tel No Salisbury 4515.

C Humphry, Esq, (Branch Treasurer), Westover, 2 Greenway Park, Chippenham, Wilts. Tel No Chippenham 2914.

Hampshire
Major T E St Aubyn, (Branch Chairman) (See under **Southern Water Authority Region**).

Southern Water Authority Region

Hampshire
Major T E St Aubyn, (Branch Chairman), Tangier House, Wotton St Lawrence, Basingstoke, Hants. Tel No Basingstoke 780240.

Dr A T Lloyd-Davies, (Branch Organiser), 12 St Anne's Close, Goodworth Clatford, Andover, Hants. Tel No Andover 2983.

East & West Sussex
J D Swatland, Esq, (Branch Chairman), Haywards Grange, Jarvis Brook, Crowborough, East Sussex. Tel No Crowborough 4242.

Kent
Vacant.

Wessex Water Authority Region

Gloucestershire, Avon & Somerset
D Gifford, Esq, (Branch Chairman), 239 Badminton Road, Downend, Bristol, Avon. Tel No Bristol 562974.

S Marsh-Smith, Esq, (Branch Secretary), 12 Richmond Hill, Clifton, Bristol, Avon, BS8 1AT. Tel No Bristol 311207.

E G Wright, Esq, GM, (Branch Organiser), Bristol Waterworks Company, Woodord Lodge, Chew Stoke, Bristol, Avon, BS18 8XH. Tel No 0272-589 2172.

Wiltshire
Dr H M Darlow, (Branch Chairman) (See under **Thames Water Authority Region**).

Dorset
Major A E Hill, (Branch Chairman), The Mill House, Hooke Springs Trout Farm, Hooke, Beaminster, Dorset. Tel No Beaminster 862553.

South West Water Authority Region

Devon and Cornwall
P D Tuckett, Esq, (Regional Chairman), c/o Michelmore, Hughes & Wilbraham, 1 Bedford Place, Tavistock, Devon, PL19 6AZ. Tel No Tavistock 3633 (office).

North Devon
Lt Colonel G P Badham, (Branch Chairman), East Stowford, Chitlehampton, Umberleigh, North Devon. Tel No Chittlehamholt 225.

South Devon
Major J C Montague, (Branch Chairman), Manorside, Couley, Exeter, South Devon. Tel No Exeter 71021.

East Devon
Colonel J M Ricketts, (Branch Chairman), Weston Manor, Weston, Devon.
S H Noar, Esq, (Branch Organiser), The Deer Park Hotel, Weston Village, Honiton Devon. Tel No Honiton 3538.

Cornwall
T E F Mutton, Esq, (Branch Chairman), Lamorran, Old Falmouth Road, Truro, Cornwall. Tel No Truro 3858.

S Gardiner, Esq, (Branch Secretary/Treasurer), 70, Causewayhead, Penzance, Cornwall.

Tamar
M Charleston, Esq, (Branch Chairman), The Gift House, Buckland Monachorum, Yelverton, Devon.

WALES
Welsh Water Authority (which includes the Wye Catchment area)

Gwynedd & Clwyd
Professor O G Williams, CBE, (Branch Chairman), Meini Gwynion, Brynsien-cyn, Anglesey, Gwynedd, LL61 6HJ. Tel No (024873) 505.
C B Briggs, Esq, DL, (Branch Organiser), Pen-y-Gwryd Hotel, Nantgwynant, Gwynedd, N Wales. Tel No Llanberis 211.
R H Roberts, Esq, (Branch Secretary), Cafnant, 38 Ffriddoedd Road, Bangor, Gwynedd, LL57 2TW.

Glamorgan and Dyfed
E P H Hopkin, Esq, (Branch Chairman), 25 Capel Road, Clydach, Swansea, Glamorgan. Tel No Clydach 843276.

Glamorgan
J C Bills, Esq, (Branch Organiser), 10, Warwick Road, Derwen Fawr, Swansea, Glamorgan, SA2 8DZ. Tel No Swansea 25020.

Dyfed
Vacant.

Powys, Gwent, Hereford & Worcester (with responsibility for the River Wye).
Captain R W Corbett, TD, (Area Chairman) (See under **Severn-Trent Water Authority Region**).

Powys (North) & Lake Vyrnwy
Lt Colonel Sir John Baynes, Bt, (Branch Organiser), Lake Vyrnwy Hotel, Via Oswestry, Shropshire, SY10 0LY. Tel No Llanwddyn 244.

Powys (South) & Gwent
N S Brabner, Esq, (Branch Chairman), Gliffaes Hotel Ltd, Crickhowell, Powys, NP8 1RH. Tel No Bwlch 730371.
R Pomfret, Esq, (Branch Organiser), c/o Digby Turner & Co, 18 Monk Street, Abergavenny, Gwent. Tel No Abergavenny 2821.

Hereford and Worcester
R W Darlington, Esq, (Branch Chairman), 1 Havelock Road, Leominster, Hereford. Tel No Leominster 2584.

SCOTLAND
R O M Williams, Esq, OBE, MC, WS, (Chairman), Cross Roads, Currie, Midlothian. Tel No Pentland (031-449) 3217.
J R Gardiner, Esq, WS, (Secretary), Brodies, 7 Rothesay Terrace, Edinburgh, EH3 7SD. Tel No 031-225 8566.

NORTHERN IRELAND
Co Tyrone
Lt Colonel J S T Reilly, (Branch Chairman), Beltony Lodge, Mountjoy, Omagh, Co Tyrone, Northern Ireland. Tel No Newton Stewart 263.

Co Fermanagh
Vacant.

Co Londonderry
T A D Martin, Esq, (Branch Chairman), 84 Strand Road, Portstewart, Londonderry, Northern Ireland.

Co Antrim
Vacant.

Co Down
Brigadier H J P Baxter, CBE, GM, (Branch Chairman), The Old Manse, Boardmills, Co Down, Northern Ireland.

Co Armagh
J H Balmer, Esq, (Branch Chairman), Ringawoody, Waringstown Road, Lurgan, Craigavon, Co Armagh, Northern Ireland.

Overseas

UNITED STATES OF AMERICA
Professor M B Wingate, Department of Perinatal Studies, University of Albany, Albany, New York, USA.

AUSTRIA
W Strelka, Esq, Lainzerstrasse 115, Vienna 1130, Austria.

INDEX TO RIVERS AND FISHING STATIONS (Great Britain and Ireland)

Entries appearing as for example "Annan (River)" with "river" or "lake", etc., in parentheses, indicate that the reference is to a town or village and a water of the same name

ADVERTISERS INDEX